SOLAR ACTIVITY

A BLAISDELL BOOK IN THE PURE AND APPLIED SCIENCES

CONSULTING EDITOR
Gordon J. F. MacDonald, University of California, Los Angeles

SOLAR ACTIVITY

EINAR TANDBERG-HANSSEN
High Altitude Observatory, National Center for Atmospheric Research

BLAISDELL PUBLISHING COMPANY

A Division of Ginn and Company

WALTHAM, MASSACHUSETTS · TORONTO · LONDON

To Erna

Preface

The aim of this book is to treat all the different manifestations of activity on the sun in a unique framework: as the inevitable results of the interaction between solar magnetic fields and the solar plasma. To study solar magnetism is to open a veritable Pandora's box, and, even though we can treat many aspects of this subject, we are still far from a complete understanding of the origin of solar magnetic fields. Observations tell us, however, that magnetic fields are there; building on this fact, we can construct plausible working models of many aspects of solar activity. Similarly, we do not understand the differential rotation of the solar atmosphere but, employing our descriptive knowledge of the phenomenon, we can infer additional properties of our models. The solar plasma portraying the different forms of activity is often subject to intricate mass motions. At times these motions can be approximated by fairly simple expressions, and the dynamics may be treated in some detail. Our theoretical interpretations are then built on the tools furnished by one or more of the fields of hydrodynamics or hydromagnetics, atomic physics, wave theory, and plasma physics.

The book is written for the advanced student in astrophysics who may want a comprehensive account of the "disturbed" conditions that can be found in a "typical" star like our sun, when magnetic fields play havoc with the "quiet" conditions. Also, some of my colleagues may find parts of the book helpful in their teaching or research. (As for a good introductory text in solar physics, Zirin (1966) is recommended.)

The observations pertaining to each aspect of activity treated (plage, sunspot, flare, prominence, corona) are reviewed first in the respective chapters. In this task I have been helped greatly by the excellent monographs on sunspots (Bray and Loughhead, 1964) and flares (Smith and Smith, 1963) published recently and by a book on the corona (Billings, 1966) that was kindly offered in manuscript form. Since the aim of the book is a physical understanding of solar activity, I have generally tried to achieve this in two steps. The first part treats the different models proposed to account for a given set of observations; the second, theoretical interpretations and speculations, in which we draw from our knowledge of hydromagnetics, atomic physics, and so on.

To provide a reasonable background of physics in a condensed form, Chapter 1 summarizes most of the necessary basic equations and principal physical assumptions to be used later. The different methods of observing solar activity are the subject of Chapter 2. Chapter 3, furnishing a bird's-eye view of the quiet sun as it would appear in the absence of activity, is the background against which the various forms of activity should be considered. The basic manifestation of activity is revealed by the plage phenomenon (faculae), which changes with time and thereby gives the sun some properties of a variable star. This is treated in Chapter 4. In Chapters 5 through 8 the other aspects of solar activity, sunspots, flares, prominences and the active corona, are discussed.

In presenting different theories of a physical phenomenon, an author is often torn between two extremes: should he discuss as objectively as possible the different theories and let them speak for themselves, as it were, or evaluate the theories according to his own judgment, giving strong priority to the one deemed most successful? While I have, in general, tried to adhere to the former philosophy, I have also felt compelled to comment at times on the physical soundness of some of the research presented.

It is a pleasure to acknowledge the valuable help from Miss C. Travis, J. Goff, and D. Tanton in preparing photographs and drawings for the figures. Special thanks are due Mrs. R. Fulk for her careful typing of the manuscript, Mrs. K. McKean for her indefatigable help in the final revision of the manuscript and in painstaking proofreading, and the staff of Blaisdell Publishing Company for their care and attention in the printing.

I have benefited greatly from discussions with a number of colleagues, to whom I give my grateful thanks: M. Altschuler, D. E. Billings, M. Cimino, J. W. Firor, C. L. Hyder, W. Jones, F. Meyer, G. Newkirk, F. Q. Orrall, H. E. Ramsey, and H. U. Schmidt.

Also, I would like to express my deepfelt appreciation to the astronomers who provided me with many of the illustrations: G. Abetti, L. Acton, G. Anderson, J. Bahng, J. D. Bohlin, R. N. Bracewell, W. N. Christiansen, T. G. Cowling, J. W. Dungey, R. B. Dunn, T. D. Kinman, R. Kippenhahn, M. Kuperus, R. B. Leighton, D. J. McLean, R. Michard, J. D. Murray, N. F. Ness, the late J. L. Pawsey, J. C. Pecker, K. A. Pounds, J. B. Rogerson, W. C. Rowe, E. Schatzman, A. Schlüter, M. Schwarzschild, S. Smith, R. T. Stewart, the late A. A. Weiss, and J. P. Wild.

Finally, for their kind permission to reproduce, without charge, figures from the books or journals indicated I am indebted to: Faber and Faber, *The Sun;* Masson et Cie, *Astrophysique Générale;* Oxford University Press,

Radio Astronomy; Annales d'Astrophysique, Centre National de la Recherche Scientifique; Australian Journal of Physics, Commonwealth Scientific and Industrial Research Organization; Journal of the Physical Society of Japan, Physical Society of Japan; Monthly Notices of the Royal Astronomical Society, Royal Astronomical Society; Recherches Astronomiques Observatoire d'Utrecht, N. V. Drukkerij D. Reidel; Science, American Association for the Advancement of Science; Zeitschrift für Astrophysik, Springer. And my thanks to the following organizations for permission to use their data: L'Observatoire de Paris-Meudon; National Aeronautics and Space Administration Ames Research Center; Naval Research Laboratory; and Sacramento Peak Observatory, Air Force Cambridge Research Laboratories.

Einar Tandberg-Hanssen

Boulder, Colorado
June, 1966

Contents

Symbols,
Physical Constants, and
Periodical Abbreviations

SYMBOLS

A Einstein coefficient; area; relative metal abundance

b parameter expressing deviation from local thermodynamic equilibrium

B Einstein coefficient; magnetic field; Planck function

c velocity of light; concentration

C collisional rate coefficient

d distance

D transport coefficient

e electronic charge

E energy; electric field

f oscillator strength; distribution function

F flux; force; electric field (in Stark effect)

g gravitational acceleration; statistical weight; Gaunt factor; Landé's g factor

G constant of gravitation

h height

H scale height

i imaginary unit ($\sqrt{-1}$)

I specific intensity

j current density or net transport

J mean intensity; total angular momentum quantum number

k Boltzmann's constant; absorption coefficient; wave number

K degree absolute; thermal conductivity

l characteristic length

L characteristic length; orbital angular momentum quantum number

m mass

M magnetic quantum number; mass

n principal quantum number; number density of particles; refraction index

N number of particles in column of cross section 1 cm²

p pressure; momentum; radius of sunspot penumbra

P rate coefficient ($P = R + C$); probability; power; period $= 2\pi/\omega$

q heat flow

Q collisional cross section

r cylindrical polar coordinate; distance

R radiative rate coefficient; Wolf's sunspot number; Reynold's number

s coefficient in force expression const/r^s

S spin quantum number; source function; solar constant

t time

T temperature

u velocity; radius of sunspot umbra

U partition function; heat energy, velocity of shock front

v flow velocity (macroscopic)

V wave velocity

w particle velocity (microscopic)

W energy; equivalent width of spectral line

x cartesian coordinate

y cartesian coordinate

z cartesian and cylindrical polar coordinate

Z atomic number

α fine structure constant; coefficient of volume expression; angle absorption coefficient per atom

β polarizability

γ ratio of specific heats; damping constant

δ delta function; angle

$\Delta\lambda$ half-width of spectral line

ϵ emissivity; dielectric constant

ϵ' complex dielectric constant ($\epsilon' = \epsilon - i(4\pi\sigma/\omega)$)

η coefficient of viscosity

η_m magnetic diffusivity

θ angle

κ continuum quantum number

λ wavelength; mean free path

λ_B Larmor radius

λ_D Debye length

μ magnetic permeability; mean molecular weight

μ_B magnetic moment
ν frequency
$\tilde{\omega}$ statistical weight
ρ density; impact parameter
σ Stefan's constant; electric conductivity; cross section
τ optical depth; collision interval; decay time
ϕ cylindrical polar coordinate; latitude; phase
Φ magnetic flux; gravitational potential
χ electric potential
ω circular frequency; angular velocity; vorticity
Ω solid angle; collision integral; circular frequency

PHYSICAL CONSTANTS

Boltzmann's constant	$k = 1.38 \times 10^{-16}$ erg $^\circ$K^{-1}
Electron rest mass	$m_e = 9.1 \times 10^{-28}$ gm
Elementary charge	$e = 4.80 \times 10^{-10}$ esu
Gravitational constant	$G = 6.67 \times 10^{-8}$ dyne cm^2 gm^{-2}
Planck's constant	$h = 6.626 \times 10^{-27}$ erg sec
Proton rest mass	$m_p = 1.67 \times 10^{-24}$ gm
Stefan–Boltzmann constant	$\sigma = 5.67 \times 10^{-5}$ erg cm^{-2} sec^{-1} $^\circ$K^{-4}
Velocity of light	$c = 2.998 \times 10^{10}$ cm/sec

SPECIAL PERIODICAL ABBREVIATIONS

A. J.	Astronomical Journal
A. N.	Astronomische Nachrichten
A. Z.	Astronomische Zeitschrift
A. Zhurn.	Astronomischeskii Zhurnal
Ann. d'Ap.	Annales d'Astrophysique
Ap. J.	Astrophysical Journal
Ap. Norv.	Astrophysical Norvegica
B. A. C.	Bulletin of the Astronomical Institute of Czechoslovakia
B. A. N.	Bulletin of the Astronomical Society of the Netherlands
C. R.	Comptes Rendus (Paris)
J. E. T. P.	Journal of Experimental and Theoretical Physics (U.S.S.R.)
J. G. R.	Journal of Geophysical Research
M. N.	Monthly Notices of the Royal Astronomical Society
P. A. S. Japan	Publications of the Astronomical Society of Japan
P. A. S. P.	Publications of the Astronomical Society of the Pacific
Z. Ap.	Zeitschrift für Astrophysik

"It is pleasant for the eyes to behold the sun," Ecclesiastes 11, 7. Sunrise over Boulder. (Courtesy R. F. Ewy, National Center for Atmospheric Research.)

Basic Equations and Principal Physical Assumptions

1.1. *The Solar Plasma*

1.1.1. Introduction

Much of the work on the solar atmosphere based on observations in the optical part of the spectrum has been carried out under the assumption that the influence of any magnetic field can be neglected. While it may be true that spectroscopic studies of many solar phenomena will not be significantly affected by the inclusion of magnetic fields, it is also true that only part of the whole story is revealed when the presence of magnetic forces is neglected.

In an atmosphere consisting of only neutral particles, the possible existence of a magnetic field is no cause for concern since the motion of such a gas is left unaffected by a magnetic field. The solar atmosphere—like all stellar atmospheres—is, however, a plasma and therefore consists of very nearly equal numbers of positive and negative electric charges in addition to neutral particles. The ratio of charged to neutral particles changes as we go from the sun's interior to superficial layers of the atmosphere, but hardly anywhere is the ratio so small that the medium is not a plasma. Thus, few indeed are the cases where the influence of the magnetic fields on mass motions may be safely neglected if we want to arrive at a sound physical picture. We shall find that a knowledge of *the electric conductivity* of the plasma and the magnitude and configuration of the *magnetic field* are of prime importance in our discussion.

The complications that arise are enormous when we go from the domain of the physics of intrinsically neutral atmospheres to that of a plasma in the presence of magnetic fields. It is therefore necessary to approximate to the neutral gas case whenever possible. Thus, we shall discuss many aspects of the excitation and ionization of atoms and ions and their interaction with radiation in the solar atmosphere independently of any assumption regarding magnetic fields, keeping in mind that no over-all picture can be derived in this way.

In addition to the electric conductivity and the magnetic field strength, the scale of the phenomenon has a decisive bearing on whether we are safely in the realm of neutral gas theory or whether a plasma-physical treatment is essential. In the former case, on a macroscopic scale, a purely hydrodynamic treatment suffices; the latter case presents us with a coupling between the hydrodynamic and electromagnetic phenomena. If the scale, or characteristic length, of the phenomenon is denoted by L and the mass density of the plasma is ρ, and if we let σ and B denote electric conductivity and magnetic field strength, the coupling between hydrodynamics and electromagnetics is important for scales

$$L > c^2 \sqrt{\rho}/\sigma B. \tag{1.1}$$

We are then in the domain of magnetohydrodynamics or hydromagnetics (Lundquist, 1952).

The realization of this coupling can hardly be overestimated, and it has had a decisive influence on our understanding of cosmic physics. The complications that arise are due not only to the difficult mathematics involved but also to the fact that phenomena occur for which we have little or no physical intuition. We know that the sun and other stars consist of ionized gases, not liquids, which are adequately described by the hydrodynamic equations. For solar and stellar plasmas, we must in addition rely on the theory of ionized gases to compute such important parameters as the electric conductivity. This hydromagnetics of ionized gases, or *plasmahydromagnetics*, has gone a long way toward explaining many aspects of solar activity, but much remains to be done. Basically, there is the question of whether the macroscopic point of view, inherent in the use of the hydrodynamic equations, is appropriate in the more tenuous parts of the solar atmosphere. It may be that we should treat the individual particles in a microscopic sense, that is, take recourse to a statistical theory where we seek information about the distribution functions for the particle velocities and introduce the Boltzmann equation. This approach is especially applicable when we study high energy particle beams in the solar atmosphere and will be used there, but a continuous plasma dynamics is an adequate means of treating sufficiently large-scale phenomena. The relevant equations are known to be valid when the mean free paths are short compared to the characteristic length of the phenomenon under investigation.

1.1.2. Parametric Description of the Plasma

In describing the properties of a plasma, we encounter several characteristic lengths and times as well as more complex parameters of great importance. To facilitate the later mathematical treatment and to get a feeling for the physically most important parameters, we will now treat these quantities in some detail. We start out with a discussion of the concept of temperature, a parameter whose importance is matched only by the confusion associated with it.

1.1.2.1. *The concept of temperature*

If the gas we consider radiates like a blackbody, the intensity distribution with wavelength, that is, the spectrum of the emitted electromagnetic radiation, from the shortest X rays to the longest radio waves, will be given by a Planck function, uniquely determined by one temperature parameter, the radiation temperature T_R. Planck's law, with the frequency $\nu = c/\lambda$ as an independent variable, has the form

$$I_\nu = \frac{2h\nu^3}{c^2} (e^{h\nu/kT_R} - 1)^{-1}. \tag{1.2}$$

With wavelength as the independent variable, Equation (1.2) takes the form

$$I_\lambda = \frac{2hc^2}{\lambda^5} (e^{hc/k\lambda T_R} - 1)^{-1}. \tag{1.3}$$

The velocity distribution $f(v)$ of the particles making up the gas—whether it be a neutral gas or a plasma—will be Maxwellian, that is, given by Maxwell's law,

$$f(v) = \left(\frac{m}{2\pi k T_K}\right)^{3/2} e^{-mv^2/2kT_K}, \tag{1.4}$$

and the temperature parameter, the kinetic temperature T_K, will be the same for all kinds of particles present.

In the radiating (emitting and absorbing) atoms and ions, the different energy states will further be populated according to Boltzmann's formula:

$$\frac{n_U}{n_L} = \frac{g_U}{g_L} e^{\chi_{UL}/kT_{ex}}, \tag{1.5}$$

which gives the ratio of the populations of an upper and a lower state in terms of the statistical weights g of the states, the excitation potential χ_{UL}, and an excitation temperature parameter T_{ex} (see Figure 1.1).

Furthermore, the distribution of ions on the different ionization stages is given by Saha's equation (1920, 1921),

$$\frac{n_{i+1}}{n_i}\, n_e = \left(\frac{2\pi m k T_K}{h^2}\right)^{3/2} \frac{2 U_{i+1}}{U_i}\, e^{-\chi_i / k T_{\mathrm{ion}}}, \tag{1.6}$$

where n_i denotes the number density of ions in the ionization stage i, and n_e is the electron density. Here χ_i is the ionization potential for ionization from

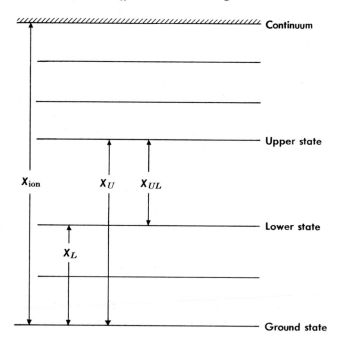

FIGURE 1.1. Atomic energy level diagram

stage i to the next stage i + 1, and T_{ion} is a temperature parameter, the ionization temperature associated with this particular process. Also, U_i and U_{i+1} are the partition functions for the two ionization stages. These are given by expressions of the form

$$U_i = \sum_i g_i e^{-\chi_i / k T_{\mathrm{ion}}}. \tag{1.7}$$

If the excitation temperature T_{ex} for all the states in all the atoms and ions present and all the ionization temperatures T_{ion} for all ionization processes in all ions present are identical and equal to the common kinetic temperature T_K for all the particles throughout the gas, and if this temperature is also equal to the radiation temperature T_R, we are in the realm of *thermodynamic equilibrium*. The radiation is then in equilibrium with the gas. This is the condition one finds in a *Hohlraum*—the blackbody—and it is the simple regime characterized by a single temperature parameter.

When we consider the solar plasma, however, we are faced with the fact that the spectrum of the sun is not continuous like that of a blackbody. It exhibits spectral lines—an indication that the solar atmosphere is not in thermodynamic equilibrium. But we can consider that any given small element of the solar plasma is in thermodynamic equilibrium, even though the temperature may be assumed to change with distance r from the solar center $T = T(r)$. This is the condition for *local thermodynamic equilibrium* (LTE) which permits spectral lines to be formed, and which is often believed to apply to stellar atmospheres, with the exception of their outermost parts.

Even though we have relaxed one requirement on the temperature (T may vary with r), the condition of LTE is still a very stringent physical regime. Only rarely do we encounter it in actual astrophysical situations. More often, we shall find, for instance, that the excitation temperature derived by some method does not coincide with a determined ionization temperature. We shall then have to be very cautious and remember that we are only dealing with temperature parameters, each one describing a different aspect of our plasma.

The electron temperature T_e is a frequently used parameter. By T_e, we understand the parameter in Maxwell's law, Equation (1.4), that is, the kinetic temperature describing the velocity distribution of the free electrons. This will often—but not always—be equal to the parameter describing the velocity distribution of the ions, the ion kinetic temperature, which we shall call T_i. Note the difference between T_i and T_{ion}, the ionization temperature.

1.1.2.2. *Characteristic lengths*

From the theory of electrolytes, we have taken the concept of the Debye length, λ_D, or Debye shielding distance, which indicates the distance to which a point charge can make its influence felt. Since the field of the charge falls off as

$$E_{pot} = 1/r \, e^{-r/\lambda_D}, \tag{1.8}$$

we see that for distance $r > \lambda_D$ the electric field is shielded by charges of opposite sign. The expression for λ_D may be found from the condition in which the energy due to the electric potential is equal to the thermal energy and is

$$\lambda_{\mathrm{D}} = \sqrt{kT/4\pi n_e e^2}\,.\tag{1.9}$$

In a plasma, λ_{D} is a measure of the distance over which strict electric neutrality ($n_{\mathrm{pos}} = n_{\mathrm{neg}}$) may not be obeyed.

From kinetic theory, we are familiar with the collisional mean free path λ of a particle. We shall let λ_e denote the mean free path for the electrons, and λ_i will pertain to ions. A completely general expression for the mean free path in a plasma is quite complicated; an often-used approximation gives

$$\lambda = \frac{\bar{v}}{\nu_e} \approx \frac{k^2 T^4}{n_e e^4}\,.\tag{1.10}$$

The definition of a plasma may now be given in terms of the parameters λ_{D} and λ, and we define an ionized gas as a plasma if $\lambda_{\mathrm{D}} < \lambda$.

In the presence of a magnetic field B, there will be superposed a systematic velocity v on the random thermal velocity v_{th} of electric charges. The charged particles will gyrate around the field lines with a radius of gyration, or Larmor radius, given by

$$\lambda_B = \frac{m v_\perp c}{eB}\,.\tag{1.11}$$

Here $v_\perp$ is the component of the velocity v perpendicular to the magnetic field. This distance is found by equating the acceleration $dv/dt = (e/mc)v_\perp B$ to the centrifugal acceleration $v_\perp^2/\lambda_B$.

In the solar corona, we find that $\lambda \approx 10^8 \lambda_{\mathrm{D}}$, and in a field of 1 gauss we find that, for electrons, $\lambda_B \approx 100 \lambda_{\mathrm{D}}$ and, for protons, $\lambda_B \approx 4000 \lambda_{\mathrm{D}}$. In general, we will encounter conditions specified by the inequalities

$$\lambda_{\mathrm{D}} \ll \lambda_B \ll \lambda.$$

1.1.2.3. Characteristic velocities

The most fundamental particle velocity is the thermal velocity v_{th}, which is simply due to the nonzero value of the kinetic temperature of the particles considered. From the gas kinetic equation

$$\tfrac{1}{2}mv^2 = \tfrac{3}{2}kT\,,$$

we find the expression for the mean thermal velocity $\bar{v}_{\mathrm{th}}$,

$$\bar{v}_{\mathrm{th}} = \sqrt{3kT/m}\,.\tag{1.12}$$

Under coronal conditions, $T = 10^6 °K$, and $\bar{v}_{th} = 1.58 \times 10^7$ centimeters per second (cm/sec) = 158 kilometers per second (km/sec). The corresponding velocity for electrons is $(m_p/m_e)^{1/2} = 43$ times greater, or nearly 6800 km/sec.

In most studies of the dynamic properties of a gas, it is of prime importance to compare the motions involved with the local velocity of sound in the gas. In ordinary gas dynamics, the characteristic velocity of acoustical waves is

$$V_s = \sqrt{\gamma(p/\rho)} = \sqrt{\gamma(\rho/m)kT} = dp/d\rho. \tag{1.13}$$

For a monatomic gas, $\gamma = \frac{5}{3}$, and for hydrogen we therefore find that

$$V_s = 1.18 \times 10^4 T \quad \text{cm/sec}.$$

Disturbances that propagate with velocities in excess of V_s are called supersonic, and those that propagate with velocities less than V_s are subsonic.

In the presence of a magnetic field, transverse waves may propagate in a plasma at a characteristic velocity, called the Alfvén velocity $\mathbf{V}_A$, given by

$$\mathbf{V}_A = \mathbf{B}/\sqrt{4\pi\rho}. \tag{1.14}$$

The velocity for general wave propagations in a plasma is given by the interaction of the purely acoustic (longitudinal) wave of velocity V_s and the purely magnetic (transverse) wave of velocity V_A. This coupling may lead to very complicated wave phenomena.

1.1.2.4. *Characteristic frequencies*

The cyclotron frequency, or Larmor frequency, ω_B, is the angular frequency with which a particle of mass m and charge e gyrates in a magnetic field:

$$\omega_B = eB/mc. \tag{1.15}$$

As we shall see later, radiation at this frequency is of great theoretical importance in solar physics.

In a plasma, longitudinal oscillations of the electrons may be set up due to electrostatic forces acting between the electrons and the neutralizing ions. The resonance frequency for such oscillations, the plasma frequency, ω_p, is given by

$$\omega_p = \sqrt{4\pi ne^2/m}. \tag{1.16}$$

A typical value for the solar corona, where $n_e = 10^8$ cm^{-3}, is 5×10^8 sec^{-1} or 500 megacycles per second (Mc/sec).

1.1.2.5. *The electric conductivity*

The electric conductivity σ is one of the most important and useful parameters in plasma physics. Conventionally, it is defined as the ratio between the electric field **E** and the electric current **j**:

$$\sigma = j/E, \tag{1.17}$$

and in the general case it is a tensor. We may also define σ in terms of the coupling between electrons and ions due to collisions. More precisely, we define

$$\sigma = en \, \frac{\mathbf{j}}{\mathbf{P_{ei}}}, \tag{1.18}$$

where $\mathbf{P_{ei}}$, the interaction term, is the momentum transferred to the electrons per unit time per unit volume by collision with ions. When there is no magnetic field present, the two definitions are identical. Otherwise, the equation $\mathbf{j} = \sigma\mathbf{E}$, Ohm's law, becomes very complicated.

The simple scalar expression often given for σ,

$$\sigma = n_e e^2 / m_e \nu_c, \tag{1.19}$$

may be deduced from elementary kinetic theory by considering the momentum gained by an electron in a collision, namely $\mathbf{p} = m_e(\mathbf{v_i} - \mathbf{v_e})$, the number of such collisions per cm^3, $n_e\nu_c$, and the current density, $\mathbf{j} = n_e e(\mathbf{v_i} - \mathbf{v_e})$, in Equation (1.18). This gives the approximate relation of Equation (1.19).

For the hypothetical Lorentz gas, a fully ionized gas in which (1) the ions are at rest and (2) there are no electron–electron collisions, it can be shown that the electron conductivity is

$$\sigma_{\mathrm{L}} = \frac{2(2kT)^{3/2}}{\pi^{3/2}m_e^{1/2}Ze^2 \ln \Lambda} = 7.36 \times 10^8 \, \frac{T^{3/2}}{Z \ln \Lambda} \, \text{sec}^{-1}. \tag{1.20}$$

The quantity Λ is a slowly varying function of temperature and density:

$$\Lambda = \frac{\lambda_{\mathrm{D}}}{\rho_0} = \frac{3}{2Ze^3} \left(\frac{k^3 T^3}{\pi n_e} \right)^{1/2}, \tag{1.21}$$

where $\rho_0 = Ze^2/m_e v^2$ is the impact parameter of binary encounter theory or the distance of closest approach for an electron with velocity v deflected through ninety degrees by the encounter. In the solar atmosphere, Λ ranges from a value of about ten in the cooler, denser parts of the chromosphere to about twenty in the hotter, more tenuous regions of the corona.

The complications that arise when electron–electron collisions are included lead to an expression for the electron conductivity of the form

$$\sigma = \gamma_E \sigma_L .$$

The factor γ_E, which depends on the charge Z, varies monotonically from $\gamma_E = 1$ for an infinite charge ($Z = \infty$) to $\gamma_E = 0.58$ for $Z = 1$.

The electric conductivity is intimately related to the energy dissipated into heat by the currents flowing through the medium. Since this Joule heating is given by

$$W_J = j^2/\sigma , \tag{1.22}$$

we see that it vanishes for a plasma of very high electric conductivity, $\sigma \to \infty$. In practice, there is always some Joule heating, but a high value of σ will always characterize the plasma that we are to treat in the solar atmosphere. This property of the solar plasma leads to considerable simplification of the basic equations of the plasma.

For the fully ionized plasma just treated, the distant encounters between electrons and ions dominate. For a slightly ionized gas, the close encounters determine the electron conductivity, and the following formula has been given by Chapman and Cowling (1952) on the assumption that the particles may be considered as rigid spheres:

$$\sigma = \text{const} \frac{\alpha e^2}{\sqrt{m_e kT}} \frac{1}{Q} .$$

Here α is the degree of ionization, and Q is the collision cross section for electron–atom interaction.

When a magnetic field is present, the electric conductivity of a fully ionized plasma is a tensor and shows that the current then has three components. The electric field may be decomposed into two components: $E_{\parallel}$, parallel to the magnetic field, and $E_{\perp}$, at right angles to it. The electric current flowing along $E_{\parallel}$ is characterized by an electric conductivity

$$\sigma_{\parallel} = n_e e^2/m_e \nu_c = \sigma_0 , \tag{1.23}$$

that is, the same as for no magnetic field. The current flowing along $E_{\perp}$ has an electric conductivity

$$\sigma_{\perp} = \frac{\sigma_0}{1 + (\omega_B/\nu_c)^2} . \tag{1.24}$$

Hence, there is a considerable reduction in the current flowing perpendicular to the magnetic field when the collision frequency ν_c is small compared to the electron cyclotron frequency ω_B. Instead of carrying a large current, the electrons are kept spiraling around the same magnetic lines of force. As the number of collisions per second increases and the importance of ν_c relative to ω_B becomes greater, the magnetic field loses its influence on the motion of the electrons, and the conductivity approaches the zero field value σ_0.

The complete analysis shows that, in addition to the currents along the two components of the electric field, there is a third current, which flows in a direction perpendicular to both the magnetic and the electric field vectors. It is called the Hall current, and the corresponding conductivity is

$$\sigma_H = \sigma_\perp (\omega_B/\nu_c). \tag{1.25}$$

1.1.3. Fundamental Equations of Plasma Physics

The general case of a multicomponent gas mixture is too complex to be analyzed in any detail here. Sometimes we try to approximate to the simplest case of a conducting gas consisting of only one kind of particle, or we may treat the actual plasma as a fully ionized gas consisting of electrons and one species of ion. The introduction of a partially ionized gas consisting of electrons, one species of positive ion, and the corresponding neutral atoms, already complicates the physics and mathematics. We shall often approximate to a fully ionized hydrogen plasma, but the equations will first be written in the more general form of a Z times ionized ion.

A roman subscript e will denote electron, and a roman subscript i will stand for ion. The quantities that describe the plasma as a whole will be written without any subscript. With this convention the total number density, which in the general case is

$$n = \sum_s n_s, \qquad s \text{ different species,}$$

reduces to $n = n_e + n_i$. Similarly, the total pressure is the sum of the partial pressures:

$$p = \sum_s p_s \rightarrow p_e + p_i.$$

For a perfect gas, we see that $p_s = n_s k T_s$ and $p = k \sum_s n_s T_s = knT$, where the kinetic temperature of the plasma is defined by

$$T = (1/n) \sum_s n_s T_s \rightarrow (1/n)(n_e T_e + n_i T_i).$$

The flow velocity $\mathbf{v}$ and the current density $\mathbf{j}$ are given in terms of the mass density

$$\rho = n_e m_e + n_i m_i \approx n_i m_i$$

by the equations

$$\mathbf{v} = (1/\rho)(n_e m_e \mathbf{v_e} + n_i m_i \mathbf{v_i}) \tag{1.26}$$

and

$$\mathbf{j} = e(n_i Z \mathbf{v_i} - n_e \mathbf{v_e}). \tag{1.27a}$$

It is often useful to introduce the diffusion velocity, which is defined for the sth species as

$$\mathbf{u}_s = \mathbf{v}_s - \mathbf{v}.$$

The current density is then

$$\mathbf{j} = e(Z n_i \mathbf{u_i} - n_e \mathbf{u_e}) + e\mathbf{v}(Z n_i - n_e)$$
$$= \text{conduction current} + \text{convection current}. \tag{1.27b}$$

The equations sufficient to describe the state of a plasma for our purposes may be obtained from the Boltzmann equation for the velocity distribution function of the particles in the plasma by taking the appropriate moments. The velocity distribution function f gives the density of particles in phase space as a function of position r and of the microscopic velocity w, and the Boltzmann equation describes how f changes (along the particle trajectories) as a result of collisions between the particles. The equation is a partial differential equation

$$\frac{\partial f}{\partial t} + \sum_i \frac{\partial f}{\partial x_i}\frac{\partial x_i}{\partial t} + \sum_i \frac{\partial f}{\partial w_i}\frac{\partial w_i}{\partial t} = \left(\frac{\partial f}{\partial t}\right)_{\text{coll}}, \quad i = 1, 2, 3\,,$$

which may be written

$$\frac{\partial f}{\partial t} + w\,\nabla_r f + \frac{F}{m}\,\nabla_w f = \left(\frac{\partial f}{\partial t}\right)_{\text{coll}}. \tag{1.28}$$

There will be one such equation for each species of particle present in the plasma, but we shall here drop the suffix. The term $(\partial f/\partial t)_{\text{coll}}$ is the collision integral, and it makes the complete solution of the Boltzmann equation very complicated. The symbol ∇_r indicates differentiation with respect to the coordinates $r = (x, y, z) = (x_1, x_2, x_3)$, and ∇_w similarly indicates differentiation with respect to the velocity components $\mathbf{w} = (w_x, w_y, w_z) = (w_1, w_2, w_3)$. That is, we have

$$\mathbf{w} \, \nabla_r f = \sum_i w_i \frac{\partial f}{\partial x_i} \quad \text{and} \quad \frac{F}{m} \, \nabla_w f = \sum_i \frac{F_i}{m} \frac{\partial f}{\partial w_i}, \qquad i = 1, 2, 3 ,$$

where F is the external force, and m is the mass of one of the particles.

When $(\partial f/\partial t)_{\text{coll}} = 0$, that is, there are no collisions, Boltzmann's equation in phase space reduces to the Liouville equation, which leads to Liouville's theorem: *For a conservative system, f is constant along a dynamic trajectory.* The collisionless Boltzmann equation—the Vlasov equation—holds approximately for a very tenuous plasma. It cannot be used to study transport phenomena which owe their existence to the collisions.

If we want to go from the microscopic description to the usual macroscopic conservation equations, we first multiply the equation by a suitable function of the microscopic velocity, then integrate Equation (1.28) over velocity space $dw_x \, dw_y \, dw_z$. If this function is unity, we find the equation of continuity of matter,

$$(\partial n/\partial t) + \nabla \cdot (nv) = 0 , \tag{1.29}$$

where the particle density n is

$$n(\mathbf{r}, t) = \iiint\limits_{-\infty}^{\infty} f(\mathbf{r}, \mathbf{w}, t) \, dw_x \, dw_y \, dw_z ,$$

and the macroscopic velocity v is

$$v(\mathbf{r}, t) = \frac{1}{n(\mathbf{r}, t)} \iiint\limits_{-\infty}^{\infty} \mathbf{w} f(\mathbf{r}, \mathbf{w}, t) \, dw_x \, dw_y \, dw_z .$$

An equation of continuity for the electric charge ρ_e,

$$\partial \rho_e/\partial t + \nabla \cdot \mathbf{j} = 0 , \tag{1.30}$$

can be derived from Maxwell's equations (see Section 1.5).

To derive the equation of motion, that is, the equation for the momentum transfer, we multiply Equation (1.28) by $m\mathbf{w}$ and integrate. This gives

$$nm \frac{d\mathbf{v}}{dt} = ne\left(\mathbf{E} + \frac{\mathbf{v}}{c} \times \mathbf{B}_0\right) - \nabla \cdot \mathscr{P} - nm \, \nabla\Phi + \mathbf{P} . \tag{1.31}$$

We know that the mobile operator $d/dt \equiv \partial/\partial t + \mathbf{v} \cdot \nabla$; g is the gravitational acceleration $g = -\nabla\Phi$; $\mathscr{P}$ is the stress tensor and reduces to the scalar pressure p in the simplest case of an isotropic distribution of the random velocities of the particles; $\mathbf{P}$ describes the momentum transfer by collisions (see Equation (1.18), etc.). The external force is taken equal to $e(\mathbf{E} + (\mathbf{v}/c) \times \mathbf{B}_0) - m\nabla\Phi$.

If, in addition to electrons and ions, there are neutral particles present, we may consider collisions between neutral and charged particles by writing

$$\mathbf{P} = \mathbf{P}_{ei} + \mathbf{P}_{en} + \mathbf{P}_{in}$$

in Equation (1.31), with $\mathbf{P}_{en}$ and $\mathbf{P}_{in}$ representing the transfer of momentum between electrons and neutral particles and between ions and neutral particles, respectively.

The general equation of motion, Equation (1.31), takes the following form for the electrons only:

$$n_e m_e \frac{d\mathbf{v}_e}{dt} = n_e e\left(\mathbf{E} + \frac{\mathbf{v}}{c} \times \mathbf{B}_0\right) - \nabla \cdot \mathscr{P}_e + n_e m_e g + \mathbf{P}_{ei}. \quad (1.32)$$

There is a similar equation for the ions. If we now simplify these equations by linearizing them (neglecting all quadratic terms in v and j and in their derivatives), assume electric neutrality ($n_e = Zn_i$), and substitute the scalar pressure for the stress tensor, we can combine the equations to give the equation of motion in the form generally used for a plasma:

$$\rho \frac{d\mathbf{v}}{dt} = \frac{1}{c}\mathbf{j} \times \mathbf{B}_0 - \nabla p - \rho \nabla\Phi. \quad (1.33a)$$

The Lorentz force, $(1/c)\mathbf{j} \times \mathbf{B}_0$, provides the coupling between the magnetic field and the material motion. We can see that this is the most important coupling from the following argument. To give a general description of the processes going on in a plasma, we must include proper interaction terms to account for the coupling between the electromagnetic phenomena (described by the Maxwell equations) and the gasdynamic motions. Because the electric conductivity in a plasma is very high, the energy in the electric field is negligible compared to that in the magnetic field. Therefore, we only treat the interaction between the magnetic and gasdynamic fields, or, in other words, the coupling between $\mathbf{B}_0$ and the gasdynamic parameters $\mathbf{v}$, p, ρ, and T. In fluid dynamics, the equation of motion generally used is the Navier-Stokes equation, which includes viscosity as a force term instead of gravity.

It has the form

$$\rho \frac{d\mathbf{v}}{dt} = -\nabla p + \frac{1}{c}\mathbf{j} \times \mathbf{B}_0 + \rho\eta \, \nabla^2\mathbf{v}, \qquad (1.33b)$$

where η is the coefficient of viscosity.

Using Equation (1.18) in Equation (1.32) and in the similar one for the ions, we derive the generalized Ohm's law

$$\frac{m_e m_i}{Ze^2\rho} \frac{\partial \mathbf{j}}{\partial t} = \mathbf{E} + \frac{\mathbf{v}}{c} \times \mathbf{B}_0 - \frac{\mathbf{j}}{\sigma} + \frac{1}{Ze\rho}(m_i \, \nabla p_e - Zm_e \, \nabla p_i)$$

$$- (m_i - Zm_e)\frac{\mathbf{j}}{c} \times \mathbf{B}_0, \quad (1.34)$$

which only under extremely simple circumstances reduces to the classical Ohm's law $\mathbf{j} = \sigma\mathbf{E}$.

To get an energy-transfer equation, we multiply Equation (1.28) by w^2 and integrate over velocity space. However, by this process we introduce third moments of the distribution function—the components of the heat-flow vector. Only if we can find an independent expression for the joint heating effects β will we have a closed system of equations. In ordinary gas dynamics, the heat flow is often small, and, if it can be ignored, the energy conservation equation reduces to the equation for the conservation of entropy

$$\frac{d}{dt}(p\rho^{-\gamma}) = 0,$$

that is, we have an adiabatic variation of pressure. In most plasmas, the heat flow is due to several effects: heat conduction, radiation, viscosity, flow of electric currents, etc., and the general expression for β becomes very cumbersome. The energy equation is

$$\rho \frac{dU}{dt} = \frac{p}{\rho}\frac{d\rho}{dt} + \beta = -p \, \nabla \cdot \mathbf{v} + \beta, \qquad (1.35)$$

where U is the heat energy per unit mass. The joint heating effect, β, per unit volume, for the effects mentioned above may be written:

$$\beta = \nabla \cdot (K\nabla T) - \nabla \cdot \mathbf{F}_{rad} + \psi + (j^2/\sigma). \qquad (1.36)$$

Here K is the thermal conductivity, so that $K\nabla T$ expresses the corresponding flux of heat due to this transport; $\mathbf{F}_{rad}$ is the net radiative flux, and the corresponding term in the energy equation accounts for the heat loss due to radiation from the plasma. The two last terms on the right-hand side of

Equation (1.36) are the dissipation due to the viscous stress tensor and the loss due to Joule heating by the electric currents.

Let us now discuss in some detail the equations governing the behavior of electromagnetic fields. The propagation of disturbances in free space is uniquely determined by Maxwell's equations, since only electromagnetic waves are possible under these conditions. In the presence of matter, for example an ionized gas, there is a coupling between the radiation field and the particles. The equations governing the electromagnetic fields and the coupled particle motions are, as already mentioned, Maxwell's equations and an equation of motion for each kind of particle found in the plasma. Maxwell's equations are, in a completely general case,

$$\nabla \times \mathbf{H} = \frac{4\pi}{c}\mathbf{j} + \frac{1}{c}\frac{\partial \mathbf{D}}{\partial t} \, , \tag{1.37}$$

$$\nabla \times \mathbf{E} = -\frac{1}{c}\frac{\partial \mathbf{B}}{\partial t} \, , \tag{1.38}$$

$$\nabla \cdot \mathbf{D} = 4\pi\rho_e \, , \tag{1.39}$$

and

$$\nabla \cdot \mathbf{B} = 0 \, . \tag{1.40}$$

The new quantities introduced are $\mathbf{D}$, the electric displacement; $\mathbf{H}$, the magnetic-field intensity; and ρ_e, the electric charge density. Both $\mathbf{E}$ and $\mathbf{B}$ (the electric field intensity and the magnetic induction or magnetic vector density) are the fundamental force vectors of free space, while $\mathbf{D}$ and $\mathbf{H}$ are derived vectors, associated with the state of matter.

The distinction between $\mathbf{B}$ and $\mathbf{H}$ disappears for a nonmagnetic medium. Therefore, eliminating the magnetic field between Equations (1.37) and (1.38), we find that

$$\nabla^2\mathbf{E} - \nabla\nabla \cdot \mathbf{E} + \frac{1}{c^2}\frac{\partial^2 \mathbf{D}}{\partial t^2} - \frac{4\pi}{c^2}\frac{\partial \mathbf{j}}{\partial t} = 0 \, . \tag{1.41}$$

It is now necessary to specify a relation between the vectors $\mathbf{D}$ and $\mathbf{j}$, on one hand, and $\mathbf{E}$ and $\mathbf{B}$, on the other. One generally states that

$$\mathbf{D} = \epsilon\mathbf{E} \tag{1.42}$$

and

$$\mathbf{j} = \sigma\mathbf{E} \, . \tag{1.43}$$

Equation (1.42) is valid only when one neglects the effects of spatial dispersion, that is, only if $\mathbf{D}$ is given by the local value of the electric field. Like the electric conductivity σ, the dielectric constant ϵ is a complicated tensor in the general case. For mathematical convenience, we often combine ϵ and σ into a complex dielectric permittivity ϵ', given by

$$\epsilon' = \epsilon - i(4\pi\sigma/\omega), \tag{1.44}$$

where ω is the angular frequency describing the assumed sinusoidal time dependence ($\exp i\omega t$) of all variables. Using this, we find that Equation (1.41) takes the form

$$\nabla^2 \mathbf{E} - \nabla\nabla \cdot \mathbf{E} + (\omega^2/c^2)\epsilon'\mathbf{E} = 0. \tag{1.45a}$$

Different approximations for the equation of motion lead to different expressions for the quantities ϵ and σ that enter the equation for $\mathbf{E}$ (and a similar equation for $\mathbf{B}$).

Equation (1.45a) is extremely complicated. When we consider a wave propagating normally to a plane parallel atmosphere, say in the z-direction, Equation (1.45a) reduces to

$$\frac{\partial^2 E_{x,y}}{\partial z^2} + \frac{\omega^2}{c^2}\,\epsilon' E_{x,y} = 0. \tag{1.45b}$$

Equations of this type are found in acoustics and, in general, in the theory of propagation of waves of any type (compare also the form of the Schrödinger equation). However, with an arbitrary function $\epsilon'(z, \omega)$, this equation has no solution in terms of known functions. Therefore, we have to consider specific cases.

Before we leave this general discussion of the basic equations in plasma physics, let us return to the fundamental question of the coupling between the electromagnetic field and the material motion. The generalized Ohm's law approximates, for many practical purposes, in a plasma to the form

$$\mathbf{j} = \sigma\left(\mathbf{E} + \frac{\mathbf{v}}{c} \times \mathbf{B_0}\right) = \mathbf{E}_v \tag{1.46}$$

where the electric field $\mathbf{E}_v$ is the field measured in a system moving with the velocity $\mathbf{v}$ of the plasma. It may contain both an externally applied component $\mathbf{E}$ as well as the one induced by the motion of the plasma, $\mathbf{v}/c \times \mathbf{B_0}$. On the other hand, the magnetic field is independent of the coordinate system in the nonrelativistic case and is made up both of any

externally applied field and the induced field. When the electric conduc-
tivity is very large, $\mathbf{E}_v$ must be very small for $\mathbf{j}$ to remain finite, and hence
we have

$$\mathbf{E} + \frac{\mathbf{v}}{c} \times \mathbf{B}_0 \approx 0, \tag{1.47}$$

that is, the electric field is approximately equal to the induced electric field
$\mathbf{v} \times \mathbf{B}_0$. If we restrict our analysis so that we do not consider very rapid
fluctuations, Maxwell's displacement current will be negligible compared to
the curl of the magnetic field. In this case, the appropriate Maxwell equation
is

$$\nabla \times \mathbf{B} = \frac{4\pi}{c} \mathbf{j}. \tag{1.48}$$

Furthermore, if we write Ohm's law in the form

$$\mathbf{E} = \frac{1}{\sigma} \mathbf{j} - \frac{\mathbf{v}}{c} \times \mathbf{B} = \frac{c}{4\pi\sigma} \nabla \times \mathbf{B} - \frac{\mathbf{v}}{c} \times \mathbf{B}, \tag{1.49}$$

Equations (1.48) and (1.49) allow us to express all the electromagnetic
variables in terms of the magnetic field $\mathbf{B}$. Therefore, in the important case
of very large electric conductivity, all but the very rapid oscillations can be
treated in terms of the interaction of the magnetic field with the gasdynamic
variables. This is equivalent to saying that the energy associated with the
electric field is vanishingly small compared to the magnetic energy. The
energy density contained in the electric field is

$$\frac{E^2}{8\pi} \approx \left(\frac{v}{c}\right)^2 \frac{B^2}{8\pi}$$

and, for all nonrelativistic applications, is much smaller than the magnetic
energy density.

We will often find that the equations of hydromagnetics can be written
in an approximation sufficient in many plasmas in a form slightly simpler
than the one given so far. By neglecting the displacement current and the
dielectric properties of the plasma (assuming no polarization of the ions)
and considering a nonmagnetic medium, we find that

$$\nabla \times \mathbf{B} = \frac{4\pi}{c} \mathbf{j}, \quad \nabla \times \mathbf{E} = -\frac{1}{c} \frac{\partial \mathbf{B}}{\partial t}, \quad \nabla \cdot \mathbf{j} = 0, \quad \nabla \cdot \mathbf{B} = 0.$$

Using Maxwell's equations in this form together with Equation (1.46) for the current density, we can deduce—provided that the electric conductivity is uniform in space—an equation that describes the changes in the magnetic field:

$$\frac{\partial \mathbf{B}}{\partial t} = \nabla \times (\mathbf{v} \times \mathbf{B}) + \frac{c^2}{4\pi\sigma} \nabla^2 \mathbf{B} . \qquad (1.50)$$

If the plasma is at rest, we have $\mathbf{v} = 0$, and Equation (1.50) reduces to

$$\frac{\partial \mathbf{B}}{\partial t} = \frac{c^2}{4\pi\sigma} \nabla^2 \mathbf{B} , \qquad (1.51)$$

an equation that shows how the magnetic field diffuses through the plasma. Here $\eta_m \equiv c^2/4\pi\sigma$ is defined as the magnetic diffusivity, and from dimensional arguments one concludes that the time of decay of the field due to this resistive diffusion, or Joule diffusion, is

$$\tau_{\text{diff}} \approx L^2/\eta_m , \qquad (1.52)$$

where L is a characteristic length of the plasma in which the currents flow. If the plasma has infinite electric conductivity, Equation (1.50) reduces to

$$\partial \mathbf{B}/\partial t = \nabla \times (\mathbf{v} \times \mathbf{B}) . \qquad (1.53)$$

If we replace the magnetic field $\mathbf{B}$ in this equation with the vorticity $\boldsymbol{\omega} \equiv \nabla \times \mathbf{v}$ (from the theory of flow of nonviscous fluids), we have the exact equation for the transport of vorticity, which states that the vortex lines move with the fluid. Consequently, we interpret Equation (1.53) to mean that in a plasma of infinite conductivity, the magnetic lines of force move with the fluid, or, if we follow the nomenclature of Alfvén, the lines of force are "frozen" into the material. Motion along the lines of force is not affected, but when material motion perpendicular to the lines of force occurs, the lines are carried with the material.

From dimensional analysis we find again that the transport expressed by Equation (1.53) dominates over the diffusion as given by Equation (1.51) when $Lv/\eta_m \gg 1$. The ratio

$$R_m \equiv Lv/\eta_m \qquad (1.54)$$

is defined as the "magnetic Reynold's number," in analogy with the equation defining the Reynold's number of fluid dynamics $R = Lv/\eta$.

1.1.4. Turbulence

1.1.4.1. *The problem of equipartition of energy*

One of the fundamental difficulties we encounter in describing the state of a plasma—and even more in understanding many physical processes going on in a plasma—is the lack of a theory of general turbulence and its interaction with magnetic fields. Even in the absence of magnetic fields, useful theories for the behavior of turbulent motions are available only for restricted types of turbulence. It has only been possible to formulate satisfactorily theories of stationary, homogeneous and isotropic turbulence. However, there is no reason to believe that the turbulent motions in the solar atmosphere and in the subphotospheric layers are homogeneous or isotropic, and they are hardly stationary. Turbulence is taken here in its "true" sense, as used in hydrodynamics, not in the sense of "astronomical turbulence," which is only another name for random mass motions different from the thermal motion of the plasma particles.

The basic idea of the phenomenon of turbulence is that the kinetic energy of the turbulent plasma cascades from the larger to the smaller eddies that make up the turbulent velocity field. We assume that the energy is supplied to the largest eddies, that is, to those components of the velocity field that have the smallest wave number k, after which the energy is transferred to higher and higher wave numbers. Finally, the energy is dissipated as heat by molecular viscosity in the highest wave numbers. In practice, there will be some extra dissipation of energy by viscosity at each wave number.

The transfer of energy from one wave number to a higher one is due to the inertial term in the equation of motion which provides a nonlinear coupling between the eddies, or otherwise stated, between the Fourier components of the velocity field. We can define a transition probability $P(E_{kin}, k_2 ; E_{kin}, k_3)$ which gives the rate at which the kinetic energy $E_{kin}(k_2)$ per unit volume and per unit wave-number interval around k_2 will be transformed into kinetic energy at wave number $k_3 > k_2$. Let the amount of viscous dissipation at wave number k be given by $\eta E_{kin}(k) \cdot k^2$. With $k_1 < k_2$, the rate of change of energy at k_2 may be written

$$\frac{\partial E_{kin}(k_2)}{\partial t} = \int_0^{k_2} P(E_{kin}, k_1; E_{kin}, k_2) \, dk_1$$

$$- \int_{k_2}^{\infty} P(E_{kin}, k_2; E_{kin}, k_3) \, dk_3 - \eta E_{kin}(k_2)k_2^2. \quad (1.55)$$

Following Heisenberg, we assume that the transition probability $P(E_{kin},$

k_2 ; E_{kin}, k_3) is proportional to an eddy viscosity $\eta(k_3)$:

$$P(E_{\text{kin}}, k_2 \; ; \; E_{\text{kin}}, k_3) = E_{\text{kin}}(k_2)k_2^2 \cdot \eta(k_3) . \tag{1.56}$$

From dimensional analysis, we further find for the viscosity the expression

$$\eta(k) = b\sqrt{E_{\text{kin}}(k)/k^3} , \tag{1.57}$$

giving for $P(E_{\text{kin}}, k_2 \; ; \; E_{\text{kin}}, k_3)$ Heisenberg's result,

$$P(E_{\text{kin}}, k_2 \; ; \; E_{\text{kin}}, k_3) = bE_{\text{kin}}(k_2)k_2^2 , \tag{1.58}$$

where b is a constant.

The coupling of magnetic and kinetic energy cascading from larger to smaller eddies has been investigated by Chandrasekhar (1952, 1955) in an attempt to develop a theory for hydromagnetic turbulence. There is a basic difference between the transition probabilities for the kinetic and the magnetic energies. This is because the equation of motion has a nonlinear term that permits transfer of kinetic energy from one wave number to another, but Maxwell's equations for the magnetic field are linear, and no *direct* transfer of magnetic energy from one wave number to another is possible. But due to the coupling with the nonlinear kinetic velocity field, such a transfer can nevertheless be realized.

Instead of Equation (1.55) which describes the purely hydrodynamic turbulence cascade, we need two equations to describe hydromagnetic turbulence transfer. According to Chandrasekhar, these equations may be written

$$\frac{\partial E_{\text{kin}}(k_2)}{\partial t} = \int_0^{k_2} P(E_{\text{kin}}, k_1; E_{\text{kin}}, k_2)\, dk_1$$

$$+ \int_0^{k_2} P(E_{\text{magn}}, k_1; E_{\text{kin}}, k_2)\, dk_1 - \int_{k_2}^{\infty} P(E_{\text{kin}}, k_2; E_{\text{kin}}, k_3)\, dk_3$$

$$- \int_{k_2}^{\infty} P(E_{\text{kin}}, k_2; E_{\text{magn}}, k_3)\, dk_3 - \eta E_{\text{kin}}(k_2)k_2^2 \tag{1.59}$$

and

$$\frac{\partial E_{\text{magn}}(k_2)}{\partial t} = \int_0^{k_2} P(E_{\text{kin}}, k_2; E_{\text{magn}}, k_3)\, dk_1$$

$$- \int_{k_2}^{\infty} P(E_{\text{magn}}, k_2; E_{\text{kin}}, k_3)\, dk_3 - K E_{\text{magn}}(k_2)k_2^2 . \tag{1.60}$$

The last term in Equation (1.60) represents the dissipation of magnetic energy to Joule heat by electric conductivity. Chandrasekhar argues that one of the new transition probabilities can be written

$$P(E_{\mathrm{magn}}, k_2 \; ; \; E_{\mathrm{kin}}, k_3) = bE_{\mathrm{magn}}(k_2)k_2^2\sqrt{E_{\mathrm{magn}}(k_3)/k_3^3}, \qquad (1.61)$$

showing that the transformation of magnetic energy at wave number k_2 into kinetic energy wave number k_3 is given in terms of the eddy resistivity

$$K(k) = b \cdot \sqrt{E_{\mathrm{magn}}(k)/k^3}\,.$$

The other transition probability, which describes the transformation of kinetic energy at wave number k_2 into magnetic energy at wave number k_3, is given by

$$P(E_{\mathrm{kin}}, k_2 \; ; \; E_{\mathrm{magn}}, k_3) = bE_{\mathrm{magn}}(k_2)k_2^2\sqrt{E_{\mathrm{kin}}(k_3)/k_3^3}$$
$$+ bE_{\mathrm{kin}}(k_2)k_2^2\sqrt{E_{\mathrm{magn}}(k_3)/k_3^3}\,. \quad (1.62)$$

Equations (1.59) and (1.60), with the definitions (1.58), (1.61), and (1.62), are the two basic equations of Chandrasekhar's hydromagnetic turbulence theory. Solutions can be found in the stationary case when $K = \eta = 0$, and we find that two modes of hydromagnetic turbulence exist. In both modes, the kinetic energy density equals the magnetic energy density for $k \to 0$. For the largest eddies, we consequently have equipartition of energy between the kinetic and magnetic energy forms, $\frac{1}{2}\rho v^2 = B^2/8\pi$. The difference between the two modes becomes evident for the smallest eddies, that is, when $k \to \infty$. In one mode, let us call it the kinetic mode, the magnetic energy density then goes to zero. In the other mode, called the magnetic mode, the magnetic energy density tends to a constant value about 2.6 times the kinetic energy density. This failure of the theory to show equipartition for the smallest eddies is in contradiction to other investigations and is not resolved.

1.1.4.2. Amplification of magnetic fields

Turbulent motions in a plasma may lead to strong spontaneous amplification of infinitesimal magnetic fields. Due to thermal fluctuations or for other reasons, there will always be small perturbations in the plasma, and these perturbations are accompanied by weak electric and magnetic fields. Depending on the properties of the plasma, the perturbations—and hence the fields—may be amplified or damped by turbulent motions.

There are two competing processes: a tendency toward damping of the fields due to their dissipation through Joule heating by the induced currents, and a tendency to strengthen the magnetic field due to the stretching of the magnetic lines of force. From a study of the conditions under which these two processes balance, we can derive a criterion to tell us when magnetic fields are amplified by the turbulent motions.

In the following material, we shall assume that the amplified field which is due to the turbulent motion does not significantly affect the turbulence itself; that is, we assume a statistically steady turbulent velocity distribution unaffected by the changing magnetic field. This means that the more general equation of motion for the plasma in the presence of a magnetic field

$$\frac{\partial \mathbf{v}}{\partial t} + (\mathbf{v} \cdot \nabla)\mathbf{v} = -\frac{1}{\rho} \nabla\left(p + \frac{B^2}{8\pi}\right) + \frac{1}{4\pi\rho}(\mathbf{B} \cdot \nabla)\mathbf{B} + \eta\nabla^2\mathbf{v}$$

reduces to the ordinary Navier-Stokes equation of fluid dynamics

$$\frac{\partial \mathbf{v}}{\partial t} + (\mathbf{v} \cdot \nabla)\mathbf{v} = -\frac{1}{\rho}\nabla p + \eta\,\nabla^2\mathbf{v}. \tag{1.63}$$

Introducing the vorticity $\boldsymbol{\omega} \equiv \nabla \times \mathbf{v}$ and assuming an incompressible gas, we can write Equation (1.63) in the form

$$\frac{\partial \boldsymbol{\omega}}{\partial t} = \nabla \times (\mathbf{v} \times \boldsymbol{\omega}) + \eta\,\nabla^2\boldsymbol{\omega}.$$

This is formally the same equation as that satisfied by the magnetic field $\mathbf{B}$ (Maxwell's equation), which is Equation (1.50):

$$\frac{\partial \mathbf{B}}{\partial t} = \nabla \times (\mathbf{v} \times \mathbf{B}) + \eta_m\,\nabla^2\mathbf{B},$$

where $\eta_m = c^2/4\pi\sigma$. Hence, if $\eta = \eta_m$, we must have a relation $\mathbf{B} = \text{const} \cdot \boldsymbol{\omega}$. In this case we have a statistically steady magnetic field where dissipation of magnetic energy through Joule heating exactly balances the increase due to the stretching of the field lines. Since the dissipation is proportional to j^2/σ, we see that for values of σ greater than that corresponding to the equilibrium condition $\eta_m = \eta$, the increase in magnetic field strength due to stretching will become dominant, and instability, that is, amplification, occurs. The condition for this is therefore

$$\eta > \eta_m \qquad \text{or} \qquad \sigma > c^2/4\pi\eta. \tag{1.64}$$

This result is due to Batchelor (1950). Since this instability criterion is derived with the assumption that we can neglect the effect of the amplified field on the hydrodynamic turbulence, it is obvious that it will break down if the amplification leads to sufficiently strong fields. Therefore, it is unlikely that we will encounter conditions far removed from equipartition.

1.2. Deviations from Thermodynamic Equilibrium

A more general approach to the problem of a radiating gas than that provided by the conditions of LTE (local thermodynamic equilibrium) replaces these conditions by the assumption of a statistically steady state in each atomic energy level. In other words, the distributions of electrons in the various energy levels of the atom or ion remain statistically constant in time. Then there are as many electrons leaving a level as there are entering it. When we include collisionally induced transitions, this treatment becomes a generalization of the "principle of reversibility" discussed by Rosseland (1926) and which has been developed by Giovanelli (1948), Thomas (1948a, 1948b), Jefferies (1953), and others. Because they are coupled, the equations governing the statistical equilibrium and the equations describing the transfer of radiation through the gas must be solved simultaneously. The difficulties encountered in this process are formidable, and the problem has been only partly solved.

We define the source function at a given frequency ν as the ratio between the emissivity of the plasma and its absorptivity:

$$S_\nu = \epsilon_\nu / k_\nu . \tag{1.65}$$

In thermodynamic equilibrium, this ratio is given uniquely by the Planck function

$$S_\nu(\text{LTE}) = B_\nu(T_e). \tag{1.66}$$

In the low-density, high-temperature plasma of the solar atmosphere, this equation is no longer generally correct. In the presence of spectral lines, we may write the source function

$$S_\nu = \frac{\epsilon_\kappa + \epsilon_L}{k_\kappa + k_L} ,$$

where subscript κ refers to the continuous radiation and subscript L to the radiation in the line. We write

$$S_\nu = \frac{S_L + r_\nu S_\kappa}{1 + r_\nu} , \tag{1.67}$$

where $r_\nu = k_\kappa/k_L$ is the ratio of the continuous absorption coefficient to the line absorption coefficient at the given frequency. Instead of the absorption coefficient, we often use the optical depth (or opacity) τ_ν defined by

$$d\tau_\nu = -k_\nu\, ds\,, \tag{1.68}$$

where ds is an element of geometric length. We have

$$d\tau_\nu = -(k_\kappa + k_L)\, ds = d\tau_\kappa + d\tau_L = (1 + r_\nu)\, d\tau_L\,. \tag{1.69}$$

It is often convenient to measure the optical depth in terms of the opacity at the line center τ_0. This is easily performed if the absorption coefficient is Gaussian over the core of the line, that is, if

$$\tau_\nu = \tau_0 e^{-(\nu/\nu_0)^2}\,. \tag{1.70}$$

We shall presently return to this form of the optical depth.

We assume that the source function for the continuum is equal to the Planck function:

$$S_\kappa = B(T_e)\,. \tag{1.71}$$

It can be shown (Pagel, 1956, 1957, 1959; Thomas and Athay, 1961) that departures from LTE in the continuous source function are negligible for $\tau_\kappa > 0.01$ (measured at 5000 Å), that is, so long as we consider emission and absorption in the photosphere and low chromosphere. The line source function is, however, not equal to the Planck function, but, quite generally, it may be written (Thomas, 1957) as

$$S_L = B(T_{\mathrm{ex}}) \frac{j_\nu}{\phi_\nu}\,,$$

where ϕ_ν and j_ν are the profiles of the absorption and spontaneous emission coefficients. In general, j_ν/ϕ_ν varies with frequency across the line. Only if $j_\nu/\phi_\nu = 1$ does T_{ex} have its usual meaning of the excitation temperature, and the source function reduces to

$$S_L = B_\nu(T_{\mathrm{ex}})\,. \tag{1.72}$$

This expression is a good approximation for the core of resonance lines. It may be written as

$$S_L = \frac{2h\nu^3}{c^2} (e^{h\nu/kT_{\mathrm{ex}}} - 1)^{-1} = \frac{2h\nu^3}{c^2} \left(\frac{n_1}{n_u}\frac{g_u}{g_1} - 1\right)^{-1}\,, \tag{1.73}$$

which shows that, to determine the line source function, we must evaluate
the ratio of the populations n_1 and n_u of the lower and upper energy levels
associated with the line in question. This is done from the equations of
statistical equilibrium, which may be written

$$dn_j/dt = \sum_{\substack{i=1, \\ i \neq j}}^{\kappa} (n_i P_{ij} - n_j P_{ji}) = 0, \qquad j = 1, 2, 3, \ldots, \kappa. \qquad (1.74)$$

Here n_j is the population of the jth level in the atom considered, and κ
denotes the continuum. Also P_{ij} is the total rate for transitions from level
i to level j and is a sum of two terms

$$P_{ij} = C_{ij} + R_{ij},$$

where C_{ij} refers to the collisionally induced transitions, while R_{ij} is the
radiative transition rate.

If $j > i$, then R_{ji} will be the Einstein coefficient for spontaneous emission,
A_{ji}, plus the transition rate due to induced (stimulated) emission, $B_{ji} \int J_v \psi_v \, dv$.
Here B_{ji} is the Einstein coefficient for induced emission, J_v is the mean
intensity of the radiation field averaged over direction, $J_v = (1/4\pi) \int I_v \, d\Omega$,
and ψ_v is the profile of the induced emission coefficient. We set

$$B_{ji} \int J_v \psi_v \, dv = \bar{J} B_{ji},$$

so that we have

$$R_{ji} = A_{ji} + \bar{J} B_{ji}. \qquad (1.75)$$

Similarly, the radiative rate for absorption is

$$R_{ij} = B_{ij} \int J_v \phi_v \, dv = \bar{J} B_{ij}, \qquad (1.76)$$

where B_{ij} is the Einstein coefficient for absorption.

The Einstein coefficients are known to satisfy the equations

$$B_{ji} = A_{ji}(\lambda^5/2hc^2) \qquad \text{and} \qquad B_{ij} = (g_j/g_i) B_{ji}, \qquad (1.77)$$

where g_i and g_j are the statistical weights of the levels i and j, respectively.
The profiles are normalized such that

$$\int \psi_v \, dv = \int \phi_v \, dv = 1,$$

and we will furthermore assume in the following that the two profiles ψ_v and
ϕ_v are equal, that is, $\psi_v = \phi_v$.

The rates to the continuum are

$$R_{i\kappa} = JB_{i\kappa} = 2\pi \int \frac{q_\nu J_\nu \, d\nu}{h\nu} = \frac{2\pi}{hc} \int q_\lambda I_\lambda \lambda \, d\lambda, \qquad (1.78)$$

where q_ν is the photo-ionization cross section; the rates from the continuum, that is, the photo-recombination rates, are $R_{\kappa i}$.

To compute the collision rates C requires knowledge of the corresponding cross sections Q for electron collisions; that is, we need to know Q_{ij} for collisional excitation, and $Q_{i\kappa}$ for collisional ionization. When these are known, we can find the rates by integrating the cross sections over the electron-velocity distribution. When this is Maxwellian, we have

$$vf(v) \, dv = \frac{8\pi m_e}{(2\pi m_e k T_e)^{3/2}} e^{-E/kT_e} \, E \, dE,$$

where E is the energy of the colliding electron, $E = \frac{1}{2}mv^2$, and we find that

$$C = \frac{8\pi m_e n_e}{(2\pi m_e k T_e)^{3/2}} \int_{E_0}^{\infty} Q(E) e^{-E/kT_e} \, E \, dE. \qquad (1.79)$$

The solution of the statistical equilibrium Equation (1.74) may be put in the form

$$n_i/n_j = P^{ij}/P^{ji}, \qquad (1.80)$$

which dates back to Rosseland (1936) and where P^{ij} is the cofactor of the element P_{ij} in the matrix of the coefficients of Equation (1.74).

This value of the ratio of the populations should now be inserted into Equation (1.73) to find the source function, but Equations (1.75) and (1.76), for instance, reveal that this ratio will depend on the radiation field J_ν. To find J_ν, we must solve the equation of transfer for the radiation through the plasma. We write the transfer equation in the Eddington approximation as

$$\frac{1}{3} \frac{d^2 J_\nu}{d\tau_\nu^2} = J_\nu - S_\nu, \qquad (1.81)$$

which shows that we need the source function to extract J_ν. Consequently, we see that the equations of the problem (the equations for statistical equilibrium, the expression for the source function and the transfer equation) are strongly coupled and must be solved simultaneously.

Using the expressions of Equations (1.67), (1.69), and (1.70), we can write Equation (1.81) in the form

$$\frac{1}{x_\nu^2} \frac{d^2 J_\nu}{d\tau_0^2} = J_\nu - \frac{S_L + r_\nu S_\kappa}{1 + r_\nu}, \qquad (1.82)$$

where

$$x_\nu = \sqrt{3}(1 + r_\nu)e^{-(\Delta\nu/\Delta\nu_D)^2}.$$

By specifying the form of the source function S_κ, we then solve Equation (1.82) in terms of a Gaussian quadrature over frequency (Jefferies and Thomas, 1960).

If we are interested in phenomena taking place in photospheric or sub-photospheric layers, the continuous source function may often be approximated by the first terms of a series expansion

$$S_\kappa = B_0(1 + \beta\tau), \tag{1.83}$$

where β is a parameter that determines a simple linear change of the source function with depth. A similar form is probably appropriate when we study the emission from prominences and flares observed well outside the solar limb (against the sky background). However, when the phenomenon investigated takes place in chromospheric regions, the form of the continuous source function becomes more complicated. Then S_κ should portray the particular temperature structure of the transition region from the approximately 4500°K photosphere to the much hotter upper chromosphere and corona. A form that suitably performs this task is

$$S_\kappa = B_0(1 + \beta\tau + Ae^{-c\tau}), \tag{1.84}$$

where the term $B_0(1 + \beta\tau)$ again represents the photospheric contribution; $B_0 Ae^{-c\tau}$ represents the subsequent chromospheric rise and the first plateau (Thomas and Athay, 1961);

$B_0 =$ Planck function at the temperature minimum between the photosphere and the chromosphere, that is, the Planck function for about 4500°K;

$\beta = \frac{3}{2}r_0$, where r_0 is the value in the center of the line of the quantity $r_\nu = d\tau_\kappa/d\tau_\nu$;

$A = B(T_{max})/B_0$ and T_{max} is the value of the temperature in the "plateau" that follows the steep temperature rise in the chromosphere;

$c =$ inverse scale height of the chromospheric temperature gradient.

By adding more terms of the form $Ae^{-c\tau}$, we may account for more complex structures of the chromosphere–corona interface.

1.3. *Transport Phenomena*

1.3.1. Unified Treatment

A plasma in strict thermodynamic equilibrium is not subjected to any transport phenomenon. We have seen that in such a gas, the velocity-distribution function f of the particles is Maxwellian, Equation (1.4):

$$f(v) = (m/2\pi kT)^{3/2} e^{-mv^2/2kT} \, ,$$

and $\nabla f = \partial f/\partial t = 0$.

If $\partial f/\partial t \neq 0$, the gas is in a nonsteady state, and if $\nabla f \neq 0$, the gas is in a *nonuniform state*. The transport phenomena (viscosity, conduction, and diffusion) are concerned with gases that are not in a uniform state, whether or not they are in a steady state.

In the case of viscosity, we are concerned with a transport of momentum, brought about by the effort of the plasma to smear out a nonuniformity in velocity among the particles. Thermal conduction is associated with a temperature difference leading to the transport of (heat) energy, while a nonuniformity in composition is responsible for diffusion. Viscosity and heat transport may, therefore, be found in a gas consisting of only one kind of particle, but to experience diffusion a gas must consist of at least two different kinds of particles. In yet another respect, diffusion is to be regarded as a transport of a special nature. The atomic or molecular properties transported in viscosity and conduction (momentum and energy) are dynamic quantities, but in diffusion it is the concentration of a particular species of particles that is transported. Nevertheless, all three types of transport phenomena may be subjected to the same mathematical treatment. They all depend on the gradient of some parameter X of the plasma associated with the transported quantity. The flow of the transported quantity, that is, the net transport per unit area per second, may be written

$$\mathbf{j} = -D \cdot \nabla X \,, \tag{1.85}$$

where D is the transport coefficient.

We should also note that the electric conductivity σ treated in Section 1.1 also governs a transport phenomenon, that of electricity, and the simplest Ohm's law, $\mathbf{j} = \sigma \mathbf{E} = -\sigma \nabla \chi$, is seen to have the same form as Equation (1.85).

If we combine Equation (1.85) with the equation of continuity for the transported quantity,

$$\partial X/\partial t = -\nabla \cdot \mathbf{j} \,,$$

we find the equation governing the transport phenomenon:

$$\partial X/\partial t = D\nabla^2 X .$$

This is called the diffusion equation [compare Equation (1.85)], and in the one-dimensional case it is the simplest form of a parabolic partial differential equation that describes a completely damped motion. The quantity governed by such an equation will, therefore, always tend toward uniformity; no oscillations can occur since there is no "overshooting," as in the case of the wave equation (where the term $\partial X/\partial t$ is replaced by $\partial^2 X/\partial t^2$).

When we consider viscosity, we identify the parameter X with the average momentum of a particle in the direction of the flow, $m\bar{v}$, and $\mathbf{j}$ denotes the net transport of momentum per unit time across unit area in a plane perpendicular to the flow, that is, the shearing stress tensor $\mathscr{P}$ over the plane

$$\mathscr{P} = -\eta\nabla\mathbf{v} ,$$

where η is the coefficient of viscosity. It is one of the purposes of kinetic theories of gases to deduce the values of this and other transport coefficients.

In the case of heat conduction, X is the amount of heat per unit volume, $X = c_v T$, where c_v is the heat capacity per unit volume, or the mean thermal energy per particle, $\frac{1}{2}mv^2 = \frac{3}{2}kT$, while $\mathbf{j}$ is the heat flow vector $\mathbf{q}$:

$$\mathbf{q} = -K\nabla T ,$$

where K, the thermal conductivity, is $c_v D$. Inserting $X = c_v T$, we find an equation for the temperature, which therefore is a solution for the diffusion equation with $D = K/c_v$.

Finally, in the case of diffusion, the property X is a probability, namely the probability that the particle considered is of the right kind, n_1 say, that is, $X = n_1/n$, where n is the total number density of particles. Here $\mathbf{j}$ is the net transport of particles n_1. In the case of a two-component gas mixture, we have

$$\mathbf{j}_1 = -D_{12}\nabla n_1, \quad \text{and} \quad \mathbf{j}_2 = -D_{21}\nabla n_2,$$

and $n = n_1 + n_2 \cdot D_{12} = D_{21}$ if we have uniform total pressure and temperature.

1.3.2. Diffusion

Diffusion covers a heterogeneous set of phenomena of great importance in plasma physics, and we shall now consider this type of transport in some detail. We have mentioned that, to experience diffusion, a gas must consist of at least two different kinds of particles. For multicomponent gas mixtures, the equations governing diffusion become considerably more complicated and the amount of work involved to solve them may become prohibitively large. Also, the physics becomes more involved, and a binary gas approximation may be quite misleading. Before we enter into the general case, we will give a treatment of a two-component gas mixture.

In a binary gas, the diffusion velocity is given by (Chapman and Cowling, 1952)

$$\bar{\mathbf{v}}_1 - \bar{\mathbf{v}}_2 = -D_{12}\left[\ln\frac{c_1}{c_2} - \frac{m_1 - m_2}{m}\nabla\ln p - \frac{m_1 m_2}{mkT}\left(\frac{\mathbf{F}_1}{m_1} - \frac{\mathbf{F}_2}{m_2}\right) + \alpha_{12}\nabla\ln T\right],$$

(1.86)

where subscripts 1 and 2 refer to the two different kinds of particles. The different terms on the right-hand side of Equation (1.86) represent the velocities of (1) concentration diffusion, (2) pressure diffusion, (3) forced diffusion, (4) thermal diffusion.

The particle mass and external force are denoted by m_1 and $\mathbf{F}_1$. It is convenient to attach the subscript 1 to symbols relating to the heavier particles. Thus we have $m = c_1 m_1 + c_2 m_2$, and we find that

$$\alpha_{12} = k_T/c_1 c_2 = \text{thermal diffusion factor, and}$$

$$k_T = \text{thermal diffusion ratio.}$$

In a plasma where a large proportion of the atoms is ionized, electrostatic forces play a dominant part in the collision processes between the ions. The interionic force is that force from a point center, $F(r) = \text{const}/r^s$, with $s = 2$, that is, we have

$$F(r) = Z_1 Z_2 (e^2/r^2),$$

and to a first approximation the diffusion coefficient and the thermal diffusion factor are given by

$$D_{12} = \frac{3}{16n}\left\{\frac{2kT}{\pi[m_1 m_2/(m_1 + m_2)]}\right\}^{1/2}\left(\frac{2kT}{Z_1 Z_2 e^2}\right)^2\frac{1}{A_1(2)},$$

$$\alpha_{12} = 5(C - 1)f(m, Z, c),$$

where

$$C = 2(3s - 5)/5(s - 1) = \tfrac{2}{5}.$$

The function $f(m, Z, c)$ is a complicated expression depending on mass, charge, and concentration.

It is interesting to note that Maxwell (1867) studied diffusion phenomena due to nonequilibrium states mathematically, but he succeeded only for a gas in which the force $F(r) = \text{const}/r^5$, that is, $s = 5$. It turns out that for this value of s, $C = 1$, that is, $\alpha_{12}(s = 5) = 0$, and the phenomenon of thermal diffusion vanishes for such a "Maxwellian" gas. The phenomenon was discovered independently by Chapman (1916) and Enskog (1917) from theoretical studies, although the Soret effect, that is, thermal diffusion in liquids, had been known since the works of Ludwig (1856) and Soret (1879, 1880a, 1880b).

In a plasma, $s = 2$ and $(C - 1)$ is negative, meaning that the heavier ions (m_1) will diffuse toward the warmer regions. In a steady state with uniform pressure and no external net force acting, Equation (1.86) takes the form

$$\nabla \ln (c_1/c_2) = -\alpha_{12} \nabla \ln T . \tag{1.87}$$

The absence of a concentration gradient implies uniform temperature. With variable temperature, a density gradient must balance the temperature gradient. If we can neglect the variation of α_{12} with c over the range of c involved, the solution of Equation (1.87) may be written

$$c_1'/c_1 = (T'/T)^{-\alpha_{12}} , \tag{1.88}$$

where a prime refers to conditions in the hotter region, and c and T refer to conditions in the adjacent, cooler atmosphere.

Large, quiet regions of the corona seem to be isothermal at an approximately constant pressure. In this case, pressure diffusion and thermal diffusion vanish, and if the gas has reached a steady state, Equation (1.86) reduces to

$$\nabla \ln \frac{c_1}{c_2} = \frac{m_1 m_2}{mkT} \left(\frac{Z_1}{m_1} - \frac{Z_2}{m_2} \right) e\mathbf{E} , \qquad \text{where} \quad \mathbf{F} = e\mathbf{E} .$$

In an electron–proton plasma, this may be written

$$\nabla \ln \frac{c_1}{c_2} = \frac{1}{c_1} \frac{e\mathbf{E}}{kT} ;$$

this illustrates how the concentration gradient balances the force due to the electric field.

The only astrophysical application of diffusion in a binary gas mixture is for a pure hydrogen plasma. In all other cases, we shall have to consider diffusion in a multicomponent gas. If, for instance, we want to study the diffusion of a tracer element in a hydrogen plasma, we take recourse to a ternary gas mixture.

The expression for the mass flux vector in a gas mixture consisting of s different atoms or ions of mass m_i and number density n_i, $i = 1, 2, \cdots s$ is

$$\mathbf{j}_i = n_i m_i \mathbf{v}_i = \frac{n^2}{\rho} \sum_{j=1}^{s} m_i m_j D_{ij} \mathbf{d}_j - D_i^T \nabla \ln T. \qquad (1.89)$$

Here $\mathbf{v}_i$ is the diffusion velocity of particles of kind i and the vector $\mathbf{d}_j$ is given by

$$\mathbf{d}_j = \nabla \left(\frac{n_j}{n}\right) + \left[\frac{n_j}{n} - \frac{n_j m_j}{\rho}\right] \nabla \ln p - \frac{n_j m_j}{\rho p} \left[\frac{\rho}{m_j} \mathbf{F}_j - \sum_{k=1}^{s} n_k \mathbf{F}_k\right].$$

Here D_{ij} is the coefficient of ordinary diffusion, D_i^T is the coefficient of thermal diffusion, $\mathbf{F}$ is the external force, and ρ is the density, while p denotes the pressure. Furthermore, let F_{ij} be given by

$$F_{ij} = (1 - \delta_{ij}) \left[\frac{n_i}{\rho D_{ij}(1)} + \sum_{l \neq i} \frac{n_e m_j}{\rho m_i D_{il}(1)}\right]$$

where $D_{ij}(1)$ are the diffusion coefficients for a binary gas (see, for instance, Chapman and Cowling, 1952). Then we have

$$D_{ij} = \frac{F^{ij} - F^{ii}}{m_j |F|}, \qquad (1.90)$$

where F^{ij} are the cofactors of F_{ij} in the determinant $|F|$ of the F_{ij} given by the equation for F_{ij}.

The expression for the coefficient of thermal diffusion is

$$D_i^T = |Q, R|/|Q| \, n_i \sqrt{m_i kT/2}, \qquad (1.91)$$

where the two determinants $|Q, R|$ and $|Q|$ are complicated functions of the collision integrals $\Omega_{ij}^{(l,s)}$ used by Chapman and Cowling (see, for instance, Curtiss and Hirschfelder, 1949).

For an ionized gas which we generally want to consider, the important external force is $F_i = e_i E_i$, where e_i is the charge of ions of type i. The expression for $\mathbf{d}_j$ then reduces to

$$\mathbf{d}_j = \nabla \left(\frac{n_j}{n}\right) + \left[\frac{n_j}{n} - \frac{n_j m_j}{\rho}\right] \nabla \ln p - \frac{n_j e_j}{p} \mathbf{E}.$$

The field E is set up due to space charge separations, and this field must be evaluated before the velocity due to ordinary diffusion can be calculated. To bring out some of the important physics, let us consider the following situation. We want to calculate the diffusion of a tracer element in a hydrogen plasma. In a binary gas approximation, one must neglect the presence of the electrons but may still evaluate the field E as being that due to the space charge separation of electrons and protons. What really happens, however, is that the tracer ions do not diffuse relative to the protons, but a complex of tracer ions, each surrounded by an appropriate electron cloud, diffuse through the protons, which similarly carry with them a certain proportion of the electrons. This difference is large enough to lead to serious errors in the binary gas approximation.

1.3.3. Transport Phenomena in the Presence of a Magnetic Field

We have seen in Section 1.1 how the electric conductivity tensor σ is affected by the presence of a magnetic field in the plasma. Similar behavior is also found for the other transport coefficients.

The equation for the heat flux vector becomes

$$\mathbf{q} = - \frac{K}{1 + (\omega_B \tau)^2} \left[\nabla T + \left(\frac{\omega_B \tau}{B} \right) \nabla T \times \mathbf{B} \right], \qquad (1.92)$$

where $\omega_B = eB/mc$, and τ is the collision interval (mean time between successive collisions). The effects of the magnetic field on the thermal flow are seen to be twofold. First, we observe a reduction of the flow along the temperature gradient by a factor $[1 + (\omega_B \tau)^2]$. The physical reason for this decrease in heat conductivity, that is, in the mobility of the plasma particles perpendicular to the magnetic field, is that the (charged) particles of the plasma are forced to gyrate around the magnetic field lines. They can do so while moving freely parallel to a line, and the conductivity along the magnetic field is therefore not affected. But perpendicular to the field, the particles can only move if they undergo collisions with other particles, whereby the spiraling is interrupted. The product $\omega_B \tau$, which determines the reduction factor, is given by (Alfvén, 1950)

$$\omega_B \tau = 10^6 \frac{B T^{3/2}}{n} . \qquad (1.93)$$

The other effect is that in addition to the ordinary thermal flow, there is a flow perpendicular to both $\mathbf{B}$ and ∇T, that is, in the direction $\mathbf{B} \times \nabla T$. This is called the Righi-Leduc effect, and the corresponding conductivity is $\omega_B \tau$ times the direct conductivity.

We have seen that when an electric field is present, there is a current flowing in the $\mathbf{B} \times \mathbf{E}$ direction called the Hall current. Now, diffusion in any direction is accompanied by a heat flow in that direction. Hence, there will be transport of heat along with the Hall current; this is known as the Ettingshausen effect.

The equation of diffusion in a binary gas, Equation (1.86), takes the following form in the presence of a magnetic field (we do not give the generalization to the more complex multicomponent gas mixture):

$$\bar{\mathbf{v}}_1 - \bar{\mathbf{v}}_2 = - \frac{D_{12}}{1 + (\omega_B \tau)^2}$$
$$\times \left[(\mathbf{d}_{12} + \alpha_{12} \nabla \ln T) + \left(\frac{\omega_B \tau}{B} \right) (\mathbf{d}_{12} + \alpha_{12} \nabla \ln T) \times \mathbf{B} \right], \quad (1.94)$$

where in this case the vector $\mathbf{d}_{12}$ is given by

$$\mathbf{d}_{12} = \nabla \ln \frac{c_1}{c_2} - \frac{m_1 - m_2}{m} \nabla \ln p - \frac{m_1 m_2}{mkT} \left(\frac{\mathbf{F}_1}{m_1} - \frac{\mathbf{F}_2}{m_2} \right).$$

The similarity between Equations (1.94) and (1.92) is obvious; the vector $\mathbf{d}_{12} + \alpha_{12} \nabla \ln T$ corresponds to the temperature gradient.

1.4. *Mathematical Background for Spectral Analysis*

Important information about the physical conditions in a plasma may be obtained from a study of its spectrum. Since the solar atmosphere is not in thermodynamic equilibrium, the observed spectrum will reveal absorption and emission lines. Both the continuous spectrum as well as the shape of the lines contain valuable clues. We shall now give some of the background necessary to utilize these clues.

1.4.1. Absorption Coefficients

In classical theory, the atoms are approximated with linear oscillators of frequency ν_0, and the energy radiated by these oscillators decays as

$$E = E_0 e^{-\gamma t},$$

where γ is the damping constant. The classical theory further predicts that the oscillators can absorb radiation around their resonance frequency ν_0 and gives the following expression for the absorption coefficient:

$$\alpha_\nu = \frac{\pi e^2}{4\pi^2 (\nu - \nu_0)^2 + (\gamma/2)^2}. \quad (1.95)$$

The total absorption per cm³ is

$$\int_0^\infty \alpha_\nu n \, d\nu = \int_0^\infty k_\nu \, d\nu = (\pi e^2/mc)n \, ,$$

where n is the number of particles (i.e., harmonic oscillators) per cm³.

In quantum theory, the corresponding expression becomes

$$\int_0^\infty k_\nu \, d\nu = (h\nu/c)B_{ij}n_i \, ,$$

where B_{ij} is the Einstein coefficient for absorption between the energy states i and j of the atom, and n_i is the number of atoms in state i. We introduce the oscillator strength f_{ij} which gives the number of classical oscillators that are required to give the same absorption as one atom in state i. It is easily seen that the classical and quantum mechanical treatments give the same results provided that (1) the decay constant γ is replaced by the sum of the inverse lifetimes of the two atomic states involved, and (2) the number of oscillators per unit volume is replaced by the product of the oscillator strength and the number density of atoms in the lower state:

$$n \to n_i f_{ij} \quad \text{and} \quad \gamma \to \sum_k A_{ik} + \sum_m A_{jm} \, .$$

Here A_{ik} is the Einstein coefficient for transition from state i to state k. The expression for the oscillator strength or Ladenburg f-value is

$$f_{ij} = \frac{h\nu m}{\pi e^2} B_{ij} \quad \text{or} \quad f_{ij} = \frac{mc^3}{8\pi^2 e^2 \nu^2} \frac{g_j}{g_i} A_{ij} \, . \tag{1.96}$$

The three main sources of continuous radiation in astrophysical plasmas are due to bound–free and free–free transitions and to scattering, mainly by electrons. The first case (photo-ionization and radiative recombination) is concerned only with quanta whose energy exceed the ionization potential χ_i of the energy state involved. The corresponding frequencies obey the inequality

$$h\nu_i \geq \chi_i \, .$$

The quantum theory predicts that the absorption coefficient for such frequencies is proportional to ν^{-3} (a result already found by Kramers in his classical treatment). We may define the oscillator strength df per frequency interval $d\nu$. For the simple—and important—case of hydrogenlike atoms and ions, the continuous absorption coefficient per atom, α_κ or α_{bf}, may be written

$$\alpha_\kappa = \frac{\pi e^2}{mc} \frac{df}{d\nu} \, . \tag{1.97}$$

Expressed in terms of the quantum number, Rydberg's constant, and the charge on the nucleus, the frequencies of the spectral lines in a series are given by

$$\nu = \text{Ry } Z^2 \left(\frac{1}{n^2} - \frac{1}{m^2} \right) .$$

Similarly, the continuous spectrum may be expressed in the same form if we introduce a quantum number κ for the continuum

$$\nu = \text{Ry } Z^2 \left(\frac{1}{n^2} + \frac{1}{\kappa^2} \right) .$$

From the expression for the energy of the expelled electron, $\frac{1}{2}mv^2 = h((\text{Ry } Z^2)/\kappa^2)$, we find (with $mv \, dv = h \, d\nu$) that

$$\frac{df}{d\nu} = \frac{df}{d\kappa} \frac{\kappa^3}{2 \text{ Ry } Z^2} .$$

Here $df/d\kappa$ can be found in terms of n and κ from quantum mechanical calculations, and this leads to

$$\alpha_\kappa(n) = \frac{32}{3\sqrt{3}} \frac{\pi^2 e^6 \text{ Ry } Z^4}{ch^3 n^5} \frac{1}{\nu^3} g_{\text{bf}} = 2.815 \times 10^{29} \frac{Z^4}{n^5} \frac{1}{\nu^3} g_{\text{bf}} . \qquad (1.98)$$

The factor g_{bf}, the Gaunt factor (Gaunt, 1930), is a correction term to the classical Kramers formula (Kramers, 1923).

Rydberg's constant is

$$\text{Ry} = \frac{2\pi^2 e^4 m_e}{h^3} = 3.287871 \times 10^{15} \text{ sec}^{-1} .$$

The Gaunt factor can be expressed as (Menzel and Pekeris, 1936)

$$g_{\text{bf}} \approx 1 - 0.1728 \sqrt[3]{\frac{\nu}{\text{Ry } Z^2}} \left[\frac{2}{n^2} \left(\frac{\text{Ry } Z^2}{\nu} - 1 \right) \right] .$$

The absorption coefficient (1.98) refers to the absorption by an atom in a particular quantum state n. The ν^{-3} dependence describes the behavior of the coefficient between any two absorption edges, and, to find the total absorption by the atom at a given frequency ν, we must sum over all the edges at frequencies $\nu_n = \chi_n/h \leq \nu$. To do this we must make some hypothesis regarding the distribution of atoms over the different quantum states. Only in LTE is this easily done, by taking recourse to the equations of Boltzmann and Saha.

The contribution by the free–free transitions, that is, the absorption (or emission) due to the acceleration (or deceleration) of electrons in the Coulomb field of a charge Ze, is given in terms of the free–free absorption coefficient

$$\alpha_{ff} = \frac{4\pi Z^2 e^6}{3\sqrt{3}\ hcm^2}\frac{1}{v}\frac{1}{\nu^3}\ g_{ff}, \tag{1.99}$$

where v is the velocity of the free electrons and g_{ff} is the free–free Gaunt factor. If the distribution of the velocities is Maxwellian at a temperature T, we find that

$$k_{ff} = \frac{16\pi^2}{3\sqrt{3}}\frac{Z^2 e^6}{hc(2\pi m)^{3/2}}\frac{n_e^2}{(kT)^{1/2}}\frac{1}{\nu^3}\ g_{ff} = 3.68\times 10^8\ \frac{Z^2 n_e^2}{T^{1/2}\nu^3}\ g_{ff}. \tag{1.100}$$

The third important source of continuous radiation in many spectra is light scattered into the direction of observation by free electrons. For any kind of particle, the scattering coefficient is given as the ratio between scattered intensity and incident intensity. With n particles per cm^3, the scattering coefficient per cm for scattering through an angle ϕ is

$$\sigma(\phi) = (32\pi^5 n/c^4)\beta^2(1 + \cos^2\phi), \tag{1.101}$$

where β is the polarizability of the particles. The classical treatment, which gives the expression

$$\beta^2 = \frac{e^4}{m^2}\frac{1}{4\pi^2(\nu - \nu_0)^2 + 4\pi^2\nu^2\gamma^2}$$

for the polarizability of the atomic electron, can be made to coincide with the quantum mechanical treatment by introducing the oscillator strengths f_j for all the spectral lines that combine with the ground state. For the polarizability, we find that

$$\beta_j = \frac{e^2}{4\pi^2 m}f_j\frac{1}{\nu_j^2 - \nu^2}, \qquad \beta = \sum_j \beta_j. \tag{1.102}$$

According to the f-sum rule, $\sum f_j$ is equal to the number of outer electrons in the atom (1 for hydrogen, 2 for helium, etc.).

By taking the mean over all directions ϕ, Equation (1.101) becomes

$$\sigma = \frac{128}{3}\frac{\pi^5 n}{c^4}\ \beta^2. \tag{1.103}$$

The important case of scattering by free electrons is characterized by $\nu_0 = 0$, and the damping constant γ may be neglected. This leads to the well-known formula for the Thomson scattering which is independent of frequency.

Let us now briefly consider scattering by atoms. For frequencies much less than the resonance frequency of the harmonic oscillator ν_0, the classical theory gives $\beta^2 = (e^2/4\pi^2 m \nu_0)^2$, and the scattering coefficient per oscillator is

$$\sigma_{osc} = \sigma_{el}\left(\frac{\nu}{\nu_0}\right)^4 = \sigma_{el}\left(\frac{\lambda_0}{\lambda}\right)^4.$$

Because of Equation (1.102), we find the quantum theoretical expression

$$\sigma_{atom} = \sigma_{el}\left[\sum f_j \frac{\nu}{\nu_j^2 - \nu^2}\right]^2. \tag{1.104}$$

Again, for $\nu \ll \nu_j$, we can approximate the ν_j by their center of gravity (Bethe, 1933) and obtain

$$\sigma_{atom} = \sigma_{el}(\nu/\nu_i)^4 \sum f_j = \sigma_{el}(\lambda_i/\lambda)^4 \sum f_j.$$

For hydrogen, $\sum f_j = 1$ and $\lambda_j = 1026$ Å (that is, the center of gravity for the Lyman series). We therefore find that for a wavelength of, say, 5000 Å the relative importance of scattering by hydrogen atoms and by electrons is

$$\frac{\sigma_H}{\sigma_{el}} = \left(\frac{1.026}{5000}\right)^4 = \frac{1}{564}.$$

Scattering by hydrogen atoms, therefore, will only be of importance if $n_H/n_e > 564$, that is, in an essentially neutral gas.

1.4.2. Radiation Damping

When we know the energy level diagram of an atom or ion (see Figure 1.1), we can predict the lines which can be absorbed or emitted. We assume that the radiation associated with the states i and j takes place according to the frequency relation

$$\nu_{ji} = (E_j - E_i/h).$$

This predicts an infinitely narrow line, and we have to admit that the energy states E_j and E_i are not sharply defined to account for the finite line widths observed even when no external broadening mechanism is present. This is in accordance with Heisenberg's uncertainty principle which, applied to this situation, shows that the smaller the lifetime of the atom in any level, the greater the broadening of that level. This is expressed quantum mechanically by Weisskopf and Wigner's (1930) probability distribution law: The energy of a state with mean energy E_j is distributed according to the formula

$$P(E_j)\, dE = \frac{A_j}{h} \frac{dE}{\frac{1}{4}A_j^2 + (4\pi^2/h^2)(E - E_j)^2}, \tag{1.105}$$

where A_j is the total probability of transition from state j. The probability function, Equation (1.105), has a sharp maximum for $E = E_j$, so that most of the atoms have energies near the mean energy, and the fraction $dn_j/n_j = P_j(E)\,dE$ of the n_j atoms in state j has energies in the range E to $E + dE$.

When two states i and j combine to form a spectral line, the intensity in the line will be given by

$$I = h\nu_{ji} A_{ji} \frac{A_j + A_i}{\frac{1}{4}(A_j + A_i) + (4\pi^2/h^2)[\nu - (E_i - E_j)]^2} , \qquad (1.106)$$

where ν_{ji} is the frequency corresponding to the two mean energies involved. We may write this in the form

$$I = \frac{\text{const}}{(\nu - \nu_{ji})^2 + (\gamma_R/4\pi)^4} , \qquad (1.107)$$

where

$$\gamma_R = A_j + A_i \qquad (1.108)$$

is called the radiation damping constant and is given by the sum of the decay constants for the two energy states involved in the radiation process. In the classical treatment of the interaction between atoms and radiation, we take recourse to the oscillator electron executing forced vibrations under the influence of the electric vector of the radiation field. We then find an expression for the intensity (or absorption coefficient, see Section 1.3.1) formally equal to Equation (1.107), but the damping constant is given by

$$\gamma_{cl}/4\pi = 2\pi e^2 \nu_0^2/3mc^3 .$$

The quantity γ_R is called the natural half-width of the line or the total half-width of the absorption coefficient. The line absorption coefficient per atom, α_ν, measures the absorption of incident radiation of frequency ν of unit intensity in a given direction. By summing over all directions, we find the total absorption. The probability of absorption by an atom of a quantum of frequency ν will be $(4\pi/h\nu)\alpha_\nu$, and we have

$$\alpha_\nu = \frac{\pi e^2}{mc} \frac{\gamma_R}{4\pi^2} \frac{f}{(\nu - \nu_0)^2 + (\gamma_R/4\pi)^2} , \qquad (1.109)$$

where f is the oscillator strength, and

$$\alpha = \int_0^\infty \alpha_\nu \, d\nu = (\pi e^2/mc) f$$

is the integral over the absorption profile.

We shall call the shape of the line whose profile is given by an expression of the form of Equation (1.107) a damping profile or a dispersion curve. The form is shown by curve D in Figure 1.2. In the idealized case when only the intrinsic width of the energy states contributes to the broadening, the width is given by γ_R, which is a fundamentally lower limit to the breadth.

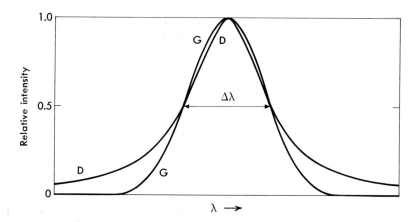

FIGURE 1.2.   Line profiles: G = Gaussian shape, D = damping profile

If we express γ in Å, the classical formula gives $\gamma_{cl} = 1.18 \times 10^{-4}$ Å. As we shall see shortly, this always constitutes only an insignificant fraction of the total broadening of solar lines.

1.4.3. Doppler Broadening

The radiation that we actually observe does not come from atoms at rest relative to the observer—as we have implied in the previous section. When the temperature is different from absolute zero, the radiating atoms and ions move with velocities whose distribution we shall assume to be Maxwellian. Let the velocity of an atom in the line of sight be v and its proper frequency ν_0. Relative to the observer, the frequency will be

$$\nu_0^1 = \nu_0 \left(1 - \frac{v}{c} \right) ,$$

and the absorption coefficient will be

$$\alpha_\nu^1 = \frac{\pi e^2}{mc} \frac{\gamma_R}{4\pi^2} \frac{f}{(\nu - \nu_0 + v\nu_0/c)^2 + (\gamma_R/4\pi)^2} .$$

To find the average absorption coefficient, we integrate α_v^1 over the velocity distribution. Since this is assumed to be Maxwellian, we find that

$$\alpha_v = \int_{v=-\infty}^{+\infty} \alpha_v^1 \, dn = \frac{\pi e^2}{\sqrt{\pi} mc} \frac{\gamma_R}{4\pi^2} f \int \frac{e^{-(\Delta v/\Delta v_0)^2} \, d(\Delta v/\Delta v_0)}{[v - v_0 + (vv_0/c)]^2 + (\gamma_R/4\pi)^2} \,, \quad (1.110a)$$

where

$$\Delta v_D/v_0 = v_0/c \,, \quad (1.110b)$$

and $v_0 = (2kT/m)^{1/2}$.

The integral in Equation (1.110a) cannot be evaluated in closed form, but numerical integrations have been carried out and tables are available (Harris, 1948). Two limiting cases are easily recognized if we put Equation (1.110a) in the following form:

$$\alpha_v = \text{const} \int_{-\infty}^{\infty} \frac{e^{-X^2} \, dX}{(X - Y)^2 + Z^2} \,,$$

where

$$X = \frac{\Delta v}{\Delta v_D} = \frac{v}{\sqrt{2kT/m}} \,, \qquad Y = \frac{v_0 - v}{v_0} \frac{c}{v_0} \,, \qquad \text{and} \qquad Z = \frac{\gamma_R c/4\pi}{vv_0} \,.$$

First, for a large Y, we may neglect X in the denominator, which means that the original form of the absorption coefficient Equation (1.109), is obtained, or that the thermal motion has no influence on the absorption of the radiation. This applies to the extreme wings of the line. Second, for Y and Z both small, it can be shown that the profile is approximately given by

$$\alpha_v = \text{const} \frac{4Z\pi}{\gamma_R} e^{-Y^2} \propto e^{-[(v-v_0)/v_0]^2} \,.$$

The original shape of the line has completely disappeared, and we see only the influence of the Maxwellian distribution of the radiating particles (see curve G in Figure 1.2).

1.4.4. Collision Damping

In our treatment of the interaction of radiation and a radiating particle, we have so far neglected the influence of neighboring atoms and ions. The collisions of the radiating atoms with surrounding particles lead to a broadening that is often called pressure broadening, since it is greater (for a given temperature) the greater the pressure in the plasma. A general treatment of the collision processes is extremely complicated, and hence only approximate solutions are known.

We may treat the collisions from two different points of view. The discrete encounter theory, or collision damping theory (Lorentz, 1905a, 1905b; Lenz, 1933; Weisskopf, 1933; Lindholm, 1942), states that the radiating atom is disturbed by separate, discrete collisions, whereby the wave emitted or absorbed by the atom is interrupted. The intensity distribution of the corresponding line is obtained by a Fourier analysis of the distorted wave train. The statistical theory (Stark, 1915; Debye, 1919; Holtsmark, 1919; Margenau, 1932) asks what will be the value, at a given atom or ion, of the field produced by the surrounding particles. To each field there corresponds a shift in the frequency of the radiation from the atom. By summing over all shifts according to their statistical probabilities, we obtain the line profile.

Collision damping and statistical broadening are two limiting cases of a general theory for pressure broadening but, since such a general theory is still beyond our knowledge, we must try to determine when one or the other approximation is valid. It turns out that within a certain critical distance $\Delta\lambda_g$ measured from the center of each line, the broadening may be described by the discrete encounter theory. For distances from the line center greater than $\pm\Delta\lambda_g$, the profile is determined by the statistical theory. In some cases, the value of $\Delta\lambda_g$ is so large (or small) that the whole line may be described by collision damping (or statistical broadening).

Let $\delta\nu$ be the change in frequency of the radiation from an atom or ion due to a neighboring particle. This change may be expressed in terms of the distance r between the two particles, and thus we have

$$\delta\nu = C/r^s \,,$$

where s is an integer and C a constant. Often C can be determined from quantum mechanical calculations or from laboratory experiments. This change in frequency is coupled with a phase change ξ of the radiated wave train:

$$\xi = 2\pi \int \delta\nu \, dt \,,$$

where we integrate over the duration of the collision. The evaluation of this integral is one of the main problems of the discrete encounter theory.

Let ρ be the distance of closest approach during a particular collision. See Figure 1.3, where ρ, also called the impact parameter, is defined in terms of the paths of two identical particles. The number of particles passing at a distance between ρ and $\rho + d\rho$ is proportional to the elementary cross section for collisions between the particles, $\sigma = 2\pi\rho \, d\rho$. Let the phase changes ξ_1, ξ_2, $\ldots$, ξ_g, correspond to the cross sections σ_1, σ_2, $\ldots$, σ_g. Lindholm's analysis (1942) now shows that the intensity of the line may be

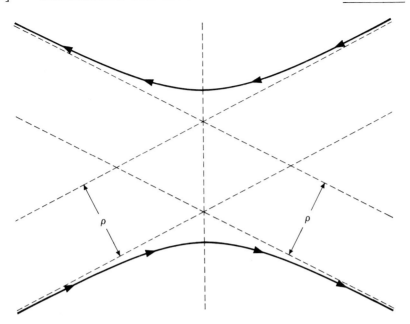

FIGURE 1.3.   Simple geometry of binary encounters

written

$$I_v = \frac{I_0}{\pi} \frac{\gamma/2\pi}{(v - v_0 + \beta/2\pi)^2 + (\gamma/2\pi)^2} , \qquad (1.111)$$

where

$$\gamma = (1/\sigma\tau) \sum_i \sigma_i(1 - \cos \xi_i), \qquad \beta = (1/\sigma\tau) \sum_i \sigma_i \sin \xi_i, \qquad (1.112)$$

and

$$\xi_i = (4\pi C/\bar{v}\rho^{s-1}) \int \cos^{s-2} \theta \, d\theta ,$$

where τ is the time between collisions, $1/\tau = \sigma\bar{v}n$, $\sigma = \sigma_1 + \sigma_2 + \cdots + \sigma_g$ is the total cross section, $\bar{v}$ is the mean velocity of the atoms, and n is the number density of atoms.

The line of Equation (1.111) has a line width

$$\gamma_c' = \frac{\gamma_c(s)}{2\pi} = \frac{\bar{v}n}{2\pi} \int_0^\infty \sin^2 \left(\frac{3\pi^2 C}{8\bar{v}\rho^{s-1}} \right) 4\pi\rho \, d\rho , \qquad (1.113)$$

and the center is displaced $\beta/2\pi$ toward the red (the Lindholm effect). Furthermore, we see that the profile is given by a dispersion curve as it is for radiation damping. In general, $\gamma'_c \gg \gamma_R$, so that the natural line width may be neglected in comparison with the effect of collision damping.

If the gas consists of neutral particles or ions and electrons, interparticle fields will still be created. Because of these fields, the frequency of the radiation of each particle is displaced relative to its normal position. For each type of radiating particle, the configuration of neighboring particles— and hence of the field affecting the particles—will be different. The spectral line that results from a superposition of a large number of differently displaced frequencies will, therefore, be broadened in a manner that depends on the interacting field. Consequently, the main task of the statistical theory is to derive the probability $P(F)$ that a particle will experience the influence of a certain field F.

A quantitative treatment of the broadening process discovered in hydrogen by Stark (1916) was given by Debye (1919) and Holtsmark (1919), who laid the foundation for the statistical theory. A more general formulation is due to Kuhn and London (1934) and Margenau (1932). It can be shown that when the exponent s in the equation $\delta\nu = C/r^s$ is equal to 2, the statistical broadening will be symmetrical. However, when $s = 4$ or $s = 6$ (van der Waals forces), the broadening is asymmetrical, and therefore the line is also shifted.

The shift corresponding to the mean distance r_0 between the radiating atom and a perturbing particle is

$$\delta\nu_0 = \frac{C}{r_0^s} = C\left(\frac{4\pi}{3}n\right)^{s/3}.$$

When we combine this with the expression for the probability that the nearest particle to the radiating atom is at a distance between r and $r + dr$,

$$P(r)\,dr = 4\pi r^2 n\,dr\,e^{-(4\pi/3)r^3 n} = e^{-(r/r_0)^3}\,d(r/r_0)^3,$$

we find an expression for the line profile due to only one perturbing particle:

$$I_\nu\,d\nu = e^{-(\Delta\nu_0/\Delta\nu)^{3/s}}\,d\left(\frac{\Delta\nu_0}{\Delta\nu}\right)^{3/s} = \frac{3}{s}\left(\frac{\Delta\nu_0}{\Delta\nu}\right)^{3/s+1}e^{-(\Delta\nu_0/\Delta\nu)^{3/s}}\frac{d\nu}{\Delta\nu_0}.\quad(1.114)$$

It is then the task of statistical theory to find out how contributions like Equation (1.114) are superposed when we are faced with simultaneous perturbations of many particles.

The best known example of statistical broadening is probably that due to the intermolecular Stark effect caused by the electrostatic field F which in turn is caused by the charged particles in a plasma. Quantum mechanically one can show that a spectral line will be split into several components in an electric field, and a given component i is displaced by an amount depending on the field. In some instances, as is the case for hydrogen, for example, there is direct proportionality between the displacement $\Delta\nu_i$ and the field F; that is, we have

$$\Delta\nu_i = c_i F = (3h/8\pi^2 me)q_i F. \qquad (1.115)$$

This is called the linear Stark effect. Here q_i is a number, and for the Balmer lines $q_i \leq n(n-1)+1$. For other atoms and ions, the displacement $\Delta\nu_i$ is proportional to the square of the electric field, if the field is not too large. Thus we have

$$\Delta\nu_i = c_i F^2. \qquad (1.116)$$

This is called the quadratic Stark effect.

We conclude this section with a resume of the different broadenings experienced for different values of the exponent s.

CASE 1: $s = 2$. This corresponds to perturbations of atoms with linear Stark effect (hydrogen and some higher terms, D, F, ... of helium). The perturbing fields are due to electrons and ions. The integral of Equation (1.113) does not converge for $s = 2$. But since the electric fields of distinct particles largely cancel, we may stop the integration at a certain $\rho = \rho_{max} = (kT/8\pi e^2 n_e)^{1/2}$. We then find that

$$\gamma'_c(2) = \frac{32\pi}{3} C^2 \frac{n}{v} (1.708 - \ln \xi_m + \cdots).$$

CASE 2: $s = 3$. In this case we treat the interaction of identical particles. The integral for $\gamma'_c(s)$ can then be integrated directly and gives

$$\gamma'_c(3) = 2\pi^2 Cn,$$

which does not depend on the velocity v. The value for C is approximately

$$C = e^2 f/16\pi^2 me v_0.$$

CASE 3: $s = 4$. Here the perturbers are electrically charged particles, and in this case of quadratic Stark effect, we have

$$\gamma'_c(4) = 3.09 C^{2/3} v^{1/3} n.$$

The displacement of the line, which is inherent in this case, is given by

$$\nu_0 - \nu_m = \beta(4)/2\pi = 5.32 C^{2/3} v^{1/3} n.$$

A closer analysis shows that the line broadening is mainly due to collisions causing phase changes $\xi \geq 1$, while the displacements are caused by encounters for which $\xi < \pi$.

CASE 4: $s = 5$. This case has no astrophysical interest.

CASE 5: $s = 6$. This corresponds to the interaction of radiating atoms with neutral particles leading to van der Waals forces. We find that

$$\gamma_c'(6) = 1.34 C^{2/5} v^{3/5} n$$

and

$$\nu_0 - \nu_m = \beta(6)/2\pi = 0.98 C^{2/5} v^{3/5} n.$$

1.5. *Waves in a Plasma*

1.5.1. Introduction

There are a bewildering number of wave modes possible in a plasma, and we shall not go into all the details regarding their generation and propagation here. We shall give, however, an account of the more important modes that may come into play in the realm of solar activity.

After a short introduction, we will first treat the simple case where all disturbances are small so that we can linearize the equations. Furthermore, we will consider that all space- and time-dependent quantities, like the field intensity $\mathbf{E}$, are of the form $\mathbf{E} = \mathbf{E}_0 \exp i(\omega t - \mathbf{k} \cdot \mathbf{r})$. For plane waves, we consider propagation along the z-axis, that is, $\mathbf{E} = \mathbf{E}_0 \exp i(\omega t - kz)$. The form $\mathbf{E} = \mathbf{E}_0 \exp i(\omega t - \mathbf{k} \cdot \mathbf{r})$ is valid with a constant $\mathbf{k}$ only in a homogeneous atmosphere where the governing equations have constant coefficients. In an inhomogeneous atmosphere, $k = k(x, y, z)$ and may be complex.

An initially small disturbance traveling out through the decreasing density of the solar atmosphere will, as a rule, ultimately steepen into a shock. In this process, nonlinear effects become important both for the propagation and the dissipation of the energy in the wave. This situation will be considered in Section 1.5.3.

In a compressible neutral gas of density ρ, pressure p, and ratio of specific heat γ, small disturbances propagate as sound waves with a velocity given by

$$V_s = \sqrt{\gamma(p/\rho)}. \tag{1.117}$$

An incompressible plasma permeated by a magnetic field $\mathbf{B}_0$ allows disturbances to propagate as the simplest type of a hydromagnetic wave, the

Alfvén mode, with velocity

$$\mathbf{V}_A = \mathbf{B}_0/\sqrt{4\pi\rho}\,. \qquad (1.118)$$

In the general case of a compressible plasma in a magnetic field, a number of mixed forms occur, and this is the complicated situation which we encounter in the solar atmosphere.

We may get a physical feeling for some of these waves from the following considerations. A completely ionized plasma consists in the simplest case of two different kinds of particles, electrons and positive ions. These particles interact strongly, and, in one mode, they may move together with the electric field and establish a soundlike wave. The restoring force, however, is not the pressure but the electric field. The possibility also exists that the electrons and the ions may oscillate in the field 180° out of phase, the restoring force still being the electric field. This will lead to plasma oscillations.

In addition to these longitudinal modes (often called electrostatic waves since there may be no magnetic field involved) we also encounter transverse modes called electromagnetic waves. In a neutral gas with no external forces, two modes appear that are distinguished by their polarization. At very high frequencies, these modes merge into one, the familiar light wave. If we consider a plasma permeated by a magnetic field, then we see that, in addition to the electromagnetic modes just mentioned, other transverse waves exist, due to the restoring forces of the anisotropic stresses exerted by the frozen-in magnetic field, that is, resulting from the $\mathbf{j} \times \mathbf{B}_0$ term in the equation of motion. These modes are called hydromagnetic waves, of which the mode occurring in an incompressible plasma is the Alfvén wave.

Finally, in a medium of changing density a restoring force can be produced by the gravitational field. This sets up another mode, called gravity waves, which may exist in neutral gases as well as in plasmas. These waves are related to the gravity waves found at the boundaries between two fluids of different densities.

Since the gravitational restoring force is independent of the charge of the particles, we expect to be able to treat gravity waves without Maxwell's equations when the electromagnetic terms in the governing equations are small. A coupling occurs when the electromagnetic terms become of the same order of magnitude as the gravitational term, and mixed wave modes are then possible.

1.5.2. Propagation of Small Disturbances

In most plasmas of astrophysical interest, the dielectric properties are negligible in comparison with the effects of the conduction current. We therefore rewrite Maxwell's equations in an approximation appropriate for the solar atmospheric plasma:

$$\nabla \times \mathbf{B} = \frac{4\pi}{c}\mathbf{j} + \frac{i\omega}{c}\mathbf{E}, \qquad (1.119)$$

$$\nabla \times \mathbf{E} = -\frac{i\omega}{c}\mathbf{B}, \qquad (1.120)$$

$$\nabla \cdot \mathbf{E} = 4\pi\rho_{\mathrm{e}}, \qquad (1.121)$$

and

$$\nabla \cdot \mathbf{B} = 0. \qquad (1.122)$$

In connection with Maxwell's equations, there is a peculiarity worth noting in that the last one is not completely independent but may be obtained from the curl $\mathbf{E}$ equation by taking the divergence. The last equation, $\nabla \cdot \mathbf{B} = 0$, therefore can be considered as an initial condition; if it holds at any time, it will hold for all times.

If we take the curl of Equation (1.120), differentiate Equation (1.119), and eliminate $\mathbf{B}$ and ρ_{e}, we find that the basic equation for electromagnetic waves is

$$\nabla^2\mathbf{E} - \nabla\nabla\cdot\mathbf{E} + \frac{\omega^2}{c^2}\mathbf{E} - i\frac{4\pi\omega}{c^2}\mathbf{j} = 0. \qquad (1.123)$$

With our coordinate system so chosen that the direction of propagation $\mathbf{k}$ is in the z-direction, Equation (1.123) becomes

$$\frac{\partial^2 E_x}{\partial x^2} + \frac{\omega^2}{c^2}E_x - \frac{4\pi i\omega}{c^2}j_x = 0, \qquad \frac{\partial^2 E_y}{\partial y^2} + \frac{\omega^2}{c^2}E_y - \frac{4\pi i\omega}{c^2}j_y = 0. \quad (1.124)$$

For the E_z component, we get only an equation that is identically zero, but from Equation (1.119) we derive a useful relation:

$$i\frac{\omega}{c}\cdot E_z + \frac{4\pi}{c}j_z = 0. \qquad (1.125)$$

Equations (1.124) are seen to be of the general form of Equation (1.45) with $\epsilon' = 1 - i(4\pi\sigma/\omega)$.

To these equations we will have to add the equations of continuity of mass and charge [Equations (1.29) and (1.30)], the equations of motion [Equation (1.32) or the equation of motion of the plasma (1.33) together with, for instance, the generalized Ohm's law, Equation (1.34)], and an energy equation [Equation (1.35)]. To survey the problem, we write these equations here in the form given in Section 1.1.3:

$$(\partial \rho / \partial t) + \nabla \cdot (\rho v) = 0, \tag{1.126}$$

$$(\partial \rho_e / \partial t) + \nabla \cdot j = 0, \tag{1.127}$$

$$n_e m_e \frac{\partial \mathbf{v}_e}{\partial t} = n_e e \left(\mathbf{E} + \frac{\mathbf{v}_e}{c} \times \mathbf{B}_0 \right) - \nabla \cdot \mathscr{P}_e + n_e m_e \mathbf{g} + \mathbf{p}_{ei}, \tag{1.128}$$

$$n_i m_i \frac{\partial \mathbf{v}_i}{\partial t} = n_i - e \left(\mathbf{E} + \frac{\mathbf{v}_i}{c} \times \mathbf{B}_0 \right) - \nabla \cdot \mathscr{P}_i + n_i m_i \mathbf{g} - \mathbf{p}_{ie}, \tag{1.129}$$

$$\rho (dU / dt) = -p \nabla \cdot \mathbf{v} + \beta. \tag{1.130}$$

Note that the equation of continuity of electric charge is not an independent equation. It is obtained by taking the divergence of the Maxwell's equation for curl $\mathbf{B}$ and eliminating $\mathbf{E}$ by the equation for div $\mathbf{E}$.

We thus have 12 equations, Equations (1.124), (1.125), (1.126), (1.127), (1.128), (1.129), and (1.130), to determine the 12 quantities $\mathbf{E}, \mathbf{j}, \mathbf{v}, p, \rho$, and T. Even though this is theoretically possible, the set of equations is extremely complicated. Therefore, we shall make a series of simplifications (see Denisse and Delcroix, 1961). Let us first consider the electric field and the velocities of the electrons and ions as the nine unknowns, using Equations (1.123), (1.128), and (1.129) as our basic set of equations. In further simplifying this set, we encounter two major difficulties. First, we want to treat our problem with macroscopic equations but, as we shall presently see, this will exclude some wave phenomena that can be adequately treated only by going back to the microscopic point of view (starting with Boltzmann's equation). The first difficulty arises because of the momentum interaction terms, $\mathbf{P}_{ei}$, etc. To be able to treat these terms, we consider the collision frequency ν_c to be a scalar, but even this case is often too difficult to treat. However, since probably all the wave modes of major interest in solar physics can be adequately understood without keeping the expression for the scalar collision frequency completely general, we shall consider a further simplification: we keep the collision frequency constant, independent of the particle velocities. In reality, the collision frequency depends on the thermal velocities of the different particles, and we shall in some instances see how this changes the wave modes and leads to interactions between different modes. It is, however, outside the scope of this book to give a detailed account of all the subtleties of wave mode coupling. For simplicity, often we shall even resort to the collisionless plasma where we ignore collisions altogether, that is, where $\nu_c = 0$. Otherwise, we will resort to the approximations inherent in Equations (1.18) and (1.19) and write $\mathbf{P}_{ei} = en(\mathbf{j}/\sigma) = -n_e m_e \nu_c(\mathbf{v}_e - \mathbf{v}_i)$.

When neutral particles (partially ionized plasma) are present, we must include terms like $\mathbf{P}_{en} = -n_e m_e \nu_{en} \mathbf{v}_e$ and $\mathbf{P}_{in} = -n_i m_i \nu_{in} \mathbf{v}_i$, where ν_{en} and ν_{in} are the collision frequencies for electrons and ions with neutral particles. Collisions are consequently treated as friction terms.

Another difficulty arises when we evaluate the pressure tensor terms $\nabla \cdot \mathscr{P}$. A proper general treatment again would have to be microscopic. We will consider, however, the macroscopic transport equations, and we shall restrict ourselves to cases where the waves produce only adiabatic changes in the scalar pressure gradients. From the standpoint of collision frequencies, this implies that we will consider the two limiting cases where the frequency of the wave is either small or large compared to the collision frequency. No simple macroscopic treatment is possible for the intermediate case. With these restrictions, we can write

$$\nabla p_e = \gamma k T \nabla n_e = m_e V_e^2 \nabla n_e, \qquad \nabla p_i = \gamma k T \nabla n_i = m_i V_i^2 \nabla n_i, \quad (1.131)$$

where V_e and V_i are the thermal velocities of the electrons and ions, and $\gamma = \frac{5}{3}$ and $\gamma = 3$ in the two limiting cases.

Furthermore, let us assume that any external magnetic field $\mathbf{B}_0$ permeating the plasma is in the yz-plane, and let us designate its two components by B_L (along the direction of propagation $\mathbf{k}$) and B_T (transverse to this direction).

Our determining set of equations then take the form

$$\left(k^2 - \frac{\omega^2}{c^2}\right)E_x + \frac{4\pi\omega}{c^2}\, in_e e v_{ex} - \frac{4\pi\omega}{c^2}\, iZn_i e v_{ix} = 0\,,$$

$$\left(k^2 - \frac{\omega^2}{c^2}\right)E_y + \frac{4\pi\omega}{c^2}\, in_e e v_{ey} - \frac{4\pi\omega}{c^2}\, iZn_i e v_{iy} = 0\,, \qquad (1.132)$$

$$\frac{\omega^2}{c^2}\, E_z - \frac{4\pi\omega}{c^2}\, n_e e v_{ez} + \frac{4\pi\omega}{c^2}\, Zn_i e v_{iz} = 0\,,$$

$$n_e e E_x + n_e m_e(\nu_c + i\omega)v_{ex} + n_e(e/c)B_L v_{ey} - n_e(e/c)B_T v_{ez} + n_e m_e \nu_c v_{ix} = 0\,,$$

$$n_e e E_y - n_e(e/c)B_L v_{ex} - n_e m_e(\nu_c + i\omega)v_{ey} + n_e m_e \nu_c v_{iy} = 0\,, \qquad (1.133)$$

$$n_e e E_z + n_e(e/c)B_T v_{ex} + n_e m_e(\nu_c - i\omega + i(k^2/\omega)V_e^2)v_{ez} + n_e m_e \nu_c v_{iz} = 0\,,$$

and

$$Zn_{i}eE_{x} - n_{e}m_{e}\nu_{c}v_{ex} + (n_{i}m_{i}i\omega + n_{e}m_{e}\nu_{c})v_{ix} + Zn_{i}(e/c)B_{L}v_{iy}$$

$$- Zn_{i}(e/c)B_{T}v_{iz} = 0,$$

$$Zn_{i}eE_{y} - n_{e}m_{e}\nu_{c}v_{ey} - Zn_{i}(e/c)B_{L}v_{ix} + (n_{i}m_{i}i\omega + n_{e}m_{e}\nu_{c})v_{iy} = 0, \qquad (1.134)$$

$$Zn_{i}eE_{z} - n_{e}m_{e}\nu_{c}v_{ez} + Zn_{i}(e/c)B_{T}v_{ix} + [n_{i}m_{i}(i\omega - i(k^{2}/\omega)V_{i}^{2})$$

$$+ n_{e}m_{e}\nu_{c}]v_{iz} = 0.$$

Equations (1.132) through (1.134) are a system of linear and homogeneous equations in the nine variables E_{x}, E_{y}, E_{z}, v_{ex}, v_{ey}, v_{ez}, v_{ix}, v_{iy}, and v_{iz}, and we find a solution, provided that the determinant of the system is zero, as shown on page 52.

This equation between ω and k is the dispersion relation for the waves. In general, it is an equation of the 4th degree in k^{2}. The four roots correspond to four different modes of propagation, and to each of the roots k^{2} there are two waves, $\pm k$, indicating that two identical waves propagate in opposite directions along the z-axis.

For the following discussion we introduce the quantities

$$\omega_{p} = \sqrt{4\pi n_{e}e^{2}/m_{e}} = \text{electron plasma frequency, Equation (1.16),}$$

$$\Omega_{p} = \sqrt{4\pi Zn_{i}e^{2}/m_{i}} = \text{ion plasma frequency,}$$

$$\omega_{0} = \sqrt{\omega_{p}^{2} + \Omega_{p}^{2}} = \text{combination plasma frequency} \approx \omega_{p},$$

$$\omega_{B} = eB_{0}/m_{e}c = \text{electron gyromagnetic frequency, the Larmor frequency,}$$

$$\text{Equation (1.15),}$$

$$\Omega_{B} = ZeB_{0}/m_{i}c = \text{ion gyromagnetic frequency.}$$

Note the following relations:

$$\omega_{p}^{2}/\Omega_{p}^{2} = \omega_{B}/\Omega_{B} = m_{i}/Zm_{e}. \qquad (1.136)$$

If we approximate the solar atmosphere with a fully ionized hydrogen plasma, we have $Z = 1$ and $m_{i}/m_{e} = 1836$.

We shall now see how the form of the magnetic field B_{0} determines the possible modes of propagation in a plasma. Let us consider the following cases.

CASE 1: $B_{0} = 0$. When the external magnetic field is vanishingly small, the dispersion relation simplifies considerably and may be written $\Delta_{1}^{2}\Delta_{L} = 0$,

$$\begin{vmatrix}
k^{2}-\dfrac{\omega^{2}}{c^{2}} & 0 & 0 & \dfrac{4\pi\omega}{c^{2}}\,in_{e}e & 0 & 0 & -\dfrac{4\pi\omega}{c^{2}}\,iZn_{i}e & 0 & 0 \\[2mm]
0 & k^{2}-\dfrac{\omega^{2}}{c^{2}} & 0 & 0 & \dfrac{4\pi\omega}{c^{2}}\,in_{e}e & 0 & 0 & -\dfrac{4\pi\omega}{c^{2}}\,iZn_{i}e & 0 \\[2mm]
0 & 0 & \dfrac{\omega^{2}}{c^{2}} & 0 & 0 & -\dfrac{4\pi\omega}{c^{2}}\,n_{e}e & 0 & 0 & \dfrac{4\pi\omega}{c^{2}}\,Zn_{i}e \\[2mm]
n_{e}e & 0 & 0 & -n_{e}m_{e}(\nu_{c}+i\omega) & n_{e}\dfrac{e}{c}B_{L} & -n_{e}\dfrac{e}{c}B_{T} & n_{e}m_{e}\nu_{c} & 0 & 0 \\[2mm]
0 & n_{e}e & 0 & -n_{e}\dfrac{e}{c}B_{L} & -n_{e}m_{e}(\nu_{c}+i\omega) & 0 & 0 & n_{e}m_{e}\nu_{c} & 0 \\[2mm]
0 & 0 & n_{e}e & n_{e}eB_{T} & 0 & n_{e}m_{e}\!\left(\nu_{c}-i\omega+i\dfrac{k^{2}}{\omega}V^{2}_{e}\right) & 0 & 0 & n_{e}m_{e}\nu_{c} \\[2mm]
Zn_{i}e & 0 & 0 & -n_{e}m_{e}\nu_{c} & 0 & 0 & n_{i}m_{i}i\omega+n_{e}m_{e}\nu_{c} & Zn_{i}\dfrac{e}{c}B_{L} & -Zn_{i}\!\left(\dfrac{e}{c}\right)B_{T} \\[2mm]
0 & Zn_{i}e & 0 & 0 & -n_{e}m_{e}\nu_{c} & 0 & -Zn_{i}\dfrac{e}{c}B_{L} & n_{i}m_{i}i\omega+n_{e}m_{e}\nu_{c} & 0 \\[2mm]
0 & 0 & Zn_{i}e & 0 & 0 & -n_{e}m_{e}\nu_{c} & Zn_{i}\!\left(\dfrac{e}{c}\right)B_{T} & 0 & n_{i}m_{i}\!\left(i\omega-i\dfrac{k^{2}}{\omega}V^{2}_{i}\right)+n_{e}m_{e}\nu_{c}
\end{vmatrix}=0.$$

$$(1.135)$$

where we have

$$
\Delta_1 = \begin{vmatrix}
k^2 - \dfrac{\omega^2}{c^2} & \dfrac{4\pi\omega}{c^2}\, i n_e e & -\dfrac{4\pi\omega}{c^2}\, i Z n_i e \\[2ex]
n_e e & -n_e m_e(\nu_c + i\omega) & n_e m_e \nu_c \\[2ex]
Z n_i e & -n_e m_e \nu_c & n_i m_i \cdot i\omega + n_e m_e \nu_c
\end{vmatrix}
\tag{1.137}
$$

and

$$
\Delta_L = \begin{vmatrix}
\dfrac{\omega^2}{c^2} & -\dfrac{4\pi\omega}{c^2}\, n_e e & \dfrac{4\pi\omega}{c^2}\, Z n_i e \\[2ex]
n_e e & n_e m_e\left(\nu_c - i\omega + \dfrac{k^2}{\omega} V_e^2\right) & n_e m_e \nu_c \\[2ex]
Z n_i e & -n_e m_e \nu_c & n_i m_i\left(i\omega - i\dfrac{k^2}{\omega} V_i^2\right) + n_e m_e \nu_c
\end{vmatrix}.
$$

$$\tag{1.138}$$

We note that this equation is satisfied with either $\Delta_1 = 0$ or $\Delta_L = 0$. In the first case the system admits one solution where only E_x, v_{ex} and v_{ix} are different from zero and another where only E_y, v_{ey} and v_{iy} are nonvanishing. This means that we have two plane-polarized transverse waves which are the electromagnetic modes. If $\Delta_L = 0$ the solution is two waves where only E_z, v_{ez} and v_{iz} are different from zero, i.e., purely longitudinal waves. One of these represents the electron plasma oscillations, the other is a pseudo-sound wave.

CASE 2: $B_T = 0$, $B_L \neq 0$. With a longitudinal magnetic field present, the dispersion relation takes the form $\Delta_T \Delta_L = 0$, where we have

$$
\Delta_T = \begin{vmatrix}
k^2 - \dfrac{\omega^2}{c^2} & 0 & \dfrac{4\pi\omega}{c}\, i n_e e & 0 & -\dfrac{4\pi\omega}{c^2}\, i Z n_i e & 0 \\[2ex]
0 & k^2 - \dfrac{\omega^2}{c^2} & 0 & \dfrac{4\pi\omega}{c}\, i n_e e & 0 & -\dfrac{4\pi\omega}{c^2}\, i Z n_i e \\[2ex]
n_e e & 0 & -n_e m_e(\nu_c + i\omega) & n_e \dfrac{e}{c} B_L & n_e m_e \nu_c & 0 \\[2ex]
0 & n_e e & -n_e \dfrac{e}{c} B_L & -n_e m_e(\nu_c + i\omega) & 0 & n_e m_e \nu_c \\[2ex]
Z n_i e & 0 & -n_e m_e \nu_c & 0 & n_i m_i i\omega + n_e m_e \nu_c & Z n_i \dfrac{e}{c} B_L \\[2ex]
0 & Z n_i e & 0 & -n_e m_e \nu_c & -Z n_i \dfrac{e}{c} B_L & n_i m_i i\omega + n_e m_e \nu_c
\end{vmatrix}.
$$

$$\tag{1.139}$$

As one solution, we find again that $\Delta_L = 0$, that is, the longitudinal modes are not affected by the presence of a purely longitudinal magnetic field. However, such a field results in a coupling between the two plane–polarized transverse waves in Case 1. In other words, the equation $\Delta_T = 0$ gives two circularly polarized transverse waves, where E_x, v_{ex}, v_{ix} as well as E_y, v_{ey} and v_{iy} are all nonvanishing.

CASE 3: $B_T \neq 0$. The general discussion of the dispersion relation is then quite complicated. The main new feature is a coupling between the two transverse and the two longitudinal modes already encountered in Cases 1 and 2. As a result, we no longer find purely transverse or purely longitudinal waves but rather four mixed modes.

Let us now consider in some detail the transverse modes in Case 2, where $B_T = 0$, but let us neglect collisions. Under these conditions, the determining equation is $\Delta_T = 0$, Equation (1.139), which leads to the dispersion relation

$$\omega \left[\frac{k^2 c^2}{\omega^2} - 1 + \frac{\omega_p^2}{\omega^2 - \omega_L^2} + \frac{\Omega_p^2}{\omega^2 - \Omega_L^2} \right] = \pm \left[\frac{\omega_p^2 \omega_L}{\omega^2 - \omega_L^2} - \frac{\Omega_p^2 \Omega_L}{\omega^2 - \Omega_L^2} \right],$$

where

$$\omega_L = -eB_L/m_e c \quad \text{and} \quad \Omega_L = Z_e B_L/m_i c.$$

Following the nomenclature generally adopted,

$$x \equiv \omega_0^2/\omega^2 \approx \omega_p^2/\omega^2, \qquad y \equiv k^2 c^2/\omega^2,$$

we can write the two solutions to this dispersion relation in the form

$$y_1 = 1 - \frac{\omega_0^2}{(\omega + \omega_L)(\omega - \Omega_L)} \tag{1.140}$$

and

$$y_2 = 1 - \frac{\omega_0^2}{(\omega - \omega_L)(\omega + \Omega_L)} . \tag{1.141}$$

The wave given by y_1 is called the ordinary wave, and that given by y_2, the extraordinary wave. For high frequency disturbances, $\omega \gg \Omega_L$, Equations (1.140) and (1.141) reduce to

$$\left. \begin{array}{c} y_1 \\ y_2 \end{array} \right\} = 1 - \frac{\omega_p^2}{\omega(\omega \pm \omega_L)},$$

and with a vanishing external magnetic field this reduces further to

$$y = \frac{k^2 c^2}{\omega^2} = 1 - \frac{\omega_0^2}{\omega^2} . \tag{1.142}$$

Hence, the phase velocity will be given by

$$V_\phi = \frac{\omega}{k} = \frac{c}{\sqrt{1 - \omega_0^2/\omega^2}} \approx \frac{c}{\sqrt{1 - \omega_p^2/\omega^2}} . \qquad (1.143)$$

Thus, electromagnetic wave propagation can occur in a plasma for $\omega^2 > \omega_p^2$, but the electromagnetic field is evanescent for $\omega^2 < \omega_p^2$ since k^2 is then negative. For $\omega = \omega_p$, either an electromagnetic or an electric sound wave oscillation can occur. We shall presently return to this latter kind of wave mode.

The polarization of the waves, given by E_y/E_x, is found from the basic Equation (1.135). It may be written

$$\frac{E_y}{E_x} = (i\omega) \left[\left(\frac{k^2 c^2}{\omega^2} - 1 + \frac{\omega_p^2}{\omega^2 - \omega_L^2} + \frac{\Omega_p^2}{\omega^2 - \Omega_L^2} \right) \Big/ \left(\frac{\omega_p^2 \omega_L}{\omega^2 - \omega_L^2} - \frac{\Omega_p^2 \Omega_L}{\omega^2 - \Omega_L^2} \right) \right],$$

and we find that $E_y/E_x = +i$ for the ordinary wave y_1, and that $E_y/E_x = -i$ for the extraordinary wave y_2. The two waves are consequently circularly polarized in opposite direction, and the electric vector of the extraordinary wave rotates in the same sense as do the plasma electrons around the field B_L. Therefore, it is easy to understand that the wave will be strongly perturbed if the wave frequency is close to the value of the gyromagnetic frequency ω_L. This interaction is portrayed by the term $1/(\omega - \omega_L)$ in Equation (1.141). A similar resonance is seen to occur for the ordinary wave when $\omega = \Omega_L$.

Let us consider next the low frequency waves, that is, $\omega \ll \omega_L$. Equations (1.140) and (1.141) then reduce to a common expression

$$y = 1 + \frac{\omega_0^2}{\omega_L \Omega_L} , \qquad (1.144)$$

and the corresponding phase velocity V_ϕ is given by

$$y = \frac{c^2}{V_\phi^2} = 1 + \frac{\omega_p^2 + \Omega_p^2}{\omega_B \Omega_B} = 1 + \frac{4\pi c^2 (n_e m_e + n_i m_i)}{B_0^2} \qquad (1.145)$$

or

$$V_\phi = c/y^{1/2} = cB_0/\sqrt{B_0^2 + 4\pi\rho c^2} . \qquad (1.146)$$

When either the magnetic field is small or the density is high, the inequality

$$\frac{4\pi c^2 \rho}{B_0^2} \gg 1 \qquad (1.147)$$

holds, and the phase velocity is

$$V_\phi = B_0/\sqrt{4\pi\rho} \equiv V_A.$$

Here V_A is called the Alfvén velocity, and these limiting hydromagnetic waves are called Alfvén waves. When Equation (1.147) is valid, the displacement current in the wave is negligible in comparison with the conduction current. Given this condition, the hydromagnetic approximation applies.

The dispersion relation, Equation (1.145), which, when the condition of Equation (1.147) holds, leads to the familiar expression for the Alfvén velocity, is derived for a collisionless plasma. This is the dispersion relation for a cold plasma, that is, a plasma in which the thermal velocities are zero. However, the equation also is valid for a hot plasma (V_{thermal} is large), provided that the pressure is isotropic. A more rigorous derivation (see, for instance, Stix, 1962) leads to the dispersion relation

$$y\left[1 + \frac{4\pi n k(T_\perp - T_\parallel)}{B_0^2}\right] = 1 + \frac{4\pi c^2(n_e m_e + n_i m_i)}{B_0^2},$$

where $T_\perp$ and $T_\parallel$ are the temperatures related to thermal motion which are perpendicular and parallel, respectively, to the magnetic field. If the pressure is isotropic, we have $T_\perp = T_\parallel$, and the equation above reduces to the expression of Equation (1.145). For large anisotropies, we find that $4\pi n k T_\parallel > B_0^2 + 4\pi n k T_\perp$, and the above equation shows that instabilities will occur (y becomes complex). This is called the garden-hose instability of Rosenbluth (1956) and of Vedenov and Sagdeev (1958). In addition to this incompressible (shear) Alfvén wave, a hot plasma also sustains the compressional Alfvén wave (called the fast mode). With increasing temperature, this last mode becomes a mixed hydromagnetic and acoustic wave, called the magnetosonic mode. Furthermore, in a hot plasma other modes occur which have no counterpart in the cold-plasma approximation.

We now turn to the two longitudinal waves that can propagate in a plasma when $B_T = 0$. We have seen that the presence of a purely longitudinal magnetic field does not alter the basic physics involved, and we shall therefore assume that $B_0 = 0$. The restoring force in the waves is electrostatic, the electric charge resulting from the divergence of the current $\mathbf{j}$. We have already found that the two possible wave modes are the electron waves (electron plasma oscillations) and the positive ion waves, the pseudo-sound mode.

After some rearrangement, the dispersion relation $\Delta_L = 0$ of the two wave modes may be written in the form

$$(k^2 V_e^2 - \omega^2 + \omega_p^2)(k^2 V_i^2 - \omega^2 + \Omega_p^2) - \omega_p^2 \Omega_p^2 = 0. \qquad (1.148)$$

From a graphic representation, we see that this dispersion relation, that is, a hyperbola, is well represented by its tangent in the domain of interest. One solution of the dispersion relation is therefore

$$k^2 V_e^2 - \omega^2 + \omega_p^2 = 0 \quad \text{or} \quad \frac{\omega^2}{k^2} = V_e^2 + \frac{\omega_p^2}{k^2} . \qquad (1.149)$$

This is the dispersion relation for the electron plasma oscillations whose phase velocity is given as

$$V_\phi = \frac{\omega}{k} = \sqrt{V_e^2 + \frac{\omega_p^2}{k^2}} , \qquad (1.150)$$

and whose group velocity is given as

$$V_g = \frac{d\omega}{dk} = \frac{k}{\omega} V_e^2. \qquad (1.151)$$

The last two equations give $V_\phi V_g = V_e^2$. Since $V_g < V_e$, the phase velocity is always greater than the electron thermal velocity.

If the thermal velocity of the electrons is zero, we see from Equations (1.149) and (1.151) that the plasma can oscillate at a fixed frequency ω_p, but this is a stationary oscillation, and no energy is transported since $V_g = 0$. When $V_e \neq 0$, the dispersion relation shows that one must have $\omega \geq \omega_p$, that is, ω_p is a critical frequency and waves for which $\omega < \omega_p$ cannot propagate. Let us designate the corresponding wavelength for the electron oscillations λ_e. It is given by $\lambda_e = 2\pi V_e/\omega_p$.

An approximate expression for the dispersion relation for the ionic oscillations can also be found from Equation (1.148). We shall consider two limiting cases.

CASE 1: $\lambda \ll \lambda_e$. Then $k^2 V_e^2 \gg \omega_p^2$, and if also $k^2 V_e^2 \gg \omega^2$, the dispersion relation of Equation (1.148) reduces to

$$k^2 V_i^2 - \omega^2 + \Omega_p^2 = \frac{\omega_p^2}{k^2 V_e^2} \Omega_p^2$$

or, approximately,

$$k^2 V_i^2 - \omega^2 + \Omega_p^2 = 0. \qquad (1.152)$$

The condition for the existence of these ion plasma oscillations can be written $m_i V_i^2/m_e V_e^2 \ll 1$ or $T_i \ll T_e$, where T_i and T_e are the ion kinetic and the electron kinetic temperatures, respectively. We therefore find that ion plasma oscillations can exist only under extreme departures from thermodynamic equilibrium.

CASE 2: $\lambda \gg \lambda_e$. Then $k^2 V_e^2 \ll \omega_p^2$, and if also $\omega \ll \omega_p$, Equation (1.148) becomes

$$k^2 V_i^2 - \omega^2 + \Omega_p^2 = \frac{\omega_p^2 \Omega_p^2}{\omega_p^2 + k^2 V_e^2}$$

or approximately

$$\omega^2 = k^2 \frac{\omega_p^2 V_i^2 + \Omega_p^2 V_e^2}{\omega_p^2 + \Omega_p^2} = k^2 V_s^2, \qquad (1.153)$$

where V_s—"the velocity of sound" in the plasma—is a weighted mean of V_i^2 and V_e^2. Also V_s is generally of the order of V_i, the ion thermal velocity. The waves whose dispersion relation is given by Equation (1.153) are called pseudo-sound waves. They have the property such that electrons and ions move together and they show no dispersion, that is, V_ϕ is independent of ω. The ions will oscillate with amplitudes which are slightly larger than those for the electrons $[v_{iz}/v_{ez} \approx 1 + (k^2 V_e^2/\omega_p^2) = 1 + (\lambda_e^2/\lambda^2)]$. This produces a very slight departure from electric neutrality, and an electric field is thereby induced. The coupling of the motions of the ions and the motions of the electrons due to this field produces these low frequency soundlike waves.

In the preceding discussion, we neglected gravitational acceleration since the wave modes considered thus far would not be significantly influenced by it. In this approximation, however, we cannot treat the gravity waves mentioned in the introduction. Therefore, we shall now treat this wave mode separately.

Let us consider the forces on an isothermal plane–parallel atmosphere due to pressure gradients, gravity and inertia. We shall later indicate how a temperature gradient may affect the problem. We write for the velocity $\mathbf{v} = \bar{\mathbf{v}} + \mathbf{v}'$, where $\mathbf{v}'$ is the perturbation velocity, and we will introduce similar expressions for the pressure and density. The static equations give the solutions for the mean values $\bar{\rho}$, $\bar{p} \propto e^{-z/H}$, where H is the scale height of the atmosphere. The linearized equations of mass conservation, motion and state are then

$$(\partial \rho'/\partial t) + \mathbf{v}' \cdot \nabla \bar{\rho} + \bar{\rho} \nabla \cdot \mathbf{v}' = 0, \qquad \bar{\rho}(\partial \mathbf{v}'/\partial t) = \rho' \mathbf{g} - \nabla p',$$

and

$$\frac{\partial p'}{\partial t} + \mathbf{v}' \cdot \nabla p_0 = V_s^2 \left(\frac{\partial \rho'}{\partial t} + \mathbf{v}' \cdot \nabla \bar{\rho} \right),$$

where we assume that all oscillations occur adiabatically. The velocity of sound is $V_s = \sqrt{\gamma \bar{p}/\bar{\rho}}$.

We may now seek solutions of the form

$$\frac{p'}{p}, \quad \frac{\rho'}{\bar{\rho}}, \quad v'_z \propto \exp i(\omega t - k_x x - k_z z),$$

where z is chosen vertically (opposite to the vector $\mathbf{g}$), and we find the dispersion relation

$$\omega^4 - \omega^2 V_s^2 (k_x^2 + k_z^2) + (\gamma - 1)g^2 k_x^2 + ig\omega k_z = 0. \qquad (1.154)$$

A word of caution is needed here. Note that we have to use $p'/\bar{p}$ and so forth for the dependent variables, not p' and so forth. This is because if p' and ρ' decrease with height in the atmosphere, v' will increase, and hence these variables will have different wave numbers k_z. A more elegant treatment involves the introduction of new variables, $p'/\sqrt{\bar{\rho}}$, $\rho'/\sqrt{\bar{\rho}}$ and $v'\sqrt{\bar{\rho}}$, which will all have the correct amplitude dependence with height and which, furthermore, are directly related to the energies involved (see, for instance, Hines, 1960).

If we neglect gravity, this equation reduces to

$$\omega^2 = V_s^2 (k_x^2 + k_z^2),$$

which is the dispersion relation for ordinary sound waves when k_x and k_z are real. When gravity is present, there is no solution of Equation (1.154) for which both k_x and k_z are real. There is one solution for which k_x is real, and k_z has the form $k_z = k_z \text{ (real)} + i\gamma g/2V_s^2$. This solution permits the phase to change in the vertical direction; hence, propagation is possible. Thus these waves include sound waves in a generalized form which show the effect of gravity, and, as we shall presently see, they also include the low frequency gravity waves.

Introducing the expression for the complex wave number k_z in Equation (1.154), we find the dispersion relation

$$\omega^4 - \omega^2 V_s^2 (k_x^2 + k_z^2) + (\gamma - 1)g^2 k_x^2 - \gamma^2 g^2 \frac{\omega^2}{4V_s^2} = 0.$$

This equation shows that for each value of the wave number, there are two positive values of ω, that is, two wave modes. For one mode, we have

$$\omega > \omega_a \equiv \gamma g/2V_s, \qquad (1.155)$$

and for the other, we have

$$\omega < \omega_g \equiv g\sqrt{\gamma - 1}/V_s. \qquad (1.156)$$

The high frequency mode whose frequency is greater than the critical frequency ω_a is called the acoustic wave mode, whereas the low frequency mode, found only for frequencies smaller than the critical frequency ω_g, is the (internal) gravity wave mode. The acoustic waves include ordinary sound waves as a limiting case. Furthermore, we see from Equations (1.155) and (1.156) that the domains of the acoustic waves and of the gravity waves are completely separated, since there is no real value of γ smaller than 2 for which ω_a and ω_g coincide.

When we allow temperature variations in the atmosphere, the wave modes just described still retain their identity; that is, for each value of the wave number we have a high frequency acoustic wave and a low frequency gravity wave. But whereas the waves propagate in straight lines, in the isothermal case we encounter curved wave paths as the result of a tempera-ture gradient. The general mathematical treatment is quite complicated, and the WKB approximation (Wentzel, 1926; Kramers, 1926; Brillouin, 1926) is generally used. We shall not treat this case further, but merely note that when the domain of the gravity waves is changed, the critical fre-quency ω_g is replaced by the Brunt frequency $\omega_{Br} = [\omega_g^2 + (g/T)(dT/dz)]^{1/2}$.

1.5.3. Shock Waves

In linear wave motion, all disturbances (which are assumed small) are propagated with a specific velocity, the velocity of sound, and the principle of superposition of solutions of the governing differential equations holds. This is not so for violent disturbances which lead to nonlinear waves. These may steepen into shocks, the velocities of which are not uniquely given by the properties of the medium itself. Furthermore, the principle of superposition does not hold any longer, and entirely new phenomena occur.

Consider the one-dimensional case of a wave propagating along the x-axis. Let the particle velocity be $u = u_x$ and the velocity of sound be V_s. Then the linear propagation of an initial wave form, $u = F(x)$, is given by

$$u = F(x - V_s t), \quad \text{where} \quad V_s = \text{const}.$$

This expresses the fact that in a linear wave the wave form is propagated unchanged. In the general, nonlinear case, the corresponding equation is

$$u = F_1(x - (u + V_s)t),$$

where

$$V_s = F_2(x - (u + V_s)t),$$

and it shows that a nonlinear wave becomes distorted as it propagates.

More specifically, the velocity profile in a compression wave steepens gradually, while that of a rarefaction wave flattens out. Hence, in the physically interesting case of a compression wave, what may have started out as a continuous linear wave cannot be maintained without a discontinuity, and then there occur jumps in velocity, pressure, density, entropy, temperature and, if present, magnetic field. To describe this mathematically, we need something in addition to the laws of conservation of mass, momentum, and energy (which surely must all still apply). The additional information is that irreversible processes take place in the jump, the shock front, generally requiring entropy to increase.

Let us consider a plane shock traveling with velocity U in the X-direction through a neutral gas. Again let $u = u_x$ be the velocity of the particles of the gas, whence $v = u - U$ is the flow velocity relative to the shock front. We often use a coordinate system moving with the velocity of the shock front and $v = u$. Using the symbols s for entropy, e for the internal energy of the gas, and j_m for the mass flux density, and letting a subscript 2 pertain to conditions behind the shock front while a subscript 1 identifies conditions in front of the shock, we can write the four basic principles on which the shock wave theory is built in the following form.

(1) Conservation of mass

$$\rho_2 v_2 - \rho_1 v_1 = 0 \tag{1.157a}$$

or

$$\rho_2 v_2 = \rho_1 v_1 = j_m. \tag{1.157b}$$

(2) Conservation of momentum

$$\rho_2 u_2 v_2 - \rho_1 u_1 v_1 = p_1 - p_2 \tag{1.158a}$$

or

$$j_m u_2 + p_2 = j_m u_1 + p_1. \tag{1.158b}$$

(3) Conservation of energy

$$\rho_2 (\tfrac{1}{2} u_2^2 + e_2) v_2 + p_2 u_2 = \rho_1 (\tfrac{1}{2} u_1^2 + e_1) v_1 + p_1 u_1 \tag{1.159a}$$

or

$$\frac{1}{2} v_2^2 + e_2 + \frac{p_2}{\rho_2} = \frac{1}{2} v_1^2 + e_1 + \frac{p_1}{\rho_1}. \tag{1.159b}$$

(4) Nondecrease of entropy

$$\rho_2 s_2 v_2 \geq \rho_1 s_1 v_1 \qquad (1.160a)$$

or

$$j_m s_2 \geq j_m s_1 . \qquad (1.160b)$$

Combining Equations (1.157b) and (1.158b), we find that

$$\left(\frac{1}{\rho_1} + \frac{1}{\rho_2}\right)(p_2 - p_1) = j_m\left(\frac{1}{\rho_1} + \frac{1}{\rho_2}\right)(v_1 - v_2) = v_1^2 - v_2^2, \qquad (1.161)$$

and eliminating the velocity between Equations (1.160a) and (1.161), we obtain

$$e_2 - e_1 = \frac{1}{2}(p_2 + p_1)\left(\frac{1}{\rho_1} - \frac{1}{\rho_2}\right),$$

which relates only thermodynamic quantities and is called Hugoniot's relation.

From the condition for mass conservation, we find the expressions

$$j_m(v_2 - v_1) = p_1 - p_2 \qquad \text{and} \qquad v_2 v_1 = (p_1 - p_2)/(\rho_1 - \rho_2).$$

From these equations, we see that for very weak shocks, that is, $p_2 - p_1 \to 0$, v_2 will approach v_1 and that

$$v_1 v_2 \to p/\rho = V_s^2, \qquad (1.162)$$

where V_s is the velocity of sound in the gas. Hence, a sound wave can be interpreted as an infinitely weak shock wave. This fact can also be stated as follows: As the shock strength, measured by $p_2 - p_1$, tends to zero, the velocity of the shock tends uniquely to the velocity of sound. The case in which the shock strength is not approaching zero is governed by Prandtl's relation $v_1 v_2 = v_{cr}^2$, where v_{cr} is called the critical speed and is given by $v_{cr}^2 = [(2\gamma - 1)/(\gamma + 1)](\frac{1}{2}v^2 + e + p/\rho)$. Prandtl's relation—which goes into Equation (1.162) for weak shocks—shows that the velocity of the gas relative to the shock front is supersonic in front of the shock but subsonic behind it. The shock strength may be measured by one of the following parameters: the excess pressure ratio, $(p_2 - p_1)/p_1$; the condensation, $(\rho_2 - \rho_1)/\rho_1$; the relative velocity difference, $(u_2 - u_1)/V_s$; and the Mach number, $M \equiv v_1/V_s$.

The fundamental system of Equations (1.157a) through (1.160a) holds for shock propagation in a neutral gas. We now generalize the system to a plasma pervaded by a magnetic field **B**, but for simplicity we assume the electric conductivity σ to be infinite, while thermal conductivity and viscosity are neglected. We then find that the equations of motion permit discontinuous flow as they do in ordinary fluid (or gas) dynamics. However, the magnetic field exerts forces on the currents induced in the plasma by the field, and these forces modify the flow. Also, the currents will modify the magnetic field, and this complex interaction requires that we treat the problem by solving both the field equations and the equations of fluid dynamics for the plasma. The field equations are Equations (1.40) and (1.50), namely

$$\nabla \cdot \mathbf{B} = 0 \quad \text{and} \quad \frac{\partial \mathbf{B}}{\partial t} = \nabla \times (\mathbf{u} \times \mathbf{B}) + \frac{c^2}{4\pi\sigma} \nabla^2 \mathbf{B}. \quad (1.163)$$

The latter reduces to

$$\partial \mathbf{B}/\partial t = \nabla \times (\mathbf{u} \times \mathbf{B}). \quad (1.164)$$

The equations of fluid dynamics for this case are the equation of continuity,

$$(\partial\rho/\partial t) + \nabla \cdot (\rho\mathbf{u}) = 0; \quad (1.165)$$

the Navier-Stokes Equation (1.33b),

$$\frac{\partial \mathbf{u}}{\partial t} + (\mathbf{u} \cdot \nabla)\mathbf{u} = -\frac{1}{\rho} \nabla p - \frac{1}{4\pi\rho} \mathbf{B} \times (\nabla \times \mathbf{B}) + \eta \nabla^2 \mathbf{u},$$

which reduces to

$$\frac{\partial \mathbf{u}}{\partial t} + (\mathbf{u} \cdot \nabla)\mathbf{u} = -\frac{1}{\rho} \nabla p - \frac{1}{4\pi\rho} \mathbf{B} \times (\nabla \times \mathbf{B}); \quad (1.166)$$

the equation of state,

$$p = p(\rho, T); \quad (1.167)$$

and the heat transfer equation,

$$\rho T \left(\frac{\partial s}{\partial t} + \mathbf{u} \cdot \nabla s \right) = \sigma_{ij} \frac{\partial u_i}{\partial x_j} + \nabla \cdot (K \nabla T),$$

which becomes

$$\rho T(\partial s/\partial t) + \mathbf{u} \cdot \nabla s = 0, \quad (1.168)$$

the equation of conservation of entropy, equivalent here to energy conservation.

Equations (1.163) through (1.168) form the complete set of equations of "magneto-fluid" dynamics. We will now proceed to the jump conditions applicable to this case. They can be derived from Equations (1.163) through (1.168), and here we shall mainly state the results.

Let a subscript n denote the component of a vector normal to the shock front, and a subscript t (for tangential) denote the component parallel to the front. Mass conservation requires an equation of the form of Equation (1.157a),

$$\rho_2 v_{2n} = \rho_1 v_{1n},\tag{1.169}$$

that is, the same as found for a neutral gas. But the equation for conservation of momentum now becomes

$$p_2 + \rho_2 v_{2n}^2 + \frac{1}{8\pi}\,(B_{2t}^2 - B_{2n}^2) - p_1 - \rho_1 u_{1n}^2 - \frac{1}{8\pi}\,(B_{1t}^2 - B_{1n}^2) = 0,\tag{1.170a}$$

and

$$\rho_2 u_{2n} u_{2t} - \frac{1}{4\pi}\,B_{2n}B_{2t} - \rho_1 u_{1n} u_{2t} + \frac{1}{4\pi}\,B_{1n}B_{2t} = 0,\tag{1.170b}$$

where the additional terms [relative to Equation (1.158a)] are due to the Maxwell stress tensor of the magnetic field.

The requirement that the energy flux through the shock front remain continuous leads to the condition

$$\rho_2 u_{2n}\left(\frac{1}{2}\,u_2^2 + e_2 + \frac{p_2}{\rho_2}\right) + \frac{1}{4\pi}\,u_{2n}B_2^2 - \frac{1}{4\pi}\,B_{2n}\mathbf{u}_2\cdot\mathbf{B}_2$$
$$- \rho_1 u_{1n}\left(\frac{1}{2}\,u_1^2 + e_1 + \frac{p_1}{\rho_1}\right) - \frac{1}{4\pi}\,u_{1n}B_1^2 - \frac{1}{4\pi}\,B_{1n}\mathbf{u}_1\cdot\mathbf{B}_1 = 0,\tag{1.171}$$

which replaces the entropy conservation condition.

Finally, at the shock front B_n, the normal component of the magnetic field, must be continuous, that is, $B_{2n} - B_{1n} = 0$; the same holds for E_t, the tangential component of the electric field. Since this induced field in our approximation is given by $\mathbf{E} = (1/c)\mathbf{u}\times\mathbf{B}$, the condition $E_{2t} - E_{1t} = 0$ leads to

$$B_{2n}u_{2t} - B_{2t}u_{2n} - B_{1n}u_{1t} + B_{1t}u_{1n} = 0.\tag{1.172}$$

Equations (1.169) through (1.172) are the basic system of equations for discontinuities in magneto-fluid dynamics and replace Equations (1.157a) to (1.160a) in ordinary gas dynamics.

Several types of discontinuities are possible. If $j_m = 0$, that is, if the mass flux density through the discontinuity is zero, we have—as in ordinary gas dynamics—a *tangential discontinuity*. If $j_m \neq 0$ but if $\rho_2 - \rho_1 = 0$, we have a *rotational discontinuity*, so called because the direction of the magnetic field, not its magnitude, is changed in the discontinuity. Since for this case $j_m \neq 0$, this type of discontinuity is sometimes treated as a noncompressive shock, also called a transverse Alfvén shock.

The discontinuities in which we are interested, the shock waves, are characterized by $j_m \neq 0$ and $\rho_2 - \rho_1 \neq 0$.

If we eliminate $u_{2t} - u_{1t}$ from Equations (1.170b) and (1.172), we find an equation for $\rho u_n \equiv j_m$ which we insert in Equation (1.171) after some rearranging. We then arrive at an equation which corresponds to Hugoniot's relation in ordinary fluid dynamics:

$$e_2 - e_1 = \frac{1}{2}(p_2 + p_1)\left(\frac{1}{\rho_1} - \frac{1}{\rho_2}\right) + \frac{1}{16\pi}(B_{2t} - B_{1t})^2\left(\frac{1}{\rho_1} - \frac{1}{\rho_2}\right). \quad (1.173)$$

The equations permit a solution in which $B_{2t} = B_{1t} = 0$, that is, the magnetic field remains perpendicular to the shock front. If this case is realized, the magnetic field has no influence on the shock, and Equation (1.173) reduces to Hugoniot's relation.

From the basic Equations (1.169) through (1.172), we can derive the equation for j_m which determines the different types of possible discontinuities. This equation is

$$\frac{1}{4}\left(\frac{1}{\rho_1} + \frac{1}{\rho_2}\right)^2 j_m \left[\frac{1}{2}\left(\frac{1}{\rho_1} + \frac{1}{\rho_2}\right)j_m^2 - B_n^2\right]$$

$$\times \left\{\frac{1}{2}\left(\frac{1}{\rho_1} + \frac{1}{\rho_2}\right)j_m^4 + \left[\frac{(1/\rho_2) + (1/\rho_1)}{(1/\rho_2) - (1/\rho_1)}(p_2 - p_1) - \frac{1}{4}(B_2 - B_1)^2\right]\right.$$

$$\left. \times j_m^2 - 2\frac{p_2 - p_1}{(1/\rho_2) - (1/\rho_1)}B_n^2\right\} = 0.$$

We note that there are the following four solutions:

(1) $j_m = 0$, that is, the tangential discontinuity.

(2) $$\frac{1}{2}\left(\frac{1}{\rho_2} + \frac{1}{\rho_1}\right)j_m^2 = B_n^2,$$

which is the noncompressive transverse shock.

(3) and (4)

$$\frac{1}{2}\left(\frac{1}{\rho_2} + \frac{1}{\rho_1}\right)j_m^4 + \frac{(1/\rho_2) + (1/\rho_1)}{(1/\rho_2) - (1/\rho_1)}(p_2 - p_1)$$

$$-\frac{1}{4}(B_2 - B_1)^2 j_m^2 - 2\frac{p_2 - p_1}{(1/\rho_2) + (1/\rho_1)}B_n^2 = 0.$$

The two solutions for j_m to this equation are the genuine shocks in which we are primarily interested. One of the solutions is called the fast magnetic shock, $j_m(\mathrm{f})$, the other the slow shock, $j_m(\mathrm{s})$. They are characterized by different propagation velocities. Furthermore, the following inequalities are satisfied:

$$j_m^2(\mathrm{f}) \geq \frac{p_1 - p_2}{(1/\rho_2) - (1/\rho_1)} \geq j_m^2(\mathrm{s})$$

and

$$j_m^2(\mathrm{f}) \geq \frac{2B_n^2}{(1/\rho_2) + (1/\rho_1)} \geq j_m^2(\mathrm{s}).$$

It can be shown that the magnetic field strength B increases across a fast shock and decreases across a slow shock.

We shall close this section with some remarks concerning the compression to be expected in a shock, using Hugoniot's relation. Assume first an ideal neutral gas. In this case, the internal energy is a function of temperature alone. If we further consider a polytropic gas where the temperature dependence of entropy is linear, with the specific heat at constant volume as the constant of proportionality, we have $e = c_v T$. These assumptions further lead to the expression $p = p(\rho, s) = A\rho^\gamma$, where the constant A depends on the entropy, and, by using $p/\rho = RT$ (R = gas constant), to $e = (p/\rho)/(\gamma - 1)$.

Since the internal energy can be considered as a function of p and ρ, we can write Hugoniot's relation in the form of Hugoniot's function

$$H(\rho, p) = e(\rho_2, p_2) - e(\rho_1, p_1) + \frac{1}{2}(p_2 + p_1)\left(\frac{1}{\rho_2} - \frac{1}{\rho_1}\right) = 0,$$

which becomes

$$H(\rho, p) = \frac{1}{2}\frac{\gamma - 1}{\gamma + 1}\left(\frac{1}{\rho_2} - \frac{\gamma - 1}{\gamma + 1}\frac{1}{\rho_1}\right)p_2 - \left(\frac{1}{\rho_1} - \frac{\gamma - 1}{\gamma + 1}\frac{1}{\rho_2}\right)p_1 = 0.$$

Hence we have

$$\frac{p_2}{p_1} = \left(\frac{1}{\rho_1} - \frac{\gamma-1}{\gamma+1}\frac{1}{\rho_2}\right)\bigg/\left(\frac{1}{\rho_2} - \frac{\gamma-1}{\gamma+1}\frac{1}{\rho_1}\right) = \left(\rho_2 - \frac{\gamma-1}{\gamma+1}\rho_1\right)\bigg/\left(\rho_1 - \frac{\gamma-1}{\gamma+1}\rho_2\right)$$

or

$$\frac{p_2}{p_1} = \left(p_2 + \frac{\gamma-1}{\gamma+1}p_1\right)\bigg/\left(p_1 + \frac{\gamma-1}{\gamma+1}p_2\right). \tag{1.174}$$

Equation (1.174) shows that the compression is restricted to the range

$$1 < \rho_2/\rho_1 < (\gamma+1)/(\gamma-1). \tag{1.175}$$

In terms of the condensation $\eta_g \equiv (\rho_2 - \rho_1)/\rho_1$, we find the restriction $\eta_g < 2/(\gamma-1)$. For example, if $\gamma = \frac{5}{3}$, the compression is always less than 4, or $\eta_g < 3$.

Using the relations $T_2/T_1 = p_2\rho_1/p_1\rho_2$ and Equation (1.174), we can compute the change of temperature across the shock.

We now generalize to hydromagnetic shocks and find that η never exceeds the gas-dynamic upper limit $\eta_g = 2/(\gamma-1)$. More specifically, for fast shocks, $\eta(f) = \eta_g$, while for slow shocks $\eta(s) < \eta_g$. The excess pressure ratio in hydromagnetic shocks, $(p_2 - p_1)/p_1$, is, however, greater than the corresponding ratio in pure gas-dynamic shocks. This is due to the transverse component of the magnetic field and may be deduced from the generalized Hugoniot relation, Equation (1.173).

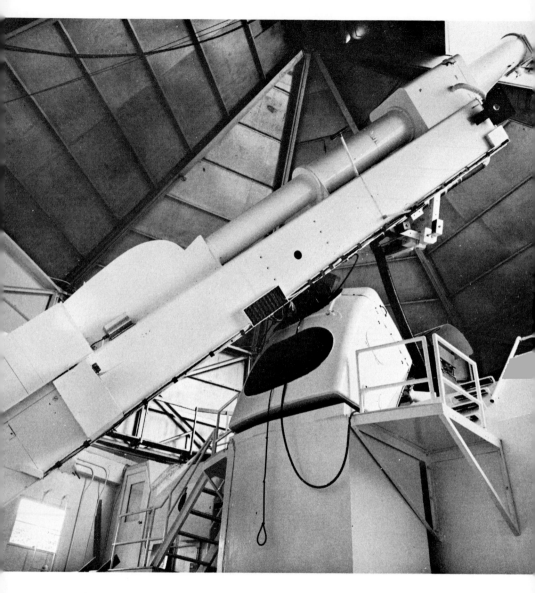

The 16-in. coronagraph at the Climax, Colorado station of the High Altitude Observatory.

Observations of 2
Solar Activity

We do not intend to give a full account of all the facets of the observational techniques employed in solar physics, techniques ranging from the classical visual observations, photography via spectroscopy, radio techniques, and photoelectrical measurements to X-ray spectroscopy and the subtleties of cosmic-ray observations. Instead, we shall assume that the reader is sufficiently familiar with the more standard observational methods of astrophysics and limit ourselves to a discussion of the techniques more specifically used in studying solar activity. Obviously, there is often no clear-cut dividing line between methods used to investigate solar activity and other methods, and thus the subject matter in this chapter is chosen with a fair degree of ambiguity.

Also we shall not discuss the advantages and disadvantages of ground-based versus airborne equipment. In some cases, it makes little difference whether the equipment is on the ground or aboard a satellite or hanging under a balloon; in other cases, it may be of crucial importance. Besides the fact that our atmosphere is not even transparent to many wavelengths and to particles of certain energies, the atmospheric gases cause distortions and serious absorption effects for many of the waves and particles transmitted. A proper evaluation of these effects will decide whether we need to get the observing instrument up above most of the earth's atmosphere.

The energy received from the sun per 1 cm^2/sec outside the earth's atmosphere (the solar constant, see Section 4.1) is 1.34×10^6 erg cm^{-2} sec^{-1}. At sea level, this is reduced to about 9.4×10^5 erg cm^{-2} sec^{-1}.

The highest mountain observatories still have about 65 % of the atmosphere above them, which causes "bad seeing." A balloon flown at 12 km [40,000 feet (ft)] sees all but 18 % of a sea-level atmosphere, while at 30 km (100,000 ft) about 1 % of the atmosphere remains overhead.

The effects generally called "bad seeing" comprise (1) atmospheric refraction (bending of the light waves reaching the telescope), (2) atmospheric dispersion (spreading of the white light into its color components), (3) atmospheric scintillation (causing point images to dance irregularly), and (4) atmospheric scattering (blurring of light from a bright source and illuminating the surrounding field of view). These effects are often of extreme importance, and it is due to them that we do not have adequate observational models of sunspots or better data on coronal streamers, to mention only a few examples.

2.1. *Optical Instruments*

2.1.1. The Spectroheliograph

This important instrument was introduced into the studies of solar physics in 1891 independently by Hale at Kenwood and Deslandres at Meudon. The principle of this adaption of the spectrograph to solar astronomy is shown schematically in Figure 2.1. An image of the sun is formed on the

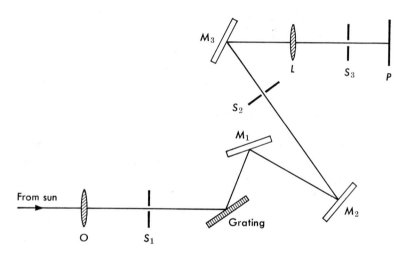

FIGURE 2.1.   Principle of the spectroheliograph

entrance slit S_1 of the spectrograph. By some means, either the slit or the objective O is moved so that the slit sweeps across the solar image at a uniform speed. Synchronized with the sweeping speed of the entrance slit, the photographic plate P or film now moves behind the slit S_3 which only lets through the particular wavelength in which we are interested. On the film, we then obtain a picture of the sun in the chosen wavelength. These photographs may correspond to filters of bandpass less than 0.1 Å and are the best monochromatic pictures of the sun we can get. Modern spectroheliographs attain a spectral purity of more than 60,000, but fall short of the best spectrographs which approach their theoretical resolution of ≈500,000.

If one chooses to transmit (through slit S_2) different parts of a strong line, like Hα or Ca II, K, we get pictures of the sun which give information from different heights in the solar atmosphere (the center of a line corresponds to a greater absorption coefficient and gives information about higher regions than do the wings of the line). A series of spectroheliograms and the corresponding white-light photograph are shown in Figure 2.2.

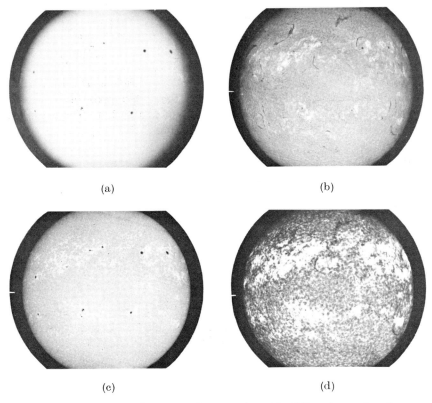

(a)   (b)

(c)   (d)

FIGURE 2.2.   The solar atmosphere as viewed in different wavelengths: (a) white light, (b) Hα, (c) Ca II, K 1, (d) Ca II, K 3 (courtesy R. Michard, L'Observatoire de Paris-Meudon)

The spectroheliograph can be modified to record the wavelength shift of the line instead of the brightness in the line. If this shift is due to mass motions (in the line of sight), we observe a Doppler effect, and we say that the spectroheliograph operates in "the Doppler mode." The shift may also be due to

Zeeman splitting of the line in a magnetic field and can be used to measure this field (Leighton, 1959). The Doppler mode of operation is an adaption of the method used to measure magnetic fields with the spectroheliograph. We shall discuss both these techniques in Section 2.2.

2.1.2. Interference (Birefringent) Filters

Spectroheliographs are fairly complicated instruments. The scanning of the solar image takes a certain amount of time, and the whole method is not particularly suited to patrolling the sun on a short-time-scale basis.

An elegant solution to the problem of obtaining an instantaneous monochromatic picture of the sun has been given by Lyot (1931, 1938a, 1938b) and independently by Öhman (1938); see also Lyot (1944) and Evans (1940, 1949). The principle of the birefringent polarizing filter (for short often called a Lyot filter) is discussed below.

The light beam from the sun is made parallel and falls on a plane–parallel piece of birefringent material (a crystal with one optical axis, like quartz or calcite) cut parallel to the optical axis (C_1 in Figure 2.3). The crystal is

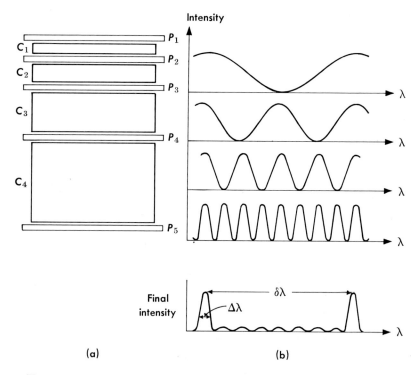

(a)   (b)

FIGURE 2.3.   Principle of the birefringent filter (courtesy J. C. Pecker and E. Schatzman, 1959)

placed between parallel polaroids (P_1 and P_2) whose plane of polarization forms a 45-deg angle with the direction of the optical axis of the quartz or calcite. In this arrangement, interference is produced between the components of light in the plane of polarization of the polaroid. The transmitted light shows a spectrum where only those wavelengths λ exist that satisfy the relation

$$d(n_{ex} - n_{ord}) = k\lambda, \qquad (2.1)$$

where d is the thickness of the quartz (or calcite), n_{ex} and n_{ord} are the extraordinary and ordinary indices of reflection, and k is an integer. If we now let this light go through another similar filter with thickness d', we find that the systems of transmitted wavelengths are commensurable only if

$$d'(n_{ex} - n_{ord}) = k'\lambda. \qquad (2.2)$$

Equations (2.1) and (2.2) lead to $d' = dk'/k$. One may, therefore, use a series of filters where the thicknesses of the quartz elements form a geometric progression: d, $2d$, $4d$, $8d$, etc. Then the final transmitted spectrum will look like the one shown schematically in Figure 2.3. The thinnest element determines the distance $\delta\lambda$ between transmitted peaks; the thickest element determines the half width $\Delta\lambda$ of the peaks.

By varying the temperature of the filter elements, we can change the wavelength of the transmitted peak. In the case of quartz elements, the transmitted wavelength decreases by about $d\lambda = 0.7$ Å for every degree of increase in temperature:

$$d\lambda/\lambda = -1.04 \times 10^{-4},$$

which corresponds to a radial velocity v ($= c\, d\lambda/\lambda$) of 31 km/sec.

The half width $\Delta\lambda$ can be brought down to about 0.5 Å in complex Lyot filters.

2.1.3. The Coronagraph

The invention of the coronagraph (Lyot, 1930) has made possible the observation of the corona outside eclipses. The importance of this instrument for studies of solar activity can hardly be overestimated. The principle of the instrument is extremely simple. Lyot realized that—at high mountain stations—the atmospheric scattered light is much fainter than the scattered light in ordinary telescopes. The scattered light in instruments is mainly due to refraction at the edge of the objective, to flaws in the glass, and to multiple reflections. Appreciating this, we find with Lyot that the ideal solution to the problem is to have a telescope free of scattered light. In praxis one uses very high quality, polished bubblefree glass to make a single objective lens (O_1 in Figure 2.4) which forms an image of the sun on an occulting disk D_1. The disk occults the photosphere and about 15″ or 20″ of the atmosphere above. The field lens F now forms a picture of the objective at D_2, where a diaphragm stops the light reflected by the edge of the objective. Near the center of the diaphragm is a small disk which stops

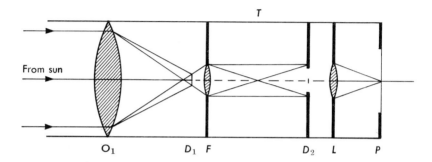

FIGURE 2.4.   Principle of the coronagraph

the light that is reflected off the faces of O_1. Finally, a well-corrected lens L forms an achromatic picture of the corona with prominences, etc. in the film plane P of a camera or on the entrance slit of a spectrograph. The whole coronagraph is encased in a tube T, where dust is kept to a minimum.

2.2. *Magnetic Field Measurements*

2.2.1. Introduction

All early observations of solar magnetism dating from the pioneering work of Hale (1907) depended on the photographic recording of Zeeman-affected lines on high-dispersion spectrograms. The underlying basic idea is very simple and utilizes the longitudinal Zeeman effect. Let us briefly recall the essence of the simplest example of this effect. It should be remembered that optical instruments are used in the magnetic field measurements, but we treat the latter separately since specific techniques are employed.

In a magnetic field, an atom radiates a spectral line split into three components designated σ_1, σ_2, and π. The π-component is unshifted from the normal position of the line, and, if we observe perpendicular to the direction of the magnetic field **B**, the π-component is linearly polarized along the field, while it disappears for observations parallel to the field **B**. The σ-components are shifted by an amount $\Delta\lambda_B$, one to each side of the normal position of the line. If we make observations perpendicular to the field **B**, we see that the σ-components are linearly polarized (in a direction perpendicular to the field), while the σ_1- and σ_2-components are circularly polarized in opposite directions when we look parallel to **B**.

In the simplest case, the shift $\Delta\lambda_B$ due to the splitting of the line of wavelength λ is given by

$$\Delta\lambda_B = (e/4\pi m_e c)\lambda^2 g B = 4.67 \times 10^{-5}\lambda^2 g B, \qquad (2.3)$$

where g, the Landé g-factor, can take values between 0 and 3. When $g = 0$, the corresponding atomic energy levels are not split in a magnetic field, and these fairly infrequent lines may be used to check the instrumental set-up.

The splitting depends on the magnetic moment of the atom in the direction of the field ($\mu_B = (eh/4\pi m_e c)Mg$, where M, the magnetic quantum number, follows the selection rule $\Delta M = 0, \pm 1$). Landé's g-factor is given by

$$g = \frac{J(J+1) + S(S+1) - L(L+1)}{2J(J+1)} + 1, \qquad (2.4)$$

and from calculations we can find which lines should give the most favorable shifts (von Klüber, 1947). This is important, since the splitting is always very small. The lines mainly used are Cr I, 5247.6; Fe I, 5250.2 (Evershed, 1939; von Klüber, 1947), and Fe I, 6173.3; Fe I, 6302.5 (von Klüber, 1947). From Equation (2.3), we see that the splitting is proportional to the square of the wavelength of the line, from whence we find that red and infrared lines have advantages over lines of shorter wavelengths.

2.2.2. Early Work

The two effects of a magnetic field on a line, namely the shift and the sense of polarization, may be used to develop two observational methods for measuring the field:

(1) We can measure the shift and thereby deduce the field, using Equation (2.3). This is practical for strong fields with their relatively large splitting effect—as observed in large sunspots.

(2) We can use the polarization in the components to render the effect more conspicuous and therefore more easily observable. This is of prime importance for weaker fields. Because we get different polarizations for the σ-components in the longitudinal effect, this is more suitable than the transverse effect.

Hale and his collaborators (Seares, 1913; Hale, 1914; Hale, Seares, van Maanen, and Ellerman, 1918) used the second method and converted the circularly polarized σ-components into linearly polarized light by introducing a quarter-wave ($\lambda/4$) plate. If the σ_1-component, for example, becomes horizontally plane polarized, the σ_2-component will be plane polarized in the vertical direction. Thus, a Nicol prism or a polaroid (linear polarizer) placed behind the ($\lambda/4$)-wave plate can suppress either one or the other of the Zeeman components, depending on its orientation.

The Mount Wilson group used a number of mica strips placed with their optical axes in alternately crossed directions. Thereby, each of the circularly polarized Zeeman components was broken up into short sections alternately perpendicular to each other. The Nicol prism then suppressed the two components alternately, resulting in a spectrum where the Zeeman affected lines showed a characteristic zigzag pattern. Nearly all of the fundamental research by Hale and his collaborators was carried out with this instrumental arrangement (Hale and Nicholson, 1938).

Later developments and variants of the method are due to von Klüber (1948), Öhman (1950), Thiessen (1946, 1949) and others, but none of them suffice to measure with certainty field strengths smaller than 10 to 20 gauss. The results obtained in this period (prior to 1952) for a general magnetic field of the sun are, therefore, probably spurious (see Chapter 4).

2.2.3. Babcock's Magnetograph

Two difficulties had to be overcome before very faint fields could be recorded. One was that the resolution of even the best gratings used was below 200,000; the other was that the photographic technique used had been pushed to its practical limit. A solution to these difficulties was pointed out by H. D. and H. W. Babcock, who—after having realized special diffraction gratings giving a very high resolving power (H. D. Babcock, 1940)—in 1952 introduced what is today the best plane grating available for this kind of work. In that same year, the Babcocks (H. D. and H. W. Babcock, 1952, 1955; H. W. Babcock, 1953) put into operation a new instrument—the magnetograph—which combined the use of the new grating with an ingenious photoelectric recording device, thereby also eliminating the limit set by photography. The idea of replacing the photographic recording of the Zeeman splitting by measuring the polarization with a photomultiplier had already been used by Thiessen (1949) in a series of observations he made while searching for the general magnetic field of the sun.

A number of changes have been made in the original Babcock magneto-graph, and different versions of it are now either in operation or planned for the future (Kiepenheuer, 1953a; Beggs and von Klüber, 1956, 1964; Nikulin, Severny, and Stepanov, 1958; Kotlyar, 1960).

Of considerable interest is the introduction of magneto-optical crystals to replace ordinary quarter-wave plates. These crystals (unsaturated potassium, KH_2PO_4, or ammonium phosphate, $NH_4H_2PO_4$) serve as $(\lambda/4)$-wave plates in that when a voltage is applied to them, they become in effect $(\lambda/4)$-wave plates for either right or left circularly polarized light, depending on the direction of the voltage. If we use an alternating voltage, the crystal passes the right-circular beam and suppresses the left-circular beam on one half-cycle, and reverses on the other.

If we use this technique, the magnetograph will separate the two partly overlapping components of a split line by viewing them one at a time. This results in an oscillation of the image of the line back and forth over a very small distance, the length of which depends on the magnetic field strength. Two slits are placed on the "shoulders" of the line (centered on the undisplaced line) and, when the magneto-optical crystal is in operation, the two slits see each displaced component in turn, so that first one slit is brighter, and then the other, etc. A photomultiplier is mounted behind each slit. The difference between the signals produced in the photomultipliers is amplified and converted to a single direct current. The strength of the current varies with the strength of the field, and the direction gives the direction of polarization of the field. Figure 2.5 shows schematically the general optical arrangement of a magnetograph (p. 78).

2.2.4. Leighton's Magnetoheliograph

Magnetographs of the Babcock type are very sensitive, having noise levels of a small fraction of one gauss. But at this high sensitivity, the angular resolution is fairly poor, $10''$ to $20''$. Furthermore, the scanning rate is then so slow that it takes several hours to cover the solar disk.

Leighton (1959) has devised a method whereby one can map the solar magnetic field quickly over large areas with good spatial resolution. This is accomplished at the sacrifice of sensitivity, which, in Leighton's instrument, is about 20 gauss.

The method is based on a comparison of two spectroheliograms which are identical except for local differences due to magnetic fields. This is done by a photographic subtraction technique which brings out these magnetic field differences. Thus the magnetoheliograph is a spectroheliograph to which is added a unit that renders the Zeeman effect visible. A diagram of the magnetic field attachment is shown in Figure 2.6 (p. 79). Here M is a mica quarter-wave plate, and B is a beamsplitter, producing two images, I_1 and I_2, on the entrance slit S of the spectroheliograph. Also D_1 and D_2 are sheets of polaroid placed one in each beam. One polaroid is so oriented as to block out right-hand circularly polarized light; the other blocks left-hand circularly polarized light. The light of the two images I_1 and I_2 now goes to the

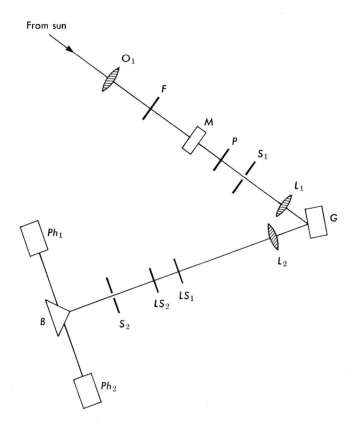

From sun

FIGURE 2.5. Principle of the magnetograph: O_1 = objective, F = filter, M = magneto-optical crystal, P = polaroid, S_1 = entrance slit of spectrograph, L_1 = collimator lens, G = grating, L_2 = camera lens, LS_1 = line shifter for Doppler compensator, LS_2 = line shifter for calibration, S_2 = exit slit of spectrograph, B = beam splitter, double slit, Ph_1 = photomultiplier, Ph_2 = photomultiplier

spectroheliograph and returns through the exit slit T. This slit is set on the shoulder of a line sensitive to the Zeeman effect, and spectroheliograms are obtained in the film plane P, where the image points P_1 and P_2 correspond to the images I_1 and I_2. The two spectroheliograms (built up of points P_1 and P_2) will show the same variation in brightness of all points, except where a sufficiently strong magnetic field exists. Here they will display opposite brightness variations. By photographically subtracting the two spectro-heliograms, we obtain a magnetoheliogram which is uniformly grey, except where points corresponding to magnetic fields are found.

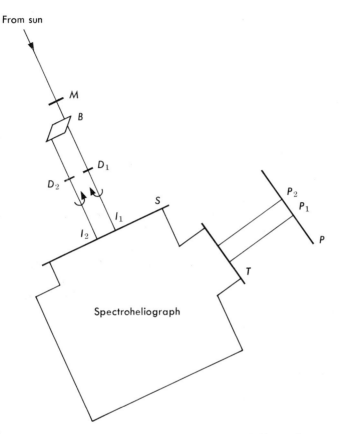

FIGURE 2.6.   Principle of the magnetoheliograph

2.2.5. Measuring the Direction of the Magnetic Field

It is clear from the previous sections that even the more favorable case
in which the longitudinal effect is utilized still confronts the observer with a
difficult task. We encounter grave difficulties if, in addition to observing
only one component of the magnetic field, we also want to determine the
direction of the field. Several methods have been outlined and a number of
techniques have been devised, and we shall treat the more important ones
in this Section.

2.2.5.1. *The work of Hale and Nicholson*

Two different methods have been used to determine the vector **B**. In the
first, a comparison of the intensities of the Zeeman components of a triplet
is made using a quarter-wave plate and a Nicol prism. According to Seares

(1913), the intensity of these components is given by

$$I(\sigma_1) = \tfrac{1}{4}(1 - \cos \alpha)^2, \qquad I(\pi) = \tfrac{1}{2} \sin^2 \alpha, \qquad I(\sigma_2) = \tfrac{1}{4}(1 + \cos \alpha)^2,$$

$$(2.5)$$

where the angle α is the inclination of **B** to the line of sight. The expressions—often referred to as Seares' relations—can be derived only for very weak lines, which strongly limits their applicability. Even more serious, Stepanov (1958a) has questioned the very validity of Equations (2.5) and has argued that a correct expression must be derived by considering the transfer problem in detail.

Nicholson (Hale and Nicholson, 1938) assumed that Seares' relations are valid for the lines he used and deduced the direction of the lines of force by measuring the intensities as given by Equations (2.5).

The second method is based on the fact that the π-component is plane-polarized for observations in a plane containing that line of sight and the line of force. Nicholson used the method to observe sunspots close to the limb. Near the limb of the sun, the direction of polarization of the π-component will coincide with the direction of the lines of force. We may, therefore, determine this direction at different points near the limb by extinguishing the π-component with a half-wave plate and Nicol prism.

2.2.5.2. *Treanor's method*

To measure sunspot fields, interference techniques have been tried by Öhman (1950) and Severny and Stepanov (1956) using a Savart plate and by Treanor (1960) using a Babinet compensator. Treanor showed that the method is well suited to determine the direction of the field vector. The principle involved is as follows. Let us consider the circularly polarized components of a normal Zeeman triplet. When observed along the field lines, the path of the amplitude vector is a circle, and when viewed normally to the field, one of the orthogonal components of the circularly polarized light is in the line of sight and ineffective, so that the light observed is plane polarized in the plane of the field (the transverse Zeeman effect). At any intermediate angle, the light will be elliptically polarized, and the ratio of the major to minor axes of the ellipse will determine the angle α between the line of sight and **B**. Furthermore, the orientation of the axes given by some angle β, for example, will determine the azimuth of the projection of the field on a plane perpendicular to the line of sight. A complete determination of the two constants which describe the shape and the orientation of the ellipse also determines the orientation in space of the magnetic field vector.

To accomplish this, Treanor set up a Babinet compensator followed by a linear polarizer in front of the entrance slit of the spectrograph. The

axis of the polarizer is inclined 45-deg to the axis of the compensator. After
having photographed the resulting fringe system of a Zeeman triplet, we
rotate the compensator with its polarizer 45-deg, and the new fringe system
is photographed. We can then measure the phase differences between
corresponding fringes in the two σ-components on each photograph, and we
obtain the values of α and β by simple calculations (Treanor, 1960).

2.2.5.3. *The work of Severny and Stepanov*

Severny and Stepanov have used the magnetograph (see Section 2.2.3)
to measure the transverse component of sunspot fields (Severny, 1962a).
In this case, the modulator that works between $-\lambda/4$ and $+\lambda/4$ is replaced
by a modulator that works between 0 and $\lambda/2$, and the two fluctuating
photomultiplier signals are added (instead of subtracted as is the case when
the longitudinal field is measured). The response signal $I(\perp)$ is proportional
to the square of the component of the magnetic field perpendicular to the
line of sight, $B_\perp = B \sin \alpha$, that is, we have

$$I(\perp) \propto B^2 \sin^2 \alpha, \qquad (2.6)$$

while in the longitudinal case, the response $I(\parallel)$ is directly proportional to
the component of the field along the line of sight, $B_\parallel = B \cos \alpha$, that is,
we have

$$I(\parallel) \propto B \cos \alpha. \qquad (2.7)$$

In this respect the transverse response is a second-order effect.

The response signal equation, Equation (2.6), also depends on the orientation of the polarizer. This orientation may be expressed in terms of an angle,
$\sin \phi$, so that each measurement $I(\perp)$ gives the product of $B^2 \sin^2 \alpha$ and
$\sin \phi$. Hence, each scan of the magnetograph must be made twice, while the
$\lambda/2$ modulator is rotated a known amount between scans. In this way, one
can determine both $B \sin \alpha$ and ϕ. If, in addition, we observe the longitudinal component $B \cos \alpha$ in the usual way, it is then possible to determine both
the strength and the direction of the magnetic field.

2.2.5.4. *The Lyot-Dollfus-Leroy polarimeter*

Lyot conceived of a very sensitive device for observing a degree of polarization as low as 10^{-5}. It is a white-light polarimeter which Dollfus (1958)
perfected and which he and Leroy used to study the transverse magnetic
field in sunspots and active regions (Dollfus and Leroy, 1962; Leroy, 1960,
1962).

The sunlight passes through a modulator consisting of a rotating $\lambda/2$ plate,
which is followed by a fixed birefringent prism. The modulator rotates the

plane of polarization 30 times/sec in discrete steps of 90-deg, and the prism divides the light into two beams which go to two photocells whose outputs are connected to a difference amplifier. As a result, any plane-polarized component of the incident light is directed in turn to each of the photocells and will produce an alternating output signal I'. If we consider the presence of a plane-polarized component to be the result of a transverse magnetic field $B \sin \alpha$, as Dollfus and Leroy claim, we find that the response of the polarimeter will measure the strength of such a field by Equation (2.6), that is, $I' = I(\perp) \propto B^2 \sin^2 \alpha$.

2.3. Radio Observations

2.3.1. Interferometers

Because of the long wavelengths involved in radio astronomy, we often need to resort to the use of interferometers when high resolution is a prime requirement. That this is true can be seen from the equation

$$\theta = 1.13 \frac{\lambda}{D} \text{ radians}, \qquad (2.8)$$

which gives the angle of the main reception cone (angle between half-power points) of an ideal quadratic antenna with an effective area D^2. Only for centimeter waves received by very large antenna arrays ($D \approx 100$ m) is the angle θ less than one minute of arc—a requirement imposed by many problems.

2.3.1.1. Simple interferometer

The principle of a simple interferometer with two antennas is shown in Figure 2.7. The two aerials, A and B, are placed a distance L from each other on a baseline AB and are connected with an appropriate transmission line (radio links are used when the distance L is very large). The receiver is coupled to the line halfway between the antennas. Let us consider the rays R_1 and R_2 from a distant source of small angular diameter. The rays form an angle θ with the normal to the baseline. Then the difference in path length from the two antennas to the source is $r = d \sin \theta$, and the difference in phase angle between the signals in antennas A and B is

$$\phi = \frac{2\pi r}{\lambda} = 2\pi L \frac{\sin \theta}{\lambda} \approx \frac{2\pi L \theta}{\lambda} \qquad \text{for} \quad \theta \text{ small.}$$

As the angle θ varies (for example, due to the rotation of the earth whereby the source drifts through the reception pattern), the phase ϕ will change, and

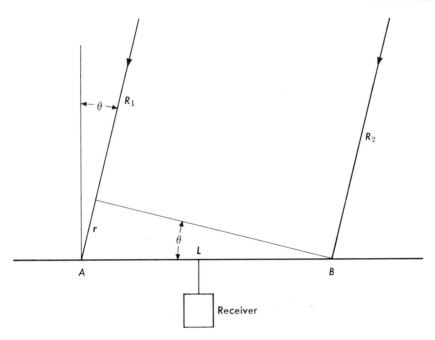

FIGURE 2.7.   Principle of a simple interferometer

the signals arriving at the receiver from the antennas will alternate between being in phase and out of phase. When $\phi = \pi$, 3π, 5π, etc., the two signals will cancel, and we get no output from the receiver. When $\phi = 0$, 2π, 4π, etc., the signals will add to amplify each other, and the output will have maximal values. If we let P_m be the power that each antenna A or B would produce separately in the receiver, then the power given by the interferometer system is

$$P'_m = P_m(1 + \cos \phi) = P_m\left(1 + \cos \frac{2\pi L\theta}{\lambda}\right) . \tag{2.9}$$

Figure 2.8 shows an antenna diagram of this type, which consists of a series of lobes that get narrower the larger L becomes.

2.3.1.2. *Interferometer with many antennas*

When several active regions are simultaneously visible on the sun, it is important to distinguish between them and to know which active region is, at any given time, in the reception pattern of the interferometer. Then we may use a composite interferometer developed in Sydney by Christiansen (1953). A large number N of antennas ($N = 32$ in Christiansen's first

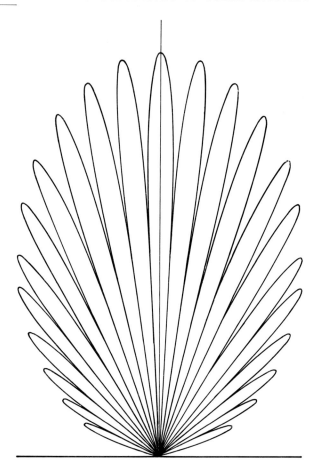

FIGURE 2.8.   Antenna diagram of a simple interferometer

system), each having a diameter D, are fed in phase and are placed equidistant on a baseline of total length L. The distance between two adjacent paraboloids is l. This system will act as a diffraction grating, giving a central maximum for $\theta = 0$ (in a direction perpendicular to the baseline), and giving first, second, and higher order maxima for values of θ given by

$$l \sin \theta = n\lambda, \qquad n = 1, 2, \ldots .$$

The total distance L determines the half-width Δ of the individual lobes by the relation $L \sin \Delta = \lambda$. For the Christiansen interferometer, $L = 217$ m, and $\Delta = 3$ min when working at $\lambda = 21$ cm. Then the angular distance between lobes is given by $\sin \theta_1 = \lambda/l = 0.03$, or $\theta_1 = 1.7$ deg. The two requirements imposed on such a system, that is, that Δ be small and θ_1 be larger than the angular diameter of the sun (so that one may know at any time with which lobe one is observing), are realized for Christiansen's interferometer (compare Figure 2.9).

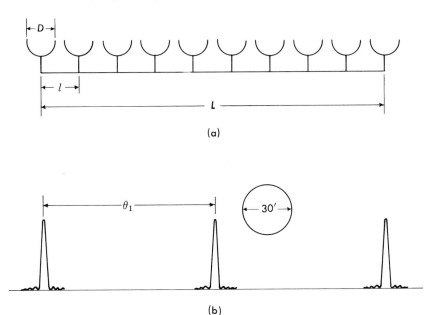

(a)

(b)

FIGURE 2.9.   Principle of a multiantenna interferometer

2.3.1.3. *Mills' cross*

We also owe to the Sydney group another interferometer system called Mills' cross (Mills and Little, 1953)—a special form of a single-lobe radiometer consisting of two arrays of dipoles shown as (a) and (b) in Figure 2.10. The two arrays are at right angles to each other (one in the east–west, the other in the north–south direction), but all dipoles receive the same direction of polarization. Each array by itself makes a fan-shaped antenna diagram, and thus it follows that the system can only "see" that part of the sky which is common to the two fan-shaped diagrams, namely the cross-hatched area shown in Figure 2.10. The output from the two arrays is sent to a phase-switching system, so that only those signals that have components in both arrays are fed to the receiver. Thus we only observe the sources that lie in the cross-hatched area; that is, we observe with a so-called "pencil beam" antenna diagram. We can obtain very considerable space resolution, since here also the half-width of the pencil beam lobe Δ is given by the total length of the dipole array.

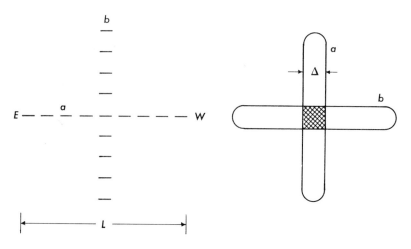

FIGURE 2.10. Principle of the pencil beam interferometer (after Mills and Little, 1953)

2.3.2. Spectrographs

In optical astronomy, we understand a spectrograph to be an instrument that can give information about the intensity of radiation as a function of wavelength. In radio astronomy, we also have instruments that can give such information, and this is accomplished in one of two different ways: (1) we observe the intensity at a certain number of fixed frequencies; in other words, we try to find a certain number of points on the spectral curve; or (2) we sweep continuously over a certain frequency range and in this fashion construct the spectrum.

If the radiation is steady (its intensity at any given frequency more or less time independent), we may use fixed frequencies and thus need only one receiver which is successively tuned to the required frequencies. If, however, the radiation varies rapidly with time (as do several components of the radio radiation from the active sun), then we are forced to observe at several frequencies simultaneously, while using many channel receivers. In addition, the radiation may vary strongly within small frequency intervals, in which case we need many channels spaced very closely together in frequency space. This procedure can become quite complicated, and it is better to use the sweep-frequency method.

The first experiments using this technique were made by Wild and McCready (1950) who built a receiver for the range 70 to 130 Mc/sec. The sweeping was done mechanically three times per second, and, to accommodate the extended frequency band, Wild employed a broadband (rhombic) antenna.

The method described is used when observing the so-called radio bursts that occur on frequencies that may vary rapidly with time. The center frequency of the bursts drifts to higher or lower frequencies with time, often covering several octaves in a few minutes or less. By studying this frequency drift, we may obtain valuable information on the physical conditions in those regions of the atmosphere where the burst is generated. A frequency–time diagram giving this relationship is called a *dynamic spectrum*. It is built up, however, of ordinary intensity–frequency spectra obtained by the sweep-frequency receiver.

The main instrument used is a receiver that can sweep a large frequency range several times per second. Each spectrum is registered on an oscilloscope, and the spectra are photographed continuously on film moving past the scope. The dynamic spectra are then constructed from these data.

If we want to cover a very large frequency range, we use several receivers simultaneously, each sweeping a part of the frequency range. Figure 2.11 (p. 88) shows a simple diagram of Wild's 40 through 240 Mc/sec spectrograph. Three receivers are used, one in the range covering 40 through 75 Mc/sec, one covering 75 through 140 Mc/sec, and one 140 through 240 Mc/sec. The output signals from the three receivers are alternately (2/sec) fed to the common oscilloscope by the method of electronic switching.

The registration on the scope may be done either by amplitude modulation or intensity modulation of the signal. When the former method is used, the frequency is recorded horizontally, and the output of the receiver is recorded vertically. The intensity may thereby be accurately determined, although this method is cumbersome and requires large amounts of film. When the intensity-modulation method is used, the frequency is still the abscissa, but the output of the receiver is recorded by modulating the intensity of the cathode ray. Since the sensitivity of the film emulsion is practically logarithmic, this method can also record very large intensity ranges, on the order of 1000:1.

2.3.3. Polarimeters

In order to have a physical understanding of the generation and propagation of radio waves in the solar atmosphere, it is often very important to know about the possible polarization of the radiation. The simplest way to determine whether a given radiation is linearly polarized is to rotate a plane-polarized antenna around the main axis of the antenna diagram. By observing possible changes in the output, we can determine the degree of polarization. In praxis this is not a very reliable method, because antenna diagrams are not sufficiently symmetrical for our purposes.

We use instead two antennas oriented at right angles to each other and alternately connected to a common receiver by a switch. The principle is shown in Figure 2.12a (p. 89), where the two antennas are designated *A* and

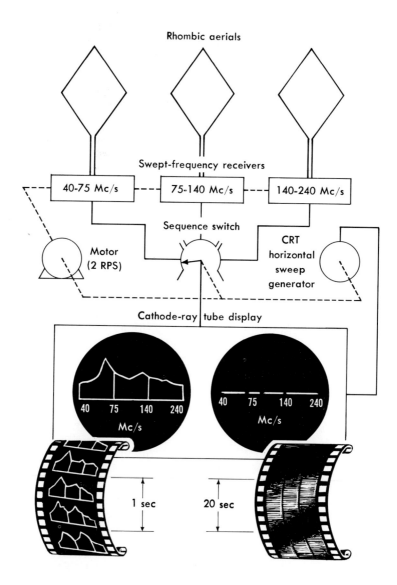

FIGURE 2.11.   Diagram of a radio spectrograph (courtesy J. P. Wild, J. D. Murray, and W. C. Rowe, 1954)

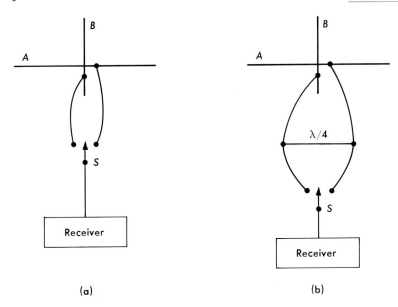

FIGURE 2.12. The radio polarimeters: (a) for linear polarization, (b) for circular polarization

B. If the signal to be detected has a plane-polarized component, the output of the receiver will depend on which antenna is connected (unless the plane of the polarized component happens to form an angle of exactly 45 deg with both antennas *A* and *B*). By rotating the antenna system, we can study all possible directions of polarization.

We can study circular polarization using the same two antennas *A* and *B*, provided that an extra $\lambda/4$ cable is inserted between them, as shown in Figure 2.12b. Depending on the position of the switch *S*, the system will be sensitive to right-hand or left-hand circular polarization. A difference in the output power observed in the two positions of the switch will serve as a measure of a circularly polarized component in the radiation.

We can place the two antennas *A* and *B* at a distance *d* apart but retain their orientation, thereby realizing an interference polarimeter of baseline *d*. This instrument combines the capabilities of an interferometer and a polarimeter.

2.4. *X-ray Astronomy*

2.4.1. Introduction

It is well known that the atmosphere of the earth is not transparent to solar radiation of wavelengths shorter than about 3000 Å. The important

TABLE 2.1

Particle energy		$T = E/k$, °K	Associated thermal velocity, km/sec		Associated wavelength λ, Å	Spectral region
eV	E, ergs		Electron	Proton		
.1	1.6×10^{-13}	1.16×10^{3}	1.875×10^{2}	4.375	123980	infrared (IR)
1	1.6×10^{-12}	1.16×10^{4}	5.927×10^{2}	13.83	12398	visible
10	1.6×10^{-11}	1.16×10^{5}	1.875×10^{3}	43.75	1239.8	ultraviolet (UV)
100	1.6×10^{-10}	1.16×10^{6}	5.927×10^{3}	1.383×10^{2}	124	extreme UV
$10^{3} = 1$ KeV	1.6×10^{-9}	1.16×10^{7}	1.875×10^{4}	4.375×10^{2}	12.4	soft X ray
10^{4}	1.6×10^{-8}	1.16×10^{8}	5.927×10^{4}	1.383×10^{3}	1.24	hard X ray
10^{5}	1.6×10^{-7}	1.16×10^{9}		4.375×10^{3}	.124	
$10^{6} = 1$ MeV	1.6×10^{-6}	1.16×10^{10}		1.383×10^{4}		
10^{7}	1.6×10^{-5}	1.16×10^{11}		4.375×10^{4}		

resonance lines of the most abundant elements and of many other ions are now found in this part of the spectrum, and bremsstrahlung (X rays) also fills the whole spectrum down to the shortest wavelengths. It is, therefore, of great importance to be able to observe this part of the spectrum, and such observations can be made only by balloons, rockets, and satellites.

We shall use the notation extreme ultraviolet (EUV) for radiation of wavelength in the range 20 to about 100 Å, and reserve the name X ray for radiation below 20 Å. The notation γ ray is sometimes used for the most energetic X rays, but this notation shall be used here to imply that the generation of the quanta is associated with nuclear processes.

There is no clear-cut definition to help us decide where the transition from soft to hard X rays takes place. This is more a matter of convenience and general practice. Here we shall designate X rays of wavelengths longer than about 1 Å as soft. Many people working in this field let the associated energy decide whether the X rays are soft or hard, calling them soft if the energy does not exceed 20 KeV (which corresponds to 0.62 Å).

There are, at present, two methods of observing solar X rays: (1) X-ray detectors are sent up with balloons or rockets, and the data are either telemetered to the ground or the payload is recovered (Peterson and Winckler, 1959; Chubb, Friedman and Kreplin, 1960; Vette and Casal, 1961); (2) X-ray detectors are flown on satellites, and the data are telemetered to the ground (Friedman, Chubb, Kupperian, Kreplin and Lindsay, 1961; Kreplin, 1961).

We measure X rays by observing one of the following two basic effects: (1) the ionization they produce; or (2) the photoelectrons they produce when hitting a surface. The form of the X-ray detector used depends on the wavelengths. For soft X rays ($\lambda > 1$ Å), the X-ray photometers operate as some form of ion chamber, while scintillation counters so far have generally been used to observe hard X rays. The detectors are also sensitive to sufficiently energetic ionizing particles. Consequently, we try to shield them, using magnets to deflect these particles. In early experiments (see references in Kreplin, Chubb and Friedman, 1962), van Allen belt electrons interfered with attempts to measure solar X rays, and in later work the results have often been affected by particles too energetic to be deflected by the magnets.

Table 2.1 gives the wavelengths associated with different particle energies, expressed in several, frequently used, units.

2.4.2. Measurements of Soft X Rays

The first measurements of solar X rays were carried out in 1948 when a group at the U.S. Naval Research Laboratory sent photographic film, placed behind a beryllium window, aloft with V–2 rockets (Burnight, 1949). Quantitative measurements started shortly thereafter when a photon-counter tube behind a beryllium window was flown on September 29, 1949 (Friedman, Lichtman and Byran, 1951). Since that time, this or a similar kind of instrument has been used extensively in the study of soft solar X rays.

The tubes may be divided into three classes depending on the way they operate, which in turn depends on the voltage across the tube.

2.4.2.1. *Ionization chambers*

The first mode of operation is achieved when the voltage is so low that no secondary ionization occurs. In other words, the free electrons produced in the tube by the X rays are not accelerated to energies great enough to enable them to knock off the electrons from the gas molecules in the tube as they travel toward the anode. The measured electron current is therefore proportional to the number of ion pairs produced by the X rays and is a linear function of the energy of the X rays. Thus the ionization chamber serves as a total energy detector and gives no information on the spectral characteristics.

2.4.2.2. *Proportional counters*

For the second mode of operation, the voltage across the tube is sufficient to cause signal amplification due to the production of secondary electrons. Each current pulse or "count" collected on the anode is—apart from statistical fluctuations—proportional in amplitude to the number of ion pairs produced by the X-ray photons. This signal is fed to a pulse-height analyzer which can count the pulses and sort them into groups by amplitude. The measured quantity is thus the number of counts per second in each amplitude interval. Therefore, we also obtain information on the spectral distribution of radiation.

2.4.2.3. *Geiger–Müller counters*

When the voltage across the tube is so high that every free electron produced by the X rays will start a cascade discharge, we are in the Geiger–Müller-counter mode of operation. The discharge will envelope the entire anode until it is stopped due to the space charge built up around the anode. The pulse amplitude is constant and independent of the photon energy. Thus the instrument is referred to as a photon counter, because it is sensitive to the photon flux rather than to the energy flux. It can give us no information on the spectrum of the X radiation.

The voltage at which the different modes of operation take place is a sensitive function of the characteristics of the individual tubes (see, for instance, Wilkinson, 1950). The regions of the X-ray spectrum to which the tubes are sensitive is determined by (1) the transmission of the window material, and (2) the absorption coefficient and ionization potential of the gas in the tube.

Let $\mu(\lambda)$ be the mass absorption coefficient of the window material and ρx the mass per unit area of the window, where ρ is the density and x the window thickness. The total attenuation of the X rays passing through the window is then given by

$$I_T(\lambda) = I_0(\lambda)e^{-\mu(\lambda)\rho x}.$$

The absorption within the gas follows the same law, and the expression for the intensity absorbed in the gas of the tube takes the form (ergs cm^{-2} sec^{-1} cm^{-1})

$$I_A(\lambda) = I_T(\lambda)(1 - e^{-\mu(\lambda)\rho y}),$$

where y is the effective depth of the tube.

We now define the spectral efficiency of the detector tube per unit window area and per unit wavelength $E(\lambda)$ as that fraction of the radiation intensity incident on the window which is absorbed in the gas of the tube. We have

$$E(\lambda) \equiv I_A(\lambda)/I_0(\lambda) = e^{-\mu(\lambda)\rho x}\left(1 - e^{-\mu(\lambda)\rho y}\right).$$

If A is the window area of the detector, the energy absorbed in the tube chamber per unit wavelength and per second is

$$U(\lambda) = A \cdot I_A(\lambda) = A \cdot E(\lambda)I_0(\lambda).$$

If we further multiply $U(\lambda)$ by the ionization efficiency G (ion pairs produced per erg of absorbed energy), which depends on the gas, and by the electric charge e, we find the ion chamber current $i(\lambda)$:

$$i(\lambda) = A \cdot G \cdot e \cdot E(\lambda)I_0(\lambda) \quad \text{amperes (amp)/cm}. \qquad (2.10)$$

Starting with $U(\lambda)$, we can also derive the counting rate $c(\lambda)$ of the Geiger–Müller counter. We divide $U(\lambda)$ by $h\nu = hc/\lambda$ to convert the energy absorbed to photons absorbed per cm (the Geiger–Müller counter is a photon counter). Thus we have

$$c(\lambda) = \frac{A\lambda}{hc} E(\lambda)I_0(\lambda) \quad \text{counts cm}^{-1}\text{ sec}^{-1}. \qquad (2.11)$$

In the above expression for the ion chamber, we have assumed that every electron produced in the tube is collected, and in the expression for the Geiger–Müller counter, we have assumed that every photon absorbed results

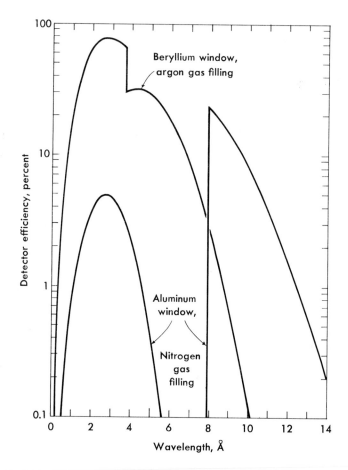

FIGURE 2.13. FIGURE 2.13.   Different X-ray detector responses (courtesy L. Acton, 1964)

in a count. This seems to be justified by experiments (Wilkinson, 1950). Furthermore, photoelectric effects both in the window material and from photons hitting the walls of the tube have been neglected. The importance of these effects changes from tube to tube and depends on the manufacturing techniques.

Both the window material and the gas will determine the part of the X-ray spectrum to which a particular tube will be sensitive. Figure 2.13 shows the detector response (spectral efficiency in percent) as a function of wavelength for two different detectors in common use.

2.4.3. Measurements of Hard X Rays

To observe the hard X-ray region (defined as $\lambda <$ about 1 Å, or $E > 20$ KeV, see Table 2.1), we generally use scintillation counters. The X-ray energy is then high enough to get through the foils and to produce enough light for adequate resolution. The resolution, however, is not as good as that obtained with proportional counters (used in the range of about 1 to 20 KeV), because the ion pairs are measured directly in those counters.

The scintillation counters are based on the following principle. When charged particles impinge on certain liquid or solid materials known as phosphors (or fluors), part of the energy dissipated in molecular excitation and ionization is re-emitted as visible or UV light. This phenomenon of luminescence (fluorescence and phosphorescence) makes it possible to observe and measure the light pulses or scintillations produced in the phosphors by individual ionizing particles. The scintillations from the phosphors are converted into amplified electrical pulses in photomultiplier tubes of high gain, which are sensitive to very small light intensities.

Different kinds of phosphors have been used. Kallmann (1949) found that large transparent blocks of naphthalene produced good scintillations, while Bell (1948) discovered that anthracene was an even more suitable phosphor. To Hofstadter (1948) we owe the discovery that sodium iodide crystals, activated by thallium [NaI(Tl)], give very large pulses. Scintillations from certain organic phosphors may also be used (Reynolds, Harrison and Salvini, 1950).

Following Birks (1953), we divide the operation of the scintillation counter into the following steps:

(1) The absorption of the incident radiation by the phosphor;
(2) The luminescent conversion of the energy dissipated in the phosphor, and the emission of photons;
(3) The transit of the emitted photons to the cathode of the photomultiplier;
(4) The absorption of the photons at the cathode, and the emission of the photoelectrons;
(5) The electron multiplication process.

When an X-ray quantum of energy $E_0 = h\nu_0$ strikes a phosphor, it will not ionize directly but transfers a fraction f_1 of its energy to charged particles. These secondary particles produce the scintillations used to detect the primary radiation. The fraction f_1 is given by $f_1 = 1 - e^{-kd}$, where d is the thickness of the phosphor and k, the absorption coefficient of the phosphor for the incident radiation, depends on the absorption processes responsible: photoelectric absorption, Compton scattering, or pair production.

Part of the absorbed energy $f_1 E_0$ will now be converted by the phosphor to photons of energy E_p. Let us call the efficiency of this conversion f_2, leading to the production of $f_1 E_0 f_2 / E_p$ photons of average energy $E_p = h\nu_p$. Not all the photons $f_1 E_0 f_2 / E_p$ will reach the cathode. Preferably, the optical absorption coefficient α should be small so that the phosphor is transparent to its own fluorescence radiation. Then the transparency T_p for the photons is large, and $T_p = e^{-\alpha d}$. But even for a completely transparent phosphor ($T_p = 1$), only a fraction f_3 of the photons falls on the cathode. The fraction f_3 is determined by the geometry of the system. The number of photons per scintillation incident on the cathode is therefore given by $f_1 E_0 f_2 T_p f_3 / E_p$.

In step (4) above, the photons are absorbed by the cathode of the photomultiplier tube and converted to electrons with an efficiency $f_4 f_5(\nu_p)$, where f_4 is the photoelectric conversion efficiency of the cathode at its optimum frequency, and $f_5(\nu_p)$ is the relative response at frequency ν_p. The number of electrons produced per scintillation will then be given by

$$n = f_1 E_0 f_2 T_p f_3 f_4 f_5(\nu_p)/E_p . \tag{2.12}$$

The efficiency f_4 depends on the cathode material, as does $f_5(\nu_p)$. This latter coefficient also depends strongly on the optical properties of the photomultiplier envelope. For glass, f_5 goes to zero at about 3200 Å and for quartz at about 2000 Å, but in the X-ray regions these tubes again have high sensitivity.

The electron-multiplication stage takes into consideration that the n photoelectrons will be multiplied at the subsequent dynodes due to secondary emissions. If there are N dynodes, each with an electron-multiplication factor f_6, the over-all gain is $N f_6 f_7$, where f_7 is the collection efficiency factor of the dynode system. The total charge of the signal at the collector plate is therefore, by Equation (2.12),

$$q = n e N f_6 f_7 ,$$

where e is the charge of an electron.

2.5. *Particle Astronomy*

Of utmost importance for our understanding of solar physics is the realization that the sun emits particles as well as photons. Some of the particles are expelled in the direction of the earth, and by measuring their flux and energy, we may obtain information about the emitting regions on the sun.

2.5.1. General Considerations

Four methods have been used so far in the observation of solar particles. Two methods are completely indirect and consist of studying different aspects of the response of the atmosphere of the earth to the ionizing particles. In the riometer method, we measure the signal strength of extraterrestrial radio noise and simultaneously monitor the magnetic field of the earth to obtain a parameter, the K index, which measures the effect of solar particles.

Another method, which is only semidirect, involves the use of detectors in which an electric signal appears after the ionizing particle has passed through the detector. These devices are also sensitive to very short-wave electromagnetic radiation, and they have been extensively used as X-ray detectors. We treated them in Section 2.4.2 (ion chambers, scintillation counters). Here we shall discuss only one version of the proportional counter that is used to measure neutrons (the neutron monitor).

In the only direct method, the actual trajectory of the particle is rendered visible over a certain distance in space. Two versions of this method are widely used: the cloud chamber and the nuclear emulsion techniques.

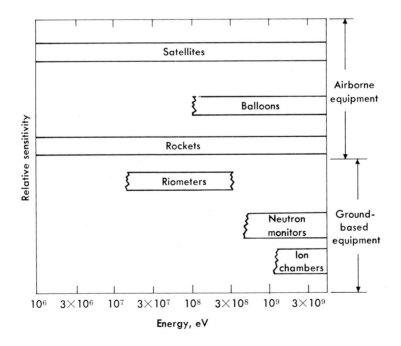

FIGURE 2.14.   The range of particle energies observable by different types of detectors (after Waddington, 1963)

Solar cosmic ray particles may be observed with detectors located on the surface of the earth, on balloons floating high in the atmosphere of the earth, (20 through 30 km), or on rockets and satellites outside the atmosphere. At typical balloon altitudes, the remaining atmosphere is about 10 grams per square centimeter (gm/cm^2) and the minimum energy required to reach down to this level is about 1×10^8 eV for vertically incident protons.

The range of particle energies observable by some ground-based detectors is shown in the lower part of Figure 2.14, where a rough indication of the sensitivity of the methods is also incorporated. In the upper part, the potentially observable energy range and the relative sensitivity of different kinds of airborne, rocket, and satellite equipment are compared (Waddington, 1963). In the following sections, we often refer to airborne equipment but may also have rocket and satellite equipment in mind.

2.5.2. The Neutron Monitor

A special application of the proportional counter (Section 2.4.2.2) is for the detection of neutrons. The counter is filled with BF_3 (boron trifluoride) enriched with the boron isotope B^{10}. When neutrons, n_0^1, strike this compound, the following reaction occurs:

$$B_5^{10} + n_0^1 \rightarrow Li_3^7 + He_2^4 + 2.5 \times 10^8 \text{ eV} .$$

The liberated energy is divided between the α-particle and the lithium nucleus, and if they are stopped in the gas of the chamber, they produce about 80,000 ion pairs. Such a quantity of ionization is easily detected.

The great importance of the neutron monitor stems from its large response to particles of low energy, where other counters are less sensitive.

The collision cross section of B^{10} is much larger for slow neutrons than for fast, and thus the neutron counter has a higher detection efficiency for the slow neutrons. A neutron counter operated at ground level, therefore, may be used to count those neutrons produced high in the atmosphere which slow down on collision with air molecules on their way downward.

Of greater interest for solar cosmic ray work is the application whereby neutron counters are used to detect fast nuclei via the neutrons produced in local interactions. These neutrons are of high energy ($\sim 2 \times 10^7$ eV), and a local moderating medium is required to slow them down so that the collision cross section with B^{10} is large enough. Several counters are generally arranged in what is called a neutron pile, or neutron monitor. The incoming nucleons interact with lead (arranged in blocks around the counters) to produce the neutrons which are slowed down in paraffin wax or, more recently, polyethylene by elastic collisions.

2.5.3. Direct Methods

When we use direct methods, it is possible to see the tracks left by the particle in the medium used. By measuring these tracks, we can determine one or more of the following quantities: the range (the distance the particle travels in the medium before it is stopped), the mass, the momentum, and the ionization caused by the particle. We shall now recall some useful relationships between the mass, momentum, and energy of high-energy particles.

The mass m of a relativistic particle is related to its velocity v by the well-known formula from the special theory of relativity,

$$m = m_0/(1 - v^2/c^2)^{1/2}, \tag{2.13}$$

where m_0 is the rest mass. The total energy E of the particle is given by Einstein's relation

$$E = mc^2. \tag{2.14}$$

Combining Equations (2.13) and (2.14) and expanding in series, we find that

$$E = m_0c^2 + \tfrac{1}{2}m_0v^2 + \tfrac{3}{8}m_0v^4/c^2 + \cdots. \tag{2.15}$$

The quantity m_0c^2 is the rest energy of the particle, and $E_{\text{kin}} = E - m_0c^2$ is the relativistic kinetic energy.

The momentum p is given by the expression

$$p = mv = \frac{m_0v}{\sqrt{1 - v^2/c^2}}. \tag{2.16}$$

Equations (2.13), (2.14), and (2.16) combine to give the general relation

$$E^2 = c^2(m_0^2c^2 + p^2). \tag{2.17}$$

For particles in the extreme relativistic energy region, $v/c \approx 1$, whence we have $E \approx pc$. In this energy range, it is customary to give momenta in units of eV/c, since the numerical values of momenta and energy then are virtually the same. For example, a proton of energy 10^{12} eV has a momentum of 10^{12} eV$/c$.

2.5.3.1. *The cloud chamber*

The cloud chamber (originally due to Wilson, 1911) consists of a closed vessel containing a gas (a typical filling is 80% argon and 20% oxygen) and a saturated vapor (for example a mixture of 50% water and 50% ethyl alcohol). If an adiabatic expansion occurs, the chamber becomes super-saturated with vapor, and some of it will condense on whatever ions are present. Each drop of liquid will then rapidly grow to visible size before it evaporates. Consequently, if we expand the chamber adiabatically just after a cosmic ray particle has passed through and left many ion pairs, a "track" of drops will be seen along the particle trajectory. This track may then be photographed by proper illumination.

The ionization is measured by counting the number of drops per unit length of track. The fluctuations in the drop count are similar to the fluctuations found in pulse heights from a proportional counter, mentioned in Section 2.4.2.

If we operate the chamber in a magnetic field, we can measure the momentum of the particles. Let a cosmic ray particle travel at right angles to an applied magnetic field B. The radius of the trajectory will be given by Equation (1.11), the Larmor radius λ_B, and the momentum may be written $p = mv = Be\lambda_B$ or

$$p = 300B\lambda_B \quad \text{for} \quad p \text{ in units of eV}/c.$$

2.5.3.2. Nuclear emulsions

The possibility of using photographic emulsion to detect individual ionizing particles was first demonstrated by Kinoshita (1910). Modern emulsions are greatly improved. They contain a variety of elements, mainly silver and bromide (about 80% as compared with some 10% in ordinary photographic emulsions). The silver-halide grains are rendered "sensitive" when struck by a cosmic ray particle, and the particle trajectory appears as a track after processing. Modern emulsions are used in strips without glass backing, so that many layers may be used, thus forming blocks of emulsion through which the particle tracks may be measured with great accuracy.

One of the great advantages in using nuclear emulsions is that range measurements can easily be made. From theoretical analyses of range-energy relations, we may deduce the particle energy. If the particle loses energy by ionization only, then the range of the particle can be expressed simply as a function of energy. The total energy loss rate by collisions is given by $-dE/dt = f(E)$ (see, for instance, Wolfendale, 1963). Denoting the range by R, we find that

$$-\int_E^0 dE/f(E) = \int_0^R dx = R.$$

At high energies $f(E)$ is nearly independent of energy, so that R is proportional to energy, but at low energies $(v \ll c)$ the relation between R and E is quite complicated.

The ionization may be measured by counting the number of grains per unit length of track provided that calibrations are available for the particular emulsion.

Magnetic deflection is not well suited for measurements of particle momenta because of the considerable scattering resulting from the high density of nuclei in the emulsion. However, by studying in detail the kinks of the track that result from the scattering, we may estimate the momentum.

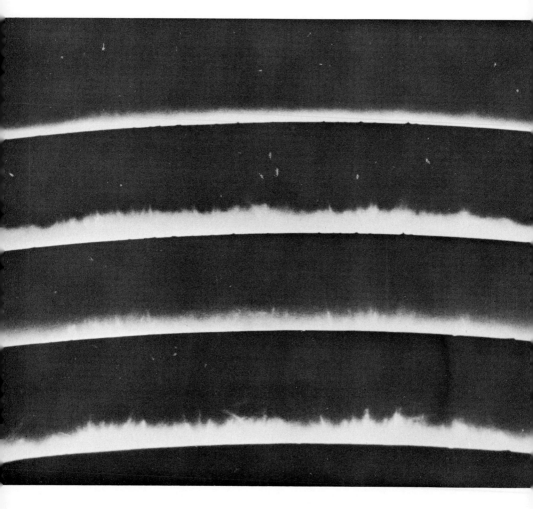

The salient feature of the quiet sun is the spicule structure here photographed in the Hα line of hydrogen and the continuum 4 Å from H: the top two pictures are the off-band observations with exposure ratio 10:1; the lower two are Hα with the same exposure ratio. (Courtesy R. Dunn, Sacramento Peak Observatory.)

The Quiet Sun | 3

3.1. *Introduction*

During times of minimum solar activity, the sun's atmosphere settles down to a state approaching the "quiet sun condition." Since there is always some degree of activity present, this idealized quiet condition is never quite realized. At the minimum phase of every sunspot cycle, some parts of the actual atmosphere do, however, approximate fairly well the "quiet sun condition." We shall now discuss this normal atmosphere and consider the physical conditions reigning there.

The temperature in the solar atmosphere is everywhere so high that the gas is more or less ionized. As we have seen in Chapter 1, the atmosphere must therefore be treated—in an over-all picture—as a plasma. We shall define the atmosphere of the sun as that part of the solar plasma from which we can get direct optical observations. Therefore, the deepest-lying layers of the atmosphere correspond, in our notation, to the *photosphere*, the seat of the continuous spectrum. At the extreme solar limb, the continuous emission drops by a factor of $e = 2.718 \ldots$ over a region of some 100 km. Hence, the solar limb which defines our zero level is very sharp. The heavy absorption that sets in as one goes down into the photosphere prevents reception of radiation from depths in excess of 400 km. The level -400 km is thus the lower boundary of the photosphere. Below this level, both temperature and ionization increase very rapidly from the boundary values $T_e = 8000\,°\mathrm{K}$ and $n_e = 10^{15}\,\mathrm{cm}^{-3}$. The faintest Fraunhofer absorption lines are formed only slightly higher than this layer, the shortest observable radio waves and the stronger Fraunhofer lines are generated in the above-lying *chromosphere*, and radio waves in the meter range as well as X-ray radiation come from the *corona*, the outer part of the atmosphere. As we go out through the atmosphere from subphotospheric layers, the temperature reaches a minimum in the lowest part of the chromosphere and thence

103

increases monotonically with height. We will define the upper boundary of the chromosphere as that layer in which the temperature becomes too high for hydrogen to give observable line emission. This occurs roughly 10,000 km above the photosphere. Higher up, the temperature increases rapidly to the 10^6 °K regime of the corona. The extent of the transition region between the chromosphere and the corona is very narrow, but its actual size is the subject of considerable controversy.

The chromospheric radiation in the optical region is characterized by emission from singly ionized metals, hydrogen and helium, while the corona exhibits emission from high ionization stages of metals (roughly nine to fifteen times ionized). We should, therefore, expect the transition region to produce emission from intermediate ions like Fe III, Fe IV, and others with similar ionization potentials, but the lines belonging to such ions are not seen in the spectrum of the solar atmosphere. The answer to this apparent paradox is that the transition region is very narrow, and thus contains too few ions in the stages Fe III, Fe IV, etc. to give observable emission.

This simple picture of the atmosphere, which implies spherical symmetry, has to be modified to include the *spicules*, one of the most important quiet sun characteristics. The spicules, which give rise to the picturesque description of the chromosphere as "the burning prairie," are not seen as individual features in the lower chromosphere. Below a level of about 2000 km, the chromosphere may thus be approximated by a spherically symmetrical atmosphere, but above this height all the optical chromospheric emission comes from the spicules. We consider these cool jets surging up into the hot corona with velocities of about 30 km/sec. In the upper chromosphere, we are thus faced with a two-component atmosphere. The name *spicule* was introduced by Roberts (1945), while the French often use the term *jet*. The spicules are more or less cylindrical or conical structures, about 1000 km across. Their average lifetime is four minutes, and at any one time there are roughly 10^4 to 10^5 present, depending on the height. The spicules seem to furnish the coupling between the subphotospheric energy reservoir and the hot outer atmosphere, bridging the region of the temperature minimum.

3.2. *The Photosphere and Chromosphere*

3.2.1. Chromospheric Structure. Spicules

We shall now consider the temperature and density structures of the chromosphere, following mainly the works of Moriyama (1961) and Athay (1963). Models differing more or less from the one presented have been discussed by van de Hulst (1953), and Thomas and Athay (1961).

The physical conditions in the lowest 500 km of the chromosphere are not well known. It is, however, somewhere in this region that the temperature minimum takes place with T_e approximately 4700 °K. Furthermore, at the top of this layer we know that the temperature is slightly in excess of 6000 °K. The hydrogen density has decreased out through this lowest region from a value of about $n_H = 10^{16}$ cm^{-3} at the top of the photosphere to $n_H = 10^{14}$ cm^{-3} at 500 km (see Figure 3.1). In this part of the atmosphere, the electron density is very small compared to the hydrogen density, $n_e = 10^{12}$ cm^{-3}, and virtually all the electrons come from singly ionized metals. It is within this region that most of the Fraunhofer lines are formed, and a proper understanding of their formation requires a more detailed knowledge of the region than is available at present.

So far as the best observations reveal, the atmosphere retains spherical symmetry also in the next 500 km, that is, up to a height of 1000 km above the photosphere. If this is a correct picture, the temperature variation is well determined, with T_e increasing to about 8000 °K at 1000 km. This is a much steeper increase than was assumed a few years ago and is due to the incorporation of non-LTE effects in the ionization theory of hydrogen. It further implies that the total hydrogen density has decreased by a factor of 50 to 100 in this region, while the electron density has remained practically unchanged.

Between 1000 and 1500 km, the picture of a spherically symmetrical atmosphere begins to change; some observations indicate that this change starts at even lower heights. We encounter here a transition region, called the middle chromosphere, where the two-component atmosphere is born. Our understanding of this region is still quite rudimentary, but we appreciate that all the optical emission (except the forbidden coronal lines) becomes concentrated in the spicules. These jets emerge as well-observed individual features at heights of about 3000 km above the photosphere, the lower boundary of the upper chromosphere. At these heights, the temperature of the interspicular plasma is very much higher than the value of 8000 °K that pertains to the lower boundary of the middle chromosphere. Estimates of the temperature made by different authors do not agree very well, but we may consider that here the hot coronal gas is reaching down between the spicules. This indicates that the distinction between an upper chromosphere and the corona becomes illusory in the interspicular region. On the other hand, within the spicules the temperature remains low, that is, $T_e \approx 10^4$ °K as one goes up into the upper chromosphere. The density, being of the order of $n_e = 10^{12}$ cm^{-3}, is from one to several orders of magnitude higher than the interspicular value. It is this dense spicule material that emits the strong Fraunhofer lines of Ca II (the H and K lines) and the Balmer lines of hydrogen, as well as the radio waves in the millimeter (mm) and centimeter (cm) region of the spectrum.

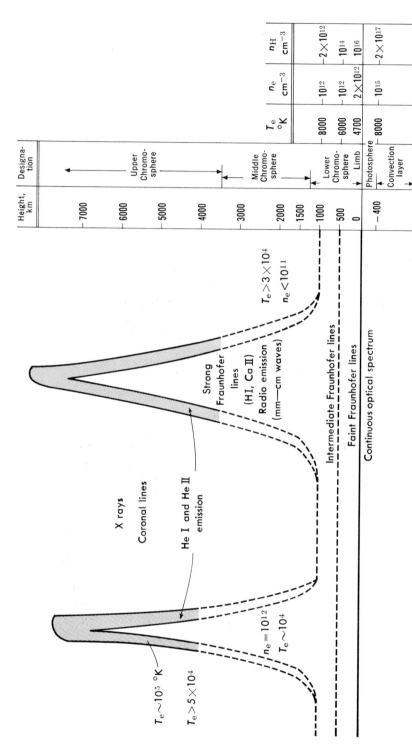

Height, km	Designa-tion		T_e °K	n_e cm^{-3}	n_H cm^{-3}
7000	↕				
6000		Upper Chromo-sphere			
5000					
4000					
3000	↕				
2000		Middle Chromo-sphere	8000	10^{12}	2×10^{12}
1500	↕		6000	10^{12}	10^{14}
1000		Lower Chromo-sphere	4700	2×10^{12}	10^{16}
500		Limb			
0		Photosphere	8000	10^{15}	2×10^{17}
−400		Convection layer			

Figure 3.1.   Density and temperature model of the chromosphere

The more recent models call for the narrow transition region to be on the surface of the spicules, where the temperature is of the order of 50,000 °K through a significant part of this "coating." This narrow region is believed to be responsible for the emission of neutral and ionized helium.

A model like the one described above explains the absence of lines of all ionization stages of metals between the second and the eight or ninth stage as being due to the extreme narrowness of the "coating layer" on the spicules. The corona outside is too hot for these intermediate ions, and the spicule material inside is too cold. Only in the steep temperature gradient in the "coating" do we find the physical conditions conducive to the emission of the missing ions, but the material involved is too sparse to produce observable lines. However, one cannot doubt that for each of the missing ions there will be a thin layer which actually emits the lines in question.

For a deeper understanding of the role played by the spicules, it is of prime importance to include their dynamics. One question that immediately arises is how the spicules can retain their identity as cool fingers reaching up into the hot corona. The answer is, in all probability, to be sought in the existence of magnetic fields threading the spicules. The spicules are those regions of the chromosphere through which the larger part of the magnetic flux is channeled. This model is pictured schematically in the left-hand portion of Figure 3.1. The magnetic field is running more or less along the axis of the spicules and prevents them from dispersing quickly into the coronal environments. A simple calculation shows what magnetic field strengths are necessary. Equality of the kinetic energy density of the spicular plasma ($\frac{3}{2} nkT$) and the magnetic energy density ($B^2/8\pi$) requires, for $T_e = 10^4$ °K and $n_e = 10^{12}$ cm^{-3}, a magnetic induction $B \approx 7$ gauss. As we go higher up into less dense regions, smaller magnetic fields may dominate the dynamics. In the corona, where $n_e = 10^8$ cm^{-3} and $T_e \approx 10^6$ °K, the field necessary to guarantee equality of magnetic and kinetic energy densities is less than one gauss.

There is reason to believe (Osterbrock, 1961) that the spicules are the manifestation of hydromagnetic waves carrying energy up into the corona from subphotospheric layers. In this picture, the spicules *are* the chromosphere, constituting the transition region between the photosphere and corona and providing the coupling between the sun and its atmosphere.

3.2.2. The Supergranulation

One of the fundamental questions concerning the photosphere and the chromosphere is how the spicules are related to the granulation phenomenon. Since the spicules form the coupling between the photosphere, with its granulation, and the outer atmosphere, we might think that the spicules are just the upward continuation of the granules. Given this simple idea, we see that a spicule would correspond to each rising granulation element. But the picture is not so simple as that, and it is not clear how the two phenomena are related in detail. Spicules are not more or less evenly distributed over the solar surface (as are the granules) but are found along the Ca II network (Beckers, 1964). This network (discovered by Hale and by Deslandres in the 1890's; see Deslandres, 1910) corresponds—at photospheric levels—to a network of large cells of horizontally moving material, *the supergranulation*. Measurements by Leighton, Noyes, and Simon (1962)

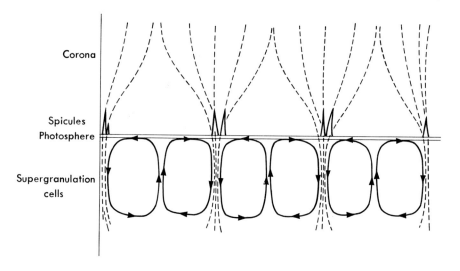

FIGURE 3.2.   Diagram of supergranulation cells and the relationship to spicules and magnetic fields

and Simon and Leighton (1964) show that the motion within each cell consists of a horizontal, outward flow from a source inside the cell. We can think of this as convective motion rising near the middle of the cell, bending over horizontally, and flowing radially outward toward the walls of the cell (see Figure 3.2). The appearance suggests that the cells are a surface manifestation of convection currents coming from deep inside the sun—whence the name supergranulation. The convective motions then generally would be directed downward in the peripheral parts of the cells, that is, in those parts which higher up correspond to the chromospheric network. It is also in this region that we find the concentrated strong upward motions that constitute the spicules. However, the spicules cover only a very small fraction of the total area of the network and probably do not significantly change the picture we have sketched of the supergranulation. The diameter of the cells is typically slightly more than 30,000 km, and at any one time there are roughly 5000 cells on the solar surface. The horizontal flow has an rms velocity of 0.3 to 0.5 km/sec, and the lifetime of cells is roughly 20 hours (10^4 to 10^5 sec). The vertical motions are about 0.1 km/sec.

The material in the cells is highly conducting, and any magnetic field existing in the region will be swept toward the boundaries between cells and concentrated there. Thus, we get cells bounded by magnetic walls along which most of the magnetic flux must be channeled. This is another way of saying that in the layers where the supergranulation exists, the interaction of material motions and magnetic fields is dominated by the former.

Leighton, Noyes, and Simon (1962) also found a distinct correlation between brightness fluctuations and vertical velocities. The area of a cell within which vertical motions were detected was found to increase with height. In a simple model, we may picture the vertical convection as a rising column near the middle of the supergranulation cell. At the level where the faint Fe I, 6102 line is formed, the column has a diameter of roughly 1700 km, and this increases to about twice this value at the (higher) level where the stronger Na I, 5896 line is emitted.

3.2.3. Wave Motions

One of the most important observations in recent years has been the detection and measurement of oscillatory motions in the photosphere and chromosphere. The pioneering work was done independently by Leighton (1959, 1960); see also Leighton, Noyes, and Simon (1962) and Evans and Michard (1961, 1962).

Leighton used a spectroheliograph operating in the "Doppler mode" (see Section 2.2), while Evans and Michard studied the shape and displacements of Fraunhofer lines on spectrograms. We shall now consider the main features of these two series of investigations.

3.2.3.1. *The 300-second period*

Leighton used the Doppler difference procedure to detect changes with time in the velocity field. At one end of a Doppler difference plate, the time difference between the two exposures involved is $\Delta t = 0$, and we see a uniform grey area. As we move away from this end of the plate, Δt increases to many minutes at the other end of the plate. If the velocity fields were only that of the rising and falling granulation, the pattern on the plate would change from the uniform grey at the $\Delta t = 0$ end to a granular field brought about by the superposition of two uncorrelated velocity fields at the other end. Actually, Leighton secured plates where the pattern changed from the uniform grey at end $\Delta t = 0$ to a maximum of contrast between dark and light grains at a distance corresponding to $\Delta t \approx 150$ sec.

Further away from the end $\Delta t = 0$, the contrast diminished again to a minimum at $\Delta t \approx 300$ sec, after which the pattern repeated itself.

This behavior of the Doppler difference plates strongly suggests that an oscillatory motion with a period around $P = 300$ sec exists in the region where the lines in question are formed.

Under certain conditions (the center of the solar disk lies in the strip where $\Delta t = 150$ sec), the oscillatory motions can also be brought out by Doppler *sum* plates. In that case, a pronounced minimum of contrast is observed for $\Delta t \approx 150$ sec, which shows that there is a strong anticorrelation of velocities after about 150 sec. This is an important observational fact because it shows that the oscillations contain essentially all the energy of vertical velocity fields in the range of linear dimensions which are resolved by Leighton's method. If there are other vertical velocity fields in the photosphere, their characteristic dimensions must be such that they are unobservable by the present techniques. The main vertical motion in the solar photosphere, therefore, seems to be an oscillatory one.

3.2.3.2. *Wiggly lines*

Evans' and Michard's work is based on time sequences of spectrograms covering both strong and faint lines. The lines show "wiggles" due to Doppler displacements, indicating more or less vertical mass motions in the layers where the lines are formed. Microdensitometer tracings were made along the slit at different distances $\Delta\lambda$ from the line center. Each spectrogram yielded a $v(x)$ curve of velocity v vs. position x along the slit, and Evans and Michard used the time sequences to construct $v(t)$ curves of velocity vs. time t for any point along the slit.

The velocity amplitudes (rms values) were found to increase from about 0.4 km/sec for a faint line like Ti I, 5174, to about 0.8 km/sec for a strong line like Mg I, 5173, which means that the amplitude increases with height in the solar atmosphere. Furthermore, the $v(t)$ curve for any point shows an oscillating nature indicating a mean period of about 240 sec, with quite a large spread (180 to 320 sec) for both faint and strong lines. The oscillations have wavelengths of a few thousand kilometers.

Another way to obtain a value for the oscillation period is to perform a time-correlation analysis on the $v(x)$ curves. This was tried by Evans and Michard, who found a maximum for the correlation function at $t \approx 300$ sec, in excellent agreement with the period determined by Leighton (1960). The large discrepancy between this value and the value of 240 sec has been explained by Evans and Michard as due to an unobserved long extension—in the Fourier spectrum of $v(t)$—of the time distribution of periods toward longer periods. Jensen and Orrall (1963) compared motions determined at different heights and found some indications of phase differences. Also, the period seems to decrease substantially with height, being of the order of 150 sec in the Ca II, K line. Evans and Michard found substantial phase shifts with height for short waves, but little shift for longer waves.

3.2.3.3. *Theoretical considerations*

One important problem is to explain the well defined period of about 300 sec in an atmosphere which supposedly is exposed to a broadband frequency spectrum of convective motions from below. There have been several attempts to show how the observed period can be singled out, and we shall trace some of the arguments here.

First, we notice that the quasi-periodic vertical motions described in this section are apparently connected with the previously discussed transfer of mechanical energy from the convection zone to the outer atmosphere. But until recently it had generally been assumed that these wave motions in the upper layers would consist of a continuous frequency spectrum. The discovery of a discrete period shows that a substantial fraction (maybe most) of the energy connected with the wave motions is concentrated in a narrow frequency interval.

The problem of vertical propagation (z-direction) of acoustical waves in an atmosphere is an old one. Lamb (1908, 1945) has pointed out that the propagation problem is characterized by a resonance, or critical, frequency ω_a, and that frequencies less than the critical one are strongly attenuated, while greater frequencies are propagated. No variation of the pertinent parameters in the horizontal direction was considered, that is, the wave number $k_x = 0$. For $\omega < \omega_a$, only standing wave solutions are possible. Waves in the domain around the critical frequency ω_a, given by Equation (1.155) for an isothermal atmosphere, are treated in Section 1.5. To the frequency ω_a there corresponds a critical period $P_a = 4\pi V_s/\gamma g = 4\pi H/V_s$, where V_s is the velocity of sound, γ the ratio of specific heats, g the gravitational acceleration, and H the scale height. Due to uncertainties in the parameters involved, P_a is not well determined in the solar atmosphere, but we can estimate it. Remember, however, that the approximation leading to Equation (1.155) implies an isothermal atmosphere and the neglect of both ionization on γ and radiative transfer problems. We need appropriate values for the scale height and the velocity of sound, and this really means that we need to know the structure of the atmosphere, since these parameters depend on the mean molecular weight μ as well as the temperature T. The value of μ varies throughout the atmosphere mainly due to the changing ionization of hydrogen, and atmospheric models giving estimates of μ are available (Pottasch and Thomas, 1960). If we use the values $V_s = 6.3\ \text{km/sec}$ and $H = 120$ km, we find that $P_a = 240$ sec. It may be that the critical period is somewhat longer, in which case the observed oscillations may exhibit frequencies within the nonpropagation range of the dispersion relation. As discussed by Schmidt and Meyer (1966), this difficulty can be removed either by assuming that the observed oscillations are built up asymptotically by the neighboring propagating modes or by taking recourse to gravity waves which propagate throughout this frequency range (see Section 1.5).

A general description of the different ways of attacking the problem of solar atmospheric oscillations has been given by Jones (1965), and we shall follow his arguments here. To explain the observed fact that vertical motions in the atmosphere are strongly concentrated in periodic or quasi-periodic narrow-band oscillations, we must consider two questions: (1) What is the driving mechanism, and (2) how do the dynamics of the atmosphere modify the motions?

We may either be quite general and assume that we can find the driving mechanism in the turbulence generated in the convection zone, or we may be more specific and assume that single granules are the proper sources of the vertical motions. We can consider these disturbances as the input to a mechanical system, namely the solar atmosphere, while the output is the oscillatory motions. The problem is, then, to find the relation between the input and the output.

There are several approaches to solve the problem. One is in terms of an analogy to the input and output of a communications system (Lee, 1960). Assuming that we know the input signal $q_{in}(t)$, we can compute the output motions $q_{out}(t)$ as a function of time from a knowledge of the response, $h(t - t_0)$, of the atmosphere to a unit impulse at $t = t_0$. Thus, we have

$$q_{out}(t) = \int_{-\infty}^{t} q_{in}(t_0) h(t - t_0)\, dt.$$

This is the philosophy behind the approach followed by Jensen and Orrall (1963), Schmidt and Zirker (1963), and Schmidt and Meyer (1966). Jensen and Orrall considered the possibility that the fluctuations are isobaric oscillations associated with the stability of the atmosphere above the convection zone. This is a rather stable situation, since the layers involved are situated above the temperature minimum. An element that is displaced from its equilibrium position will be subjected to an oscillating motion, all the time being in pressure equilibrium with its surroundings. The period of the oscillations is given (Eliassen and Kleinschmidt, 1957) by

$$P = \frac{2\pi}{\sqrt{g}} \left[\frac{T}{(\nabla T)_0 - (\nabla T)_{ad}} \right]^{1/2},$$

where $(\nabla T)_0$ is the temperature gradient in the undisturbed atmosphere, and $(\nabla T)_{ad}$ is the adiabatic temperature gradient. Using reasonable models for the solar atmosphere, we find, with Jensen and Orrall, that the predicted periods for the oscillations in the photosphere and chromosphere are in good agreement with observations.

If we consider the granule as the driving force of the oscillations, it is necessary to remember that the lifetimes of granules are not negligible compared to the average periods of lifetimes of the oscillations. This means that we are dealing with an inhomogeneous boundary-value problem, where the inhomogeneity at the boundary, that is, the spicule, influences the solution throughout the interesting range of time. Schmidt and Meyer used a superposition of many modes fitting initial and boundary values, and they used this superposition to explain the observed time lags of the oscillations at different heights in the chromosphere.

Another approach to finding the input–output relation is to Fourier-transform the problem into the frequency domain. If $Q_{out}(\omega)$, $Q_{in}(\omega)$, and $H(\omega)$ are the transforms of $q_{out}(t)$, $q_{in}(t)$, and $h(t)$, respectively, then we have

$$Q_{out}(\omega) = H(\omega)Q_{in}(\omega).$$

Lamb (1908) had already studied the response of an atmosphere to periodic disturbances of given frequency ω, and this is also the approach used by Noyes and Leighton (1963), Moore and Spiegel (1964), and Kato (1963).

The third approach to the problem is a stochastic one, where we consider the input to be a random variable of known statistical characteristics, and the problem is to find the statistical characteristics of the output. If

$$\phi_{in}(\tau) = \lim_{T \to \infty} \frac{1}{2\pi} \int_{-T}^{T} q_{in}(t)q_{in}(t + \tau)\, dt$$

is the autocorrelation function of the input and

$$\Phi_{in}(\omega) = \frac{1}{2\pi} \int_{-\infty}^{\infty} \phi_{in}(\tau)e^{-i\omega\tau}\, dt$$

is the input power density spectrum, then the output power density spectrum is (Lee, 1960)

$$\Phi_{out}(\omega) = |H(\omega)|^2\, \Phi_{in}(\omega).$$

If the frequency response $H(\omega)$ of the atmosphere has marked peaks in the frequency domain of the input power spectrum, then the output power spectrum will show these peaks. Also, the output autocorrelation will show pronounced maxima at time intervals corresponding to the resonant frequencies of $H(\omega)$. Much of the data of small-scale motions is effectively

recorded in the form of autocorrelations, so that the stochastic method seems
appropriate, and indeed this is the approach indicated by Jones.

The atmosphere can exhibit two types of resonances, both of which may
amplify certain wave modes. One resonance is due to the local wave
propagation characteristics of the plasma and is referred to as the propagation
resonance. It is independent of the boundary conditions for the plasma, and
it is the resonance studied by Noyes and Leighton, Moore and Spiegel,
Kato, Schmidt and Zirker, and Schmidt and Meyer in their descriptions of
the vertical oscillatory motions.

The other type of resonance is a result of the spatial characteristics of the
atmosphere and may be referred to as the free oscillation resonance. It depends critically on the boundary conditions and is determined by the trapping
of waves between layers in the atmosphere. This resonance has been studied
by Kahn (1961, 1962), Bahng and Schwarzschild (1963), and Uchida (1961,
1966). Jones found a new wave mode in this domain characterized by a
nondivergent velocity field. He was able to show that for certain frequencies
and wavelengths, both types of resonances will be effective, and that strongly
amplified excited oscillations are obtained.

Many of the treatments referred to above appear to reproduce satisfactorily periods of about 300 sec. A more crucial test is to account for
phase shifts with height (which are still inadequately observed) and for the
observed changes in wavelength with height. Depending on the approach
used in attacking the problem (see above), we find that some of the investigations mentioned can determine a wavelength for the wave motions, while
others are inherently incapable of doing this.

3.3. *The Corona*

3.3.1. Electromagnetic Radiation

At heights of about 12,000 km above the photosphere, the last traces
of spicules—and hence of the Ca II and the Balmer lines—disappear. This
height defines the outer boundary of the upper chromosphere in the simplified
spherically symmetric picture of the solar atmosphere. Here the temperature
of the interspicular plasma has reached a value of about half a million
degrees, and we are entering the corona proper. In a distance of about 2 %
of a solar radius, the temperature has—through the chromosphere—increased from the photospheric boundary value of less than 5000 °K to the
10^6 °K regime of the outer atmosphere. In contrast to this sharp gradient,
in the corona we encounter a nearly isothermal plasma. The electron density
has fallen to a value of between 10^9 and 10^8 cm^{-3}, and it continues to decrease
monotonically as we go out through the corona. It is this outer layer of the
solar atmosphere that is responsible for the emission of radio waves in the

dm and especially the m range and for important parts of the X-ray spectrum.
We shall now treat in some detail the different components of the radiations
observed from the corona.

3.3.1.1. *The F corona*

In the optical wavelength region, the most important source of emission
is scattered photospheric light. The light is scattered by two agencies,
electrons and "dust particles," the first giving rise to what has become

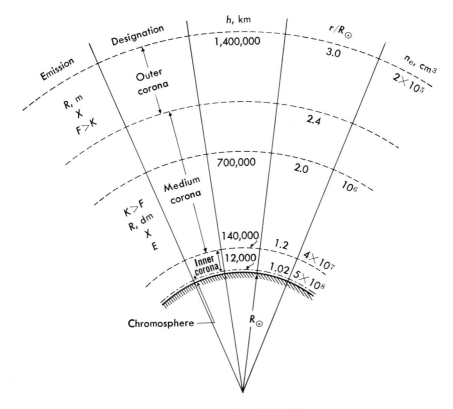

FIGURE 3.3.   Schematic model of the corona

known as the *K corona*, the second to the *F corona*, or inner zodiacal light.
Together they form the *white-light corona*. The outer corona is now defined as
that part of the atmosphere where the *F*-component is greater than the
K-component (that is, for $r/R_\odot > 2.4$, see Figure 3.3). The apparent difficulty
in having to account for nonevaporating solid particles in the 10^6 °K hot
corona was overcome by Allen (1946) and van de Hulst (1947), each working

independently. They argued that scattering of light by small particles—the Tyndall scattering—will take place under very small angles, that is, in a forward direction (the so-called Mie effect), and will not follow the Thomson scattering of electrons which presents a broad diagram $(1 + \cos^2 \phi)$. The light from the F corona, therefore, does not come from the inner corona which is subjected to a temperature of a million degrees, but from the far outer reaches of the much cooler atmosphere.

The F-component may be distinguished from the K-component by several methods. First, by observing the Fraunhofer lines which in the F-component show ordinary intensity and width (whence the designation F for Fraunhofer), whereas in the K-component they are broadened beyond recognition by Doppler motions. Second, by noting the fact that the F corona shows no polarization, while scattering by electrons results in easily measurable polarization in the K corona. Third, by observing the photometry of the F corona, which indicates that this component has spherical symmetry, while the shape of the K corona shows greater equatorial extension than polar extension.

3.3.1.2. *The K corona, or the electron corona*

This is the stronger white-light component in the inner and middle corona. The form of the K corona varies with the sunspot cycle, and here we should treat only the minimum, or quiet, corona. The distinction is not easy to make, since we do not know how inactive the sun must be before we see the quiet corona—if we ever see it. We shall return to this question in Chapter 8. Due to the large thermal velocities of the electrons (at $T_e = 10^6$ °K , $v_{th} = 6.8 \times 10^3$ km/sec), the Fraunhofer lines in the light scattered by these electrons will be so smeared out as to be almost, but not quite, unobservable. In fact it was these very broad and shallow depressions, instead of proper lines, that made Grotrian (1931b) realize the possibility of a very high temperature in the corona. The polarization of the K corona—which seems to vary somewhat with the solar cycle—reaches a maximum of approximately 70% in the inner part of the outer corona (Öhman, 1947).

3.3.1.3. *The E corona, or emission line component*

This is, in many ways, the most interesting component observed. Numerous studies have been made of these lines since the first one was discovered in 1869 by Young and Harkness (Young, 1896). The nature of these lines remained a mystery until Grotrian (1939) determined that two lines were caused by forbidden transition in very highly (9 and 10 times) ionized iron. Since then Edlén (1942, 1954) has identified many of the lines. The wavelengths of these lines are found in the visible part of the spectrum, as well as in the infrared, ultraviolet, and X-ray domains. Tables 3.1 and 3.2 list lines for which identifications seem fairly certain, plus a few others.

TABLE 3.1.   Optical coronal emission lines. (Van de Hulst, 1953; Pecker–Wimel, 1960; Billings, 1966.)

λ, Å	Ion	Transition	Ionization potential
3010	Fe XII	$^2P_{1/2}-^2D_{3/2}$	291
3170	Cr XI	$^1D_2-^3P_1$	246
3327	Ca XII	$^2P_{1/2}-^2P_{3/2}$	592
3388	Fe XIII	$^1D_2-^3P_2$	330
3533	V X	$^1D_2-^3P_1$	206
3601	Ni XVI	$^2P_{3/2}-^2P_{1/2}$	455
3643	Ni XIII	$^1D_2-^3P_1$	350
3685	Mn XII	$^1D_2-^3P_2$	288
3801	Co XII	$^1D_2-^3P_1$	306
3987	Fe XI	$^1D_2-^3P_1$	262
3998	Cr XI	$^1D_2-^3P_2$	246
4086	Ca XIII	$^3P_1-^3P_2$	655
4220	Mn X	$^1D_2-^3P_1$	248
4232	Ni XII	$^2P_{1/2}-^2P_{3/2}$	321
4256	K XI	$^2P_{1/2}-^2P_{3/2}$ $(^2P_{3/2}-^2P_{1/2})$	504
4312	V X	$^1D_2-^3P_2$	206
4351	Co XV	$^2P_{3/2}-^2P_{1/2}$	412
4412	Ar XIV	$^2P_{3/2}-^2P_{1/2}$	687
4566	Cr IX	$^1D_2-^3P_1$	185
4744	Ni XVII	$^3P_2-^3P_1$	500
5116	Ni XIII	$^3P_1-^3P_2$	350
5188	Co XI	$^2P_{1/2}-^3P_2$	290
5303	Fe XIV	$^2P_{3/2}-^2P_{1/2}$	355
5446	Ca XV	$^3P_2-^3P_1$	820
5536	Ar X	$^2P_{1/2}-^2P_{3/2}$	423
5620	Ca VII	$^1D_2-^3P_2$	109
5694	Ca XV	$^3P_1-^3P_0$	820
5774	Co XVI	$^3P_2-^3P_1$ $(^3P_1-^3P_0)$	444
5926	Ar XV	$^3P_2-^3P_1$	755
6374	Fe X	$^2P_{1/2}-^2P_{3/2}$	235
6535	Mn XIII	$^2P_{3/2}-^2P_{1/2}$	315
6702	Ni XV	$^3P_1-^3P_0$	430
6740	K XIV	$^3P_2-^3P_1$	717
6917	Ar XI	$^3P_1-^3P_2$	479
7060	Fe XV	$^3P_2-^3P_1$	390
7144	Ni IX	$^1G_4-^1D_2$	169
7892	Fe XI	$^3P_1-^3P_2$	262
8024	Ni XV	$^3P_2-^3P_1$	430
8425	Ni XV	$^3P_2-^3P_1$	430
8476	Ar XIII	$^3P_2-^3P_1$	621
10747	Fe XIII	$^3P_1-^3P_0$	330
10798	Fe XIII	$^3P_2-^3P_1$	330

TABLE 3.2.   XUV coronal emission lines (limited to ionization potential > 100 volts)(Alexander, Feldman, Fraenkel, Hoory, 1965; Jordan, 1965; Billings, 1966)

λ, Å	Ion	Transition	ΔJ
1058.7	Al VIII	$2p^2\ ^3P_1-2p^2\ ^1S_0$	
1037.6	O VI	Multiplet 1	
1031.9	O VI	Multiplet 1	
780.3	Ne VIII	$2s\ ^2S_{1/2}-2p\ ^2P^o_{1/2}$	
770.4	Ne VIII	$2s\ ^2S_{1/2}-2p\ ^2P^o_{3/2}$	
625.3	Mg X	$2s\ ^2S_{1/2}-2p\ ^2P^o_{1/2}$	
609.8	Mg X	$2s\ ^2S_{1/2}-2p\ ^2P^o_{3/2}$	
558	Ne VI	Multiplet 1	
521.1	Si XII	$2s\ ^2S_{1/2}-2p\ ^2P^o_{1/2}$	
499.4	Si XII	$2s\ ^2S_{1/2}-2p\ ^2P^o_{3/2}$	
465.3	Ne VIII	$2s\ ^1S_0-2p\ ^1P^o_1$	
436.7	Mg VIII	$2s^22p\ ^2P^o-2s2p^2\ ^2D$	$1\frac{1}{2}-1\frac{1}{2}$
430.5	Mg VIII	$2s^22p\ ^2P^o-2s2p^2\ ^2D$	$\frac{1}{2}-1\frac{1}{2}$
368.1	Mg IX	$2s^2\ ^1S-2s2p\ ^1P^o$	0-1
360.8	Fe XVI	$3s\ ^2S-3p\ ^2P^o$	$\frac{1}{2}-\frac{1}{2}$
349.9	Si IX	$2s^22p^2\ ^3P-2s2p^3\ ^3D^o$	2-3
347.4	Si X	$2s^22p\ ^2P^o-2s2p^2\ ^2D$	$\frac{1}{2}-1\frac{1}{2}$
346	Fe X	$3s^23p^5\ ^2P^o-3s3p^6\ ^2S$	$1\frac{1}{2}-\frac{1}{2}$
345.1	Si IX	$2s^22p^2\ ^2P-2s2p^3\ ^3D^o$	1-2
342	Fe XIV	$3s^23p\ ^2P^o-3s3p^2\ ^2D$	$\frac{1}{2}-1\frac{1}{2}$
339.0	Mg VIII	$2s^22p\ ^2P^o-2s2p^2\ ^2S$	$1\frac{1}{2}-1\frac{1}{2}$
335.3	Fe XVI	$3s\ ^2S-3p\ ^2P^o$	$\frac{1}{2}-1\frac{1}{2}$
332.8	Al X	$2s^2\ ^1S-2s2p\ ^1P^o$	0-1
319.8	Si VIII	$2s^22p^3\ ^4S^o-2s2p^4\ ^4P$	$1\frac{1}{2}-2\frac{1}{2}$
317.0	Mg VIII	$2s^22p\ ^2P^o-2s2p^2\ ^2P$	$1\frac{1}{2}-\frac{1}{2}$
316.2	Si VIII	$2s2p^3\ ^4S^o-2s2p^4\ ^4P$	$1\frac{1}{2}-1\frac{1}{2}$
315	Mg VIII	$2s^22p\ ^2P^o-2s2p^2\ ^2P$	$1\frac{1}{2}-1\frac{1}{2}$
314.3	Si VIII	$2s^22p^3\ ^4S^o-2s2p^4\ ^4P$	$1\frac{1}{2}-\frac{1}{2}$
313.8	Mg VIII	$2s^22p\ ^2P^o-2s2p^2\ ^2P$	$\frac{1}{2}-\frac{1}{2}$
312.0	Mg VIII	$2s^22p\ ^2P^o-2s2p^2\ ^2P$	$\frac{1}{2}-1\frac{1}{2}$
308.3	Si VIII	$2s^22p^3\ ^2P^o-2s2p^4\ ^2D$	$1\frac{1}{2}-2\frac{1}{2}$
303.4	Si XI	$2s^2\ ^1S-2s2p\ ^1P^o$	0-1
296.2	Si IX	$2s^22p^2\ ^3P-2s2p^3\ ^3P$	2-1, 2
292.8	Si IX	$2s^22p^2\ ^3P-2s2p^3\ ^3P^o$	1-0, 1; 1-2
290.7	Si IX	$2s^22p^2\ ^3P-2s2p^3\ ^3P^o$	0-1
284.1	Fe XV	$3s^2\ ^1S^o-3s3p\ ^1P^o$	0-1
278.3	Mg VII	$2s^22p^2\ ^3P-2s2p^3\ ^3S^o$	2-1
	Si VII	$2s^22p^4\ ^3P-2s2p^5\ ^3P^o$	1-2
277.1	Si VIII	$2s^22p^3\ ^2D^o-2s2p^4\ ^2D$	$2\frac{1}{2}-2\frac{1}{2}$
275.3	Si VII	$2s^22p^4\ ^3P-2s2p^5\ ^3P^o$	2-2; 1-1
274.2	Fe XIV	$3s^23p\ ^2P^o-3s3p^2\ ^2S$	$\frac{1}{2}-\frac{1}{2}$
272.0	Si X	$2s^22p\ ^2P^o-2s2p^2\ ^2S$	$\frac{1}{2}-\frac{1}{2}$

TABLE 3.2   *Continued*

λ, Å	Ion	Transition	ΔJ
270.4	Fe XIV	$3s^23p\ ^2P^o-3s3p^2\ ^2P$	$1\frac{1}{2}-\frac{1}{2}$
264.5	Fe XIV	$3s^23p\ ^2P^o-3s3p^2\ ^2P$	$1\frac{1}{2}-1\frac{1}{2}$
264.3	S X	$2s^22p^3\ ^4S-2s2p^4\ ^4P$	$1\frac{1}{2}-2\frac{1}{2}$
259.5	S X	$2s^22p^3\ ^4S^o-2s2p^4\ ^4P$	$1\frac{1}{2}-1\frac{1}{2}$
258.2	Si X	$2s^22p\ ^2P^o-2s2p^3\ ^2P$	$1\frac{1}{2}-1\frac{1}{2}$
257.3	S X	$2s^22p^3\ ^4S^o-2s2p^4\ ^4P$	$1\frac{1}{2}-1\frac{1}{2}$
253.8	Si X	$2s^22p\ ^2P^o-2s2p^2\ ^2D$	$\frac{1}{2}-1\frac{1}{2}$
251.8	Fe XIV	$3s^23p\ ^2P^o-3s3p^2\ ^2P$	$\frac{1}{2}-1\frac{1}{2}$
249.3	Si VI	$2s^22p^5\ ^2P^o-2s2p^6\ ^2S$	$\frac{1}{2}-\frac{1}{2}$ (?)
248.6	C V	$2p\ ^3P^o-3d\ ^3D$	?
246.1	Si VI	$2s^22p^5\ ^3P-2s2p^6\ ^2S$	$1\frac{1}{2}-\frac{1}{2}$
235.4	Si VIII	$2s^22p^3\ ^2P^o-2s2p^4\ ^2P$	$1\frac{1}{2}-1\frac{1}{2}$
233.0	Si VIII	$2s^22p^3\ ^2P^o-2s2p^4\ ^2P$	$1\frac{1}{2}-\frac{1}{2}$
231.4	Fe XV	$3p\ ^3P^o-3d\ ^3D$	$2-3$ (?)
227.1	Si IX	$2s^22p^2\ ^3P-2s2p^3\ ^3S^o$	$2-1$
225.1	Si IX	$2s^22p^2\ ^3P-2s2p^3\ ^3S^o$	$1-1$
224.7	Si IX	$2s^22p^4\ ^3P-2s2p^5\ ^3P^o$	$1-1$; $2-2$
223.7	Si IX	$2s^22p^2\ ^3P-2s2p^3\ ^3S^o$	$0-1$
217.0	Si VIII	$2s^22p^3\ ^2D^o-2s2p^4\ ^2P$	$2\frac{1}{2}-1\frac{1}{2}$
214.7	Si VIII	$2s^22p^3\ ^2D^o-2s2p^4\ ^2P$	$1\frac{1}{2}-\frac{1}{2}$
211.7	Fe XIV	$3p\ ^2P^o-3d\ ^2D$	$\frac{1}{2}-1\frac{1}{2}$
196.7	Fe XII, XIII		
195.1	Fe XII, XIII		
193.5	Fe XII, XIII		
192.3	Fe XII, XIII		
191.2	Fe		
190.2	Fe XIII		
	S XII		
188.2	Fe XI, XII		
187.0	Fe XIII	$3p^3\ ^2D^o-3p^2(^1D)3d\ ^2F$	$2\frac{1}{2}-3\frac{1}{2}$
185.5	Fe VIII	$3p^63d\ ^2D-3p^53d^2\ ^2F^o$	$2\frac{1}{2}-3\frac{1}{2}$
184.7	Fe XI, XII		
183.9	O VI	Multiplet 3	
182.2	Fe XI	$3p^4\ ^3P-3p^3(^2P)3d\ ^3D^o$	$1-2$
179.8	Fe XI	$3p^4\ ^1D-3p^3(^2P)3d\ ^1F^o$	$2-3$
177.1	Fe X	$3p^5\ ^2P^o-3p^4(^1D)3d\ ^2P$	$1\frac{1}{2}-1\frac{1}{2}$
175.3	Fe X	$3p^5\ ^2P^o-3p^4(^1D)3d\ ^2D$	$\frac{1}{2}-1\frac{1}{2}$
174.5	Fe X	$3p^5\ ^2P^o-3p^4(^1D)3d\ ^2D$	$1\frac{1}{2}-2\frac{1}{2}$
173.1	O VI	Multiplet 4	
172.9	O VI	Multiplet 4	
171.1	Fe IX	$3p^6\ ^1S-3p^53d\ ^1P^o$	$0-1$
164.1	Ni XIV	$3p^3\ ^2D^o-3p^23d\ ^2F$	$2\frac{1}{2}-3\frac{1}{2}$ (?)

Table 3.2 *Continued*

λ, Å	Ion	Transition	ΔJ
160.0	Ni X	$3p^6 3d\ ^2D$–$3p^5 3d^2\ ^2F^o$	$1\frac{1}{2}$–$2\frac{1}{2}$
158.8	Co X	$3p^6\ ^1S^o$–$3p^5 3d\ ^1P_1$	
158.4	Ni X	$3p^6 3d\ ^2D$–$3p^5 3d^2\ ^2F^o$	$2\frac{1}{2}$–$3\frac{1}{2}$
157.7	Ni XIII	$3p^4\ ^3P$–$3p^3(^2P)3d\ ^3D^o$	2–3
154.1	Ni XII	$3p^5\ ^2P^o$–$3p^4(^1D)3d\ ^2D$	$1\frac{1}{2}$–$1\frac{1}{2}$
153.0	Ni XII	$3p^5\ ^2P^o$–$3p^4(^1D)3d\ ^2D$	$\frac{1}{2}$–$1\frac{1}{2}$
152.1	Ni XII	$3p^5\ ^2P^o$–$3p^4(^1D)3d\ ^2D$	$1\frac{1}{2}$–$2\frac{1}{2}$
150.0	O VI	Multiplet 2	
148.4	Ni XI	$3p^6\ ^1S$–$3p^5 3d\ ^1P^o$	0–1
145.0	Ni X	$3p^6 3d\ ^2D$–$3p^5 3d^2\ ^2D^o$	$2\frac{1}{2}$–$2\frac{1}{2}$
144.2	Ni X	$3p^6 3d\ ^2D$–$3p^5 3d^2\ ^2D^o$	$1\frac{1}{2}$–$1\frac{1}{2}$
129.9	O VI	Multiplet 5	
116.4	O VI	$2p\ ^2P^o$–$5d\ ^2D$	?
115.8	O VI	$2s\ ^2S$–$4p\ ^2P^o$	?
111.0	Ca X	$3s\ ^2S$–$4p\ ^2P^o$	$\frac{1}{2}$–$1\frac{1}{2}$ (?)
106.1	Ne VII	$2s2p\ ^3P^o$–$2s3d\ ^3D$	1–2
105.3	Fe IX	$3p^6\ ^1S$–$3p^5 4s\ ^3P^o$	0–1
104.8	O VI	$2s\ ^2S$–$5p\ ^2P^o$	?
103.7	Fe IX	$3p^6\ ^1S$–$3p^5 4s\ ^1P^o$	0–1
98.1	Ne VIII	$2p\ ^2P^o$–$3d\ ^2D$	$\frac{1}{2}$–$1\frac{1}{2}$
96.6	Fe X	$3p^5\ ^2P^o$–$3p^4 4s\ ^2P$	$\frac{1}{2}$–$\frac{1}{2}$
96.1	Fe X	$3p^5\ ^2P^o$–$3p^4 4s\ ^2P$	$\frac{1}{2}$–$1\frac{1}{2}$
95.3	Fe X	$3p^5\ ^2P^o$–$3p^4 4s\ ^2D$	$\frac{1}{2}$–$1\frac{1}{2}$
94.1	Fe X	$3p^5\ ^2P^o$–$3p^4 4s\ ^2P$	$1\frac{1}{2}$–$1\frac{1}{2}$
90.1	Fe XI	$3p^4\ ^3P$–$3p^3 4s\ ^3S^o$	1–0
89.2	Fe XI	$3p^4\ ^3P$–$3p^3 4s\ ^3S^o$	2–1
88.1	Fe XI	$3p^4\ ^3P$–$3p^3 4s\ ^3D^o$	1–2
	Ne VIII	$2s\ ^2S$–$3p\ ^2P^o$	$\frac{1}{2}$–$1\frac{1}{2}$
86.8	Fe XI	$3p^4\ ^3P$–$3p^3 4s\ ^3D^o$	2–3
82.9	Mg VIII	$2p\ ^2P^o$–$3s\ ^2S$	$1\frac{1}{2}$–$\frac{1}{2}$ (?)
82.6	Mg VIII	$2p\ ^2P^o$–$3s\ ^2S$	$\frac{1}{2}$–$\frac{1}{2}$ (?)
81.7	Mg VIII	$2p^2\ ^4S$–$2p3s\ ^4P^o$	
81.6	Si VII	$2p^4\ ^3P$–$2p3s\ ^3D^o$	2–3
79.5	Fe XII	$3p^3\ ^4S^o$–$3p^2 4s\ ^4P$	$1\frac{1}{2}$–$2\frac{1}{2}$ (?
77.7	Mg IX	$2p\ ^1P^o$–$3s\ ^1S$	1–0
75.8	Fe XIII	$3p^2\ ^3P$–$3p4s\ ^3P^o$	1–1 (?)
74.8	Mg VIII	$2p\ ^2P^o$–$3d\ ^2D$	?
74.3	Si VIII	$2p^3\ ^2P^o$–$2p^2 3s\ ^2P$	?
72.4	Si VIII	$2p^3\ ^2D^o$–$2p^2 3s\ ^2P$	$1\frac{1}{2}$–$\frac{1}{2}$ (?)
72.3	Mg IX	$2p^2\ ^1D$–$2p3d\ ^1D^o$	2–2 (?)
69.9	Mg IX	$2p^2\ ^1D$–$2p3d\ ^1F^o$	2–3
	Fe XV	$3s3d\ ^3D$–$3s4f\ ^3F^o$	?
69.5	Si VIII	$2p^3\ ^4S^o$–$2p^2 3s\ ^4P$	

TABLE 3.2 Continued

λ, Å	Ion	Transition	ΔJ
68.5	Mg VIII	$2p\ ^2P^0\text{--}3p\ ^2S$	?
67.2	Ne VIII	$2s\ ^2S\text{--}4p\ ^2P^0$	?
	Mg IX	$2s2p\ ^3P^0\text{--}2s3d\ ^3D$	?
66.4	Fe XVI	$3d\ ^3D\text{--}4f\ ^2F^0$	$2\frac{1}{2}\text{--}3\frac{1}{2}$
65.7	Mg X	$2p\ ^2P^0\text{--}3s\ ^2S$	$1\frac{1}{2}\text{--}\frac{1}{2}$
65.6	Mg IX	$2p\ ^2P^0\text{--}3s\ ^2S$	
63.7	Fe XVI	$2p\ ^2P^0\text{--}4s\ ^2S$	$1\frac{1}{2}\text{--}\frac{1}{2}$
63.3	Mg X	$2p\ ^2P^0\text{--}3d\ ^2D$	
	Si VIII	$2p^3\ ^2P^0\text{--}2p^23d\ ^2P$	$1\frac{1}{2}\text{--}1\frac{1}{2}$
62.8	Si VIII	$2p^3\ ^2P^0\text{--}2p^23d\ ^2P$	$\frac{1}{2}\text{--}\frac{1}{2}$
	Mg IX	$2s^2\ ^1S\text{--}2s3p\ ^1P^0$	$0\text{--}1$
62.7	Mg IX	$2s^2\ ^1S\text{--}2s3p\ ^1P^0$	
61.9	Si IX	$2p^2\ ^3P\text{--}2p3s\ ^2P^0$	$2\text{--}1$
61.6	Si IX	$2p^2\ ^3P\text{--}2p3s\ ^3P^0$	$1\text{--}2$
61.1	Si VIII	$2p^3\ ^4S^0\text{--}2p^23d\ ^4P$	$1\frac{1}{2}\text{--}\frac{1}{2},\ 1\frac{1}{2};\ 1\frac{1}{2}\text{--}2\frac{1}{2}$
60.7	Ne VIII	$2s\ ^2S\text{--}5p\ ^2P^0$	$\frac{1}{2}\text{--}\frac{1}{2},\ 1\frac{1}{2}\ (?)$
59.3	Fe XIV	$3p\ ^2P^0\text{--}4d\ ^2D$	$1\frac{1}{2}\text{--}2\frac{1}{2}$
58.8	Fe XIV	$3p\ ^2P^0\text{--}4d\ ^2D$	$\frac{1}{2}\text{--}1\frac{1}{2}$
57.6	Mg X	$2s\ ^2S\text{--}3p\ ^2P^0$	$\frac{1}{2}\text{--}\frac{1}{2},\ 1\frac{1}{2}$
56.8	Si X	$2s2p^2\ ^2P\text{--}2s2p3d\ ^2D^0$	$1\frac{1}{2}\text{--}2\frac{1}{2}\ (?)$
56.6	Si X	$2s2p^2\ ^2P\text{--}2s2p3d\ ^2D^0$	$1\frac{1}{2}\text{--}2\frac{1}{2}\ (?),$
56.0	Si IX	$2p^2\ ^1D\text{--}2p3d\ ^1F^0$	$2\text{--}3\ (?)$
55.3	Si IX	$2p^2\ ^3P\text{--}2p3d\ ^3D^0$	
55.1	Si IX	$2p^2\ ^3P\text{--}2p3d\ ^3P^0$	
54.8	Fe XVI	$3p\ ^2P^0\text{--}4d\ ^2D$	?
54.6	Si X	$2p\ ^4P^0\text{--}3s\ ^4P$	?
54.2	Fe XVI	$3s\ ^2P^0\text{--}4p\ ^2D$	$\frac{1}{2}\text{--}1\frac{1}{2}\ (?)$
	S IX	$2p^4\ ^3P\text{--}2p^33s\ ^3D^0$	$2\text{--}3\ (?)$
52.8	Si IX		
52.5	Si X	$2s2p^2\ ^2D\text{--}2s2p3d\ ^2F$	$2\frac{1}{2}\text{--}1\frac{1}{2}\ (?)$
52.3	Si XI	$2s2p\ ^1P^0\text{--}2s3s\ ^1S$	$1\text{--}0\ (?)$
52.1	Si X	$2s2p^2\ ^2P^0\text{--}2s2p3d\ ^2D$	
50.7	Si X	$2p\ ^2P^0\text{--}3d\ ^2D$	$1\frac{1}{2}\text{--}2\frac{1}{2}$
50.5	Si X	$2p\ ^2P^0\text{--}3d\ ^2D$	$\frac{1}{2}\text{--}1\frac{1}{2}$
50.3	Fe XVI	$3s\ ^2S\text{--}4p\ ^2P^0$	$\frac{1}{2}\text{--}1\frac{1}{2}\ (?)$
49.7	Si X	$2s2p^2\ ^2D\text{--}2s2p3d\ ^2F^0$	?
49.2	Si XI	$2s2p\ ^1P^0\text{--}2s3d\ ^1D$	$1\text{--}2$
47.6	Si XI	$2s2p\ ^3P^0\text{--}2s3d\ ^3D$	?
	S X	$2p^3\ ^4S^0\text{--}2p^23s\ ^4P$	
46.3	Si XI	$2s2p\ ^3P^0\text{--}2s3d\ ^3D$	
45.7	Si XII	$2p\ ^2P^0\text{--}3s\ ^2S$	$1\frac{1}{2}\text{--}\frac{1}{2}$
44.2	Si IX	$2p^2\ ^3P\text{--}2p4d\ ^3D^0$	
	Si XII	$2p\ ^2P^0\text{--}3d\ ^2D$	

TABLE 3.2   *Continued*

λ, Å	Ion	Transition	ΔJ
	Mg X	$2s\,{}^2S\text{–}4p\,{}^2P^o$	
43.8	Si XI	$2s^2\,{}^1S\text{–}2s3p\,{}^1P^o$	0–1
42.5	S X	$2p^3\,{}^4S^o\text{–}2p^23d\,{}^4P$	$1\frac{1}{2}\text{–}\frac{1}{2};\ 1\frac{1}{2}\text{–}1\frac{1}{2},\,2\frac{1}{2}$
40.9	Si XII	$2s\,{}^2S\text{–}3p\,{}^2P^o$	$\frac{1}{2}\text{–}\frac{1}{2},\,1\frac{1}{2}$
33.8	C VI	$1s\,{}^2S\text{–}2p\,{}^2P^o$	$\frac{1}{2}\text{–}\frac{1}{2},\,1\frac{1}{2}$
24.8	N VII	$1s\,{}^2S\text{–}2p\,{}^2P^o$	$\frac{1}{2}\text{–}\frac{1}{2},\,1\frac{1}{2}$
23.2	N VI	$1s^2\,{}^1S\text{–}1s4p\,{}^1P^o$	0–1 (?)
21.7	O VII	$1s^2\,{}^1S\text{–}1s2p\,{}^3P^o$	0–1
21.6	O VII	$1s^2\,{}^1S\text{–}1s2p\,{}^1P^o$	0–1
20.8	N VII	$1s\,{}^2S\text{–}3p\,{}^2P^o$	$\frac{1}{2}\text{–}\frac{1}{2},\,1\frac{1}{2}$
18.8	O VIII	$1s\,{}^2S\text{–}2p\,{}^2P^o$	$\frac{1}{2}\text{–}\frac{1}{2},\,1\frac{1}{2}$
18.6	O VII	$1s^2\,{}^1S\text{–}1s3p\,{}^1P^o$	0–1
17.7	O VII	$1s^2\,{}^1S\text{–}1s4p\,{}^1P^o$	0–1
16.3	Fe XVII	$2p^6\,{}^1S\text{–}2p^53s\,{}^1P^o$	0–1
16.0	O VIII	$1s\,{}^2S\text{–}3p\,{}^2P^o$	$\frac{1}{2}\text{–}\frac{1}{2},\,1\frac{1}{2}$
15.3	Fe XVII	$2p^6\,{}^1S\text{–}2p^53d\,{}^2P^o$	0–1
15.0	Fe XVII	$2p^6\,{}^1S\text{–}2p^53d\,{}^3P^o$	
13.7	Fe XVII	$2s^22p^6\,{}^1S\text{–}2s2p^63p\,{}^1P^o$	0–1

Many of the lines are always seen in the corona and may be considered as part of the minimum—if not the quiet normal—coronal emission. Others are seen only during times of solar activity and indicate disturbed conditions in the solar plasma. The first group, the semipermanent lines, are seen in the inner and lower part of the middle corona. The only exceptions are the strongest lines that, on occasion, may be seen throughout the entire middle corona. The sporadic lines, whose presence indicate more or less strong activity, are confined to well-defined regions of the corona, and their spatial distribution will be discussed in Chapter 8.

3.3.1.4. *The R corona (radio component)*

This component was discovered with the advent of radio-astronomy, and new information regarding the solar atmosphere has been gained through the study of this emission. The observed radio waves of different wavelengths originate at different levels in the solar corona, and from an analysis of different parts of the radio spectrum, we may study the physical conditions in different strata of the solar atmosphere. The R-component is also a source of continuous radiation as are the F and K coronas, but although the radiation from the latter components is scattered photospheric light, that from the former is thermal radiation. A study of its intensity may therefore give us an estimate of the temperature of the radiating plasma. At times of solar activity, when dense regions form in the corona, thermal radiation at radio frequencies is generated, much in excess of the quiet sun R-component.

3.3.1.5. *The X corona*

The introduction of rockets and satellites as observing platforms for solar studies has revealed the existence of this last newcomer to the list of coronal components. Here we shall define X rays as electromagnetic radiation of wavelengths shorter than about 20 Å which are produced by bremsstrahlung. In the hot coronal plasma, the fast-moving free electrons will emit radiation quanta in their collisions with heavy ions. These bremsstrahlung quanta will correspond to a continuous spectrum if the velocity distribution of the electrons is Maxwellian. The short wavelength part of this free–free radiation accounts for the X-ray emission, while the long wavelength part is responsible for the radio emission in the R-component. Only in the visible region of the spectrum is this source of continuous emission superseded by another mechanism: the previously discussed photospheric light scattered by free electrons (K corona). This is because the photospheric radiation has its strong maximum around 5000 Å.

In the X-ray region, there also may be electromagnetic radiations due to sources other than free–free transitions. Line emission produced by transitions within atomic nuclei led to the discovery of γ rays from radioactive elements. They are also of great significance in the solar interior. We will discuss the possible importance of this radiation in the solar atmospheric plasma in Chapter 6.

The preceding discussion of the different components of the electromagnetic radiations from the corona may be summarized in a physically more satisfactory way if we neglect the historical development and divide the radiation up into the following components: (1) the bremsstrahlung component (free–free transitions, R and X coronas); (2) the Thomson scattered component (electron scattering, K corona); (3) the emission line component (bound–bound transitions, E corona).

The F corona has been dropped from this classification since it is not an intrinsic coronal radiation but may be considered as part of the zodiacal light phenomenon. The free–bound transitions will all give rise to continua, but their intensities are generally less than the free–free continua. However, as we shall see later, these continua may at times attain considerable strength in prominences and flares and will then furnish valuable information on the emitting plasma.

3.3.2. Corpuscular Emission

Electromagnetic radiation is by far the most important way in which the sun loses energy. However, direct mass losses in the form of corpuscular streams or flows are observed during times of activity. We then witness the ejection of energetic *cosmic rays* and *plasma clouds* from certain active regions. In addition, there is a smaller, continuous mass loss from the quiet sun. Some theories dealing with the corona are based on the idea that, due to the high temperature, coronal matter is "boiled off" the atmosphere, resulting in a steady flow of gas from the sun—*the solar wind* (Parker, 1958a, 1961). The hydrodynamic equations show that the corona is steadily expanding with a velocity that ranges from a value of a few kilometers per second in the lower corona to supersonic values at large distances from the sun. While this solar wind model is due to Parker, Biermann (1951, 1952) had previously pointed out that the observed outward acceleration and the ionization of certain comet tails require a continuous flux of corpuscles from the sun.

Given the equation of motion, Equation (1.33), with $\mathbf{B}_0 = 0$,

$$nm(d\mathbf{v}/dr) = -\nabla p - nm\nabla\Phi,$$

where n is the number of atoms per unit volume, and m is the mass of the hydrogen atom, we find that the governing equation for a purely radial,

$$\mathbf{v} = \begin{pmatrix} v \\ 0 \\ 0 \end{pmatrix},$$

and stationary ($\partial\mathbf{v}/\partial t = 0$) expansion of the fully ionized gas ($p = 2nkT$) is

$$nmv\frac{dv}{dr} = -\frac{d}{dr}(2nkT) - nmG\frac{M_0}{r}. \tag{3.1}$$

Here G is the gravitational constant, and M_0 is the solar mass. During the expansion, mass is conserved, that is, we have

$$nv\pi a^2 = n_0 v_0 \pi a_0^2,$$

where the subscript zero denotes the values at a reference level $r = r_0$ and a is the radius of a section through the cone whose top is in the center of the sun and whose generatrix is along a solar radius. Then we have

$$nvr^2 = n_0 v_0 r_0^2 \qquad \text{or} \qquad n = n_0(v_0 r_0^2/vr^2). \tag{3.2}$$

Eliminating n between Equations (3.1) and (3.2), we find that

$$d(\tfrac{1}{2}v^2) = 4kT/mr \cdot dr + 2kT/m \cdot dv/v + d(GmM_0/r), \tag{3.3}$$

which may be integrated under the assumption of an isothermal corona:

$$\frac{1}{2}(v^2 - v_0^2) = \frac{2kT}{m} \ln \frac{v}{v_0} - \frac{4kT}{m} \ln \frac{r}{r_0} + GM_0 m \left(\frac{1}{r} - \frac{1}{r_0} \right). \qquad (3.4)$$

Thus we find, along with Parker, that the velocity of expansion of the coronal plasma—the solar wind—is a function of the distance r for any given value of T_0, keeping v_0 as a parameter. Further analysis now shows that to get an appreciable wind [like the $v_0 = 500$ km/sec required by Biermann's (1957) arguments concerning the tails of comets], the isothermal corona must remain at a high temperature ($\sim 1.5 \times 10^6\,°K$) out to several solar radii. If the temperature decreases outward through this region, the magnitude of the wind will be greatly reduced. Observations (Ness and Wilcox, 1965) have shown that solar plasma—carrying with it photospheric magnetic fields—travels the earth–sun distance with a mean velocity of about 300 km/sec.

3.3.3. The Conduction Corona

If the expansion velocity considered in the previous section is so small that it renders the solar wind phenomenon insignificant, other effects will dominate the energy balance of the corona. Heat conduction will then be the important transport mechanism and will keep the corona at an approximately uniform temperature. Also, from the plateau of maximum temperature, conduction will occur inward to heat the chromosphere (Giovanelli 1949; Woolley and Allen, 1950).

The flow of heat due to conduction (by the free electrons) may be written

$$F'_{\text{cond}} = K \nabla T,$$

where K, the thermal conductivity of a proton-electron gas, is (Chapman, 1954)

$$K = 0.324 \frac{25}{2A_2(2)} \frac{k^{7/2} T^{5/2}}{e^4 \sqrt{m\pi}},$$

and

$$A_2(2) = 2 \ln (1 + x^2) - \frac{2x^2}{1 + x^2},$$

where

$$x = (4kT/e^2)\sqrt{kT/8\pi e^2 n}.$$

Putting in numerical values, we find the total outward flux for a spherically symmetric corona,

$$F_{\text{cond}}^{\text{out}} = \int_{\text{sphere}} F_{\text{cond}}' \, dA = 4\pi R^2 k (dT/dR) = 5.2 \times 10^{-7} 4\pi R^2 T^{5/2} (dT/dR).$$

$$(3.5)$$

This flux F is independent of the radius R, and an expression for it is obtained in the following way (see Chapman, 1957). We set

$$K = K_0 (T/T_0)^{5/2}.$$

Let $T \to 0$ as $R \to \infty$, and set

$$\left(\frac{5}{2} + 1 \right) F_{\text{cond}}^{\text{out}} \frac{T_0^{5/2}}{4\pi K_0} = C.$$

Then the expression for the flux takes the form

$$\frac{dT(\frac{5}{2} + 1)}{d(1/R)} = C,$$

which integrated gives

$$T^{7/2} - T_0^{7/2} = C \left(\frac{1}{R} - \frac{1}{R_0} \right).$$

Since $C = R_0 T_0^{7/2}$, we see that

$$F_{\text{cond}}^{\text{out}} = 4\pi R_0 K_0 (T_0)/(7/2) \tag{3.6}$$

and

$$T = T_0 (R_0/R)^{2/7}. \tag{3.7}$$

According to this model, the temperature decreases as $R^{-2/7}$ and hence remains high at large distances from the sun.

The thermal flow inward to the chromosphere depends critically on the temperature gradient in this region. If we use the value $dT/dR = 12.5°/\text{km}$, we find that

$$F_{\text{cond}}' = 2 \times 10^4 \text{ ergs cm}^{-2} \text{ sec}^{-1} \quad \text{or} \quad F_{\text{cond}}^{\text{in}} = 1.1 \times 10^{27} \text{ ergs/sec}.$$

$$(3.8)$$

This amount is nearly an order of magnitude larger than the total outward

flux from a one million degree corona. This is due to the very steep temperature gradient found in the corona-to-chromosphere transition region.

The question now arises as to the nature of the energy supply in the solar
atmosphere. If we adopt the description found in this section, we must
account for the high temperature of the corona and then explain the chromospheric heat supply as secondary (by conduction inward). Other hypotheses
first attempt to ascribe the energy supply to the chromosphere as the primary
process and then explain the heating of the corona as due to transport from
below. We shall return to this question in Section 3.3.5, but first we shall
discuss the temperature structure in the corona.

3.3.4. The Temperature of the Corona

The problem of the temperature of the corona has been one of the most
vigorously debated issues in solar physics in recent years. Even though
there are still difficulties to be ironed out, the following conclusions are now
emerging: (1) Different—and often closely adjacent—parts of the corona
have significantly different temperatures; (2) The various line emissions (see
Section 3.3.1) come from the regions of different temperatures; (3) The
temperature ranges from values close to 0.5×10^6 °K in the cooler regions
(where, for instance, we see lines of Fe X) to about 2×10^6 °K (in regions
producing X-ray emission and lines from Fe XVI); (4) During times of
greater solar activity, localized "hot spots" develop where the temperature
increases to about 4×10^6 °K (producing lines from ions like Ca XV).

There are a number of methods available to determine the temperature
of the corona. The different methods—and the principle upon which each
one is based—are as follows: (1) The smearing out of the Fraunhofer lines
in the K corona; (2) The intensity of the radio wave emission (meter waves);
(3) The reflection of radar pulses from the corona; (4) The density scale
heights in the corona; (5) The widths of coronal lines; (6) The ionization
equilibrium of coronal ions.

We shall now discuss the kind of temperature that results from each of
these methods as well as the numerical values deduced from the analyses.
The implications of the first method were discussed by Grotrian (1931b),
who came very close to suggesting that the temperature of the corona was
about one million degrees. For the electrons to smear out the Fraunhofer
lines to the degree observed, Grotrian estimated that the electron velocity is
about 8×10^8 cm/sec. This would correspond to a kinetic temperature (from
$\frac{1}{2}mv^2 = 3/2kT_e$) of somewhat over one million degrees. It is very difficult to
make precise observations of the smearing out of the lines, and therefore the
deduced temperatures cannot be given with great accuracy.

In Section 1.5 we saw that the radio waves bearing information about the
corona have wavelengths greater than approximately one-half meter. A

study of the observed brightness temperature T_{br} of such radio emission should, therefore, lead to a determination of the electron temperature in the corona. However, we have also seen that T_{br} is made up of contributions from a long path length along which the electron temperature probably changes quite strongly. We have the relation

$$T_{br} = \int_0^\tau e^{-\tau} T_e \, d\tau, \qquad (3.9)$$

and we find that a wide range of coronal models (T_e, τ) satisfy the observed T_{br}. Smerd (1950) concluded that any value $3 \times 10^5 < T_e < 3 \times 10^6 \, °K$ is compatible with observations. Again it is likely, according to later work by Newkirk (1959) and Firor (1959a), that the electron temperature of the corona is about one million degrees, but the second method is not suitable for a more precise determination. Only when we are dealing with optically thin radiation, when Equation (3.9) reduces to

$$T_{br} = T_e(1 - e^{-\tau}) \approx \tau T_e, \qquad \tau < 1,$$

may we conclude that the observed brightness temperature is a lower limit to the electron kinetic temperature.

Attempts at determining the temperature of the corona by radar methods (the third method) had failed for several years when Eshleman, Barthle, and Gallagher (1960) succeeded in obtaining the radar reflection from the sun shortly before Abel, Chisholm, Fleck, and James (1961) made the first rough estimate of the temperature. The reflectivity is mainly limited by the absorption of the radar pulses in the corona, and the absorption depends on the temperature of the free electrons, since it is the collisions of electrons with protons that cause the absorption. For the time being, only an estimate of the temperature necessary to produce the observed absorption is possible, and Abel, Chisholm, Fleck, and James (1961) arrived at a value of $T_e \approx 500,000 \, °K$.

The fourth method utilizes as basic data the observed electron density distribution with height h above the photosphere. Most of the work along this line has assumed that hydrostatic equilibrium holds in the corona and has deduced a scale height

$$H = kT/mg, \qquad (3.10)$$

from the equation governing this equilibrium,

$$n(h) = n(0)e^{-(mg/kT)h}.$$

Unless the corona is isothermal, the scale height is a function of height.

One of the first determinations of the electron temperature based on the temperature gradient is due to Waldmeier (1945) who found that $T_e = 1.3 \times 10^6$ °K. From a more elaborate study, van de Hulst (1953) differentiated between the electron distribution at sunspot maximum and at sunspot minimum. He obtained for sunspot maximum $T_e = 1.6 \times 10^6$ °K and for sunspot minimum 1.15×10^6 °K. A careful study by von Klüber (1961) of the density gradient above different portions of the limb resulted in temperatures ranging from 1.4×10^6 to 2.1×10^6 °K. Several years earlier, Hepburn (1955) had found evidence that temperatures associated with the density gradient were higher in coronal streamers than in the more quiet corona.

Since the streamers may be of a dynamic, rather than a static, nature, the findings of von Klüber and Miss Hepburn immediately raise the question whether the assumption of hydrostatic equilibrium is a sound one. The solar wind effect is the equivalent of increasing gravity and leads to an estimated temperature lower than the one corresponding to hydrostatic equilibrium. This is seen from Parker's (1960) equation governing the hydrodynamic equilibrium of the corona, that is, Equation (3.1), which—after being differentiated and rearranged slightly—may be written

$$\frac{1}{T}\frac{dT}{dr} = -\frac{1}{n}\frac{dn}{dr} - \frac{m}{2kT}\left(g + v \cdot \frac{dv}{dr}\right). \tag{3.11}$$

The "effective" gravity, $g_{\text{eff}} = g + v \cdot dv/dr$, is greater than g for an expanding corona (v positive outward). Consequently, the corresponding scale height—and hence T—will be decreased relative to the purely hydrostatic value of Equation (3.10). In other words, if the hydrodynamic effect ($v \cdot dv/dr$) is at all noticeable, an evaluation of the temperature of the corona from the density gradient will tend to underestimate the temperature.

The idea that the scale height of an atmosphere may be influenced by nonthermal effects was developed by McCrea (1929) for the case of the chromosphere. He tried to account for the very large scale height and low temperature ($\sim$6000 °K) believed to reign in the chromosphere by postulating macroscopic mass motions of a turbulent nature. This "turbulence effect" works in the opposite way from the hydrodynamic effect discussed above in that it imparts vertical, upward momentum to the coronal plasma (which is equivalent to pressure) and thereby tends to increase the scale height.

The fifth method—together with the sixth—is probably the most widely used. This is partly due to its simplicity. Referring to Section 1.4 we note that the width of an observed coronal line is related to the temperature of the emitting ions by

$$\Delta\lambda = \frac{\lambda}{c}\sqrt{\frac{2kT_i}{m} + v_t^2} = \frac{\lambda}{c}\sqrt{\frac{2kT_{\text{equiv}}}{m}}. \tag{3.12}$$

The great limitation of this method is at once obvious. We have no way of knowing how much of the line broadening is due to the velocity of large scale mass motion v_t—the astrophysical "turbulence"—and how much is caused by the thermal motion of the ions. The turbulent motions mimic the effect of the genuine thermal motion on the line profile, and the deduced equivalent temperature T_{equiv} is therefore always an upper limit to the ion kinetic temperature.

Observations show that the deduced temperature depends on the line studied, indicating that we are dealing with regions of different temperature and/or velocity. According to Billings (1962, 1966), the temperature ranges from about 1.2×10^6 °K and up for the regions where the red coronal line is formed (Fe X, 6473) to more than 3.5×10^6 °K for regions of the yellow line (Ca XV, 5694).

The "line width temperature" is sensitive to the solar wind, that is, to the hydrodynamic effect as is the temperature deduced from the density distribution. Yallop (1961) has calculated the profile which would result from the combined effect of thermal broadening and of the motion due to an expanding corona. If v_{exp} is the expansion velocity at a point P in the corona and θ the angle between the radius vector and the line of sight through P, then the observed wavelength of a line will be given by

$$\frac{\lambda - \lambda_0}{\lambda_0} = \frac{v_{\text{exp}} \cos \theta}{c} \, . \tag{3.13}$$

Here v_{exp} depends on the temperature and distance above the photosphere, from whence we see that the profile of a line emitted by ions partaking in the general expansion also depends on these parameters.

Yallop used Parker's values of v_{exp} as a function of the temperature and concluded that to explain the observed profiles as a sum of the expansion profile and the thermal profile, the ion kinetic temperature must be less than 1.5×10^6 °K. In this case, the expansion accounts for only about 10 % of the total width of the coronal lines.

The ionization-equilibrium method (the sixth method) was used by Waldmeier (1945) to deduce an electron temperature of about 700,000 °K. Later, more refined analyses have yielded essentially the same result (see, for instance, Elwert, 1952). The basic idea of this method is that transitions from higher to lower stages of ionization are produced mainly by radiative recombination (rate: $n_{\kappa+1} n_e R_{\kappa+1,\kappa}$), while electron collisions are responsible for ionizations (rate: $n_\kappa n_e C_{\kappa,\kappa+1}$). Equating these rates in a statistically steady state, as an especially simple case of Equation (1.80), we find that

$$\frac{n_{\kappa+1}}{n_\kappa} = \frac{C_{\kappa,\kappa+1}}{R_{\kappa+1,\kappa}} \, , \tag{3.14}$$

an expression which is independent of electron density (Woolley and Allen, 1948).

Radiative ionizations are considered rare because the radiation field, which is the photospheric field, contains very few high energy photons which are necessary to ionize these high stages. Also, the low coronal density is not favorable for three-body collisional recombinations.

Equation (3.14) does not hold if radiative ionization can take place in two steps *via* a metastable level. Under these circumstances, radiative excitation to the metastable level, followed by ionization, may be important (Athay and Hyder, 1963).

If we want to compare the populations of more widely separated stages of ionization, n(Fe X) and n(Fe XIV) for example, we apply Equation (3.14) four times to obtain

$$\frac{n(\text{Fe XIV})}{n(\text{Fe X})} = \frac{C(\text{XIII} \to \text{XIV})}{R(\text{XIV} \to \text{XIII})}\frac{C(\text{XII} \to \text{XIII})}{R(\text{XIII} \to \text{XII})}\frac{C(\text{XI} \to \text{XII})}{R(\text{XII} \to \text{XI})}\frac{C(\text{X} \to \text{XI})}{R(\text{XI} \to \text{X})}.$$

This ratio is the product of four strongly increasing functions of temperature, and the ratio itself is a sharply peaked function of temperature. Calculations based on a single electron temperature, therefore, give a sharp maximum at a particular ion, lower and higher ionization stages not being very abundant. Actual measurements (Firor and Zirin, 1963; Aly, Evans and Orrall, 1963) fall off much less rapidly.

The recombination rate $R_{\kappa+1,\kappa}$ used in Equation (3.14) is determined by multiplying the recombination cross section σ_R over the Maxwellian distribution of recombining electrons,

$$R_{\kappa+1,\kappa} = \int_0^\infty \sigma_R v f(v)\, dv. \tag{3.15}$$

During the 1950's and early 1960's, all those studying the problem of ionization equilibrium in the corona used, in essence, an expression for σ_R derived by Elwert (1952). He started with Equation (1.98) for the free-bound absorption coefficient $k_\kappa(n)$ and derived the recombination cross section by noting that in LTE the rate of radiation-absorbing transitions between discrete and continuous levels is equal to the rate of radiative recombinations between the same pair of levels or that

$$n_{\kappa,n}k_\kappa(n)I_v \frac{dv}{hv}(1 - e^{-hv/kT}) = n_{\kappa+1,1}n_e\sigma_R f(v)v\, dv,$$

where the double subscripts (κ and n) refer to stages of ionization and excitation, respectively. Since the ratio $n_{\kappa+1,1}/n_{\kappa,n}$ can be found from Saha's equation, we obtain

$$\sigma_R = \frac{2^7\pi^4}{3\sqrt{3}} \frac{Z^2 e^{10}}{m_e c^3 v^2 h^3} \frac{1}{n^3} \frac{g}{h\nu}. \tag{3.16}$$

Equation (3.16) does not depend on the radiation field, so even though it was derived from the assumption of LTE, it is applicable to the corona. We can then find the recombination rate from Equation (3.15) by assuming that recombination is a simple two-body process, where the free electron is captured and gives up, as radiation, energy equal to its kinetic energy plus the binding energy involved. By using this method, we can obtain ion kinetic temperatures that are only about 50% of the electron kinetic temperatures found when using the fifth method (Seaton, 1962) as well as very sharply peaked abundance-vs.-temperature curves. When dielectronic recombinations are considered—in which no radiation is immediately emitted—the ion will temporarily end up with two excited electrons. The rate for this process is much greater in highly ionized iron atoms than for the simple two-body process (Burgess, 1964). The deduced temperatures are about twice the value found by neglecting dielectronic recombination. Furthermore, the temperature range over which a given stage of ionization is present is greatly broadened, so that we should be able to observe an increased number of stages of ionization at a given temperature. Still, it is not enough to explain the observations of Firor and Zirin, and of Aly, Evans, and Orrall quoted above, and it is highly unlikely that lines of Fe X and of Fe XIV are formed in the same region. This "multiple temperature corona" model was advocated by Shklovsky (1962) more than a decade ago.

The two last methods—the line width method and the ionization theory—both give strong evidence that different regions of the corona have different temperatures, ranging from less than 1.5×10^6 °K in the cooler parts to more than 3.5×10^6 °K in the hot regions.

3.3.5. The Energy Supply

The very existence of the extended solar atmosphere demands an extra lifting force over and above the hydrostatic support at the boundary temperature of about 5000 °K. If the solar atmosphere were uniquely determined by the hydrostatic equations, we know that the density would decrease by $1/e$ over a distance $H = kT/mg$, that is, over the hydrostatically determined scale height. At a temperature of $T = 5000$ °K, the scale height for the lightest element, hydrogen, is about 150 km. In Section 3.1 we saw that at the extreme limb of the sun, the intensity of the continuous emission, in optical wavelengths, does in fact decrease by $1/e$ over a region of some 100 km, but the intensity of the emission lines in the chromosphere has very much larger scale heights. This constitutes the classical problem of the chromosphere: the large scale height of its emission.

Apart from one hypothesis which states that the extra heating of the solar atmosphere comes from outside (Hoyle, 1949), it is generally believed that the support mechanism of the chromosphere and corona may be traced back to motions in the subphotospheric layers, and that the spicules provide the necessary coupling between the photosphere and the supported regions of the chromosphere and the corona. There are essentially two ways in which the support mechanism may operate. (1) We have momentum transfer but insignificant energy transfer. This case, where we have a purely dynamic support, would require most of the atmosphere to be filled with spicules to make the support strong enough. In this model, the temperature of the outer atmosphere is much smaller than that required to give the observed scale height, and the expression for the scale height is written $H = (1/g)[(kT/m) + \frac{1}{2}v_t^2]$, where v_t is the supporting "turbulent" velocity. (2) The energy transfer is dominant in that the energy is transported by the spicules and dumped into the interspicular plasma. This is achieved in one of the following ways: (a) by the mass motions, that is, the spicule atoms collide with the atoms of the corona, thereby producing a high temperature—which is equivalent to a large scale height or (b) by the mechanical motions generated by the moving elements (granules, spicules) leading to waves (hydromagnetic, acoustic, gravity) that propagate up into the higher atmosphere and develop into shocks which dissipate their energy in the chromosphere and the corona.

Theories along the lines of the momentum support mechanism have been advocated by Milne (1924), McCrea (1929), and Rosseland (1929), while the concept of a high temperature is inherent in the theories of Alfvén (1941, 1947), Biermann (1946), Schwarzschild (1948), Thomas (1948a, 1948b), Schatzman (1949), and Schirmer (1950). The final word on the energy supply of the outer solar atmosphere has still not been said, but today it seems to be generally agreed at least that the energy is found in the subphotospheric convection zone, and that it is transported to the outer atmosphere by wave motions. But this is where the ambiguity arises, since there are several modes generated in the convection zone which are capable of propagating into the corona. In addition, there are several mechanisms capable of dissipating these waves in the corona and of generating sufficient heat.

A flat spectrum of acoustic waves (noise) will be generated by turbulent motions in a plasma, and this process has been studied by Lighthill (1952, 1954), and Proudman (1952). It can be shown that the emission coefficient, that is, the rate of generation of acoustical noise per unit volume, is given by

$$q = \alpha\rho \frac{[\langle v_t^2 \rangle]^4}{V_s^5 L} \text{ erg cm}^{-3} \text{ sec}^{-1}, \qquad (3.17)$$

where $\sqrt{\langle v_t^2 \rangle}$ is the root mean square of one component of the turbulent velocity, L is the scale length of turbulence, ρ the density, and α is a numerical factor depending on the turbulence spectrum (α is 38 for the Heisenberg spectrum). The flow of energy out of the plasma in the form of sound waves is found by integrating q through the emitting layer (outward direction r in the sun). Thus, we have

$$F = \tfrac{1}{2} \int q \, dr .$$

Because of the functional dependence of q on v_t, the energy generation is a sharply peaked function of depth with a maximum around $h = -500$ km. Practically all the energy is generated in a narrow (100 km thick) region around this level of the deep photosphere.

Whitaker (1963) showed that internal gravity waves are preferentially generated in the convection zone and are propagated to the corona, where they dissipate by thermal conduction.

When magnetic fields are present, we find that turbulent motions generate hydromagnetic waves, and this process has been investigated by Kulsrud (1955) and Osterbrock (1961). Fluctuating magnetic fields and turbulent velocity give rise to a quadrupole emission of sound, while a constant magnetic field will generate additional dipole terms. However, so long as the magnetic fields are small—quiet sun conditions—the effects of the dipole terms may be neglected. Furthermore, given these conditions the energy generated is almost exclusively fed into the fast mode of the hydromagnetic waves, with hardly anything delivered to the slow and the Alfvén modes. The effects which we have neglected here when treating the quiet sun will be incorporated in later chapters when we discuss plages and sunspots, which are characterized by strong magnetic fields.

The waves generated in the convection zone will consequently have both hydromagnetic and acoustic characteristics, and as they propagate through varying density and magnetic field strengths, their character will change. The different propagating modes are (see Section 1.5): (1) hydromagnetic waves (three modes); (2) acoustic waves; (3) gravity waves. According to Osterbrock (1961), the energy carried upward by waves generated in the convective layers is sufficient to replace the loss of energy from the corona by radiation. The waves propagate with a velocity which is a function of both the sound velocity V_s and the Alfvén velocity V_A,

$$V = \{\tfrac{1}{2} V_s^2 + V_A^2 + [(V_s^2 + V_A^2)^2 - 4 V_s^2 V_A^2 \cos^2 \theta]^{1/2}\}^{1/2} ,$$

and they become more and more hydromagnetic in character as they pass through the outer chromosphere. The waves steepen and build up to shocks, and their dissipation (which is much greater than the Joule heating or frictional damping of the linear waves) is the main energy source for the chromosphere-corona region.

From the equations of motion for nondissipative magnetic fluids

$$\frac{\partial(\rho v_i)}{\partial t} + \frac{\partial}{\partial x_j}\left(\rho v_i v_j - \frac{1}{4\pi}B_iB_j\right) = -\frac{\partial}{\partial x_i}\left(p + \frac{B^2}{8\pi}\right) \qquad (3.18)$$

and

$$\frac{\partial\rho}{\partial t} + \frac{\partial}{\partial x_i}(\rho v_i) = 0, \qquad (3.19)$$

we find that

$$\frac{\partial^2\rho}{\partial t^2} - \frac{\partial^2}{\partial x_i \partial x_j}\left(\rho v_i v_j - \frac{B_iB_j}{4\pi}\right) = \frac{\partial^2}{\partial x_i \partial x_i}\left(p + \frac{B^2}{8\pi}\right). \qquad (3.20)$$

We shall briefly show how we can estimate the production of noise using this last equation. So long as the Mach number is small, we can assume adiabatic compressions and expansions. We then decouple the kinetic and magnetic energies, in the sense that changes in the magnetic pressure $B^2/8\pi$ are completely balanced by corresponding changes in the magnetic energy. The changes in gas pressure are then given by

$$dp = V_s^2\, d\rho. \qquad (3.21)$$

Combining Equations (3.20) and (3.21), we arrive at the equation for sound propagation as given by Kulsrud,

$$\frac{\partial^2\rho}{\partial t^2} - V_s^2\frac{\partial\rho^2}{\partial x_i \partial x_i} = \frac{\partial^2}{\partial x_i \partial x_j}\left(\rho v_i v_j - \frac{B_iB_j}{4\pi} + \frac{B^2}{8\pi}\delta_{ij}\right). \qquad (3.22)$$

If there is no turbulent magnetic field $(B = 0)$, this equation reduces to the equation given by Lighthill:

$$\frac{\partial^2\rho}{\partial t^2} - V_s^2\frac{\partial^2\rho}{\partial x_i \partial x_i} = \frac{\partial^2}{\partial x_i \partial x_j}(\rho v_i v_j). \qquad (3.23)$$

The right-hand sides of Equations (3.22) and (3.23) are the source terms or the density of the source functions. These inhomogeneous scalar wave equations are amenable to Kirchhoff's (1850) techniques of integrating by retarded potentials. For small Mach numbers, the viscous stresses are approximately $\rho_0 v_i v_j$, and the solution of the wave equation may be written

$$\rho - \rho_0 = \frac{1}{4\pi V_s^2}\int \frac{\delta^2 W_{ij}[x', t - (|x - x'|/V_s)]}{\partial x_i \partial x_j}\frac{dx'}{|x - x'|},$$

where

$$W_{ij} \equiv \rho_0 v_i v_j - \frac{B_i B_j}{4\pi} + \frac{B^2}{8\pi} \delta_{ij}$$

is the generalized stress tensor, incorporating both velocity and magnetic stresses. The intensity of the sound generated is

$$I(x,t) = \left(\frac{V_s^3}{\rho_0}\right) \langle (\rho - \rho_0)^2 \rangle,$$

and we find the rate of generation of noise per unit volume in all directions by integrating $I(x,t)$ over the surface containing the sources. Thus, we obtain

$$q = \int \rho I(x,t) x^2 \, dx.$$

To evaluate this expression, it is necessary to make a number of approximations. Assuming isotropic turbulence and neglecting the retarded times, we first find that

$$q = \frac{\rho}{4\pi V_s^5} \int \left\langle \frac{\partial^2 W_{ij}}{\partial t^2} \frac{\partial W'_{ii}}{\partial t^2} \right\rangle dr.$$

The fourth-order correlations contained under the integral have been calculated by Proudman under the assumption that they are normal (that is, that they have the form

$$\langle ABA'B' \rangle = \langle AA' \rangle \langle BB' \rangle + \langle AB' \rangle \langle BA' \rangle + \langle AB \rangle \langle A'B' \rangle),$$

and by using the theory of isotropic turbulence to evaluate the lower-order correlations. The final result is that

$$q = \alpha \rho \epsilon M^5, \tag{3.24}$$

where ϵ is the rate of dissipation per unit mass,

$$\epsilon = \frac{(\langle v^2 \rangle)^{3/2}}{L}, \tag{3.25}$$

given in terms of a characteristic length L of the turbulence. Combining Equations (3.24) and (3.25), we arrive at

$$q = \alpha\rho \frac{[\langle v_t^2 \rangle]^4}{V_s^5 L} \text{ erg cm}^{-3} \text{ sec}^{-1},$$

which is the desired Equation (3.17).

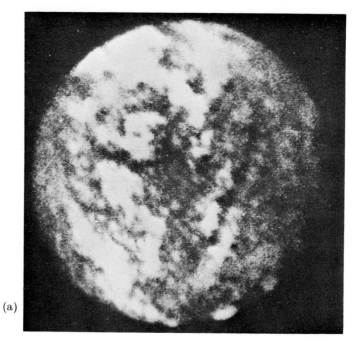

(a)

(a) Lyman-α photograph of the sun taken from an Aerobee-hi rocket, 19 April, 1960. (Official U.S. Navy photograph; courtesy U.S. Naval Research Laboratory.) (b) X-ray photograph of the sun (32 Å and 44 Å $< \lambda <$ 48 Å) taken from a Skylark rocket, 20 October, 1965. (Courtesy K. A. Pounds, University of Leicester; Russell and Pounds, 1966.)

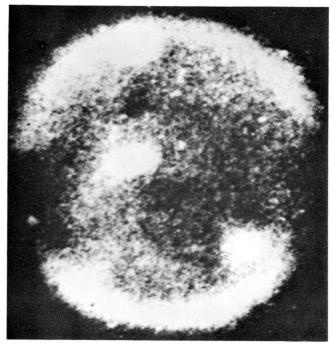

(b)

The Sun as a
Variable Star

4

4.1. *Introduction*

When we think of a variable star, we generally have in mind a star with
a time-dependent light output. Disregarding the cases where the observed
light changes are due to the presence of a second star (binary systems), we
note that the (intrinsic) variability of a star may range from a cyclic nature
to impulsive or burstlike manifestations. The stars that show more or less
periodic light variations are believed to be pulsating, and the physics
involved is fairly well understood—even though there are still important
gaps in the theories. In the impulsively variable stars, the light bursts may
range from small "flare-ups" to enormous light increases. The former are due
to the sudden appearance of localized hot spots or "flares" in the star's
atmosphere, the latter to violent explosions encompassing the whole stellar
atmosphere and even the whole star (supernovae).

In addition to those stars with light variations, there are also stars whose
spectral lines vary in intensity due to a changing magnetic field in the
atmosphere. This magnetic variability is portrayed by a number of the
spectral lines being broadened, the so-called Zeeman effect. The total light
output of these stars may not change noticeably with time.

The number of "bright areas" in the sun's atmosphere varies with a
mean period of roughly eleven years, and in this sense the sun may be considered a variable star. Also, the number of sunspots varies with this same
mean period. The sunspots are the seats of strong magnetic fields, and the
sun is, therefore, also a magnetically variable star. Furthermore, it is possible
that the sun has a general magnetic field that may change with time. As
we shall see later, the sunspots appear in pre-existing bright areas, *faculae,*

which in turn owe their existence to localized magnetic fields. Thus there is a coupling between the sun's light variations, as portrayed by the appearance of faculae, sunspots, etc., and the varying magnetic fields found in the sun's atmosphere. Therefore, we cannot exhaustively discuss one aspect without having the other in mind. Remembering this, in Section 4.2 we shall treat the different electromagnetic radiations, and in Section 4.3 we shall discuss more specifically the sun's magnetic field. First, however, let us for a moment consider the *constancy* of the sun's radiation in the optical region.

The intensity of the sun's radiation at different wavelengths as well as the total flux have been measured over a period of many years. The radiation is generally given in terms of *the solar constant*, S, defined as the flux of total radiation received outside the earth's atmosphere per unit area at mean sun–earth distance, and has the value

$$S = 1.34 \times 10^6 \text{ ergs cm}^{-2} \text{ sec}^{-1}.$$

Often the solar constant is given in units of calories (cal) per cm^2 per minute (min) (cal cm^{-2} min^{-1}) (that is, in langleys min^{-1}):

$$S = 1.99 \pm 0.02 \text{ cal cm}^{-2} \text{ min}^{-1}.$$

A useful concept is the radiation from the whole sun per second, that is, the radiant energy loss L,

$$L = 3.90 \times 10^{33} \text{ erg/sec}.$$

Furthermore, the radiation intensity at the center of the sun's disk is

$$I(0) = 2.49 \times 10^{10} \text{ ergs cm}^{-2} \text{ sec}^{-1} \text{ sr}^{-1} \text{ (sr = steradian)},$$

while the mean radiation intensity of the sun's disk, $\bar{I}$, is

$$\bar{I} \equiv F = 2.04 \times 10^{10} \text{ ergs cm}^{-2} \text{ sec}^{-1} \text{ sr}^{-1}.$$

From this we find the "effective temperature" of the sun

$$T_{\text{eff}} = (\pi F/\sigma)^{1/4} = 5800 \text{ }^\circ\text{K},$$

where σ is Stefan's constant, $\sigma = 5.67 \times 10^{-5}$ ergs cm^{-2} sec^{-1} $(^\circ K)^{-4}$.

Most of the sun's radiant energy (about 93%) is emitted between the wavelengths 3500 and 24,000 Å, as can be seen from Table 4.1. No significant changes with time can be found in the value of the solar constant for wavelengths between 3500 and 24,000 Å, and especially for the visual region

TABLE 4.1   The solar constant

Wavelength region	Contribution to solar constant	
	In cal cm^{-2} min^{-1}	In percent
<3500	0.07	3.5
3500–7000	0.89	44.5
7000–24,000	0.97	48.5
>24,000	0.07	3.5
Whole spectrum	2.00	100

4000 to 8000 Å. In this sense, the solar constant approximates closely a true constant. At times of solar activity, we find, however, large increases in the ultraviolet and X-ray emission as well as in the radiation at radio wavelengths. In this respect, the sun behaves like a semiregularly or irregularly variable star, with a period or cycle of about 11 years, superposed upon which there are short-lived variations. Most of these changes are associated with the appearance of *plages*, the primary optical sign of variability. We shall discuss shortly the nature of plages in some detail.

Over the years, several attempts have been made to determine whether the sun's diameter, that is, the diameter of the photosphere as defined by optical observations, varies with time. Secchi (1872, 1873) and Rosa (1871) discussed the problem using all observations available at that time. They concluded that at times when the number of spots and prominences are at a minimum, the sun's equatorial diameter is maximal. This has been referred to as the Secchi-Rosa law by Wolf (1892), who came to the same conclusion using different data. Cimino (1945, 1953) and Meyermann (1950) have re-examined the problem and find indications of a periodic variation, which is about 22 years according to Cimino, and 11 years according to Meyermann. See also Fortini (1949), and Giannuzzi (1953, 1955a, 1955b).

The sun's diameter is measured regularly at Greenwich Observatory and at Rome's Monte Mario Observatory (previously at Campidoglio). It seems today that due to a number of instrumental effects and effects of the terrestrial atmosphere, the measurements are still inconclusive regarding any real variation in the photospheric dimensions (Abetti, 1963).

Leaving the problem of the photospheric diameter, we shall consider briefly some measurements of the extent of the chromosphere. We define the height of the chromosphere by the length of a suitable emission line when observed with the spectrograph slit oriented perpendicularly to the sun's limb. For example, one may measure the length of the reversed Hα line with a micrometer from the end of the absorption line to the point where the emission line merges with the sky background. The results of such observations may be summarized as follows (Abetti, 1963): the mean height of the Hα reversal, averaged over several solar cycles, is about 8000 km. Small variations in the yearly means seem to follow the 11-year cycle, but no final conclusion can be reached.

On the other hand, the shape of the optical corona as seen during eclipses undoubtedly changes with the solar cycle. At times of maximum sunspot number, the corona is roughly spherical, while the equatorial regions are brighter than the polar regions in minimum years. Photometric measurements (van de Hulst, 1949) indicate that at a given height in the corona, the density at maximum is about 1.8 times the density at minimum.

Observations at radio wavelengths also reveal some interesting variations. Avignon and Malinge (1961) measured the equatorial diameter of the sun at a wavelength of 1.8 m over the period 1957 to 1962. The diameter (defined as the angular distance between the points in the antenna diagram where the power has fallen to 33.3% of the peak power) remained fairly constant at 52 seconds of arc for the two years 1957–1959 around sunspot maximum, after which it began to decrease, reaching a value of 47 seconds of arc toward the end of 1961. This is in agreement with O'Brien's (1953) results at a wavelength of 1.4, which indicate a decrease of about 20% during the corresponding period in the previous sunspot cycle.

Avignon and Malinge found no change in the polar diameter. Thus, the ellipticity of the corona at meter wavelengths changes during the solar cycle, but in a sense opposite to that of the optical corona. Their value between 0.7 and 0.8 for the ellipticity in 1961 is in good agreement with Hewish's (1957) determination in 1954, which gave a value of 0.8 at a wavelength of 1.4 m.

4.2. *The Plage Phenomenon*

4.2.1. Observations

4.2.1.1. *Faculae and plages. Definitions and descriptions*

On a white-light photograph of the sun, we notice areas—especially toward the limb—which are brighter than the surrounding photosphere. These areas are called faculae, or more specifically *photospheric faculae*, to emphasize that they are observed in the lowest part of the sun's atmosphere. On the other hand, a picture of the sun taken in the nearly monochromatic light of a strong spectral line—like Hα or the Ca II, *K* line—also reveals bright areas. The location of these areas corresponds rather closely with the photospheric faculae. Since strong spectral lines give information about higher layers in the sun's atmosphere, these bright areas are called *chromospheric faculae*. The French designation is *plage faculaire*, and the word "plage" is fairly generally adopted in astrophysical terminology as an alternative name for a chromospheric facula.

There is a continuous transition from the deep-lying photospheric faculae to the chromospheric faculae or plages. The two types resemble each other with respect to shape, occurrence, and their correlation with sunspots. The transition may be studied spectrographically and with the help of spectroheliograms, the reason being that the cores of strong lines are formed high in the chromosphere, while the wings of moderate to faint lines are formed deeper in the atmosphere. Thus a K_3 spectroheliogram will portray the chromospheric appearance at a height of roughly 7000 km (Mohler, 1960), while the sodium-D lines give information about the middle chromosphere, around 1500 km. Finally, by observing the wings of very faint lines, we probe the atmospheric conditions down in the photosphere proper.

It was not until 1939 that the fine structure of the photospheric faculae was discovered, due to studies by Waldmeier (1939a) and ten Bruggencate (1939). Their works, as well as later investigations, show that the faculae have a *granulation* structure, not unlike that of the undisturbed photosphere. The fact that chromospheric faculae show a granulation has been known since the pioneering work by Hale and Ellerman (1903).

4.2.1.2. *Radio plages and magnetic plages*

During the last decade, a wealth of new information on plages has become available, thanks to radio-astronomical observations and to airborne equipment. Let us first consider the radio observations, and ask what kind of information they may give about the physical conditions in plage regions. The first question to decide is what are the frequencies of those waves that originate in or near the faculae and hence can give information about these layers of the solar atmosphere. To answer this, we need to consider the way in which radio waves propagate in the atmospheric plasma. If the index of refraction n differs from unity, the waves follow curved paths, and the optical depth must be integrated along these paths. For a given wavelength λ, the solar radio emission comes from the so-called isodiaphanous surface, given by

$$r = \text{const}/n. \tag{4.1}$$

Lorentz' law for the refraction index gives this as

$$n^2 = 1 - (n_e e^2 \lambda^2 / \pi m c^2).$$

The smaller the wavelength, the larger n is and the smaller r becomes; in other words, the smaller wavelengths come from deeper layers in the atmosphere. By utilizing models of the corona, namely $n_e = f(r)$, the isodiaphanous surfaces of Equation (4.1) may be determined.

In the presence of an external magnetic field, two wave modes are possible, corresponding to two solutions for the refractive index. These two modes— treated in Section 1.5—are the ordinary and extraordinary waves which reach us from different levels of the solar atmosphere. It turns out that for λ greater than about 50 cm, the isodiaphanous surfaces lie well out in the corona, so that these waves cannot escape from the chromospheric plage regions and thus cannot give information about these layers. However,

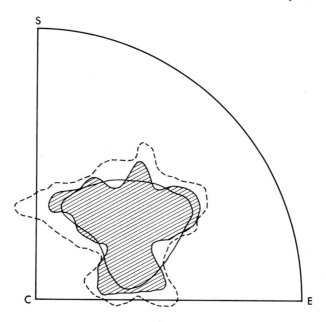

FIGURE 4.1. The relationship between the magnetic field and the optical and radio plages (courtesy W. N. Christiansen *et al.*, 1960)

waves with $\lambda \approx 10$ to 20 cm should be well suited for studies of the middle and upper chromosphere and of the lowest coronal regions. It is, therefore, fortunate that one of the most reliable series of solar radio observations has been carried out on 10.7 cm. Covington (1948) discovered that this 10 cm radiation shows a slow variation from day to day, in phase with the number, or area, of sunspots present. By using directional antennas, it later became possible to determine the location of the regions emitting this *slowly varying component* of the solar radio radiation. It is now well established that the emission in the cm and dm range comes from fairly thin areas directly above the plages—let us call these areas *radio plages*. Of special interest are the measurements on 21 cm made by Christiansen *et al.* (1960) in Sydney (see Figure 4.1). We note the strong correlation between optical plages and radio plages and conclude that the radio plages as observed with cm and dm radio waves are the continuation upward of the chromospheric plages as these chromospheric plages or faculae are the continuation of the photospheric faculae.

Figure 4.1, which has been reproduced from a joint paper by Australian, French, American, and Japanese radio astronomers (Christiansen *et al.*, 1960), is another illustration of the close similarity between the facula and the radio plage. The optical plage (cross hatched) is compared to the radio plage (solid curve), and the correlation is very convincing. The dashed curve outlines the area within which the magnetic field strength was observed to be increased relative to the surrounding photosphere. We may, therefore, introduce the concept of a *magnetic facula or plage*. This concept brings a new element into the discussion of plages—probably the most fundamental of them all: the underlying magnetic field. The dashed curve in Figure 4.1 defines the area where the magnetic field strength was larger than about 10 gauss according to Babcock's magnetograph. Studies by Leighton (1959) and Martres, Michard, and Soru-Iscovici (1966a, 1966b) also reveal the close geometrical relationship between the magnetic plages and the Ca II plages. According to these investigations, there will be Ca II plages whenever the magnetic field strength exceeds the limiting sensitivity of the apparatus.

A photospheric facula (and hence most of the complex plage phenomenon) is generally a condition for the possible appearance of a sunspot, and often the facula remains after the death of the sunspot. Similarly, there will always exist a magnetic plage where an optical facula forms, and the magnetic field strength remains above the value of the surrounding quiet photosphere until the optical facula has disappeared. This indicates that the magnetic field is of primary importance for the development of any active solar region. If spicules form the cornerstone of our understanding of the chromosphere, so the magnetic plage is the foundation of a study of solar activity.

4.2.1.3. *UV and X-ray emission*

During the last five years or so, answers to some questions of great importance for our understanding of the physics of active solar regions have been found. The reason for this is the increased use of airborne equipment. Since air effectively absorbs radiations in the ultraviolet and X-ray regions of the spectrum, we have to get above most of the earth's atmosphere to observe the solar spectrum below about 2000 Å. The most important transition in hydrogen gives rise to the resonance line Ly_α at 1216 Å, which until a few years ago was in a hopelessly inaccessible region of the spectrum. This is even more true of neutral and ionized helium, whose resonance lines are at 584 and 304 Å, respectively. It is, therefore, of utmost importance that we can now get spectrographs and cameras up above the earth's atmosphere and secure solar spectra down into the hard X-ray region.

The first spectrogram of the sun in the light of the Ly_α line (Purcell and Tousey, 1960) clearly revealed the existence of Ly_α *plages*. Comparisons between the extent of the Ly_α plages and of Ca II plages, for instance, show that the Ly_α radiation comes from areas right above the more familiar plages, the main difference being that the Ly_α plage is larger (horizontally) than the underlying H_α or Ca II plage. In other words, we are sampling a higher region of the chromosphere when observing in the light of Ly_α.

If we now go to even shorter wavelengths, that is, if we observe in the X-ray region, we might expect to find *X-ray plages*. Friedman (1960) succeeded in obtaining pictures of the sun in the 20 to 60 Å region, and since then several similar photos have been secured. Again one finds that the X rays originate in areas above normal chromospheric plages (Blake, Chubb, Friedman, and Unzicker, 1963; Russell, 1965; Giacconi, Reidy, Zehnpfennig, Lindsay, and Muney, 1965). To every X-ray plage there corresponds a chromospheric facula. Since the X-ray emission does not originate in the chromosphere, our plage concept has now led us into the corona proper.

4.2.2. Models of Photospheric Faculae

Over the years, spectrographic observations have been used to derive models of faculae. For example, St. John (1921), see also Kremer (1930), showed that lines emitted by neutral metal atoms are fainter in the spectra of faculae than in the normal photospheric spectrum, while the opposite holds true for lines from ionized metals. This points to a higher ionization temperature in faculae than in the photosphere. This is confirmed by the more recent work by Mitropolskaya (1954, 1955), who from curve-of-growth analyses finds a temperature difference, $T_f - T_{ph} = \Delta T$, of between 100 and 300 °K, depending on which lines are used. De Jager (1959) believes that these values are much too small and suggests that they be increased by a factor of 2 or 3 to take into consideration the blending of the facular spectrum with the photospheric spectrum. If this is correct, the real temperature difference may be as high as 900 °K.

Mitropolskaya also used line profiles and central intensities to study the different excitation in faculae and in the photosphere. Generally speaking, the early Balmer lines H_α, H_β (and H_γ for very intense faculae) show greater central intensities in faculae than in the photosphere, while the higher Balmer lines reveal dark faculae. Since the latter are formed considerably deeper in the atmosphere than the strong early Balmer lines, we may conclude that the excitation temperature in faculae increases with height.

Faculae are most easily observed toward the limb and practically disappear at the center of the disk. The center-to-limb contrast variation is roughly given by curve I in Figure 4.2. This simple observation means that in higher

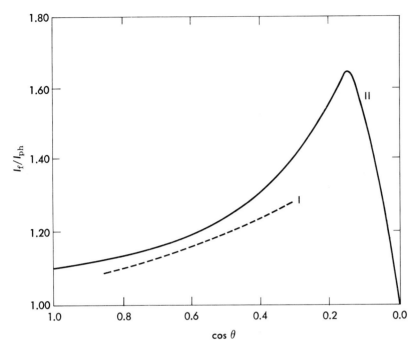

FIGURE 4.2.   The center-to-limb contrast variation in faculae (courtesy J. B. Rogerson, 1961)

parts, the emission from the facula is greater than that from the photosphere at the same monochromatic optical depth. The total emission near the center is roughly the same from the facula and from the photosphere, which means that less emission comes to us from deeper layers of the facula. Measurements in white light (Wormell, 1936) and in monochromatic light (Richardson, 1933) show the center-to-limb contrast variation, that is, the ratio I_f/I_{ph} as a function of the heliocentric distance θ ($\cos \theta = 1$ is the center, $\cos \theta = 0$ is the limb). (Compare curve I in Figure 4.2). Measurements beyond $\cos \theta = 0.3$ are difficult and uncertain [see also Waldmeier (1949a)].

Let us write the solution of the transfer equation for the photosphere in the form

$$I(0, \theta) = \tfrac{1}{2}F(1 + \tfrac{3}{2} \cos \theta), \qquad (4.2)$$

and for the mean intensity (averaged over all directions)

$$J(\tau) = \tfrac{1}{2}F(1 + \tfrac{3}{2}\tau). \qquad (4.3)$$

Using these expressions, we can satisfy Wormell's measurements by

$$I(0\,,\,\theta) = \tfrac{1}{2}F(1.1 + 1.4\cos\theta) \qquad \text{and} \qquad J(\tau) = \tfrac{1}{2}F(1.1 + 1.4\tau)\,.$$

At the surface $\tau = 0$ and, since the total radiation is proportional to the fourth power of the effective temperature, we deduce that

$$T_{\mathrm{f}} = (1.1)^{1/4}T_{\mathrm{ph}}\,.$$

For $T_{\mathrm{ph}}(\tau = 0) = 4830\ {}^{\circ}\mathrm{K}$, we have $T_{\mathrm{f}} = 4950\ {}^{\circ}\mathrm{K}$ and $\Delta T = 120\ {}^{\circ}\mathrm{K}$. Reichel (1953) used these data to construct a model of faculae and found that ΔT had a maximum $= 350^{\circ}\mathrm{K}$ for $\tau_{4100} = 0.2$. For an optical depth $\tau_{4100} = 0.9$, we see that $\Delta T = 0$, and in greater depths ΔT is negative (see Table 4.2).

TABLE 4.2   Reichel's model of faculae

τ_{4100}	T_{f}	T_{ph}	ΔT
0.05	5500	5370	130
0.1	5810	5540	270
0.2	6260	5880	380
0.3	6370	6100	270
0.4	6420	6280	140
0.8	6860	6840	20
1.0	7030	7070	−370
2.0	7580	7950	−40

More recent observations by balloon-borne equipment indicate a sudden drop in the center-to-limb contrast at the extreme limb. To account for this, Rogerson (1961) has suggested a tentative model where the facula has a granular structure, and he identifies the facular granules with the brighter photospheric granules seen at the center of the disk. The problem is, then, to modify the source function of a photospheric granule in such a way as to produce center-to-limb contrast variations of the type observed. Rogerson does this by taking a "typical" photospheric granule of diameter d and ascribing to it an additional hot layer between depths h_1 and h_2 (corresponding to optical depths τ_1 and τ_2) (see Figure 4.3). The excess brightness of the facula will then come from this hot layer of the granules, and the center-to-limb contrast variation is brought about by the combined influence of this layer and the cooler part above it.

Let the hot layer have a source function S_{f} that is simply aS_{ph}, where a is a constant. The observed intensity will then be

$$I_{\mathrm{f}} = I_{\mathrm{ph}} + a[e^{-\tau_1/\mu} - e^{-\tau/\mu}]\,,$$

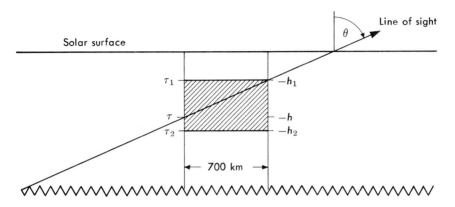

FIGURE 4.3. Tentative model of a facula according to Rogerson (courtesy J. B. Rogerson, 1961)

where $\mu = \cos\theta$ and $\tau = \tau_2$ for $\tan\theta < d/(h_2 - h_1)$ and $\tau = \tau(h)$ for $\tan\theta > d/(h_2 - h_1)$, where $h = d/\tan\theta + h_1$. Rogerson used Minnaert's (1953) photospheric model to relate the geometrical depth h to the optical depth. He further forced his solution to satisfy the (observed) boundary conditions

$$\frac{I_f(\theta = 0)}{I_{\mathrm{ph}}(\theta = 0)} = 1.1\,, \qquad \frac{I_f(\theta = 82°)}{I_{\mathrm{ph}}(\theta = 0)} = 0.65\,, \qquad \frac{I_f(\theta = 87°)}{I_{\mathrm{ph}}(\theta = 0)} = 0.45\,.$$

The solution, then, is

$$a = 0.46 I_{\mathrm{ph}}(\theta = 0)\,, \qquad \tau_1 = 0.05\,, \qquad \tau_2 = 0.31\,.$$

Comparing this with Minnaert's model, we find that these optical depths correspond to $h_1 = -147$ km and $h_2 = -253$ km, where $h = 0$ is taken at $\tau = 0.003$. This model gives the predicted center-to-limb contrast variation designated as curve II in Figure 4.2. The deduced value $a/I_{\mathrm{ph}}(\theta = 0) = 0.46$ corresponds to a mean temperature excess of about 900 °K for the hot layer between depths h_1 and h_2.

A number of empirical models have been computed by Kuz'minykh (1962, 1963, 1964), Livshits (1963), and Kozhevnikov and Kuz'minykh (1964). They use different expressions for the assumed source function in faculae, $S_f(\tau)$, and determine the "best" model by finding the "best" fit with observations. From the source function, one gets the emergent intensity

$$I_f(\mu) = \int_0^\infty S_f(\tau) e^{-\tau/\mu}\, d(\tau/\mu)\,. \tag{4.4}$$

The source function is often set equal to

$$S_f(\tau, \lambda) = a_\lambda + b_\lambda \tau_\lambda + c_\lambda E_2(\tau_\lambda), \qquad (4.5)$$

where $E_2(\tau_\lambda)$ is the exponential integral, since this is a good representation for the photosphere. Kozhevnikov and Kuz'minykh (1964), on the other

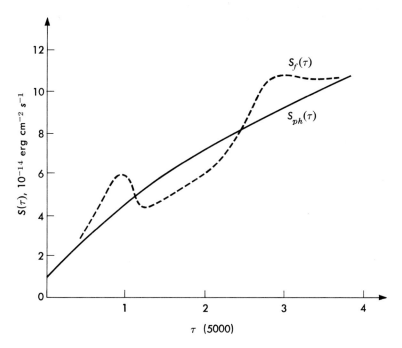

FIGURE 4.4. Variation of the source function with depth in faculae according to Kozhevnikov and Kuz'minykh (1964)

hand, used the equation

$$I_f(\mu) - I_{ph}(\mu) = \int_0^\infty [S_f(\tau) - S_{ph}(\tau)] e^{-\tau/\mu} d(\tau/\mu) \qquad (4.6)$$

instead of Equation (4.4) to calculate $S_f(\tau)$ by a method of trial functions. The photospheric source function was assumed to have the form of Equation (4.5). The intensities $I_{ph}(\mu)$ were taken from Sitnik (1960) and Peyturaux (1955), and data on the facular contrast were from Kuz'minykh (1962, 1963). To get the best fit, the authors arrived at a variation with depth of the source function $S_f(\tau)$ as portrayed in Figure 4.4 for $\lambda = 5095$ Å.

We note that on this model there is—in addition to the hot layer between $\tau = 0.8$ and $\tau = 1.5$—another layer where the facula is hotter than the

TABLE 4.3   Kozhevnikov's and Kuz'minykh's model of faculae

τ_{5096}	T_f	T_{ph}	ΔT	τ_{5096}	T_f	T_{ph}	ΔT
0.4	6020	5950	70	2.4	7270	7530	-260
0.6	6640	6240	400	2.6	7600	7650	-50
0.8	6980	6430	550	2.8	8000	7770	230
1.0	6760	6620	140	3.0	8110	7860	250
1.2	6570	6790	-220	3.2	8140	7960	150
1.4	6540	6930	-390	3.4	8190	8040	100
1.6	6670	7070	-400	3.6	8270	8150	40
1.8	6790	7190	-370	3.8	8270	8250	20
2.0	6930	7300	-400	4.0	8340	8330	10
2.2	7070	7410	-340				

photosphere, namely below about $\tau = 2.5$. From $\tau = 1.5$ to $\tau = 2.5$, the facula is cooler than the surroundings, as also found by Reichel (1953). Kozhevnikov's and Kuz'minykh's model is shown in Table 4.3.

4.2.3. Models of Radio Plages

We have seen in Section 4.2.1 that the radio plages invariably overlie photospheric faculae and chromospheric plages and extend radially outward. Furthermore, a study of the isodiaphanous surfaces—Equation (4.1)—shows that the longer the wavelength, the higher in the solar atmosphere the region of emission. We may thus sample the depth of a radio plage by observing on different wavelengths. The height is most reliably determined either from the apparent displacement of the radio center from the optical center of the region as it moves across the disk or by direct measurement at the limb. Individual radio plages are formed at very different heights, as exemplified by a series of measurements on 3.2 cm made by Tanaka and Kakinuma (1959). These authors found that the heights of ten plages ranged from 3000 to 40,000 km. They gave a mean value of 22,000 km for this wavelength, while Kakinuma and Swarup (1962) found the average height of 3.2 cm plages to be about 12,000 km. Some approximate mean values are given in Table 4.4, based on observations by Gutman and Steinberg (1959), Christiansen and Mathewson (1959), Ikhsanova (1959), Vauquois (1959), Swarup and

TABLE 4.4   Height h of radio plages as a function of wavelength λ

λ, cm	3.2	7.5	9.1	21	60	88	178
$h \times 10^3$, km	10 to 20	20	20 to 30	20 to 40	40	130	>200

Parthasarathy (1958), Avignon, Boischot, and Simon (1959), and Christiansen *et al.* (1960).

To specify the model of plages further, we would like to determine the temperature. The radiation temperature T_R may simply be inferred from the observed intensity if we have blackbody radiation (see Equation 1.4). For wavelengths corresponding to the radio spectrum, this equation reduces to the Rayleigh-Jeans formula

$$I_\lambda = 2ckT_R/\lambda^4 \qquad \text{or} \qquad I_\nu = 2kT_R/\lambda^2 \,. \tag{4.7}$$

The transfer of radiation through the plasma is governed by Schwarzschild's equation

$$dI_\nu/dr = \epsilon_\nu - k_\nu I_\nu \qquad \text{or} \qquad dI_\nu/d\tau_\nu = I_\nu - S_\nu \,, \tag{4.8}$$

where τ_ν is the radial optical depth and S_ν the source function (ϵ_ν/k_ν). For simplicity, we consider radiation leaving the gas along the normal to the surface, this being in the direction of the observer. The treatment may easily be generalized to radiation making an arbitrary angle θ with the normal. Also, the effect of a varying refraction index may be included but, in this connection, adds nothing new. In local thermodynamic equilibrium (LTE), due to Equation (4.7), Equation (4.8) takes the form

$$dI_\nu/d\tau_\nu = I_\nu - 2kT_e(\tau_\nu)/\lambda^2 \,.$$

This may be solved after multiplication with the integrating factor $e^{-\tau_\nu}$, yielding

$$I_\nu = I_\nu(0)e^{-\tau_\nu} - (2k/\lambda^2) \int_0^{\tau_0} T_e(\tau_\nu)e^{-\tau_\nu} \, d\tau_\nu \,, \tag{4.9a}$$

where $I_\nu(0)$ is the intensity at optical depth τ_0. Equation (4.9a)—or its more generalized form—may be integrated numerically to find the specific intensity in a given direction from a plasma cloud. To do this, we need to know (1) the path of radiation in the plasma, (2) the optical depth of the plasma along each considered path, and (3) the electron temperature along each path.

When we observe the solar disk, we find from Equation (4.9a), since $\tau \to \infty$, that

$$I_\nu = (2k/\lambda^2) \int_0^\infty T_e(\tau_\nu)e^{-\tau_\nu} \, d\tau_\nu \,. \tag{4.9b}$$

For an isothermal atmosphere this gives

$$I_\nu = 2kT_e/\lambda^2 \,,$$

and the corresponding monochromatic radiation temperature is $T_R = T_e$, that is, blackbody radiation. When we observe a thin plasma cloud, which is not illuminated from behind, $I_\nu(0) = 0$, the intensity is given by

$$I_\nu = (2k/\lambda^2) \int_0^{\tau_0} T_e(\tau_e) e^{-\tau_\nu} \, d\tau_\nu, \tag{4.9c}$$

and τ_0 is small compared to unity. Again, if the cloud is isothermal, we find that

$$I_\nu = (2k/\lambda^2)\tau_0 T_e,$$

and the corresponding radiation temperature is $T_R = \tau_0 T_e$.

The absorption coefficient for free–free transitions in a fully ionized hydrogen plasma is

$$k_\nu = \frac{8e^6 n_e^2}{3(2\pi)^{1/2} e \nu^2 (m_e k T_e)^{3/2}} \ln \frac{kT_e}{1.44 e^2 3 n_e^{1/2}} = \frac{a n_e^2}{\nu^2 T_e^{3/2}}, \tag{4.10}$$

where a is a slowly varying function of n_e and T_e. The absorption coefficient is proportional to the number of collisions between electrons and protons, and this collision frequency is proportional to $T_e^{-3/2}$. For the radiation temperature from a gas cloud of depth $h_0 = \tau_0/k_\nu$, we then find that

$$T_R = a n_e^2 h_0/\nu^2 T_e^{1/2}. \tag{4.11}$$

We note that the radiation temperature decreases with the increasing kinetic temperature of the plasma. This decrease in emission from the gas is because the cross section for electron–proton collisions decreases strongly with increasing relative velocity between the particles, that is, with increasing temperature. In Figure 4.5 we show schematically the variation of the radiation temperature and of the specific intensity as functions of frequency for an isothermal hydrogen plasma. The absorption coefficient—and hence the optical depth—decrease with increasing frequency, $\tau_\nu \propto \nu^{-2}$. For small frequencies, where $\tau \gg 1$ (blackbody radiation), T_R will be constant and equal to T_e, and $I_\nu \propto \nu^2$ (since $I_\nu = 2kT_e/\lambda^2$). For large frequencies, where $\tau \ll 1$, I_ν is constant (since $I_\nu = 2kT_e\tau_\nu/\lambda^2$), and $T_R \propto \nu^{-2}$. Schematically, we have

$$\begin{aligned}
&\nu \text{ small: } \tau \gg 1, \quad T_R = T_e, \quad I_\nu \propto \nu^2, \\
&\nu \text{ large: } \tau \ll 1, \quad T_R = \tau_\nu T_e, \quad I_\nu \propto \nu^{-2}.
\end{aligned} \tag{4.12}$$

It turns out that those layers of the atmosphere that contribute most to the observed radiation are situated at optical depths around unity. These are—as shown in Figure 4.5—unfortunately those layers in which the

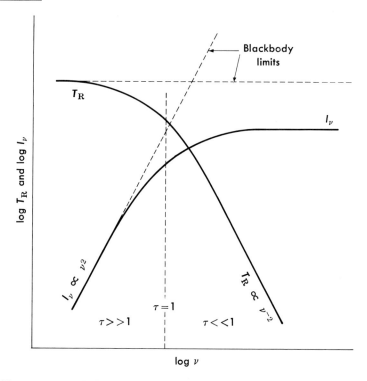

FIGURE 4.5.   Variation of radiation temperature (T_R) and specific intensity (I_ν) as functions of frequency in an isothermal hydrogen plasma (courtesy J. L. Pawsey and R. N. Bracewell, 1955)

deviations from the approximate formulas, Equation (4.12), are the greatest. The observed spectrum, therefore, will rarely be as simple as Equation (4.12) indicates.

A number of investigations have been carried out to determine the electron temperature and electron density in radio plages, essentially using Equation (4.9a) or the specific forms (4.9b) or (4.9c). Newkirk (1961) used data for the electron density obtained by K coronameter observations and found the temperature by integrating Equation (4.9b) along the paths with the absorption coefficient given by Equation (4.10). He found that the electron density in plage regions is somewhat higher—about three times—than in the surrounding normal atmosphere. Similar studies based on assumed exponentially varying electron densities have been conducted by Christiansen *et al.*, (1960). These authors also conclude that plages are denser than their quiet surroundings. The radiation temperature as determined by Newkirk is given in Table 4.5 together with Athay's (1959) values for the quiet chromosphere. However, only at the shortest wavelengths considered in Table 4.5 does the chromospheric temperature regime dominate the observed spectrum. At these wavelengths ($\lambda < 1$ cm), both the chromosphere and the corona are transparent. Hence, a slightly increased electron density in a fairly high-lying plage region will have little effect on the optical depth. At longer waves, 1 cm $< \lambda < 10$ cm , there is an increase in the coronal contribution due to growing optical depth in the corona, and the temperature of the chromosphere is also higher in the regions that now contribute ($\tau \sim 1$). Both these effects are enhanced in the higher densities in plages, and a steep rise in the observed radiation temperature is to be expected. For waves longer than

TABLE 4.5   Radiation temperature in plages (Newkirk) and quiet chromosphere (Athay) from radio data

λ, cm	T_R, *plage*	T_R, *chrom*
1	10,000	9500
3	40,000	16,000
7.5	150,000	23,000
21	400,000	40,000
40	(500,000)	(50,000)

10 cm, the optical depth of the corona becomes appreciable, and the corresponding radiation dominates over the chromospheric contribution. Hence, we expect the radiation temperature to reflect coronal conditions. At long waves, $\lambda = 100$ cm and above, the optical depth is large for all paths, and the resulting radiation temperature is the same as that observed outside the plage, $T_R(\text{plage}) \approx T_R(\text{quiet})$. Since this approximates the conditions of Equation (4.12), we expect that the radiation temperature will be the electron temperature of the corona.

The spectrum of the thermal radiation from a plage—the slowly varying component—according to this should take the form illustrated schematically in Figure 4.6. Calculations performed by Newkirk confirm this. The results of the 1958 eclipse observations made by Tanaka and Kakinuma (1958) also are given in Figure 4.6 on page 156.

The radio emission from plages seems, consequently, to be well accounted for by a model having an electron density several times higher than the surrounding chromosphere and corona, and an electron temperature about equal to the surroundings. However, it should be remembered that when the magnetic field is ignored, as is often the case, we introduce errors whose magnitude is difficult to assess. Observations show that the radiation is circularly polarized for wavelengths less than about 10 cm and randomly polarized for longer waves. This points to the influence of magnetic fields in the lower parts of the atmosphere, and Kakinuma and Swarup (1962) have

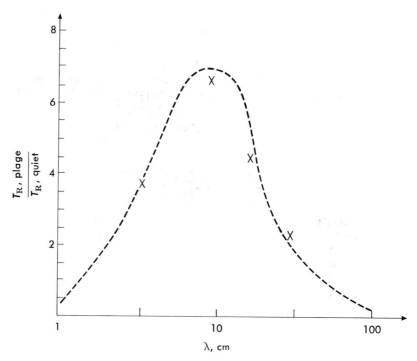

FIGURE 4.6.   The spectrum of the slowly varying component; the X's represent observations by Tanaka and Kakinuma (1958) (after Newkirk, 1961)

suggested that the radiation emitted by thermal electrons at the gyro-frequency (see Equation (1.15)), and its harmonics should also be taken into consideration to explain the spectrum of the slowly varying component.

4.2.4. Models of X-Ray Plages

The X-ray fluxes F_X, measured at the earth, in the years near sunspot minimum may be assumed to be due to one, or a few, plage areas. The value of F_X ranges from about 10^{-3} ergs cm^{-2} sec^{-1} to a few times 10^{-2} ergs cm^{-2} sec^{-1}, (Kreplin, 1961; Kreplin, Chubb and Friedman, 1962; Pounds and Sanford, 1963; White, 1964; Culhane, Willmore, Pounds and Sanford, 1964). Fluxes of this order of magnitude have been described as thermal radiation from the hot plasma making up the X-ray plages (Acton, 1964). In his model Acton assumes the plasma to be isothermal at a temperature of 2.3×10^6 °K and computes the X-ray flux to be expected. The temperature chosen seems to be in reasonable agreement with the observations of profiles of coronal lines originating above plage areas (Billings, 1959). The computations are carried out for $\lambda < 14$ Å, and the flux is given in terms of the square of the electron density, integrated over the volume of the plage plasma, V, that is, in terms of the parameter S

$$S \equiv \int_{v} n_{\mathrm{e}}^{2} \, dV \, . \tag{4.13}$$

The bremsstrahlung (ff) emissivity was determined from the equation

$$\epsilon_{\mathrm{ff}}(T, \nu) = n_{\mathrm{i}} n_{\mathrm{e}} k_{\mathrm{ff}} T^{-1/2} \, e^{-h\nu/kT} \, , \qquad \text{ergs cm}^{-3} \text{ sec}^{-1} \, (\text{c/sec})^{-1}, \quad (4.14)$$

where the absorption coefficient k_{ff} for free–free transitions is given by Equation (1.100). The contribution from free–bound transition to quantum level n may be calculated from the expression for the emission from electrons of energy E which are captured on level n, namely

$$\epsilon_{\mathrm{fb}}(n, E, \nu) = n_{\mathrm{i}} n_{\mathrm{e}} k_{\mathrm{fb}}(\sqrt{2E} \, h_{\nu}/\sqrt{m}) \qquad \text{ergs cm}^{-3} \text{ sec}^{-1} \, (\text{unit energy})^{-1} \, ,$$

$$(4.15a)$$

where the absorption coefficient for free–bound transitions k_{fb} is given by Equation (1.98). To find the emission resulting from captures to all levels, one sums over those levels whose ionization potential χ_{n} is less than the energy of the emitted photon. For a Maxwellian gas, the result is

$$\epsilon_{\mathrm{fb}}(T, \nu) = n_{\mathrm{i}} n_{\mathrm{e}} k_{\mathrm{fb}} T^{-3/2} \, e^{-h\nu/kT} \sum_{n} n \chi_{n}^{2} g \, e^{\chi_{n}/kT} \, , \qquad \text{ergs cm}^{-3} \text{ sec}^{-1} \, (\text{c/sec})^{-1} \, .$$

$$(4.15b)$$

Finally, the line emission (bb) was calculated using Elwert's (1954) expressions for the emissivity

$$\epsilon_{\mathrm{bb}} = 4\sqrt{\pi} \, c \alpha a_{0}^{2} \chi_{\mathrm{H}} \sqrt{\chi_{\mathrm{H}}/kT} \, n_{\mathrm{e}}^{2} Y_{\mathrm{Zi}} \, , \qquad \text{ergs cm}^{-3} \text{ sec}^{-1} \qquad (4.16)$$

for the transition in elements with atomic number Z in stage of ionization i. In this expression, the function Y_{Zi} takes the form

$$Y_{\mathrm{Zi}} = (n_{\mathrm{i}}/n_{\mathrm{e}}) \sum_{l_{1}} b(n_{1} l_{1}) \sigma(n_{1} l_{1} \to n) \, e^{-h\nu/kT} G_{3}(h\nu/kT) \, ,$$

where

$$G_{3}(x) = 1.2(1 - x \, e^{x} Ei(x)) - 0.2/x \, ,$$

and

α = the fine structure constant, 1/137,

a_0 = radius of Bohr's first orbit,

n = principal quantum number of excited state,

n_1, l_1 = principal and azimuthal quantum numbers of ground state,

$b(n_1 l_1)$ = number of electrons in the $n_1 l_1$-shell,

$\sigma(n_1 l_1 \rightarrow n)$ = collisional cross section between state $n_1 l_1$ and state n .

Acton's computations include all ions which he believed could make significant contributions to the X-ray flux below 14 Å from a 2.3×10^6 °K region. These include for bremsstrahlung, H II and He III; for free–bound, H II, He III, C VII, O VIII, O IX, N VII, and N VIII; and for line emission, Ne IX at 13.5 Å, Mg XI at 9.2 Å and Si XIII at 6.6 Å. The total emission was

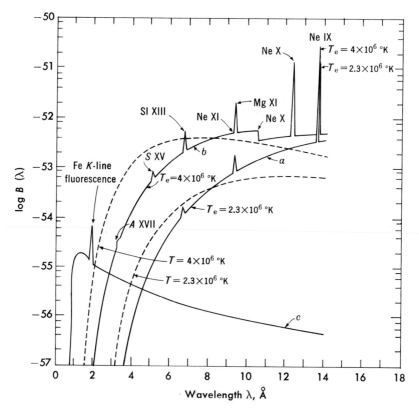

FIGURE 4.7. The spectral distribution of radiation below 14 Å (courtesy L. Acton, 1964)

found to be $2.35 \times 10^{-52} S$ ergs cm^{-2} sec^{-1}, of which free–free emission accounts for $6.5 \times 10^{-54} S$ ergs cm^{-2} sec^{-1}, free–bound for $1.2 \times 10^{-52} S$ ergs cm^{-2} sec^{-1}, and bound–bound for $1.1 \times 10^{-52} S$ ergs cm^{-2} sec^{-1}. The predominant emission processes are recombination radiation (mainly from O VIII and O IX) and line emission (mainly from Ne IX). Bremsstrahlung contributes relatively little at these wavelengths and this temperature. This is substantiated by the work of Kawabata (1960). The spectral distribution of the radiation below 14 Å is shown in Figure 4.7.

Acton determined the value of the parameter S corresponding to an observed flux of 4×10^{-3} ergs cm^{-2} sec^{-1} from the plages seen on June 29,

TABLE 4.6   Acton's model of X-ray plages;
$T_{\mathrm{e}} = 2.3 \times 10^{6}$ °K

Assumed vertical dimension, km	Resulting (uniform) electron density, cm^{-3}
2×10^{7}	1×10^{8}
8×10^{5}	5×10^{8}
2×10^{5}	1×10^{9}
4×10^{4}	2×10^{9}
8×10^{3}	5×10^{9}

1961: $S(\lambda < 14 \text{ Å}; T_{\mathrm{e}} = 2.3 \times 10^{6} \text{ °K}) = 4 \times 10^{-3} \cdot 2.35 \times 10^{-52} = 1.7 \times 10^{49}$ cm^{-3}. The area of the Ca II plages that day was about 8.5×10^{20} cm^{2}, and if one assumes that the entire X-ray flux for $\lambda < 14$ Å came from the corona overlying these plage regions, one can obtain an estimate of the (uniform) electron density by assigning a certain thickness to the emitting region (see Table 4.6).

Somewhat different models have been proposed by White (1964) and by Culhane, Willmore, Pounds, and Sanford (1964) to interpret their observations. White considers an X-ray emitting region of the same horizontal extent as the Ca II plage and of thickness proportional to its horizontal dimension. The electron temperature is about 2.8×10^{6} °K and the electron density 5×10^{9} cm^{-3}. The line emission from such an X-ray plage should be about 20 times stronger than the continuous emission, which is not observed.

The model presented by Culhane, Willmore, Pounds, and Sanford is even more extreme. It requires very hot regions, $T_{\mathrm{e}} \approx 5 \times 10^{6}$ °K, that are also very dense, $n_{\mathrm{e}} = 10^{10}$ cm^{-3}.

4.2.5. Theoretical Considerations

Several hypotheses have been advanced to account for the extra heating in the upper layers of plages, all of them relying on energy from below being absorbed by the plage plasma. Most of the convective energy below the photosphere is dissipated in the convection zone, but a certain fraction of it (the curl free part of the velocity field) may proceed upward as acoustic waves. The development of an aerodynamic theory for the generation of acoustic noise—to be dissipated higher up in the atmosphere—is due to Lighthill (1952). In Chapter 3 we saw how the aerodynamic theory may be used to explain the heating of the normal chromosphere and corona, but without any modifications, it does not explain the extra heating of the plages.

The crucial observation that plages are defined by their magnetic field makes it reasonable to try to explain them as a hydromagnetic phenomenon. Alfvén (1947) already had considered the Joule heating from hydromagnetic waves. This heating is given by j^2/σ, where j is the electric current density and σ the electric conductivity. However, it turns out that the σ to use in the expression for the Joule heating is an effective—Cowling—conductivity, $\sigma_3 = \sigma_\perp + \sigma_H^2/\sigma_\perp$, where $\sigma_\perp$ is the conductivity perpendicular to the magnetic field **B** and in the plane of the electrical field vector **E** (the Pedersen conductivity) and σ_H is the Hall conductivity [see Equation (1.25), perpendicular to both **B** and **E**]. This Cowling conductivity is so large that the Joule heating becomes insignificant for the plage problem.

Viscosity is another effect that may cause absorption of waves. This has been studied by van de Hulst (1949). The ratio between the heating due to viscosity and that due to Joule losses is given by $4\pi\sigma\eta$, where η is the kinematic viscosity, Equation (1.36). This ratio may be greater than unity in certain parts of the chromosphere, but the heating effect is still much too small to be of importance for plages.

Piddington (1956) proposed a new approach by including the effect of neutral atoms. In his theory, heating is produced by hydromagnetic waves due to friction between the oscillating ion plasma and the neutral atoms. This dissipation process is not an ordinary Joule heating, but a Joule loss due to the Hall drift in a ternary gas (ions, electrons, atoms). Note that the Hall drift may be considerable, even though the Hall current is small and negligible due to the plasma moving as a whole.

One is consequently led to discuss the transport of energy by waves in an ionized gas pervaded by a magnetic field. Under these conditions, the four modes of waves are (see Section 1.5):

(1) Space charge waves. These may be ignored for wavelengths significantly longer than radio waves.

(2) A modified acoustic wave, velocity $V = V_s$. This is the so-called S-wave for which there exists no adequate theory for heating effects.

(3) The ordinary, transverse wave, the O-wave.

(4) The extraordinary, transverse wave, the E-wave.

The two last waves have velocities $V_A = B_0/(4\pi\rho)^{1/2}$, and in the limit of large frequencies they go over into the well-known waves of the magnetoionic theory.

In his treatment, Piddington approximated to the case where the ion plasma and the neutral gas could be treated separately. He used the field equations in the form

$$\nabla^2\mathbf{B} = 4\pi\sigma_3\left[\frac{\partial\mathbf{B}}{\partial t} - \nabla \times (\mathbf{v} \times \mathbf{B})\right] + \frac{\sigma_H}{\sigma_\perp}\frac{\partial}{\partial z}\nabla \times \mathbf{B},$$

where the magnetic field $\mathbf{B}$ has a component $\mathbf{B_0}$ along the axis OZ. The electric conductivity and the velocity $\mathbf{v}$ of the gas refer to the fully ionized plasma, meaning that σ_3 is very large when the collision frequency is small (ions and electrons oscillate in phase).

The effect of the neutral particles is included by considering the friction they impose on the ion plasma, whence two equations of motion result. Since the absorption of the O- and E-waves does not depend on the gas pressure, it is neglected in the equations, which then take the form

$$\frac{\partial\mathbf{v}}{\partial t} + (\mathbf{v} - \mathbf{v}_a)\frac{\mu}{\tau_a} + \frac{V_A^2}{B_0^2}[\mathbf{B_0} \times (\nabla \times \mathbf{B})] = 0,$$

$$\frac{\partial\mathbf{v}_a}{\partial t} = (\mathbf{v} - \mathbf{v}_a)\frac{1}{\tau_a}, \tag{4.17}$$

where $\mathbf{v}_a$ is the velocity of the neutral atoms, τ_a their collision period, and μ is the ratio between the mass density of atoms and ions. With Piddington, we seek solutions proportional to $\exp[i(\omega t - k\zeta)]$, where ζ is in the XZ-plane. The equations determining the problem then become

$$(k^2 + i4\pi\sigma_3\omega)B_x + i4\pi\sigma_3 B_0 \cos\psi\, v_x + \frac{\sigma_H}{\sigma_\perp}\cos^2\psi\, k_z B_y = 0,$$

$$(k^2 + i4\pi\sigma_3\omega)B_y + i4\pi\sigma_3 B_0 \cos\psi\, k v_y - \frac{\sigma_H}{\sigma_\perp}k^2 B_x = 0,$$

$$B_0 \cos\omega\left(1 + \frac{\mu}{1 + i\omega\tau_a}\right)\omega v_x + V_A^2 k B_x = 0,$$

$$B_0\omega v_y\left(1 + \frac{\mu}{1 + i\omega\tau_a}\right) + V_A^2 \cos\psi\, k B_y = 0$$

and give a dispersion relation

$$\frac{\omega^2}{k^2} = \frac{V_A^2 S^2}{1 + [\mu/(1 + i\omega\tau_a)]} + \frac{i\omega}{4\pi\sigma_3}, \tag{4.18}$$

where $S = \cos\psi$ for the O-wave and $S = 1$ for the E-wave.

When no neutral atoms are present, $\mu = 0$, we get the special case of a binary gas. The conditions $\omega \approx 1/\tau_a$ and $\mu \neq 0$ lead to forced oscillations, and strong absorption occurs.

The absorption coefficient is the imaginary part of k. When $\mu = 0$, the absorption is given by the last term in the dispersion relation (collision between ions and electrons). This has been shown to be negligible (Cowling, 1953). The remaining part gives

$$\text{Im}\,(k) = -\text{Im}\left\{\frac{\omega}{SV_A}\,\sqrt{1 + [\mu/(1 + i\omega\tau_a)]}\right\}.$$

If $\omega \ll 1/\tau_a$, this simplifies to

$$\text{Im}\,(k) = \omega^2\tau_a\mu/2V_A S\sqrt{1 + \mu}\,. \tag{4.19}$$

In that part of the chromosphere where the gas is half ionized ($\mu = 1$), $n_e \approx 3 \times 10^9$ cm^{-3}, $\sigma \approx 10^{-8}$ electrostatic units (esu) and $\tau_a = 1s$. A magnetic field of $B = 100$ gauss will there lead to an absorption $\approx 10^9$ times larger than the absorption due to ordinary Joule heating.

4.3. The 22-Year Period

4.3.1. Observation of a Possible Poloidal Field

The most basic variability, to which all the above mentioned manifestations of activity can be attributed, is that of the sun's magnetic field or fields. Ever since 1908, when Hale discovered sunspot magnetism (Hale and Nicholson, 1938), we have known that sunspots are the seat of strong, varying magnetic fields. The behavior of these fields is fairly well–known. In particular, we can state that they are hardly ever found at latitudes greater than 45 to 50 deg from the equator. Less clear–cut is the problem of the sun's general magnetic field. In 1913 Hale reported the discovery of what has been believed to be a general solar field, poloidal in nature, and recognizable only at high latitudes. But the intensity of this field is the source of much confusion, to the point where even its very existence is questioned.

With the modern magnetographs (Babcock, 1953; Beggs and von Klüber, 1964; see also Thiessen, 1953; Kiepenheuer, 1953a), it is at times possible to measure a weak field of about one gauss around the north and the south poles of the sun. These fields extend toward the equator to latitudes about ± 55 deg (Babcock and Babcock, 1955). In the years around the 1955 sunspot minimum, the fields around the two poles had opposite polarities, the north polar cap showing a field of positive polarity, the south polar cap one of negative polarity (magnetic vector into the sun). This could be taken as the manifestation of a dipole, poloidal magnetic field of the sun. Consequently, in many textbooks on astrophysics and solar physics one may find descriptions of "the dipole field of the sun" or similar statements. Few observations are available to support such a notion. The reason for assuming a dipole field is due to analogies made with the earth's magnetic field, whose main component can be fairly well approximated by a dipole field.

Let us briefly discuss what the general field would be like if it were such a dipole field. The easiest way to describe it would be by its magnetic potential Φ_M, which in turn is given by the magnetic moment M:

$$\Phi_M = -(M/r^2) \cos \theta . \tag{4.20}$$

Here r is the radius vector from the center of the sun, $\theta = 90 - \phi$ is the polar distance, and ϕ is the latitude. The components of this dipole field are

$$B_r = \frac{\partial \Phi_M}{\partial r} = \frac{2M}{r^3} \cos \theta$$

and

$$B_\theta = \frac{\partial \Phi_M}{r \, \partial \theta} = \frac{M}{r^3} \sin \theta ,$$

giving a total field strength $B = (B_r^2 + B_\theta^2)^{1/2} = (M/r^3)(1 + 3 \cos^2 \theta)^{1/2}$. Observations perpendicular to the magnetic axis will then pertain to the longitudinal field

$$B_L = B_r \sin \theta - B_\theta \cos \theta = (M/r^3) \sin \theta \cos \theta , \tag{4.21}$$

which is seen to have a maximum at $\theta = 45$ deg.

Instead of the magnetic moment, one often gives the polar field strength $(\theta = 0)$, that is, $B_p = 2M/r^3$. The early Mount Wilson measurements gave $B_p \approx 50$ gauss, which seems to be between one and two orders of magnitude too high.

The more recent observations of the polar cap fields also have been interpreted in terms of a general poloidal magnetic field. An order-of-magnitude estimate of the total magnetic flux through the polar caps was made by Babcock (1960) and gives 8×10^{21} maxwell. It is not clear in detail what happened to this poloidal field in the immediate post minimum years 1955–1956, whether it stayed constant or decreased in intensity. The latter alternative is the more probable, for in 1957 the south polar cap reversed its polarity. The sun then had two positive magnetic poles and this apparent anomaly lasted for about 18 months, until the north pole also reversed its polarity in 1958, that is, around the time of sunspot maximum. Since then, observations have been infrequent but the indications are that the general magnetic field remains fainter than that observed during the 1954 sunspot minimum. Indeed, at times it is not even possible to detect the field at one or the other pole at all (Babcock, 1963; Beggs and von Klüber, 1964).

It is well–known—and we shall return to this in Chapter 5—that the polarity of the sunspot magnetic field shows a reversal after any 11-year sunspot cycle, leading to a 22-year magnetic period. Even though both the quantity and the quality of the observations of the sun's poloidal field are very inferior to the sunspot observations, the observed 1957–58 reversal just described strongly suggests a connection between the magnetic fields of sunspots and the general poloidal magnetic field.

However, before we discuss a possible interaction of the two fields, it may be worthwhile to look at the attempts that have been made to explain the general field *per se*. One is then led to ask how can a field continue to exist at all in the hot solar gases. If the field is part of the birth history of the sun, why has it not long since died away? Or if a possible primordial field has died away, how is the present-day field continuously being rejuvenated? The answers to these deep searching questions are not well understood, but a key to the problem seems to have been found. This key is the dynamo theory, which ascribes the maintenance of the magnetic field to electric currents generated in the plasma as a result of the coupling between the motion of this plasma and the field itself. Since the field is maintained by a motion of the plasma across the magnetic lines of force, one may say that there is a resemblance to the behavior of a self-exciting dynamo.

4.3.2. Dynamo Maintenance

The complete theory of the dynamo action in maintaining cosmic magnetic fields is extremely complicated and has not been worked out. The theory should show both that a motion exists which can maintain a given magnetic field and that this motion can be maintained by the forces available (Cowling, 1957). To do this properly, one would need to solve the hydrodynamic and electromagnetic equations simultaneously—which cannot be done. One therefore simplifies the problem by assuming that the motions are known and then asks if these motions can maintain a magnetic field.

Larmor (1919) has already attempted to explain sunspot magnetism by an axisymmetric dynamo. However, Cowling (1934) showed that a dynamo cannot work in the axially symmetric case, and this seems to have put a temporary stop to further developments. After World War II, Frenkel (1945) and Gurevich and Lebedinski (1945) rediscussed the dynamo, but it was Elsasser (1946a, 1946b, 1947, 1950) and Bullard (1949) who put new life into the discussion and in essence brought the theory to where it stands today [see also Parker (1955), Batchelor (1950), Cowling (1957) and Chandrasekhar (1961)].

With Elsasser, we shall consider magnetic fields due to motions in a uniform incompressible sphere and neglect the displacement currents $\partial \mathbf{D}/\partial t$. Hence $\nabla \times \mathbf{B} = 4\pi\mathbf{j}$ and $\nabla \cdot \mathbf{j} = 0$. If $\mathbf{v}$ is the material velocity, the equation for the magnetic induction will be [see Equation (1.50)]

$$\nabla^2 \mathbf{B} = 4\pi\sigma[(\partial \mathbf{B}/\partial t) - \nabla \times (\mathbf{v} \times \mathbf{B})]. \tag{4.22}$$

The only restriction on the velocity field $\mathbf{v}$ is that it satisfy the continuity equation, and since we assume incompressibility, $\nabla \cdot \mathbf{v} = 0$.

Elsasser obtained a formal solution to Equation (4.22) by an analogy to the simpler equation resulting from putting $\mathbf{v} = 0$. We then have the equation for the decay of the magnetic field due to the currents being dissipated as Joule heat:

$$\frac{\partial \mathbf{B}}{\partial t} = \frac{1}{4\pi\sigma} \nabla^2 \mathbf{B}.$$

The field, given in terms of currents inside the sphere, can be expressed by a series

$$\mathbf{B} = \sum_n b_n \mathbf{B}_n, \tag{4.23}$$

where the fields $\mathbf{B}_n$ form a complete set and are those normal modes which decay exponentially:

$$\mathbf{B} = \mathbf{B}_n e^{-\lambda_n t}. \tag{4.24}$$

Elsasser then assumed that when $\mathbf{v} \neq 0$, the field $\mathbf{B}$ in Equation (4.22) still satisfies an equation of the form (4.23), where the constants b_n are replaced by time dependent coefficients

$$\mathbf{B} = \sum_n b_n(t)\mathbf{B}_n. \tag{4.25}$$

It can then be shown that the coefficients $b_n(t)$ satisfy an equation of the form

$$db_n/dt = -\lambda_n b_n(t) + 4\pi \sum_n b_n(t) \int (\mathbf{v} \times \mathbf{B}_n) \cdot \mathbf{j}_n \, d\tau, \tag{4.26}$$

where the integration is over all space. The problem now is to show that real solutions exist, and this has turned out to be a formidable problem.

Bullard (1949) has discussed the case of steady motions to see if such special conditions exist which are capable of maintaining a stationary magnetic field. In this case, Equation (4.26) reduces to

$$\lambda_n b_n = 4\pi \sum_n b_n \int (\mathbf{v} \times \mathbf{B}_n) \cdot \mathbf{j}_n \, d\tau . \tag{4.27}$$

Searching for the appropriate motion, we may put the velocity equal to $k\mathbf{v}$ and try to find the values of k that give motions capable of sustaining a magnetic field. Presumably, there will only be a discrete set of k-values that can lead to dynamo maintenance, and the problem therefore resembles an eigenvalue problem. The equation—found by replacing $\mathbf{v}$ by $k\mathbf{v}$ in (4.27)—becomes

$$\lambda_n b_n = k \left[4\pi \sum_n b_n \int (\mathbf{v} \times \mathbf{B}_n) \cdot \mathbf{j}_n \, d\tau \right] , \tag{4.28}$$

which is similar to the matrix equations of eigenvalue theory. Unfortunately, it has not been possible to give a rigorous proof that real eignvalues exist, which is the same as saying that we cannot be sure that nontrivial solutions for the b_n coefficients are inevitable consequences of the assumed motions.

Bullard's (1949) great contribution to this field is that he actually solved the set of Equations (4.28) for a very large value of n (about 100) and showed that a real k existed under certain circumstances. Thus, the *possibility* of dynamo maintenance of magnetic fields is established, but it remains to be shown that dynamo maintenance is a logical consequence of the material motions. The most extensive work in this direction has been done by Parker (1955). By an ingenious combination of motions to be expected in the sun (i.e., nonuniform rotation, thermally induced convection affected by Coriolis forces), he was able to show that certain field configurations will be amplified.

The problem of dynamo maintenance of nonsteady fields is closely linked to the action of turbulent motions. Some of the basic difficulties encountered in studies of this kind are treated in Section 1.4 and are basically due to the fact that no general theory for turbulence has been developed. Important contributions to the discussion of a possible dynamo action have been given by Elsasser (1946a, 1947, 1950), Batchelor (1950), Cowling (1957), Chandrasekhar (1961), and others, but we are still far from understanding the process completely. No basic studies like those of Bullard (1949) for the steady dynamo exist which show that turbulent motions can sustain a magnetic field. Since subphotospheric regions—where the dynamo action is supposed to take place, if anywhere—show strong signs of a turbulent nature, one is forced to conclude that the theory for a general magnetic field of the sun still rests on rather shaky ground.

With our present tools for analyzing these problems, we therefore are not in a position to decide beyond doubt whether dynamo maintenance of magnetic fields is possible in the solar case. There are hence two points of view, one which with confidence awaits the final proof of the dynamo theory and another which is seeking new ways out of the dilemma. We shall now consider theories in which the so-called general, poloidal field of the sun is but a by-product of plage and sunspot fields.

4.3.3. Explanation of the General Field in Terms of Small-Scale Fields

4.3.3.1. *Leighton's theory*

We shall now discuss a new approach to the problem of the solar magnetic fields. While most theories rely on a general field to explain the formation of a sunspot field, Leighton (1964) turns the question around. He starts with the observed fact that there exist magnetic fields in active regions, fainter ones in plages, stronger ones in sunspots, and shows how these fields by the action of convective motions and nonuniform rotation lead to an explanation of the observed polar fields—that are often considered part of a general field.

The basis for Leighton's approach is the convective circulatory field in the sun called the supergranulation. Due to the great electric conductivity of the solar plasma, the convective motions will drag magnetic fields laterally and displace the field lines. This will gradually lead to a dispersion of the localized fields. The magnetic lines of force are considered to be a special kind of "atom" in the solar atmosphere so far as their lateral motions are concerned. One may then treat the motion of the magnetic fields as a random walk.

Let a field line make N lateral steps per unit time and let L be the average length of the steps. At time t the "atom" will then be at a distance r from the starting point given by

$$r = L(rt)^{1/2},$$

L will be approximately equal to the extent of a convection cell, and N will measure a reciprocal cell lifetime t_0. All the atoms that were initially within a given cell will be dispersed over an area A given by

$$A = \pi L^2 t/t_0 \ (=\pi r^2).$$

The dispersal rate of magnetic field, i.e., the growth rate of the active region of area A, may be estimated using the values $L = 15,000$ km and $t_0 = 7 \times 10^4$ sec (Simon, 1963):

$$dA/dt \approx 10^4 \ \mathrm{km^2/sec}.$$

At this rate, it will take a time $= 2\pi R_\odot^2/10^4 \approx 10$ years for the field "atoms" to spread over a solar hemisphere. In order to include the case when more than one active region is present, Leighton made the assumption that any active region disperses independently of other regions.

The just-described random walk is a two-dimensional analogy to the more familiar three-dimensional diffusion process of atoms in a gas. Leighton defined a mixing coefficient D and an average lateral drift rate or current c of the lines of force given by [see Equation (1.85)]

$$\mathbf{c} = -D\nabla n \,, \tag{4.29}$$

where n is the number surface density of points at which lines of force enter the sun, i.e., the concentration of the diffusing objects. To conserve the magnetic flux, we need

$$(\partial n/\partial t) + \nabla \cdot \mathbf{c} = 0 \,,$$

which—by Equation (4.29)—gives

$$\partial n/\partial t = D\nabla^2 n \,. \tag{4.30}$$

The mixing coefficient D is expressed in terms of the step-length L and the rate N as

$$D = \tfrac{1}{2}L^2 N \,.$$

In the above derivation, the medium in which the diffusion takes place has been assumed to be at rest. The random walk process is, however, modified by the drift due to the sun's nonuniform rotation (see Section 5.3.3). Let $\mathbf{v}$ be the drift velocity; then Equation (4.30) takes the modified form

$$\partial n/\partial t = D\nabla^2 n - (\mathbf{v} \cdot \nabla)n \,. \tag{4.31}$$

The relative velocity $\mathbf{v}$ is given by $\mathbf{v} = \omega(\theta)R_\odot \sin\theta \, \mathbf{c}_\phi$, where $\omega(\theta)$ is the angular velocity in nonuniform rotation at latitude $\phi = 90 \deg - \theta$. In spherical coordinates (r, θ, λ), Equation (4.31) then takes the form

$$\frac{\partial n}{\partial t} = \frac{D}{R_\odot^2} \left[\frac{1}{\sin\theta} \frac{\partial}{\partial\theta} \left(\sin\theta . \frac{\partial n}{\partial\theta} \right) + \frac{1}{\sin^2\theta} \frac{\partial^2 n}{\partial\lambda^2} \right] - \omega(\theta) \frac{\partial n}{\partial\lambda} \,. \tag{4.32}$$

The mean flux at latitude ϕ, averaged around the sun, that is, over λ, is defined as

$$\bar{n} = \bar{n}(\theta, t) = \frac{1}{2\pi} \int_0^{2\pi} n(\theta, \lambda, t) \, d\lambda \,.$$

It is easy to see that this mean flux satisfies a simplified form of Equation (4.32), namely

$$\frac{\partial\bar{n}}{\partial t} = \frac{D}{R_\odot^2} \frac{1}{\sin\theta} \frac{\partial}{\partial\theta} \left(\sin\theta \frac{\partial n}{\partial\theta} \right) \,. \tag{4.33}$$

Leighton obtained numerical solutions of (4.32) for different values of D corresponding to different assumed decay times $T_0 = R^2/D$. The numerical value of the longitudinal displacement due to nonuniform rotation was taken to be consistent with Newton and Nunn's (1951) empirical formula

$$\zeta = 14.38° - 2.77° \sin^2 \phi,$$

where ζ is the daily sidereal rotation.

Figure 4.8 (page 170), from Leighton's (1964) paper, shows the development of a bipolar spot group. The coordinates of the equally strong preceding and following spots were originally $\cos \theta_p = 0.40$, $\lambda_p = +6$ deg, $\cos \theta_f = 0.42$, $\lambda_f = -6$ deg. The solutions show that the neutral line between the two regions of opposite polarity becomes increasingly more deformed by the nonuniform rotation. One notices furthermore that a fairly strong magnetic field gradient across the neutral line continues to persist for many months. Also, the p-region retains a higher absolute field strength over a smaller area than does the f-region. Hence, the latter becomes more drawn out in longitude. The f-region may therefore lose its identity sooner, and we may in this way explain the so-called unipolar regions as surviving p-regions (Leighton, 1964).

The average field strength $\bar{n}(\theta, t)$ follows Equation (4.33), the f-region dominating in higher latitudes, the p-region in lower. Finally, the distance between the centers of the two spots increases steadily with time. This is here simply explained as due to the random walk in the presence of nonuniform rotation, and no *ad hoc* assumptions are necessary.

By superposing dispersed fields from many bipolar groups, one may now account for the polar cap fields, provided that the p- and f-parts of the spot groups are separated in latitude as well as in longitude. That there is such a tilt of the bipolar groups is an observed fact, but the reason for this is not understood. The p-parts tend to lie closer to the equator than the f-parts. Remembering this and the other observed fact that the polarities of spots are reversed in opposite hemispheres (Section 5.1), we find that the magnetic doublet moments of the spot groups in both hemispheres will have meridional components of the same sign. Leighton's random walk process therefore provides a large scale polar field of dipolar nature.

We know that when a new sunspot cycle begins, the polarities will be reversed. Hence, every 11 years the f-regions dispersing toward the poles will neutralize the existing fields and cause a reversal of the "general field"— which is simply the combined effects of many superposed f-regions.

In his paper, Leighton built on Babcock's (1961) theory for the assumed general poloidal field and incorporated it into his own theory. However, Babcock's theory does not readily explain the tilt of the sunspot group, and even though Leighton makes it more plausible, this is hardly a reason necessarily to couple the two theories. It may be an equally fruitful point

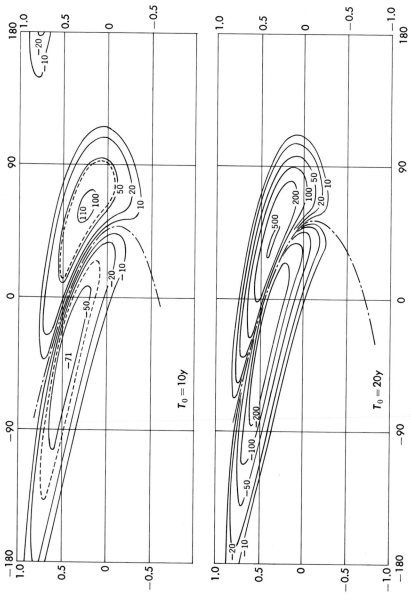

FIGURE 4.8.   Development of a bipolar region according to Leighton (courtesy R. B. Leighton, 1964)

of view to assume the tilt and then explain the so-called general field as a necessary consequence of the dispersion of active regions. This does not lead to a theory for spot fields, but so far that has not been Leighton's main contribution.

4.3.3.2. Hoyle's and Wickramasinghe's theory

We conclude this Section by noticing that Hoyle and Wickramasinghe (1961) also have considered the possibility that the polar magnetic field is but a consequence of low-latitude, small-scale fields that are carried toward the polar regions. These authors build on Gold's (1958) and Alfvén's (1958) deductions that the shape of the coronal rays and other structures maps out the magnetic field lines. They then consider the transport of local photospheric fields into the corona through the agency of particle streams. This will lead to the emergence of loops of the type described by Gold and Alfvén. Another main point in their theory is that Ohmic dissipation plays an important, even crucial, part.

Consider first a loop with both feet lying in the same hemisphere. The loop is drawn out more or less radially by the particles, but no net polarity can arise from this in either hemisphere. However, if the feet straddle the equator, then both hemispheres acquire a net polarity, and if such loops overwhelmingly possess the same sense of polarity in any one cycle, then an excess of emergent, respective entrant, lines of force will be added to the hemispheres during the cycle.

To accomplish the transport toward the poles, Hoyle and Wickramasinghe resort to the effects of resistive diffusion of lines of force in pairs of loops. The diffusion time due to this dissipation is given by Equation (1.52), namely

$$\tau_{\text{diff}} = 4\pi\sigma L^2/c^2 \,,$$

where L is a characteristic length and σ is the electric conductivity. Consider the outward motion of two adjacent loops at the equator. The outward-going lines of force in one loop may press against the inward-going lines of force of the other loop, with the result that resistive diffusion will lead to the annihilation of such interpenetrating lines of force. Reconnection of the remaining lines may then take place in the corona, and we are left with outward-going lines of force on one side of the equator, and inward-going lines on the other side. Consequently, the lines of force that carry the net magnetic polarity have been transported away from the equator. A continued process of this kind is then necessary to achieve the diffusion of the fields all the way to the poles. It is not obvious that loops will emerge continuously in such a way as to accomplish this transport, even though this seems like a promising way of producing isolated coronal loops and arches.

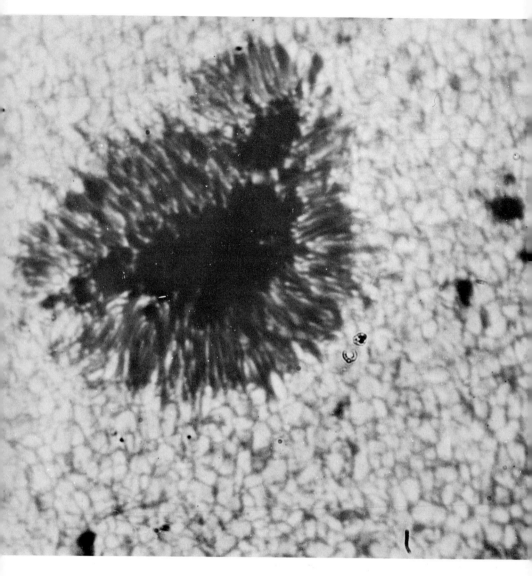

A balloon photograph of a portion of the solar disk showing granulation, pores, and sunspot structures in detail; Stratoscope flight, 17 August, 1959. (Courtesy Bahng and Schwarzschild, 1961.)

Sunspots | 5

5.1. *Observational Data*

5.1.1. Introductory Description

As discussed in Section 4.2, the first manifestation of activity in photospheric levels is the appearance of a magnetic field. If the strength of the field in a magnetic plage exceeds a certain threshold, a brightening will occur and we will have a photospheric plage or facula. The granular structure of the photosphere does not seem to be significantly changed by the plage field, and often this development is the extent of "the active region." At other times, a localized magnetic field appears somewhere in the plage and a sunspot is formed. Sunspots start out as *pores*—small regions much darker than the surrounding photosphere—and often do not develop further, but die away after hours or days. The localized fields seem to sink down below the observable photospheric levels. The field strength in such pores is of the order of 100 gauss.

In other cases, the magnetic field strength increases significantly beyond this value and a full-fledged sunspot group develops. The spots are concentrated in the preceding (west) and the following (east) ends of the group. The preceding spots usually appear before the following. One spot at each end usually develops more than the others. The magnetic field has different polarity in the spots belonging to the preceding and to the following end, so that we typically get a *bipolar* sunspot group.

A fully developed spot consists of the central dark *umbra*, through which most of the magnetic flux is channeled, and the less dark *penumbra*. The magnetic field strength has a maximum value near the center of the spot, or where the spot is darkest—the *core* of the umbra. By and large, the field often remains fairly constant over the umbra and drops in intensity as one

173

goes out through the penumbra. It gradually merges with the plage field at some distance outside the optical penumbra (Hale and Nicholson, 1938; von Klüber, 1947; Bumba, 1960a; Leroy, 1962). It is not clear what is the relationship—if any—between the pre-existing plage field and the much stronger localized spot field.

The fully developed spot may exist for days, weeks, or months, but eventually it breaks up or decreases in size as the field decreases and diffuses. After the death of the optical spot, the plage brightness will also eventually decrease as the magnetic plage breaks up and merges with the surroundings as the field becomes unobservably small.

5.1.2. Fine Structure and Velocity Fields in the Normal Photosphere

In the introduction we discussed the development of sunspots relative to the behavior of associated magnetic fields, the main key to a (still lacking) complete theory of the sunspot phenomenon. We shall now consider two other aspects of sunspots and their surroundings that may well furnish other very important clues, namely the fine structure and the velocities observed. It is of importance to compare these qualities in sunspot areas with the structure and velocities in the quiet photosphere, and we shall therefore start out by considering the undisturbed conditions.

Since the first high-resolution photographs of the quiet sun granulation (Janssen, 1896; Hansky, 1905; Chevalier, 1908) an impressive amount of data have been obtained and analyzed (Keenan, 1938; Macris, 1953; Rösch, 1955, 1956; Leighton, 1957; Bray and Loughhead, 1958; Blackwell, Dewhirst and Dollfus, 1959; Schwarzschild, 1959). The upshot of this is that the photosphere may be interpreted in terms of a cellular granulation pattern of convective origin. The material is rising in the bright granules of diameter generally between 700 and 1500 km. Individual granules can be observed for an average period of 8 to 10 minutes (Bray and Loughhead, 1964) and change little during this period. This supports Leighton's view that the motion of the rising granule material is laminar, rather than turbulent.

The darker lanes between the granules have widths comparable with the resolving limits of telescopes used, i.e., about 300 km (Leighton, 1957). It is in this part of the granulation pattern (the darker) that material moves downward (Plaskett, 1954; Stuart and Rush, 1954). Superposed on these, presumably convective, motions, we find the vertical oscillatory motions discussed in Chapter 3.

With Bray and Loughhead (1964) we define *a mean cell size*, ζ, of the pattern as the average distance between centers of adjacent granules. The photospheric granulation is then characterized by a mean cell size $\zeta = 2000$ km, with 70% of the values lying between 1500 and 2600 km.

5.1.3. Fine Structure in Sunspots

We shall presently see that the fine structure in the central parts of sunspots is quite different from the fine structure of the normal photosphere. The question then arises whether or not there is a gradual change in the granular structure as one approaches a sunspot region. Observations show that the presence of a spot has no effect on the surrounding granulation except when the spot is forming or changing. In that case, disturbances in the granulation pattern are observed. Bray and Loughhead (1964) describe this in the following way. In one case, the disturbance lasted for about three hours and took the form of a number of dark lanes lying between two groups of pores, probably of opposite magnetic polarities. This phenomenon has been interpreted as evidence of the existence of a rising loop of magnetic flux accompanying the birth of the new pores. Apart from this, the properties of the normal granulation remain unaltered right up to the boundary of the spots.

The fine structure of penumbrae consists of narrow bright filaments on a darker background. Generally speaking, the filaments are oriented in a radial direction, especially in regular (circular) spots. The filaments may be quite long, extending over a substantial fraction of the width of the penumbra, but they are very narrow. Representative values are: length 5000 to 7000 km, width 300 to 400 km (Danielson, 1961a; Bray and Loughhead, 1958). The lifetime of these filaments has been measured by Bray and Loughhead (1958), who found values ranging from thirty minutes to six hours. They are thus much longer-lived than the normal photospheric fine structure.

The umbra-penumbra border is sharply marked due to the filaments ending abruptly at the inner boundary of the penumbra. Secchi (1875) had already found that the border was also characterized by bright granules in the umbra close to the inner ends of the penumbral filaments. According to Bray and Loughhead (1964), these granules are much brighter than the granules found further within the umbra.

Until recently, it was generally believed that the convection in sunspots was inhibited by the magnetic field. This may have been because on ordinary photographs no fine structure is seen in the umbra. However, Chevalier (1916) had already reported the existence of a fine structure in umbrae consisting of bright granules on a general dark background, and this was substantiated by Thiessen's (1950) visual observations. Photographically, the umbral granules were first recorded by Rösch (1956, 1957) and a wealth of new information on this granulation is due to Bray and Loughhead (Bray and Loughhead, 1959; Loughhead and Bray, 1959, 1960a, 1960b).

We now know that the granules in the umbra also form a cellular pattern, but the cell size ζ is significantly less than for the photospheric granulation, namely 1600 km, compared with 2000 km for the photosphere. Another difference is that the lifetime of the umbral granules is much longer than the lifetime of the photospheric granules. While the latter have a lifetime of about 10 minutes, most granules found in umbrae last for 30 minutes.

We do not understand much of the basic nature of the sunspot mechanism, but it is probably of great importance to realize both that convection is active even in umbral regions and that the coupling with the magnetic field leads to a granulation whose cell size and lifetime differ significantly from what is found in the surrounding quiet photosphere.

Before we leave the domain of fine structure, we must briefly discuss the *light bridges*. These may take the form of masses of bright material extending over an appreciable part of the umbra, from one side to another, or they may be long thin streamers less than 1000 km wide extending into or crossing the umbra. As a rule, they develop slowly and last for hours or days.

The appearance of a light bridge often means that the final stage of the sunspot is approaching (Chevalier, 1916; Bray and Loughhead, 1964). Division of the spot may then take place and dissolution follows. Otherwise, light bridges seem to be an integral part of the fine structure of many umbrae, dividing a spot into parts of very different brightness.

5.1.4. Velocity Fields in Sunspots—the Evershed Effect

We now turn to the velocity fields found in sunspots. The largest components of these motions were discovered by Evershed (1909), who found that in photospheric layers the motion in the penumbra is predominantly radial and outward, away from the umbra. If one studies the behavior of strong Fraunhofer lines—which give information from chromospheric layers—one finds on the other hand that the radial component is directed inward, toward the umbra. Extensive work on the characteristics of these motions, the Evershed effect, has been conducted by St. John (1913) and later by Abetti (1929), Michard (1951), Kinman (1952, 1953), Maltby (1960, 1964), Holmes (1961), Servajean (1961), Bumba (1960b, 1960c), and others.

The magnitude of the radial velocity, v_r, at photospheric levels is a few km/sec (1 to 6 according to different observers), and it drops off as one goes from the penumbra into the umbra or into the quiet photosphere [see Figure 5.1 (page 177), taken from Kinman's work (1952)]. The variation of v_r with height in the atmosphere is schematically portrayed in Figure 5.2. The inward flow at chromospheric heights is less well determined, but seems to be of about the same magnitude as the outflow below.

There has been considerable controversy as to whether other components (tangential and vertical) of the Evershed effect are present and of importance, and the issue is still not solved. Both Abetti and Maltby reported substantial tangential velocities, while Kinman found no evidence of this component. A

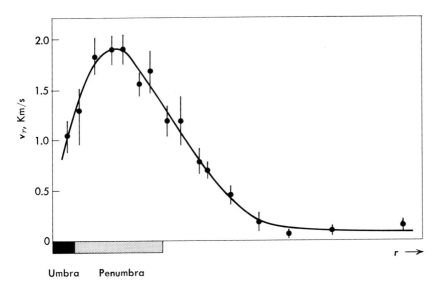

FIGURE 5.1.   The Evershed effect: the radial velocity (v_r) as a function of distance from the umbra (courtesy T. D. Kinman, 1952)

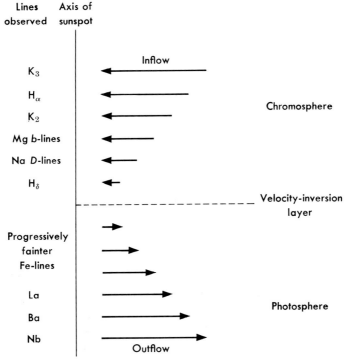

FIGURE 5.2.   The Evershed effect: the radial velocity (v_r) as a function of height in the solar atmosphere (after St. John, 1913)

small, 0.3 km/sec, vertical (downward) component was found by Servajean, but it is difficult to evaluate the reality of such small effects.

5.1.5. The Magnetic Field

As stated in the introduction, the magnetic field strength has a maximum where the spot brightness has a minimum, i.e., in the core of the umbra. The core is often not found in the central part of the umbra, whence the classical picture of the sunspot field being of simple axial symmetry and therefore purely longitudinal at the axis is not correct. Hale and Nicholson (1938) and Evershed (1941) had already observed the Zeeman π-component (see Section 2.2), and hence a transverse field in the umbra, even though they did not give the correct interpretation. Later work seems to confirm these earlier observations (Severny, 1959a; Bumba, 1962).

With this information in mind, we must consider the empirical formulas proposed from time to time to describe the variation of the field strength across individual spots only as fairly crude approximations. The best known of these formulas is due to Broxon (1942) and has been used to develop several sunspot models. The formula may have rather restricted physical significance in individual cases, but it is of value for statistical purposes. The relation is

$$B = B_m \left(1 - \frac{r^2}{\mathrm{p}^2} \right), \tag{5.1}$$

where r is the radial distance from the center of the spot where the field has its maximum strength B_m and p is the radius of the spot, including the penumbra. According to Mattig (1953), the field distribution may be written

$$B = B_m \left(1 - \frac{r^4}{\mathrm{p}^4} \right) e^{-2(r/\mathrm{p})^2} \tag{5.2}$$

and Bumba (1960a) gives the following expression:

$$B = B_m \, e^{-2.1 r^2/\mathrm{p}^2} . \tag{5.3}$$

If measurements of the field distribution within spots may be called difficult, this statement is even more true of observations of the field direction. By comparing the intensities of the two σ-components of a Zeeman triplet when viewed through a $\lambda/4$ plate analyzer (see Section 2.2.5) the Mount Wilson observers (see Hale and Nicholson, 1938) found the following empirical relation to represent the data

$$\delta = \frac{r}{\mathrm{p}} \, 70°, \tag{5.4}$$

where δ is the inclination of the field to the vertical at a distance r from the center of the spot. This result has been substantiated by work at the Crimea Observatory (Bumba, 1960a, 1960b, 1960c). Equation (5.4) indicates that the field is along the vertical axis at the center of the spot (longitudinal), but it becomes more and more inclined to the vertical as one moves away from the center, reaching an angle of 70 deg at the outer boundary of the penumbra $(r = \mathrm{p})$. Again, the relation is of value mainly in a statistical sense, since transverse fields often exist in central parts of the umbra.

We have already mentioned that most sunspots appear in groups where the polarity is opposite at the two ends (west and east) of the group. This *bipolar* character is often confused by spots of one polarity being found among the members of the opposite polarity, leading to *complex groups*. A group is termed complex when the polarities are so irregularly distributed that it cannot be classified as bipolar. Also, one often finds only the members of one polarity present, whence the group seems to be *unipolar*. A classification using this kind of observation has been given by the Mount Wilson observers (Hale and Nicholson, 1938). Hale had already realized that the unipolar spot group is a physical monstrosity and introduced the calcium plages into his classification, whereby a bipolar nature could be re-established. One then assumes that the sunspot magnetic field returns to a localized magnetic region of the opposite polarity in the plage (Hale's invisible sunspots). The Mount Wilson magnetic classification is given in Table 5.1.

Of great importance for any theoretical understanding of the sunspot

TABLE 5.1   Magnetic classification of sunspot groups

| Main class | Finer subdivision | | Percentage occurrence |
	Symbol	Description	
Unipolar	α	Distribution of faculae symmetrical around spot	15
	$\alpha\,p$	Spot followed by faculae	28
	$\alpha\,f$	Spot preceded by faculae	3
Bipolar	β	Preceding and following spots of approximately equal area	11
	$\beta\,p$	Preceding spot is the principal member of group	29
	$\beta\,f$	Following spot is the principal member of group	10
	$\beta\,\gamma$	Bipolar characteristics present, but dividing line between polarities not well marked	3
Complex	γ	Polarities irregularly distributed	1

phenomenon is the fact that the sense of the polarity is different in the two hemispheres. If the preceding spots show north polarity (and therefore the following spots south polarity) for spot groups in the northern hemisphere, then the preceding spots in the southern hemisphere will show south polarity (and the following spots north polarity).

Cowling (1946) studied the growth and decay of the magnetic field in long-lived sunspots, and the essence of his results is portrayed in Figure 5.3.

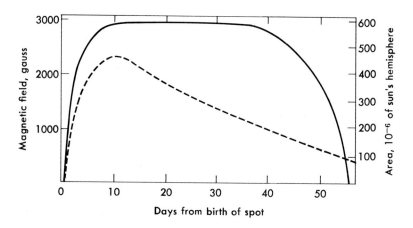

FIGURE 5.3. The growth and decay of the magnetic field in sunspots (courtesy T. G. Cowling, 1946)

The solid line is the magnetic field curve (maximum field intensity in gauss vs. time) and the broken line represents the variation of the area of the spot (in millionths of the visible hemisphere). We see that the magnetic field as well as the area of the sunspot increase very rapidly to the maximum value, after which the field remains fairly constant through the greater part of the lifetime of the spot. The area, however, soon begins to decrease after having reached its maximum value.

Many of the empirical formulas for the magnetic field use the maximum field strength B_m in the spot as a parameter. The value of B_m depends to some extent on the size of the spot, i.e., the spot area A, and several workers have studied the relationship between B_m and A (Nicholson, 1933; Houtgast and van Sluiters, 1948; Mattig, 1953; Ringnes and Jensen, 1960). The most widely used empirical expression is due to Houtgast and van Sluiters and takes the form

$$B_m = 3700A/(A + 66).\tag{5.5}$$

Field strengths in excess of 3700 gauss are found in some large spots, even though the statistically derived expression would indicate that this is an upper limit. Fields exceeding 3000 gauss are already fairly rare (5 % according to Bell, see Ringnes and Jensen, 1960), but values as high as 4300 gauss have been observed (von Klüber, 1948).

An empirical expression for the $B_m = B_m(A)$ relation which differs somewhat from Equation (5.5) has been given by Ringnes and Jensen. According to these authors, the magnetic field strength of a regular spot of area A can be written

$$B_m = a \log A + b \,, \tag{5.6}$$

where a and b are constants. Since the darkness of a spot increases with size, expressions like (5.6) indicate an important correlation between darkness of a spot and its magnetic field intensity.

In concluding this section on magnetic observations of sunspots, we shall consider the behavior of the total magnetic flux Φ through a sunspot. The flux through a circular spot of radius p($A = \pi p^2$) is (Chapman, 1943)

$$\Phi = \int B(r) \cos \delta \cdot r \, dr \,.$$

If we use Broxon's expression (5.1) we find

$$\Phi \text{ (Broxon)} = 0.315 \pi p^2 B_m \,,$$

and Mattig's expression (5.2) leads to a value 80 % of the preceding, namely

$$\Phi \text{ (Mattig)} = 0.25 \pi p^2 B_m \,.$$

5.1.6. Sunpot Cycles and Secular Variations

5.1.6.1. *The 22-year cycle*

After Schwabe (1844) discovered the *sunspot cycle of period of approximately 11 years* in 1843, Carrington (1859) discovered the *law of latitude drift* which states that the average latitude of the spots decreases steadily from the beginning to the end of any 11-year cycle. Further work on this drift was carried out by Spörer (1874). The first spots of a new cycle appear at about latitude ± 30 deg, while the last spots of a dying cycle are found close to the equator.

To the two fundamental properties concerning the variability of sunspot activity, namely the 11-year cycle and the latitude drift, we add the third, a basic observation concerning the magnetic field: the *change of polarity* of the sunspot magnetic fields with the coming of a new cycle. In other words, the preceding spots of a new cycle have the same polarity as the following spots of the previous cycle, and the following spots in a new cycle have the same polarity as the preceding spots in the previous cycle. There are exceptions to the law of sunspot polarity, but they are rare, 3.1% according to Richardson (1948). However, the fact that exceptions do exist is of importance for any theory claiming to understand the sunspot phenomenon and in the following sense. We may either have theories that can or cannot explain the exceptions to the law of polarities or we may have theories that cannot allow exceptions. The first type might, in the worst case, possibly be refined to encompass exceptions (and therefore could be on the right track), while the second type is inherently wrong.

The sunspot activity is measured in different ways by different observers. One method is to measure the total *area*, A, of all sunspots on the visible hemisphere at any one time. The area is generally given in millionths of the area of the hemisphere. This may be considered the most reliable and objective way. Another is to count the *number* of spots present, and this is generally done in the fashion developed by Wolf (1855) in Zürich. The Wolf sunspot number is defined as

$$R = K(10g + f) \qquad (5.7)$$

where f is the total number of spots, regardless of size, and g is the number of spot groups. The number will depend on the instrument used, the observer, and the observing conditions. To fix the scale, the constant K was put equal to unity for the early Zürich observations.

The correlation between A and R for single days is not very high, but the monthly means reveal a close connection. Hence, for statistical purposes either method may be used. When A is measured in millionths of the solar hemisphere (corrected for foreshortening toward the limb), the relationship between A and R is (Waldmeier, 1955)

$$A = 16.7R. \qquad (5.8)$$

The first two fundamental properties, namely the 11-year cycle and the latitude drift, may be portrayed as shown in Figures 5.4 and 5.5 (pp. 183 and 184). The ordinate in Figure 5.4 is the annual mean sunspot number. A first perusal of Figure 5.4 already reveals that the 11-year sunspot cycle is not a very well-behaved variation, both amplitude and period vary by large amounts. Following Waldmeier (1961a), we can give the characteristics of the periodicity as compiled in Table 5.2 on page 185.

Very roughly, the time of rise (t_1) and the time of fall (t_2) of the sunspot curve can be found from two empirical formulas relating these times to the

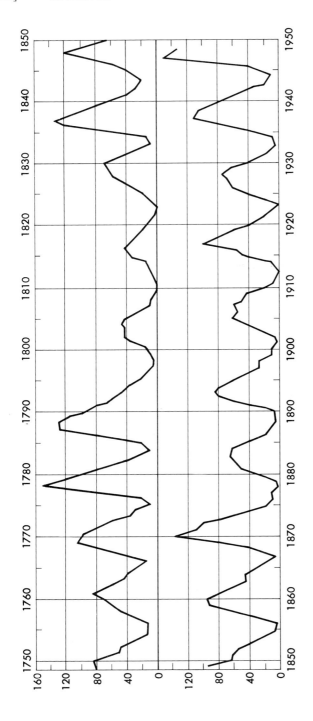

FIGURE 5.4.   The 11-year period in the variation of sunspot number (courtesy G. Abetti, 1963)

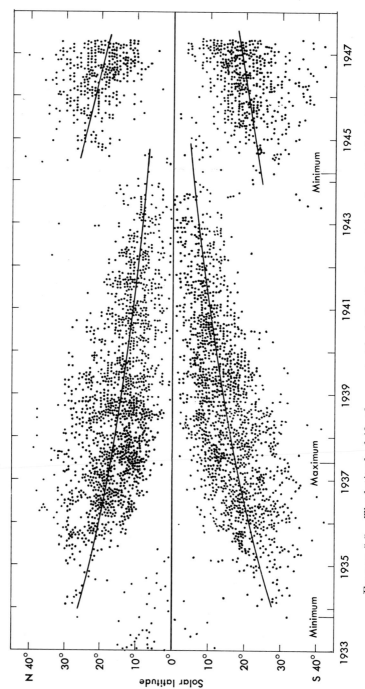

FIGURE 5.5.   The latitude drift of sunspots (the butterfly diagram) (courtesy G. Abetti, 1963)

TABLE 5.2   Periodicity of the sunspot cycle (courtesy Waldmeier, 1961a, p. 18)

	Mean	Extreme values
Period between maxima (in years)	10.9	7.3–17.1
Period between minima (in years)	11.1	9.0–13.6
Time from min to max (t_1, in years)	4.5	2.9–6.9
Time from max to min (t_2, in years)	6.5	4.0–10.2
Maximum sunspot number (R_{max}, monthly means)	108.2	48.7–201.3
Minimum sunspot number (monthly means)	5.1	0–11.2

maximum value of the sunspot number (R_{max}) in the cycle. Then t_1 and t_2 are given by

$$t_1 \approx 19 - 0.13 \log R_{max}, \qquad t_2 \approx 3 + 0.03 \log R_{max}.$$

We have repeatedly stated that the magnetic field is the most important aspect of sunspot activity. Since the polarity of sunspot fields changes with every 11-year cycle, we are really faced with a *22-year cycle*. This, therefore, is the basic periodicity of solar activity.

5.1.6.2. *Other possible cycles*

Other periodicities have been looked for and, many claim, found. However, great caution should be exercised in the type of analysis involved in these cases. The effects are very small and the statistics are often inadequate.

Hansky (1904) drew attention to the presence of secular variations in the solar activity, and already a perusal of the variation with time of the annual mean sunspot number R reveals such changes (see Figure 5.4). But to determine a long-period variation is more complicated. There is an indication that very high and very low peaks in the 11-year period occur with intervals of seven or eight 11-year cycles, and this secular variability is known as the *80-year period*. According to Kopecký (1962), who has given a review of our knowledge of the 80-year period with references to earlier work, this period manifests itself in the variation of a number of physically different sunspot parameters. Probably one of the most important changes was detected by Ringnes and Jensen (1960), who found that the constants a and b in Equation (5.6) show secular changes. The constant a has increased from a value of about 10.5 in the latter part of sunspot cycle number 15 (around 1920) to a value around 20 just prior to the maximum of cycle 19 (in 1958). Similarly, the constant b has decreased in this same interval from a slightly positive value to a value of about -21. The interval studied is believed to be the rising part of a long cycle of about 80 years which had its minimum just after the turn of the last century.

Another effect that seems to follow the same rough 80-year cycle is that the zone of sunspot group occurrence spreads toward the poles of the sun (the zone royal becomes wider) during the maximum epochs of the 80-year cycle (Kopecký, 1958).

When we subject the sunspot numbers to a power spectrum analysis, we find small peaks at about 25- or 26-month intervals, which Shapiro and Ward (1962) consider significant. From meteorological circles (Westcott, 1964), it has been suggested that this period is responsible for the pronounced 25-month periodicity in the stratospheric winds (Veryard and Ebdon, 1961). No other astronomical data seem to bring out this periodicity.

5.1.7. Brightness Distributions

From the preceding discussion in this chapter it is evident that the two most obvious characteristics of any sunspot are the presence of a strong magnetic field and the fact that the sunspot plasma is less hot than the surroundings. We shall now discuss the brightness of sunspots and the resulting appearance (umbra and penumbra).

A comparison of the brightness of a sunspot with its surroundings leads to an evaluation of the temperature difference between them. This may be done by comparing the total radiation, that is, integrated over all wavelengths, from the spot umbra, I_u, with the corresponding value for the undisturbed photosphere, I_{ph}. The measurements can then be translated into effective temperatures by Stefan's law,

$$T_u = T_{ph}(I_u/I_{ph})^{1/4}.$$

Extensive measurements of I_u and I_{ph} have been made by Pettit and Nicholson (1928), Wormell (1936), and others. We find that I_u/I_{ph} ranges from about 0.1 to 0.8 and that there is a definite correlation with the size of the umbra, larger umbrae generally having smaller I_u/I_{ph} values. The problem of scattered light is extremely severe, and should not be under-estimated. A typical value for I_u/I_{ph} is probably 0.3 for fairly large umbrae. With $T_{ph} = 5800\ °K$, this would indicate a temperature difference between photosphere and umbra of about 1600 °K. For very large sunspots with extra dark cores through which large fluxes of magnetic field are channeled, the temperature difference may be significantly greater. Table 5.3, taken from Bray and Loughhead (1964), gives the umbral temperatures as a function of the umbral diameter. As pointed out by the cited authors, the data in Table 5.3 (p. 187) should be quite reliable since they are based on a large number of independent determinations.

Also, even though the penumbra looks dark, it is considerably brighter than the umbra. According to Bray and Loughhead, there is a gradual decrease in

TABLE 5.3 Temperature T of the umbra at unit optical depth as a function of the diameter d, km, of the umbra (courtesy Bray and Loughhead, 1964, Table 4.2, p. 112)

d	$T_u(\tau_u = 1)$	$(T_{ph} - T_u)(\tau_u = \tau_{ph} = 1)$
7250	5200	1200
14500	4700	1700
21700	4300	2100
29000	4200	2200
36200	4100	2300
43000	4000	2400

brightness from the photosphere ($I_{ph} = 1.0$) to the inner part of the penumbra ($I_p = 0.7$). Over a large part of the penumbra the brightness is fairly constant, $0.7 < I_p < 0.8$. A ratio, I_p/I_{ph}, of between 0.7 and 0.8 corresponds, for a photospheric temperature of 5800 °K, to a temperature difference between penumbra and photosphere of only 300 to 500 °K. Hence, the overwhelming part of the cooling in a sunspot takes place in the umbra. Previously we have also seen that most of the magnetic flux is channeled through the umbra. From these facts alone we therefore reach the tentative conclusion that the umbra is the really important part of the sunspot phenomenon. The penumbra, as a transition region, seems to be mainly of accidental interest. But we shall see in Section 5.2 that the energy transport in the penumbra poses some interesting problems.

It is known (Jensen, Nordö and Ringnes, 1955; Ringnes and Jensen, 1960) that the ratio between the area of the penumbra and the area of the umbra varies with the 11-year cycle, and that this may reflect a change of the magnetic field in dominating the structure of sunspots. We define the ratio q of the diameter of the penumbra (p) to the diameter of the umbra (u) as (Waldmeier, 1939b; Jensen, Nordö and Ringnes, 1955)

$$q = p/u = \sqrt{A_p/A_u} ,$$

where A_u and A_p are the corrected area of the umbra and the total area of the sunspot in millionths of the solar hemisphere. The ratio q varies roughly from a value of about 2.3 in years of sunspot minimum to 2.5 in maximum years. Also, q is smaller for regular than for complex spots (Tandberg-Hanssen, 1957) and therefore smaller for the preceding than for the following spots in most bipolar groups. According to Ringnes (1964), q shows a secular variation that may reflect the 80-year cycle.

The q-value measures not only the ratio of two areas of very different brightness but is a parameter that should be able to tell us something about the structure of sunspots. Since the structure seems to be determined by the magnetic field and its configuration, the correct interpretation of the variations of the q-ratio might therefore lead us toward a model of the field and how it changes.

5.1.8. Sunspot Curve of Growth

From observation of the equivalent width, W, of a number of absorption lines from the same element in sunspots it is possible to deduce an excitation temperature T_{ex} of the umbra. This is done by the curve of growth method. We plot the equivalent width—or in practice log W/λ—vs. a quantity depending on the excitation temperature. This temperature is determined by plotting curves of growth for a number of values of T_{ex} and deciding which value of T_{ex} best represents the observations. If we then construct curves of growth for successive stages of ionization of a given element, we can obtain the electron pressure p_e—provided Saha's equation is a sufficiently good approximation. The curve of growth has a transition region between the part corresponding to weak lines (where W/λ is proportional to the number of absorbing ions, Nf) and the part corresponding to strong lines [where $W/\lambda \propto (Nf)^{1/2}$]. The height of this flat transition region depends on the nonthermal component, v_t, of the atomic or ionic velocity. If one already has determined T_{ex}, it is therefore possible to infer the value of v_t (often called the turbulent velocity component).

Sunspot curves of growth have been obtained by ten Bruggencate and von Klüber (1939, 1944), Abhyankar and Ramanathan (1955), Zhuravlev (1957), Howard (1958), Zwaan (1959), and Kornilov (1961). There seems to be agreement that the transition part lies above that of the quiet photosphere. The position of the transition region indicates a nonthermal velocity of 1.7 km/sec in the photosphere (Allen, 1963) and approximately 3 km/sec in sunspots. Smaller values, however, have also been reported (Zhuravlev, 1957; Zwaan, 1959).

Most of the curve of growth analysis has been made using lines of Ti I and Fe I. There is a fair amount of scatter in the data, but we may conclude that the corresponding excitation temperatures are roughly 4000 °K, that is, about 1000 °K lower than in the photosphere. The Fraunhofer line spectrum therefore seems to give results on the physical parameters in sunspots in satisfactory agreement with the results obtained from the continuous spectrum.

5.1.9. Molecules in Sunspots

The spectra of sunspots reveal a number of bands indicating the existence of numerous molecular compounds in the umbra (Richardson, 1931; Babcock, 1945). The occurrence of molecules is, however, not restricted to spots; all identified bands belong to molecules that also give observable bands in the normal disk spectrum. On the other hand, there are many weak bands due to unidentified molecules that are found only in spot spectra.

Of the compounds found both in the normal photosphere and in spots, we mention the hydrides, CaH, CH, MgH, NH, OH, SiH, BH; the oxides, AlO, ScO, TiO, YO, MgO; the fluorides, MgF, SrF; and the compounds, CN, C_2, and O_2. Richardson reports bands due to H_2, but Babcock failed to see them. Of the more uncertain identifications, we mention AlH, BO, ZrO and SiF.

The relative intensities of the different bands often vary from spot to spot. This indicates that the temperature of spot umbrae varies from spot to spot, as found from studies of the continuous spectrum. By measuring the intensity of the bands, we may therefore infer the temperature of the plasma where the band lines are formed. The theory shows that the lines in a given band differ only in the value of the rotational quantum number, n_{rot}, involved. The intensity $I_{n_{rot}}$ of a line is given by

$$I_{n_{rot}} = \text{const} \, (2n_{rot} + 1) \exp\left[-n_{rot}(n_{rot} + 1)h^2/8\pi^2 \mathscr{I} kT_{rot}\right], \qquad (5.9)$$

where $\mathscr{I}$ is the moment of inertia of the molecule and T_{rot} is called the rotational temperature. One way of using Equation (5.9) to determine T_{rot} is to find the most intense line, $I_{n'_{rot}}$, in the band. The temperature is then given by

$$T_{rot} = \frac{h^2(2n_{rot} + 1)^2}{16\pi^2 \mathscr{I} k} \; .$$

For spots and quiet photosphere T_{rot} has been obtained by Richardson (1931) and Laborde (1961). The probable errors are large. Richardson found for the C_2 bands $T_{rot} = 4900\,°K$ in the umbra compared to $T_{rot} = 5800\,°K$ in the photosphere. For the hydrides, MgH, CH, NH, and OH, Laborde found $T_{rot} = 3800\,°K$ in spots and $4700\,°K$ in the photosphere.

5.1.10. The Wilson Effect

Wilson (1774) discovered that spot areas decrease toward the limb more than would be expected in normal foreshortening. This has been taken to mean that spots are saucerlike depressions in the solar surface. The umbra of a regular spot, which looks circular at the center of the solar disk, shrinks steadily as the spot approaches the western limb, as does the eastern half of the penumbra. But the western part of the penumbra, nearest to the limb, contracts more slowly, and very close to the limb this part of the penumbra is all that is visible of the spot. If the spot is long-lived enough to reappear at the eastern limb some two weeks later, the same sequence of events will be observed in the reverse order as the spot moves toward the center of the disk. This has been substantiated by later workers. According to Chistyakov (1961), spots with areas in the range 300 to 1400 millionths of the solar hemisphere show foreshortening of the umbra in general agreement with the cos θ law. But the foreshortening of the penumbra varies for different sides of the spot and gives rise to the Wilson effect.

Wilson's naïve model of a saucerlike depression has, of course, to be modified, but when optical depth is substituted for geometrical depth, his picture may still give a fair description of a sunspot. Due to the temperature and density differences between a sunspot and the normal photosphere, the optical depths in a spot and outside are quite different at the same geometrical depth. As we shall see in the next Section, most models of sunspots indicate that one sees to deeper layers in the umbra than in the quiet photosphere.

5.2. *Physical Conditions in Individual Sunspots; Models*

5.2.1. General Remarks

Any complete sunspot theory will have to account for all the data discussed in the first section of this chapter—and for quite a few more. A much less ambitious goal is to make a model of a sunspot that is in accordance with some chosen set of data and does not come in contradiction with the rest. While no complete theory of the sunspot phenomenon exists, several simplified models of individual sunspots have been worked out. Zwaan (1965) has made a detailed study of several sunspot models. Before we discuss these in some detail, we shall consider two basic questions regarding the sunspot plasma, namely (1) how closely does hydrostatic equilibrium apply, and (2) is radiative equilibrium a good approximation or not?

The mechanical stability of sunspots is sometimes viewed as a purely *hydrostatic* equilibrium, but *a priori* this assumption is neither obvious nor justified. Instead, we need to consider the possibility of a *magnetohydrostatic* equilibrium. The basic equations necessary are found in Section 1.1.3 and may be written as follows.

The equation of motion (1.33)

$$\rho \frac{d\mathbf{v}}{dt} = \frac{1}{c} \mathbf{j} \times \mathbf{B} - \nabla p + \rho \mathbf{g}. \tag{5.10}$$

The energy transfer equation (1.35)

$$\rho \frac{dU}{dt} = -p \nabla \cdot \mathbf{v} - \nabla \cdot \mathbf{F} + \mathbf{j} \cdot \left(\mathbf{E} + \frac{1}{c} \mathbf{v} \times \mathbf{B} \right). \tag{5.11}$$

The convective motions in sunspots, $\mathbf{v}$, are significantly smaller than the velocity of sound, V_s, in photospheric layers ($V_s \approx 7$ km/sec). Consequently, we consider only a magnetohydrostatic situation (not a dynamic description) and Equations (5.10) and (5.11) reduce to

$$\nabla p = \rho \mathbf{g} + \frac{1}{c} \mathbf{j} \times \mathbf{B}, \qquad (5.12)$$

and

$$\nabla \cdot \mathbf{F} = j^2/\sigma. \qquad (5.13)$$

Since the electric conductivity is very large, the Ohmic losses may be neglected and Equation (5.13) reduces to the equation of radiative equilibrium,

$$\nabla \cdot \mathbf{F} = 0.. \qquad (5.14)$$

Mattig (1958) assumed purely hydrostatic equilibrium, while the magneto-hydrostatic case has been treated by Schlüter and Temesváry (1958), Deinzer (1960, 1962), and Makita (1963).

If the magnetic field is force free, that is, $\mathbf{j} \times \mathbf{B} = 0$ or

$$(\nabla \times \mathbf{B}) \times \mathbf{B} = 0, \qquad (5.15)$$

Equation (5.12) reduces to the ordinary equation of hydrostatic equilibrium. This simpler case has been treated by Schatzman (1961) and is assumed to hold in Mattig's model of sunspots. Equation (5.15) is equivalent to $\nabla \times \mathbf{B} = f(x, y) \cdot \mathbf{B}$. Schatzman studied the case where the function $f(x, y)$ is a constant and found solutions where the magnetic field bears some resemblance to the classical picture of sunspot fields. However, no justification could be given for the assumption of a force-free field.

Since a deductive description of the interaction between magnetic fields and turbulent convection presents an unsolved problem, certain tentative suggestions for treating the energy transport in sunspots have been made in the past. Biermann (1941) considered the case where the magnetic field completely inhibits convective motions in the umbra. Radiative equilibrium then results within the sunspot, that is, all energy is carried by radiation. This requires a much steeper temperature gradient than in the surroundings where convection is active. The result is that the spot region must be cooler than the quiet photosphere.

Quite a different view has been taken by Hoyle (1949), who suggested that the only effect of the magnetic field consists in making the convective motions follow the lines of force (the electric conductivity is very high). If the lines of force spread out as they approach and reach the solar surface in the spot, the energy transported by convection is also spread over a greater area than further down. Consequently, the flux is decreased and the spot is cooler than its surroundings.

Hence the cooling of the spot, as caused by the presence of a magnetic field, may theoretically be achieved from very different starting points. Cowling (1953) suggested that the truth must lie somewhere between Biermann's and Hoyle's assumptions. In other words, there is a certain, nonnegligible, amount of energy transported by convection in a sunspot, but it is significantly smaller than in the quiet photosphere.

Numerical solutions to the problem in the approximation given by Equations (5.12) and (5.14), that is, using Biermann's hypothesis, have been attempted by Schlüter and Temesváry (1958) and Deinzer (1960). They conclude that it is necessary to have some transport of energy by convection ($\mathbf{v} \neq 0$), in order to obtain a realistic sunspot model. An attempt along these lines is due to Deinzer (1962, 1965), who assumes a fixed reduction of the convective energy flux in the presence of a magnetic field using the mixing length theory. He concludes that Hoyle's funneling effect is not effective enough to explain the observed umbra temperatures.

5.2.2. Models in which the Magnetic Field is Accidental

In most work on model atmospheres, one is generally satisfied when the run of temperature and pressure with optical depth has been established and when a geometrical depth can be associated with the optical depth. This constitutes the model. A similar philosophy has been adopted by many workers on sunspot models, even though most of them have realized that neglecting the magnetic field may seriously affect the pressure distribution.

5.2.2.1. Waldmeier's model

The center-to-limb variation of the intensity ratio $I(\text{umbra})/I(\text{photo-sphere})$, I_u/I_{ph}, was calculated by Minnaert and Wanders (1932) for the case of radiative equilibrium. They found that the ratio I_u/I_{ph} under these conditions should be practically independent of the heliocentric angle θ. Observations of I_u/I_{ph} at different wavelengths (Richardson, 1933; Wanders, 1935; Michard, 1953; Makita and Morimoto, 1960) and in integrated light (Wormell, 1936; Sitnik, 1940) are in agreement with Minnaert's and Wanders' predictions. This was used as an argument by Waldmeier (1942) to construct a *radiative* model of the umbra.

The dependence of temperature with optical depth in the photosphere is given by

$$T^4_{ph} = \tfrac{1}{2}(T_{eff})^4_{ph}(1 + \tfrac{3}{2}\tau_{ph}), \qquad (5.16)$$

and with Waldmeier's assumption, a similar expression holds for the temperature structure in the umbra:

$$T_u = \tfrac{1}{2}(T_{\text{eff}})_u^4(1 + \tfrac{3}{2}\tau_u). \tag{5.17}$$

Furthermore, Waldmeier assumed hydrostatic equilibrium, $dp/dh = -\rho g$. This equation, with $d\tau = -\bar{k}\rho \, dh$, takes the form (for convenience we drop the subscript u)

$$dp/d\tau = g/\bar{k}. \tag{5.18}$$

To find an expression for the absorption coefficient $\bar{k}$, Waldmeier used Saha's (1920, 1921) formula,

$$\log \frac{n_H}{n_{H^-}} p_e = -k_{H^-} \frac{5040}{T} + \frac{5}{2} T - 0.48 + \log \frac{2U_H}{U_{H^-}},$$

and considered only the absorption by the negative hydrogen atom. With the notation, $\phi(T) = n_{H^-}/n_H p_e$, we find with Waldmeier, that

$$\log \phi(T) = 0.70 \frac{5040}{T} - \frac{5}{2} \cdot \log T - 0.12 \tag{5.19}$$

and

$$\bar{k} = \frac{\bar{k}_{H^-}}{m_H} p_e \phi(T) = C p_e \phi(T) = \frac{Cp}{A} \phi(T), \tag{5.20}$$

where $A = n_H/n_{\text{metal}}$. Furthermore, Waldmeier assumed that the number of free electrons n_e is equal to the number of metal ions, that is,

$$p/p_e = A. \tag{5.21}$$

Equations (5.18) and (5.20) give

$$p \, dp = \frac{gA}{C} \frac{d\tau}{\phi(T)}. \tag{5.22}$$

The temperature T is uniquely determined by Equation (5.17). Hence, we may use $\phi(\tau)$ instead of $\phi(T)$. Equation (5.22) may then be integrated to give

$$p(\tau) = \sqrt{gA/C} \sqrt{2 \int_0^\tau [d\tau/\phi(\tau)]}, \tag{5.23}$$

since for $\tau = 0$ we have $p = 0$. Using Equation (5.21), we obtain from

Equation (5.23) the following expression for p_e:

$$p_e(\tau) = \sqrt{g/AC} \sqrt{2 \int_0^\tau [d\tau/\phi(\tau)]}. \qquad (5.24)$$

We arrive finally at Waldmeier's model by fixing the effective temperatures of the spot umbra and of the quiet photosphere as 4620 °K and 5740 °K, respectively (see Table 5.3).

To go from optical depth to geometrical depth, we combine the hydrostatic equation with the equation of state $p = R\rho T/\mu$ to get $dp/p = d \ln p = -(g\mu/R\tau)\, dh$. In the case treated by Waldmeier, this reduces to $dh = $ const $T\, d \log p$, where the constant is about -7×10^3. This equation was

TABLE 5.4   Waldmeier's model (courtesy Michard, 1953, Table V,
        p. 280; Bray and Loughhead, 1964, Table 4.3, p. 116)

τ	T_{ph}	T_u	p_{ph}	p_u	h_{ph}	h_u
0.01	4830	3890	9.8×10^3	5.8×10^3	398	399
0.10	4995	4020	3.2×10^4	1.95×10^4	223	255
0.50	5545	4460	7.95×10^4	5.0×10^4	82	136
1.00	5930	4875	1.25×10^5	8.1×10^4	0	69
2.00	6825	5490	2.1×10^5	1.4×10^5	-96	-13
4.00	7845	6310	3.7×10^5	2.5×10^5	-222	-114

graphically integrated by Waldmeier using values of $\log p$ from Equation (5.23) and T from Equation (5.17). The zero-points of the scales were first put at $\tau = 1$ independently for umbra and quiet photosphere. To get them on the same scale, Waldmeier used a previous argument (Waldmeier, 1941) that there should be pressure equilibrium at $\tau = 1.25$. This gives a difference in the zero-points for the two scales of about 69 km.

Waldmeier's model, Table 5.4, shows that we see to deeper layers in the quiet photosphere than in the umbra, a result in contradiction to most later investigations. His model therefore also cannot give an interpretation of the Wilson effect.

5.2.2.2. Michard's model

Instead of assuming radiative equilibrium, Michard (1953) used the observed center-to-limb variation of I_u/I_{ph} to construct *observational models* of the umbra. Michard's work refers to fairly large spots (diameter of the order 15,000 km) and provides one of the most extensively used sunspot models.

For each of several wavelengths, Michard measured the dependence $I_u(\lambda)/I_{ph}(\lambda) = f(\cos \theta)$. From these measurements, the variation of the source function $S_\lambda(\tau_u)$ with optical depth in the umbra could be determined. A unique dependence of T_u on τ_u was then established by assuming $S_\lambda(\tau_u) = B_\lambda(\tau_u)$, where $B_\lambda(\tau_u)$ is the Planck function. The derived temperature distribution is given in Table 5.5.

Ten Bruggencate and von Klüber (1944) measured the equivalent widths of Fe I, Ti I, and Ti II multiplet lines in sunspot umbrae and in the quiet photosphere and deduced corresponding excitation temperatures and electron pressures. Michard used their data on equivalent widths but reanalyzed them completely and came up with very different results. Michard's values for the electron pressure p_e are given in Table 5.5. They are deduced on the

TABLE 5.5   Michard's model (courtesy G. Abetti, 1963)

$\tau_{ph}(5000) = \tau_u(5000)$	T_{ph}	T_u	$(p_e)_{ph}$	$(p_e)_u$	p_{ph}	p_u	h_{ph}	h_u
0	4270	3550						
0.02	4520	3720	0.89	0.13	1.29×10^4	6.17×10^3	0	0
0.05	4760	3880	1.70	0.25	2.34×10^4	9.12×10^3	-77	-413
0.10	5010	4060	2.88	0.45	3.47×10^4	1.32×10^4	-132	-733
0.15	5200	4180	4.17	0.63	4.37×10^4	1.59×10^4	-167	-927
0.25	5490	4340	7.76	0.93	5.89×10^4	1.91×10^4	-206	-1190
0.50	5930	4590	19.1	1.6	7.76×10^4	2.5×10^4	-256	-1600
1.00	6450	4870	58.2	2.7	9.77×10^4	3.5×10^4	-300	-2100
2.00	7100	5250	214	5.4	1.15×10^5	5.3×10^4	-332	-2700

basis of the theory that the equivalent widths of faint Fraunhofer lines formed by pure absorption depend in a simple way on the electron pressure. For greater optical depths, Michard used the observed Balmer discontinuity to find p_e.

In turn, the electron pressure depends on the total gas pressure, p, the temperature, T, and the ratio of the metals to hydrogen, $1/A$. This last parameter is included because easily ionized metals contribute significantly to the electron pressure at the temperatures in question. In other words, Michard used the dependence $p = f(p_e, T, A)$ to find p, taking $A = 10^4$ and completely neglecting the abundance of helium. The value for the deduced gas pressure is entered in Table 5.5.

In Table 5.5 we compare the physical parameters temperature and pressure at the same optical depth in the umbra and the photosphere. To find the temperature and pressure difference between umbra and photosphere at a given geometrical depth, Michard assumed the perfect gas law to hold, $p = nkT = (\rho/\mu)RT$, and calculated the depth, h, from this equation and the expression defining the optical depth, $d\tau = -k\rho\,dh$, where k is the continuous absorption coefficient due to the negative hydrogen ion. After integration, this leads to

$$h_u = \text{const} \int_{\tau_u(0)}^{\tau_u} T_u \, d\tau_u / k_u \rho_u . \qquad (5.25)$$

The main ambiguity in Michard's model is due to the fact that the zero-points of the height scales for spot and photosphere cannot be determined independently. They were arbitrarily taken to coincide at $\tau_{\mathrm{ph}} = \tau_{\mathrm{u}} = 0.02$. However, no large error can be involved because of the steep pressure gradient in these outer layers of the atmosphere. Values for geometrical depths are given in Table 5.5.

Even allowing for a fair amount of uncertainty in Michard's model as portrayed in Table 5.5, we may conclude that the gas pressure is significantly less in the umbrae than in the normal photosphere just outside. Michard suggested that equilibrium could be restored by the magnetic field, but he did not follow the idea any further.

We may draw another conclusion of great importance from an inspection of Table 5.5, namely that the umbra is much more *transparent* than the photosphere. While direct information is not available from the photosphere below about 300 km (corresponding to optical depth about unity), one can probably see down to 5 or 6 times this depth in umbrae. This behavior is consistent with the observed Wilson effect, even though a complete explanation would require a detailed discussion of radiative transfer in spots.

5.2.2.3. *Mattig's model*

Mattig's (1958) work is based on the classical interpretation of magnetic field observations which states that the magnetic lines of force are perpendicular to the solar surface in the umbra. On this basis, Mattig concluded that magnetic forces cannot contribute to the support of material in the umbra, and his model is based on the assumption of hydrostatic equilibrium. Hence, he has $dp_{\mathrm{u}} = \rho_{\mathrm{u}} g \, dh_{\mathrm{u}}$ and $d\tau_{\mathrm{u}} = \rho_{\mathrm{u}} k_{\mathrm{u}} \, dh_{\mathrm{u}}$, whence [see Equation (5.25)]

$$dp_{\mathrm{u}}/d\tau_{\mathrm{u}} = g/k_{\mathrm{u}}.$$

In the following discussion we drop the index u which signifies umbra. Mattig assumes the hydrogen/helium ratio H/He $= 5$ and the the hydrogen/metal ratio H/metal $= 1/A = 2 \times 10^4$. The absorption coefficient k is that due to neutral hydrogen and H^- (k_{H} and k_{H^-}), both of which are well known. Consequently,

$$k = (\mathrm{const}/m_{\mathrm{H}})(k_{\mathrm{H}} m_{\mathrm{H}} + k_{\mathrm{H}^-} p_{\mathrm{e}}).$$

Introducing with Mattig the degree of ionization of the metals x_{i}, we find the following expression for the ratio p_{e}/p:

$$\frac{p_{\mathrm{e}}}{p} = \mathrm{const} \left[\frac{n(\mathrm{H\,II})}{n(\mathrm{H\,I})} + \frac{x_{\mathrm{i}}}{A} \right].$$

Mattig calculates $n(\text{H II})/n(\text{H I})$ by Saha's formula and arrives at the following expressions for p and p_e:

$$p\frac{dp}{d\tau} = 1.8g \Big/ \left[\frac{k_H}{p} + \frac{k_{H^-}}{1.2m_H}\left(\frac{n(\text{H II})}{n(\text{H I})} + \frac{x_i}{A}\right)\right], \qquad (5.26)$$

$$p_e = \frac{px_i}{2.4A} + \sqrt{\left(\frac{px_i}{2.4A}\right)^2 + \frac{n(\text{H II})}{1.2n(\text{H I})}p}. \qquad (5.27)$$

By a method of successive approximations (since besides p and p_e, x_i also is unknown) Equations (5.26) and (5.27) yield the variation of pressure with depth in Mattig's model (see Table 5.6).

TABLE 5.6   Mattig's model (courtesy Mattig, 1958,
Table 3, p. 284; Bray and Loughhead, 1964;
Table 4.5, p. 120)

$\tau_u(5000)$	T_u	$(p_e)_u$	p_u	h_u
0.001	3300	0.037	8.13×10^3	0
0.005	3520	0.10	1.18×10^4	-57
0.01	3620	0.16	2.75×10^4	-83
0.02	3720	0.26	3.89×10^4	-110
0.05	3880	0.49	6.17×10^4	-144
0.10	4060	0.89	8.71×10^4	-171
0.20	4270	1.70	1.23×10^5	-206
0.30	4400	2.40	1.48×10^5	-224
0.50	4590	3.80	1.91×10^5	-246
1.00	4870	6.76	2.63×10^5	-278
2.00	5250	12.9	3.80×10^5	-314

Comparing this model with Michard's (Table 5.5), we note the great differences in p, p_e, and h. Mattig's model presents us with a spot that is in reality less transparent than the surrounding quiet photosphere.

5.2.2.4. Van't Veer's model

This model is, in van't Veer's own words, only to be considered a preliminary working model (van't Veer, 1962). It is based on a method developed by van't Veer (1961) to determine the ratio of the gas pressure between a spot and the quiet photosphere by using the measured intensities in the wings of certain Fraunhofer lines. The temperature has to be known from other sources.

The intensity I_λ in the wing of an absorption line whose central intensity is I_0 is given by

$$I_\lambda = I_0 - I_\lambda[s/(\Delta\lambda)^2]$$

for a pressure-broadened line. The quantity s determines the intensity in the wing.

Van't Veer used observations in the far wings, where the following approximation for I_λ, in terms of the residual intensity r, may be used:

$$r = (I_0 - I_\lambda)/I_0 = s/(\Delta\lambda)^2 .$$

For the case of pure absorption, the expression for r in the wings is (Minnaert, 1936)

$$r = \frac{\sec\theta \int_0^1 B\tau_\lambda\, dx - \int_0^1 B(k_\lambda/k)\, dx}{\int_0^1 B\, dx},$$

where B is the Planck function, $x = e^{-\tau\sec\theta}$, k_λ is the line absorption coefficient, and k is the continuous absorption coefficient. Using Unsöld's (1955) formula for k_λ in the wing,

$$k_\lambda = \frac{1}{4\pi}\frac{e^2}{mc^3}\frac{\lambda^4}{(\Delta\lambda)^2}\, Nf\gamma ,$$

we find with van't Veer

$$s = \left(\frac{1}{4\pi}\frac{e^2}{mc^3}f\lambda^4 \int_0^1 B\left[\sec\theta\int_0^\tau \frac{N\gamma}{k}\, d\tau - \frac{N\gamma}{k}\right] dx\right)\Big/\int_0^1 B\, dx .$$

The ratio $s(\text{umbra})/s(\text{photosphere}) = s_u/s_{ph}$ may then be written as

$$s_u/s_0 = \left(\int_0^1 B_{ph}\left[\sec\theta_{ph}\int_0^{\tau_{ph}} \frac{N_{ph}\gamma_{ph}}{k_{ph}}\, d\tau_{ph} - \frac{N_{ph}\gamma_{ph}}{k_{ph}}\right] dx_{ph} \cdot \int_0^1 B_u\, dx_u\right)$$

$$\div \left(\int_0^1 B_u\left[\sec\theta_u\int_0^{\tau_u} \frac{N_u\gamma_u}{k_u}\, d\tau_u - \frac{N_u\gamma_u}{k_u}\right] dx_u \cdot \int_0^1 B_{ph}\, dx_{ph}\right) .$$

Van't Veer uses the photospheric model of Böhm-Vitense (1954) and Mattig (1958). If we then assume a certain model, $p = p(\tau)$ and $T = T(\tau)$, we may compute the corresponding ratio s_u/s_{ph}. On the other hand, this ratio may be observed. Van't Veer then showed that for a given temperature difference, $\Delta T = T_{ph} - T_u$, it is possible to deduce the gas pressure from the observed ratio s_u/s_{ph}. This is done by changing $p = p(\tau)$ and $T = T(\tau)$ until $(s_u/s_{ph})_{\text{computed}} \approx (s_u/s_{ph})_{\text{observed}}$.

Each model is consequently characterized by two parameters, ΔT and p_u at a certain depth τ_u. Van't Veer's first model (1961) was characterized by $\Delta T = 1385\,°\text{K}$ and $p_u = 1.07 \times 10^5$ dynes cm^{-2}, while the subsequent

TABLE 5.7   van't Veer's model (courtesy van't Veer, 1961, Table 6, p. 183; 1962, Table 5, p. 216)

$\tau_{\mathrm{ph}}(5000) = \tau_{\mathrm{u}}(5000)$	T_{ph}	T_{u}	$(p_{\mathrm{e}})_{\mathrm{ph}}$	$(p_{\mathrm{e}})_{\mathrm{u}}$	p_{ph}	p_{u}	h_{ph}	h_{u}
0.01	4700	3570	0.71	0.14	1.95×10^4	1.3×10^4	0	0
0.05	4930	3700	1.82	0.31	4.8×10^4	2.7×10^4	-130	-370
0.10	5066	3780	3.16	0.43	6.9×10^4	3.7×10^4	-185	-550
0.30	5510	4020	8.32	1.05	1.2×10^5	6.2×10^4	-260	-875
0.50	5830	4180	17.78	1.66	1.5×10^5	7.8×10^4	-295	-1030
1.00	6405	4480	63.10	3.09	1.8×10^5	1.1×10^5	-330	-1270
2.00	7180	4840	282	5.25	2.0×10^5	1.4×10^5	-355	-1555
4.00	8100	5240	1380	7.94	2.2×10^5	2.0×10^5	-370	-1950

model, given in Table 5.7, corresponds to $\Delta T = 1925\,^{\circ}\mathrm{K}$ and $p_{\mathrm{u}} = 3.7 \times 10^4$. Van't Veer finds that the larger the spot (and therefore the greater the value of ΔT), the larger is the pressure difference between the umbra and the photosphere. Because of the relatively smaller pressure in the umbra, one sees deeper down into the spot than into the photosphere (see Table 5.7). The geometrical scale is fixed by using the definition $d\tau = k\rho\, dh$ and by letting the scales coincide for $\tau = 0.01$.

5.2.3. Models Including Magnetic Field

5.2.3.1. *Makita's model*

Makita's model (1963) rests on the observations (Nishi, 1962) and theoretical considerations that the radial mass flow in the penumbra (the Evershed effect) must be parallel to the magnetic lines of force. The vertical component of the electromagnetic force $(\nabla \times \mathbf{B}) \times \mathbf{B}$, which may provide some additional lifting force on the matter in the penumbra, then reduces to $-\frac{1}{2}(\partial B_r^2 / \partial z)$. For the umbra, Makita considers the magnetic field to be vertical. In that case, the lifting force

$$[(\nabla \times \mathbf{B}) \times \mathbf{B}]_z = B_r \left(\frac{\partial B_z}{\partial r} - \frac{\partial B_r}{\partial z} \right)$$

reduces to zero not only at the axis, $r = 0$, but over the whole umbra.

The vertical balance in the penumbra is given by

$$\frac{\partial p}{\partial h} = \rho g - \frac{\partial}{\partial h}\left(\frac{B^2}{8\pi} \right),$$

whence we find the field necessary to ensure equilibrium,

$$B^2 = 8\pi \int_{h_0}^{h} (\rho g - dp/dh)\, dh, \tag{5.28}$$

where h_0 is the height above which hydrostatic equilibrium breaks down.

While the vertical balance in the penumbra is taken care of by the magnetic field (5.28), other forces are necessary to bring about horizontal balance. Makita here draws on the Evershed effect, which is assumed to follow the magnetic lines of force, the matter streaming radially with velocity v_r. Equilibrium will prevail if this velocity is governed by the equation

$$\tfrac{1}{2}\rho v_r^2 = p_{\mathrm{ph}} - p_{\mathrm{p}}, \tag{5.29}$$

where p_{ph} and p_{p} are the pressures in the photosphere and the penumbra, respectively. Makita finds that the magnetic field and the radial velocity needed, according to Equations (5.28) and (5.29), lead to a very reasonable model for the penumbra. He even finds an explanation for the bright ring observed around sunspots. This ring is interpreted as the region where the Evershed flow stops, since the velocity v_r has a maximum at about $\tau_{\mathrm{ph}} = 1$, just where the ring is hotter than the photosphere.

The umbra has to be in hydrostatic equilibrium in Makita's model. The only other lifting force (in addition to the rejected electromagnetic effect) would be a vertical velocity field v_z. However, the required values of v_z are impossibly large. The equilibrium conditions lead to the equation

$$\frac{dp}{dh} = \rho g - \frac{1}{2}\rho \frac{dv_z^2}{dh} \quad \text{or} \quad v_z^2 = 2 \int_{h_0}^{h} \left(g - \frac{1}{\rho}\frac{dp}{dh} \right) dh, \tag{5.30}$$

which requires v_z to be of the order of 40 km/sec.

Makita was unable to find a consistent uniform model for the umbra because of the presence of high excitation lines in the umbral spectrum. These lines require low pressure, and the only restoring force available $(\nabla \times \mathbf{B}) \times \mathbf{B}$ was rejected. The solution offered consists of a two-component

TABLE 5.8   Makita's penumbra model (courtesy Makita, 1963, Table 3, p. 165)

$\tau_{\mathrm{p}}(5000)$	T_{p}	$(p_e)_{\mathrm{p}}$	p_{p}	h_{p}
0.001	3810	0.20	3.2×10^3	0
0.0025	3960	0.33	5.1×10^3	−24
0.01	4240	0.82	1.0×10^4	−73
0.025	4400	1.40	1.6×10^4	−121
0.063	4540	2.09	2.2×10^4	−183
0.10	4620	2.57	2.6×10^4	−223
0.16	4890	3.55	2.7×10^4	−278
0.25	5180	5.50	3.4×10^4	−348
0.40	5470	9.12	4.6×10^4	−420
1.00	6020	26.0	6.9×10^4	−539
2.50	6760	117.5	1.2×10^5	−651

model: a hot component in hydrostatic equilibrium where the high excitation lines are formed and a cold component likewise in hydrostatic equilibrium where the remaining lines are formed. To satisfy observations, Makita concluded that the hot component occupies about $\frac{1}{10}$ of the umbral area. The radiation temperatures of the hot and the cold components are 5700 °K and 4000 °K, respectively.

Makita uses the magnetic field in building part of his model. However, while this is done for the penumbra, the much stronger field in the umbra is completely accidental.

The physical quantities in the penumbra are given in Table 5.8.

5.2.3.2. Schlüter's and Temesváry's model

This is not a model in the classical sense of the word since the authors (Schlüter and Temesváry, 1958) are not primarily interested in the run of temperature and pressure with depth. Instead, they treat the interaction of the magnetic field with the sunspot plasma which is assumed to be at rest [**v** in Equations (5.10), (5.11), (5.12) and (5.18) is identically zero]. Furthermore, it is assumed that the spot and its field are axially symmetric $(B_\phi = 0)$, and on the axis, $r = 0$, B_z has its maximal value while $B_r = 0$. To single out a simple class of solutions, Schlüter and Temesváry further assumed that the relative distribution of the vertical component of the magnetic field is the same across the flux tube of the spot at all depths. This similarity condition may be written in cylindrical coordinates

$$B_z(r, z) = B_z(0, z) \frac{D(\alpha)}{D(0)} , \qquad (5.31)$$

with $\alpha = r \cdot \zeta(z)$. Then the reciprocal of the scale factor $\zeta(z)$ describes the dependence on depth of the diameter of a flux tube constituting the sunspot field, and the function $D(\alpha)$ determines the shape.

The assumption underlying Equation (5.31) is reasonable only if there are no returning lines of force in the same sunspot, i.e., if the total magnetic flux Φ has a finite constant value throughout the spot. Recent observations (Bray and Loughhead, 1964) seem to contradict the older interpretation of the shape of the magnetic field according to which a spot always has only one polarity. Nevertheless, Equation (5.31) may imply a suitably good first approximation.

We chose $D(0)$ so that the following normalization condition applies:

$$2\pi \int_0^\infty D(\alpha)\alpha \, d\alpha = \Phi .$$

Then the components of the magnetic field according to Equation (5.31) may be written

$$B_z(r, z) = D(\alpha)\zeta^2(z), \tag{5.32}$$

$$B_r(r, z) = -D(\alpha)\alpha\,(d\zeta/dz), \tag{5.33}$$

$$B_\phi(r, z) = 0. \tag{5.34}$$

The r-component of Equation (5.11) is

$$B_z\left(\frac{\partial B_r}{\partial z} - \frac{\partial B_z}{\partial r}\right) = 4\pi\,\frac{\partial p}{\partial r}\,. \tag{5.35}$$

Introducing Equations (5.32), (5.33), and (5.34) into Equation (5.35), we find the following equation for the magnetic field:

$$fy\,\frac{d^2y}{dz^2} - y^4 + 8\pi[p(0, z) - p(\infty, z)] = 0, \tag{5.36}$$

where

$$y \equiv \sqrt{B_z(0, z)} \tag{5.37}$$

and

$$f = \frac{\Phi}{\pi}\,\frac{\displaystyle\int_0^\infty [D(\alpha)/D(0)]^2\,\alpha\,d\alpha}{\displaystyle\int_0^\infty [D(\alpha)/D(0)]\,\alpha\,d\alpha}\,. \tag{5.38}$$

The z-component of Equation (5.19) leads to a simple expression for the pressure difference between the axis and the undisturbed photosphere at the same depth

$$\frac{dp(\infty, z)}{dz} - \frac{dp(0, z)}{dz} = g[\rho(\infty, z) - \rho(0, z)] \tag{5.39}$$

because the magnetic force $(\nabla \times \mathbf{B}) \times \mathbf{B}$ vanishes at the axis ($r = 0$) and at infinity. Due to the similarity assumption, one only needs to know the physical conditions along the axis of the field tube. Consequently, the equation governing the field reduces to an ordinary differential equation with depth as the independent variable. If, therefore, the horizontal pressure difference is known as a function of depth, the magnetic field may be found from Equation (5.36).

Several forms may reasonably be assumed for the horizontal distribution of the sunspot flux $D(\alpha)$. Taking $D(\alpha) = D(0)\,e^{-\alpha^2}$, that is, Gaussian, we find from Equation (5.38) $\Phi = 2\pi f$. The use of Broxon's formula, Equation

(5.1), leads to

$$B_z = B_0 \frac{1 - r^2}{\mathrm{p}^2} \cdot \cos \left(\frac{\pi}{2} \frac{r}{\mathrm{p_p}} \right)$$

and gives approximately

$$\Phi = 2\pi \int_0^\infty B_z r \, dr \approx B_m \mathrm{p}^2 .$$

With $\alpha = (\pi/2)(r/\mathrm{p})$, we get, for $r < \mathrm{p}$,

$$D(\alpha) = D(0) \left(1 - \frac{4}{\pi^2} \alpha^2 \right) \cos \alpha$$

and $\Phi = 1.7\pi f$, which is not significantly different from the result obtained for a purely Gaussian distribution.

The expressions for $B_r(r, z)$ and $B_z(r, z)$ in terms of $D(\alpha)$ lead to

$$\frac{B_r}{B_z} = -r \frac{d \ln \zeta}{dz} , \tag{5.40}$$

that is, the ratio B_r/B_z increases linearly with r according to the similarity relation. Under these conditions also, the increase with depth of the field on the axis follows from Equation (5.40), and one finds with Schlüter and Temesváry a gradient

$$dB/dz \approx 4(B/r) .$$

For $B = 2{,}000$ gauss and $\mathrm{p} = 10{,}000$ km, the vertical magnetic field gradient is $dB/dz \approx 0.8$ gauss/km in fair agreement with the value 0.5 gauss/km found by Houtgast and van Sluiters (1948).

Schlüter and Temesváry tried to make reasonable assumptions regarding the effects of convection in the spot when solving Equation (5.36). They, however, had to conclude that the neglect of mass motions ($v = 0$) seriously limited the validity of any sunspot model based on this assumption. Their work has been continued by Deinzer, and we shall now consider his treatment of the problem of sunspot models.

5.2.3.3. Deinzer's model

Deinzer's work (1960, 1962, 1965) may be considered an extension of the investigations started by Schlüter and Temesváry. The basic new idea is to account for a partial inhibition of convective energy transport in the sunspot due to a magnetic field. This is done by an application of Prandtl's mixing length theory of convection. According to this theory, turbulent elements are formed in the deeper parts of the atmosphere, then they rise and mix with the surroundings after they have traveled a distance l, the mixing length. The elements are responsible for convective energy transport in as much as they give up their energy excess to the surroundings while moving the distance l. This distance is usually believed to be of the order of the pressure scale height H. The ratio l/H will then govern the efficiency of convection in transporting energy, and may be used as a parameter to describe partial inhibition of convection by a magnetic field. Let $(l/H)_{\text{ph}}$ denote the value appropriate to the quiet layers outside sunspots. The condition $l/H \to (l/H)_{\text{ph}}$ then indicates no inhibition of convection by the magnetic field and corresponds to the idea of Hoyle (1949) mentioned in the introduction to this chapter. The limit $l/H \to 0$ corresponds to complete inhibition, as advocated by Biermann (1941). Deinzer accounts for the coupling of the magnetic field with the convective motions through the parameter l/H and avoids the difficulty of solving the complete magneto-hydrodynamic equations. Like Schlüter and Temesváry, Deinzer uses the magnetohydrostatistic equations, but he goes further than the first-mentioned authors in coupling these equations with the equation for the energy balance. The latter gives a relation between the temperature gradient and the energy flux as governed by the magnetic field through the parameter l/H.

Deinzer, therefore, starts with the momentum equation as given in (5.11) and assumes the same similarity law for the vertical component B_z as Schlüter and Temesváry, i.e., Equation (5.31). Consequently, he gets as the equation for the magnetic field the relation (5.36):

$$fy(d^2y/dz^2) - y^4 + 8\pi[p(0, z) - p(\infty, z)] = 0.$$

To solve Equation (5.36), we need the horizontal pressure difference, which again can be found from the vertical component of (5.19). Instead of the form (5.39) used in the previous section, Deinzer combines it with the equation of state for an ideal gas and obtains the relation

$$\frac{dz}{d \log p} = (\ln 10) \frac{RT}{\mu g} = \ln 10 \cdot H. \qquad (5.41)$$

This equation has to be combined with the equation for the energy balance to obtain two simultaneous equations for T and p as functions of depth. The total flux is the sum of the convective flux F_C and the radiative flux F_R, where

$$F_C = \tfrac{1}{2} c_p \rho \bar{v} l[(dT/dz) - (dT/dz)_t] \qquad (5.42)$$

and

$$F_R = \frac{4\sigma c T^3}{3k\rho} \frac{dT}{dz}. \qquad (5.43)$$

The quantity $l\rho\bar{v}$ is called the turbulent *Austausch* and is a measure of the energy convected with velocity $\bar{v}$ over the mixing length distance. We have dT/dz as the actual temperature gradient, while $(dT/dz)_t$ is the temperature gradient governing the change of state of the turbulent elements partaking in the convective energy transport. These elements have a mean velocity $\bar{v}$ given by

$$\bar{v}^2 = \frac{1}{8} l^2 \frac{g}{T} \left[\left(\frac{dT}{dz}\right) - \left(\frac{dT}{dz}\right)_t \right].$$

Instead of the temperature gradient dT/dz, we introduce with Deinzer, in the following equations the logarithmic temperature gradient

$$(d \ln T)/(d \ln p) \equiv \nabla T.$$

When convection is inhibited, all energy is transported by radiation. The logarithmic temperature gradient is then the radiative gradient ∇T_R, which assumes the form

$$\nabla T_R \equiv \left(\frac{d \ln T}{d \ln p}\right)_R = \frac{3}{16} \frac{k\rho H}{\sigma T^4}. \tag{5.44}$$

When this radiative temperature gradient is less than the adiabatic gradient, the atmosphere is stable against convection. For a pure hydrogen atmosphere (which is a good approximation since hydrogen is the only element undergoing ionization in the region considered), the adiabatic temperature gradient takes the form

$$\nabla T_{ad} \equiv \left(\frac{d \ln T}{d \ln p}\right)_{ad} = \frac{2 + x(1 - x)(\frac{5}{2} + \chi/kT)}{5 + x(1 - x)(\frac{5}{2} + \chi/kT)^2}.$$

When $\nabla T_R > \nabla T_{ad}$, turbulent convection sets in and convective energy transport must be included. Introducing the logarithmic temperature gradients and the parameter l/H, we may write Equations (5.42) and (5.43) in the form

$$F_R = \frac{3}{16} \frac{\sigma T^4}{k\rho H} \nabla T \tag{5.45}$$

and

$$F_C = \frac{1}{2} c_p \rho T \bar{v} \frac{l}{H} (\nabla T - \nabla T_t). \tag{5.46}$$

The rising turbulent elements, whose mean velocity now may be written

$$\bar{v}^2 = \frac{1}{8} \frac{RT}{\mu} \left(\frac{l}{H}\right)^2 (\nabla T - \nabla T_t), \tag{5.47}$$

would undergo adiabatic changes were it not for radiative exchange of energy with the surroundings. Assuming the elements to be optically thick, we find with Deinzer for the radiative exchange the following approximate expression

$$\frac{\nabla T - \nabla T_t}{\nabla T_t - \nabla T_{\mathrm{ad}}} = \frac{1}{24} \frac{c_p \rho^2 T k H \bar{v}}{\sigma T^4} \frac{l}{H} \,. \tag{5.48}$$

Deinzer solves this system of equations by a method envisaged by Kippenhahn (1963). Equations (5.47) and (5.48) give

$$(\nabla T - \nabla T_t) + 2U\sqrt{\nabla T - \nabla T_t} - (\nabla T - \nabla T_{\mathrm{ad}}) = 0 \,, \tag{5.49}$$

where

$$U = 12 \frac{\sigma T^4}{c_p \rho^2 T k H} \left(\frac{H}{l}\right)^2 \sqrt{\frac{8\mu}{RT}} \,. \tag{5.50}$$

By combining Equations (5.46), (5.47), (5.48), and (5.49), we find

$$(\nabla T - \nabla T_{\mathrm{ad}}) - (\nabla T_{\mathrm{R}} - \nabla T_{\mathrm{ad}}) + V\{\sqrt{U^2 + (\nabla T - \nabla T_{\mathrm{ad}})} - U\}^3 = 0 \,, \tag{5.51}$$

where the positive root for $\sqrt{\nabla T - \nabla T_t}$ from Equation (5.49) has been used, and where

$$V = \frac{3}{32} \frac{c_p \rho T k H}{\sigma T^4} \left(\frac{l}{H}\right)^2 \sqrt{\frac{RT}{8\mu}} \,.$$

As the equations describing his model, Deinzer then uses Equation (5.48) and the root of Equation (5.51). The solution of these two simultaneous differential equations gives the temperature and pressure along the axis of symmetry. Values for k were taken from the work of Böhm-Vitense (1951), and the expressions for μ, c_p, and x from Kippenhahn, Temesváry, and Biermann (1958).

The influence of the magnetic field is realized by decreasing the quantity l/H below the value corresponding to the hydrogen convection zone. When l/H decreases sufficiently, the turbulent elements become optically thin and U is redefined (Böhm-Vitense, 1953)

$$U = 12 \frac{\sigma T^4 k H}{c_p T} \sqrt{\frac{8\mu}{RT}} \,.$$

We shall not go into all the details concerning the important boundary conditions of the problem. However, some comments are in order. At the upper boundary Deinzer fits the interior solution for temperature and pressure to those of the quiet photosphere, using Böhm-Vitense's (1951) model atmosphere. The magnetic field above the photosphere is required to be that of a monopole and decrease in the outward direction. This means that $y \equiv [B_z(0, z)]^{1/2}$ and dy/dz go identically to zero at infinity. The corresponding necessary and sufficient condition can be obtained directly from Equation (5.43). The difference $p(0, z) - p(\infty, z)$ decreases rapidly above the photosphere and may be put equal to zero. We can then integrate the reduced Equation (5.43) and find

$$\tfrac{1}{2}f\,(dy/dz)^2 - \tfrac{1}{4}y^4 = C_1\,, \tag{5.52}$$

where $C_1 = 0$ to satisfy conditions at infinity. Equation (5.52) leads to

$$dy/dz = y^2/(2f)^{1/2}\,, \tag{5.53}$$

which integrates to

$$y = -\sqrt{2f}\big/(z + \text{const}).$$

This goes to zero at infinity as do its derivatives, whence (5.53) is the correct upper boundary condition for **B**.

The position of the upper boundary relative to the outside geometrical scale is a difficult quantity to assess. It would be natural to choose the zero-point of the spot's geometrical scale to coincide with the undisturbed photosphere outside. Then we would have to specify the depth, z_D, of the photospheric level at the center of the spot. This depth is referred to as the geometrical depression of the sunspot. However, the pressure varies rapidly with depth and z_D will therefore enter the pressure difference very sensitively and greatly affect the calculations. Since the value of z_D is poorly known from observations, Deinzer prefers to establish the relation between the inside and outside geometrical scales by choosing an appropriate condition at the lower boundary of the spot region, z_0, and predict z_D.

We do not know anything about the magnetic field at the lower boundary, z_0, of the spot. But it turns out that a useful condition is the requirement that **B** become independent of depth at and below z_0, that is,

$$dy/dz = 0\,, \qquad d^2y/dz^2 = 0 \qquad \text{at} \quad z = z_0\,. \tag{5.54}$$

Using Equation (5.43), we can transform Equation (5.54) into

$$p(0\,, z) - p(\infty\,, z) = y^4/8\pi \qquad \text{at} \quad z = z_0\,.$$

The final set of boundary conditions may be put in the following form:

At the upper boundary,

$$p = p(T_{\text{eff}}), \qquad dy/dz = y^2/(2f)^{1/2} .$$

At the lower boundary,

$$p(0 , z) - p(\infty , z) = y^4/8\pi$$

and

$$dy/dz = 0, \; T(0 , z) - T(\infty , z) = T/p[p(0 , z) - p(\infty , z)] .$$

It turns out that a model is uniquely determined by specifying the three parameters z_0, T_{eff}, and Φ. In the actual calculations, Deinzer first determined temperature and pressure for the undisturbed convection zone, starting with the boundary conditions at $z = 0$, namely $\log p = 4.85$, $T_{\text{eff}} = 5800 \, °\text{K}$, and $l/H = 1$. A value of z_0 was chosen and $p(0 , z_0) - p(\infty , z_0)$ was guessed at. With these values inserted into an equation of the form (derived from the condition $d[p(0 , z_0) - p(\infty , z_0)]/dz = 0$),

$$\frac{p(0 , z_0) - p(\infty , z_0)}{p} = \frac{T(0 , z_0) - T(\infty , z_0)}{T} ,$$

we obtain the temperature difference at $z = z_0$. From this, one finds the temperature and pressure at the spot axis by adding $p(0 , z_0) - p(\infty , z_0)$ and $T(0 , z_0) - T(\infty , z_0)$ to the values in the normal convection zone at $z = z_0$. Using Böhm-Vitense's (1951) results, we can find the photospheric pressure at the spot axis at $\tau = \frac{2}{3}$ for the chosen value of T_{eff}.

We now know T and p at two points on the axis of the spot and the basic differential Equation (5.43) can be solved by trial and error since solutions only exist for discrete values of l/H (l/H is an eigenvalue of the problem). One then knows the horizontal pressure difference $p(0 , z) - p(\infty , z)$, and by choosing the flux Φ, solutions for $y = y(z)$ can be obtained from Equation (5.43).

The characteristics of several models (obtained by choosing different values for T_{eff} in the spot) are portrayed in Table 5.9. In the last line, corresponding data for the quiet photosphere are given for comparison. We see that the pressure in sunspots at photospheric levels is larger than in the quiet photosphere. Now, the horizontal pressure difference must be positive to balance magnetic forces. Consequently, the visible level in the sunspot must be lower than in the quiet photosphere. The visible level must lie at a depth where the pressure outside has increased to a value sufficient

TABLE 5.9   Models according to Deinzer (courtesy Deinzer, 1962, Table 1)

Model	T_{eff}	p	z_D, km	Φ, 10^{10} ergs/cm^2 sec	l/H	$B_z(0, z_D)$	$B_z(0, -\infty)$
1	3800	1.48×10^5	815	1.17	0.185	3850	9600
2	4000	1.41×10^5	700	1.43	0.226	3430	8660
3	4200	1.32×10^5	590	1.75	0.277	3080	7580
4	4400	1.20×10^5	480	2.10	0.345	2660	6720
5	5000	9.95×10^4	240	3.50	0.556	1810	4640
Photosphere	5800	7.08×10^4	0	6.42	1.000	0	0

to make $p(0, z) - p(\infty, z) > 0$. In accordance with this reasoning, column 4 of Table 5.9 shows that the geometrical depth z_D is several hundred km, in general agreement with the observed Wilson effect.

Columns 2 and 7 give a relation between T_{eff} of a spot and the corresponding vertical component of the magnetic field on the axis $B_z(0, z_D)$. From columns 6 and 7, we similarly find the $B_z(0, z_D) =$ function (l/H) relation, portraying the effect of inhibition of convective transport by the magnetic field. It is interesting that an extrapolation of $l/H \to 0$ results in an upper limit of the field of about 5000 gauss. This occurs for a spot where the inhibition of convective motions is complete, and corresponds to Biermann's suggestion (see Section 5.2.1). It may also be noted that the flux-decrease from small to large spots (T_{eff} 5000 °K and 3800 °K, respectively) according to column 5 is much larger in Deinzer's models than one would expect if Hoyle's picture were correct (see Section 5.2.1).

5.2.3.4. Danielson's penumbra model

In an attempt to interpret the outstanding solar photographs obtained by balloon-borne telescopes, Danielson (1961b) has derived a penumbra model of great interest. The main idea is that the observed long filaments, generally radially oriented, may be explained as long narrow convection cells, so-called convection rolls. The axis of the roll is parallel to the magnetic field, which is nearly horizontal in the penumbra.

One of the reasons why Danielson interprets the penumbra structure in terms of convection rolls is that when convection is neglected, the cooling times are so rapid that one cannot account for the observed penumbral filaments. Consider, for instance, the filaments simply as hot material flowing in streams about 300 km wide across the penumbra along horizontal magnetic lines of force. It would then be necessary for the cooling time of streams 300 km wide to be at least as long as the time needed to flow across the penumbra. If the flow velocity is taken to be the observed Evershed velocity, one finds that the cooling time should be of the order of an hour. Danielson estimated the cooling time for an infinite homogeneous system using the results of Spiegel's investigations (1957). A sinusoidal plane wave perturbation of amplitude $A(k, t)$ was assumed, where k is the wave number and the following expression for $A(k, t)$ may be derived:

$$A(k, t) = A(k, 0)e^{-t/t_0}.$$

The cooling time t_0 is then given by

$$t_0 = \sqrt{\rho c_p} \bigg/ 4 \sqrt{\bar{k}\sigma T^3 \left(1 - \frac{\bar{k}}{k} \cot^{-1} \frac{\bar{k}}{k}\right)}, \qquad (5.55)$$

where $\bar{k}$ is the mean absorption coefficient per cm.

The cooling time was computed as a function of optical depth τ for the normal photospheric model (Minnaert, 1953) and for Mattig's umbra model (see Table 5.6). The conditions in penumbrae would then presumably be intermediate between these two models. Danielson concludes that the cooling time t_0 for a 300 km wide stream of hot material for optical depths less than 5 is probably shorter than one minute.

On the other hand, when convection is involved, the lifetime of tempera- ture differences is determined not by the cooling time but by the time during which it is possible to maintain a given pattern of convective velocities. Danielson considers the penumbral filaments as hot rising tubes of force and the darker parts of the penumbra between the filaments as cool sinking material. Theoretically, one may here rely on Chandrasekhar's work (1952, 1954), where it is shown that the most unstable mode in the presence of a magnetic field is an infinitely long convection roll. The natural thing there- fore is to consider convection in the presence of a magnetic field and try to tie the results to the observed structure of the penumbrae. Danielson did this in the framework of Chandrasekhar's investigations of convection by thermal instability in a conducting medium in the presence of a magnetic field. A more detailed discussion of this problem will be given in Section 5.3, when we treat the general theory of sunspots. Here we simply state the equations and the results as an illustration of the application of the theory to the penumbral convection rolls. We consider a horizontal layer of fluid of depth d confined between two parallel planes $z = 0$ and $z = d$. The equations describing this situation are the equation of motion

$$\rho \frac{\partial \mathbf{v}}{\partial t} + \rho(\mathbf{v} \cdot \nabla)\mathbf{v} = \frac{1}{c}\mathbf{j} \times \mathbf{B} - \nabla p + \rho\eta \, \nabla^2\mathbf{v} - \rho\mathbf{g},$$

the energy equation, which is the equation of heat conduction,

$$\partial T/\partial t + (\mathbf{v} \cdot \nabla)T = K\nabla^2 T,$$

where η is the kinematic viscosity and K is the thermal conductivity, and

Maxwell's equations

$$\nabla \times \mathbf{B} = \frac{4\pi}{c}\mathbf{j}, \quad \nabla \times \mathbf{E} = -\frac{1}{c}\frac{\partial \mathbf{B}}{\partial t}, \quad \nabla \cdot \mathbf{B} = 0, \quad \mathbf{j} = \sigma\left(\mathbf{E} + \frac{\mathbf{v}}{c}\times \mathbf{B}\right).$$

This set of equations was solved in the Boussinesq approximation for the case of a uniform magnetic field making an angle θ with the vertical. Let us take the field to lie in the x, z plane and let the time-dependence of the perturbation on the field (B') and temperature (T') as well as of the vertical velocity (v_z) be given by $\exp{(\omega t)}$. It can then be shown that the equation for ω takes the form

$$(\omega - K\nabla^2)(\omega - \eta_m\nabla^2)(\omega - \eta\nabla^2)\nabla^2 v_z$$

$$= \frac{B^2}{4\pi\rho}\left(\sin\theta\,\frac{\partial}{\partial x} + \cos\theta\,\frac{\partial}{\partial z}\right)^2(\omega - K\nabla^2)\nabla^2 v_z$$

$$+ \left|\frac{dT}{dz}\right|g\alpha(\omega - \eta_m\nabla^2)\left(\frac{\partial^2 v_z}{\partial x^2} + \frac{\partial^2 v_z}{\partial y^2}\right), \quad (5.56)$$

where η_m is the electric resistivity, $c^2/4\pi\mu\sigma$, and α is the volume coefficient of expansion. For either a vertical ($\theta = 0$) or a horizontal ($\theta = \pi/2$) field, the following expression for v_z satisfies Equation (5.56) when both boundaries are free:

$$v_z = \text{const} \cdot \cos{(k_x x)}\cos{(k_y y)}\cdot\sin{(k_z z)}.$$

Here k_x, k_y, and k_z are the wave numbers in the x-, y-, and z-directions, respectively, $k_z = \pi/d$. Under these circumstances, Equation (5.56) reduces to

$$\left[\omega\frac{d^2}{\pi^2} + K\left(\frac{k_x^2 + k_y^2}{k_z^2} + 1\right)\right]\left[\omega\frac{d^2}{\pi^2} + \eta_m\left(\frac{k_x^2 + k_y^2}{k_z^2} + 1\right)\right]$$

$$\times\left[\omega\frac{d^2}{\pi^2} + \eta\left(\frac{k_x^2 + k_y^2}{k_z^2} + 1\right)\right] + \frac{Q}{\pi^2}\eta_m\eta\left[\omega\frac{d^2}{\pi^2} + K\left(\frac{k_x^2 + k_y^2}{k_z^2} + 1\right)\right]$$

$$- \frac{R}{\pi^4}K\eta\left[\omega\frac{d^2}{\pi^2} + \eta_m\left(\frac{k_x^2 + k_y^2}{k_z^2} + 1\right)\right]\frac{k_x^2 + k_y^2}{\eta k_z^2} = 0, \quad (5.57)$$

where the Rayleigh number R is defined as

$$R = \frac{g\alpha d^4}{K\eta}\left|\frac{dT}{dz}\right|$$

and the magnetic number Q is

$$Q = \frac{d^2}{4\pi\mu\rho\eta_m\eta} \, B_{\text{eff}}^2 .$$

The effective magnetic field $B_{\text{eff}} = B$ for $\theta = 0$ and $B_{\text{eff}} = B \, d/l = B \, k_x/k_z$ for $\theta = \pi/2$, where l is the length of the convection roll.

The discussion of Equation (5.57) is rather lengthy, and we shall not reproduce it here. Suffice it to say that Danielson determined the three roots of ω, that is, the growth rates of convective cells of a given length (given k_x) and a given width (given k_y) for values of the parameters K, η_m, η, B_{eff}, and α appropriate to penumbral conditions (see Table 5.10). He finds

TABLE 5.10   Parameters in Danielson's penumbra model
(courtesy Danielson, 1961b)

Parameter	B_{eff}, gauss	d, km	l, km	K, cm²/sec	η_m, cm²/sec	η, cm²/sec
Numerical value	1000	300	5000	10^{12}	4×10^6	10^3

Parameter	$\dfrac{\overline{dT}}{dz}$, °K/km	α, °K⁻¹	R	Q		
Numerical value	-10	10^{-4}	2×10^{11}	10^{14}		

that convection will occur in the penumbra if the magnetic field is horizonta- or nearly horizontal, and suggests that the penumbral filaments are conl vection rolls. To predict lifetimes and dimensions of these convection rolls in agreement with observations, it is necessary to assume that the depth d of the convection layer in the penumbra is about half the depth of the layer in the undisturbed photospheric granulation.

In Section 5.1 we saw that the granulation remains normal up to the edge of the penumbra. This can be accounted for in Danielson's model by the fact that the magnitude of the magnetic field changes rapidly at the outer edge of the penumbra. Going from the normal granulation into the pen-umbra, we find that the field increases to a point where the magnetic energy density $B^2/8\pi$ exceeds the turbulent energy density $\frac{1}{2}\rho\langle v\rangle^2$. One then needs specially shaped cells for convection to take place, i.e., convection rolls. The equipartition magnetic field, B_{eq}, is about 250 gauss. Since the transition from a field smaller than B_{eq} to one larger takes place in a very short distance (of the order of a normal granule) at the edge of the penumbra, we expect the granulation to appear normal up to the very edge of a sunspot.

5.3. General Theory

5.3.1. Introduction

In the previous section, we have mainly been interested in the structure of a sunspot—the model stratification—and considered the underlying causes as given. In some cases, we assumed the cooling of the spot to be due to a magnetic field, but the existence of the field was not investigated. There is, of course, no clear-cut distinction between a thorough discussion of the parameters determining a model and a more general theory of the sunspot phenomenon. However, in Section 5.2 we concentrated on the models as such; now we shall try to discuss the causes leading to them.

Any complete theory of sunspots should answer two questions, namely (1) what is the cause of the magnetic field which produces the sunspot cooling, and (2) why do the frequency and distribution of sunspots vary with a 22 year period ?

Several theories have been proposed to explain the cooling of sunspots without invoking the magnetic field. Even if such theories should succeed in explaining a cooling mechanism, we would be left with an uncomfortable feeling that we had forgotten the most important aspect of the sunspot phenomenon. Therefore, any theory to which the magnetic field is accidental or even secondary should be viewed with suspicion.

If the problem of single sunspots is complicated, this is even more true of the questions facing us when we consider the cause of the 22 year cycle. So far as the degree of activity on the solar surface is concerned (as manifested by sunspots, flares, prominences, etc.), this cycle seemingly is broken down into two cycles of approximately 11 years. But the nature of the magnetic fields that cause the sunspots is subjected to the previously discussed 22 year cycle. No theories of the cycle of sunspots can neglect the magnetic field, and they do not, but the role played by the field is quite different in the few theories that do exist.

The simple fact that we always find strong magnetic fields in sunspots raises the question whether the field is generated—and in due time destroyed—in the sunspot region or whether it is carried to the surface by large-scale material motions—that in due time will carry it away again. Bjerknes (1926) and others considered the first possibility where the field is created *in situ*. Cowling (1953) showed that under certain conditions—often believed to reign in sunspots—this is not a possible solution. His argument is that the time scale for creating and destroying magnetic fields in the photo-spheric plasma is much longer than the lifetime of sunspots. It is therefore generally assumed that the magnetic fields are transported from a deeper-lying reservoir to the surface, where they produce the visible sunspots. Partly following Cowling (1953), Spitzer (1956), and Chandrasekhar (1961), we shall now discuss the growth and decay times of sunspot magnetic fields.

Equation (1.51) shows how the magnetic field diffuses through the plasma in the absence of large-scale motions. From this equation, we deduce the time of decay, τ_{diff}, of the field, Equation (1.52),

$$\tau_{\text{diff}} \approx 4\pi\sigma L^2/c^2 ,$$

where L is a characteristic length of the phenomenon. The time τ_{diff} is the time required for Ohmic losses to dissipate an amount of energy comparable with the magnetic energy $B^2/8\pi$.

Cowling assumes L to be of the order 3000 km. He further puts $\sigma = 2.7 \times 10^{13}$ e.s.u. and deduces a value $\tau_{\text{diff}} \approx 1000$ years (Gurevich and Lebedinski, 1945; Cowling, 1946). Bray and Loughhead (1964) take $\sigma = 10^{11}$ e.s.u. and $L = 1500$ km (their assumed scale of the fine structure of the magnetic field) and find $\tau_{\text{diff}} \approx 1$ month. Since the decay time goes as the square of the dimension L, it is very sensitive to the assumed scale of the fine structure. This scale is not known and remains one of the pressing observational problems of solar activity. The convection rolls in the penumbra probably have diameters of the order of 300 km (Section 5.2.3), and it is not inconceivable that the umbral field has similar characteristic dimensions. If this were the case, the generation and destruction of magnetic fields would be accomplished *in situ* in times comparable to or shorter than the lifetimes of many sunspots.

5.3.2. Theories of Single Spots—the Cooling Mechanism

5.3.2.1. *Convective and hydrodynamic theories*

(a) THE RUSSELL-ROSSELAND MECHANISM OF ADIABATIC COOLING — In this theory (Russell, 1921; Rosseland, 1926), a stable layer is assumed to exist below the visible surface, where the temperature gradient is less than the adiabatic gradient. A spot will arise when, in such a layer, there is a circulation leading to matter rising and cooling adiabatically. The circulation will have to be such that the cooled material will flow outward from the spot and then sink down to be heated again. The Evershed motions could be taken as a partial verification of this.

The theory meets with severe difficulties (Cowling, 1953) and must be rejected—apart from the fact that it ignores the magnetic field. The reason is that when the material arrives at a given level cooler than its surroundings it will also be heavier and will sink back, thereby rapidly destroying the required circulation. The motion can exist only in an unstable layer, and there the rising material will actually arrive at the surface hotter than its surroundings.

(b) BJERKNES' "TERRESTRIAL TORNADO" MODEL — Bjerknes' (1926) theory of single sunspots is closely connected with his theory of the 22 year period which we shall treat in Section 5.3.5. It is assumed that the magnetic field of a spot is due to the rotation of ionized matter, and in Bjerknes' theory the spot is considered the seat of vortex motions around a vertical axis. He assumes that the vortex motions lead to centrifugal pumping and that the resulting adiabatic cooling causes the visible spot. His model can therefore be considered a convection theory of cooling similar to that of Russell and Rosseland, and hence subject to the same objections. In addition, observations show (Richardson, 1941) that only a minority of spots exhibits recognizable vortex motions, and a certain sense of rotation is not uniquely associated with one sense of magnetic polarity. Also, there is no known reason why whirling of a plasma should produce the necessary magnetic fields.

(c) WASIUTYNSKI'S VORTEX MODEL — Wasiutynski (1946) builds on Bjerknes' idea of a vortex model and assumes the vortex motions to be generated by the sun's nonuniform rotation. The nonuniform rotation is in turn built up by circulations in meridian planes and is destroyed in the sunspot vortex.

The model is subject to many of the objections valid for Bjerknes' theory. In addition, Wasiutynski had to assume circulation velocities far in excess of observed values.

5.3.2.2. *Magnetic theories*

In Section 5.2.1 we have already mentioned the two proposals put forth to explain how a magnetic field may lead to cooling of the photospheric plasma, namely Biermann's (1941) inhibition of convection and Hoyle's (1949) dilution of the convective motions by spreading them out over a larger area. Before we discuss these ideas further, we shall with Cowling (1953) determine the depth at which the coolness originates.

First, we remark that the sunspot cannot be mainly in the thin radiatively stable layer above the hydrogen convection zone. The reason is that this layer is too thin to significantly obstruct radiation from hotter regions. On the other hand, the coolness cannot originate at depths of many thousand kilometers, since then the observed sharp edge of a spot would be totally blurred out as the radiation streams out from the cool regions to the surface.

This places the origin of the coolness in the top few thousand kilometers of the convection zone. It will therefore be necessary either to create a magnetic field in that layer or to transport an already existing field into the layer.

The questions to be answered regarding the sunspot magnetic field are therefore: (1) How is the magnetic field created or amplified? (2) If not created *in situ*, how is the field transported to the surface? (3) By what mechanism does the magnetic field accomplish the cooling of sunspots?

We shall now discuss the problem of magnetic cooling and leave the equally fundamental questions of creation, amplification, and transport of the magnetic flux tubes to Section 5.3.3 and 5.3.4.

(a) THE BIERMANN-COWLING THEORY — In subphotospheric layers unaffected by sunspot magnetic fields, the (superadiabatic) temperature gradient causes thermal instability, leading to convective motions. We expect a cellular convection pattern, and an important part of the energy flux is transported by convection in this part of the sun. The solar plasma is highly conducting, and if a magnetic field is present, it is apparent that it will have profound effects on the onset of thermal instability. Biermann (1941) suggested that the field would partly or wholly inhibit the convective motions. The heat energy will then be dammed back and we get a cool spot. This is the basic idea in Biermann's theory. Cowling (1957) has extended the idea and discussed under what conditions the sunspot magnetic field would be strong enough to be of importance.

Naïvely, we may look at the magnetic effects in different ways. Let us suppose the sunspot magnetic field to be perpendicular and consider the convective motions in an ordinary three-dimensional cell. Since the plasma is highly conducting, the material motions may proceed unhindered in the vertical direction (along the field, upward and down) but the necessary bending-over horizontally to form the cells is inhibited. We may also observe that in ordinary convection energy will be dissipated by viscosity. In a steady state, this loss is balanced by the energy released by the buoyancy force acting on the fluid. When a magnetic field is present, there will in addition be loss due to Joule heating. To balance this extra energy loss, the buoyancy force must rely on a higher temperature gradient than is sufficient in the absence of Joule heating.

The detailed mathematical treatment of thermal instability in the presence of a magnetic field is due to Thompson (1951) and Chandrasekhar (1952, 1961), but Walén (1949) had already argued that if the dimension of the convective cells along the magnetic field is small enough, the thermal instability will be strongly influenced by the field. The presence of the field is equivalent to having to consider two mechanical effects, namely a hydrostatic pressure $B^2/8\pi$ (that is balanced by the gas pressure) and a tension $B^2/4\pi$ along the lines of force. This tension will prevent the lines of force from being bent beyond a certain limit, thereby inhibiting any motion that would try to accomplish this. Let the convective motions bend the (initially straight) lines of force into sine-curves with wavelength L. We consider the displacement, d, of any point from the initial position as small. The curvature of the line is $4\pi^2 d/L^2$, and the tension leads to a volume force $\pi B^2 d/L^2$. This is the force that will inhibit any further bending. For small wavelengths L, the force is large and can effectively prevent the convective motions.

Let us consider a uniform vertical magnetic field $\mathbf{B_0}$ and a liquid under gravity, heated from below, between horizontal planes $z = 0$ and $z = L$ (Cowling, 1957). Any small vertical displacement will lead to a small increase ΔT, in temperature, from its undisturbed value $T_0 - (dT/dz)z$ to

$$T = T_0 - (dT/dz) \cdot z + \Delta T \tag{5.58}$$

where dT/dz is the temperature gradient due to the heating. When the material motion is zero, $\mathbf{v} = 0$, the heat will be transported according to Equation (1.85) which—with $X = c_v T$—takes the form $\partial T/\partial t = K\nabla^2 T$. If the fluid velocity is different from zero, the heat equation will be of the form

$$\partial T/\partial t + (\mathbf{v} \cdot \nabla)T = K\nabla^2 T. \tag{5.59}$$

Combining this equation with Equation (5.58) for T, we find to first-order in $\mathbf{v}$ and ΔT

$$\frac{\partial}{\partial t}(\Delta T) = \frac{dT}{dz}v_z + K\nabla^2(\Delta T). \tag{5.60}$$

The magnetic field $\mathbf{B}$ will be composed of the undisturbed uniform field $\mathbf{B_0}$ and the perturbation field $\mathbf{B'}$. The changes in the magnetic field will be given by Equation (1.50), which to first-order in $\mathbf{v}$ and $\mathbf{B'}$ is

$$\partial \mathbf{B'}/\partial t = (\mathbf{B_0} \cdot \nabla)\,\mathbf{v} + \frac{c^2}{4\pi\sigma}\,\nabla^2\mathbf{B'}. \tag{5.61}$$

To our set of equations for ΔT and $\mathbf{B'}$ [Equations (5.58), (5.60), and (5.61)] we add the equation of motion, see Equations (1.33a) and (1.33b),

$$\rho\frac{d\mathbf{v}}{dt} = -\nabla\left(p + \frac{B^2}{8\pi}\right) + \frac{(\mathbf{B} \cdot \nabla)\mathbf{B}}{4\pi} + \rho\eta\,\nabla^2\mathbf{v} + \rho\mathbf{g}.$$

To simplify this, we take $\rho = \rho_0$ everywhere except in the last term on the right. In that term we consider the change in ρ due to the volume expansion

$$\rho = \rho_0[1 + \alpha\{(dT/dz) \cdot z - \Delta T\}],$$

where the coefficient of volume expansion, α, is considered small. Now, putting $\mathbf{B} = \mathbf{B}_0 + \mathbf{B}'$ and linearizing, we find

$$\frac{\partial \mathbf{v}}{\partial t} = -\nabla \left(\frac{p}{\rho_0} + \frac{B^2}{8\pi\mu\rho_0} + gz + \frac{1}{2}\,\alpha g\,\frac{dT}{dz}\,z^2 \right)$$
$$+ \frac{(\mathbf{B}_0 \cdot \nabla)\mathbf{B}'}{4\pi\rho_0} + \eta\nabla^2\mathbf{v} - \alpha\mathbf{g}\Delta T. \quad (5.62)$$

We now solve the system of Equations (5.60), (5.61), and (5.62) remembering that $\mathbf{B}'$ and $\mathbf{v}$ satisfy the additional equations

$$\nabla \cdot \mathbf{B}' = 0, \qquad \nabla \cdot \mathbf{v} = 0. \qquad (5.63)$$

A single equation for v_z will then be obtained,

$$\left(\frac{\partial}{\partial t} - K\nabla^2 \right) \left(\frac{\partial}{\partial t} - \eta\nabla^2 \right) \left(\frac{\partial}{\partial t} - \eta_m\nabla^2 \right) \nabla^2 v_z$$
$$= \frac{B_0^2}{4\pi\rho_0} \left(\frac{\partial}{\partial t} - K\nabla^2 \right) \nabla^2 \frac{\partial^2 v_z}{\partial z^2} + \alpha g\,\frac{dT}{dz} \left(\frac{\partial}{\partial t} - \eta_m\nabla^2 \right) \left(\frac{\partial^2 v_z}{\partial x^2} + \frac{\partial^2 v_z}{\partial y^2} \right). \quad (5.64)$$

Assuming periodic solutions of the form

$$\exp\left[\omega t + i(k_x x + k_y y)\right] \sin\left(\pi k_z z\right),$$

we replace Equation (5.64) with

$$(\omega + Kk^2)(\omega + \eta k^2)(\omega + \eta_m k^2)k^2 = \alpha g\,\frac{dT}{dz}\,(\omega + \eta_m k^2)(k_x^2 + k_y^2)$$
$$- \frac{B_0^2 k^2}{4\pi\rho_0\mu k_z^2}\,(\omega + Kk^2), \quad (5.65)$$

where $k^2 = k_x^2 + k_y^2 + k_z^2$.

This is the equation (5.57) used by Danielson in his study of the penumbral convection rolls (see Section 5.2.10).

Let us ignore dissipation effects, that is, $K = \eta = \eta_m = 0$. Then Equation (5.65) reduces to

$$\omega^2(k^2)^3 = \alpha g\,\frac{dT}{dz}\,(k_x^2 + k_y^2) - \frac{B_0^2 k^2 k_z^2}{4\pi\mu\rho_0}\,.$$

For a given set of values k_x, k_y, and k_z, the condition for the onset of instability is that ω goes from imaginary to real values. We may, therefore, inhibit convection, i.e., preserve stability, when

$$B_0^2 > \frac{4\pi\mu\rho_0\alpha g}{k_z}\,\frac{dT}{dz}\left(1 - \frac{k_z^2}{k^2} \right).$$

For a given vertical dimension, k_z, stability is most likely for small wave numbers, whence inhibition occurs for

$$B^2 > \frac{4\pi}{k_z^2} \rho_0 \alpha g \frac{dT}{dz} .$$

(5.66)

(b) HOYLE'S THEORY — This theory, which is sometimes considered a variant of Biermann's idea, has briefly been outlined in Section 5.2.1. We described there the fanning out of magnetic lines of force near the photosphere as the essence of Hoyle's idea. In the original work, Hoyle (1949) considered the darkening of a sunspot to be due to the combined effects of two causes, namely (1) Russell's mechanism and (2) Eddington's process. Russell's mechanism (1921) (Section 5.3.2.1a) intended to explain a general darkening of the whole spot by transferring more material in the upward convection than in the downward and by cooling it adiabatically. Eddington (1942) developed a theory for the hydrogen convection zone, and Hoyle used in his cooling mechanism the feature of Eddington's theory that the convective flux arises from an excess ionization of hydrogen in the ascending part of the convection (regardless of whether there is an excess of material). This excess of ionization is coupled with the fanning out of the magnetic lines of force near the photosphere to produce an additional darkening over the umbra of the spot.

Chapman (1943) already had pointed out that the Lorentz term, $\mathbf{B} \times (\nabla \times \mathbf{B})$, in the equation of motion (1.33a) will produce a spreading out of the magnetic lines of force. Since the spot is a fairly stable configuration, the tendency to spread the lines of force must be overcome by an excess hydrostatic pressure outside the spot. This is made possible by the cooling of the spot. Hence, near the base of the spot the term ∇p must balance $\mathbf{B} \times (\nabla \times \mathbf{B})$ in a horizontal plane. The relative importance of the Lorentz term and the pressure term can be roughly estimated by comparing the gas pressure and the magnetic energy density (p and $B^2/8\pi$). Hoyle estimated the pressure at the base of the spot to be about 10^7 dynes/cm². To hold a spot together with such a pressure, $\mathbf{B}$ should not exceed 10,000 gauss.

Higher up, near the photosphere, the magnetic energy density dominates over the pressure ($\approx 10^4$ dynes/cm²) and we get the fanning out of the field lines. Also, the material motions will fan out, which provides an explanation of the Evershed effect.

5.3.3. Theories of Single Spots—the Nature of the Magnetic Field

The most promising approaches to the question of how the sunspot magnetic field is formed seem to rely on the effects of the sun's nonuniform rotation. One school of thought assumes the existence of a general poloidal field in the sun and uses the nonuniform rotation to create a toroidal field. This azimuthal field may then be transported to the surface, where it produces the spot. Theories along these lines have been advocated by Cowling (1953), Bullard (1955), Elsasser (1956), and Babcock (1961).

A different point of view has been taken by Biermann (1950), who uses the nonuniform rotation to create electric fields that under certain conditions will set up electric currents. These currents will then produce azimuthal magnetic fields. A unique feature of this theory is that it does not depend on a hypothetical general magnetic field in the sun.

There are also theories that do not invoke the aspect of differential rotation—even though they all depend on the existence of the general poloidal field. The necessary additional parameter is then either an observed phenomenon or a postulated characteristic. In one case (Weiss, 1964a), the well observed—if not so well understood—subphotospheric convection is used; in other cases, speculations as to the effects of hydromagnetic waves and the properties of the sun's core (Alfvén, 1943a, 1943b, 1945a, 1945b; Walén, 1947) or the effects of prominence action (Menzel, 1950) are employed.

To finish this preliminary survey of sunspot theories, we note that there are several ways of classifying them. One might subdivide them according to whether they depend on a general field or not. Since only one theory does not rely on an assumed poloidal field, this is not a very practical scheme. The study of the influence of the hydrogen convection zone on magnetic fields, or, better, the coupling between the field and the convective motions might be used in this classification. It is a fundamental problem and deserves more attention. However, the practical objection raised to the use of the general field also applies here.

Another fundamental, and well-observed, property of the solar photosphere is its nonuniform rotation. We shall organize the present section according to how this characteristic enters the different theories of the sunspot magnetic field.

5.3.3.1. *Theories depending on nonuniform rotation*

(a) THE LAW OF ISOROTATION — At least the outer parts of the sun exhibit differential rotation, i.e., the angular velocity ω is a function of the solar latitude ϕ_0. The dependence $\omega = \omega(\phi_0)$ is such that the equatorial regions rotate faster than the polar regions. From sunspot data, Newton and Nunn (1951) derived the formula

$$\xi = 14.38° - 2.77° \sin^2 \phi_0, \tag{5.67}$$

where ξ is the daily sidereal rotation.

The solar gas is highly conducting, and if there is a magnetic field present it will be effectively frozen into the plasma. It is therefore easy to imagine that the differential rotation will have a profound influence on a possible general magnetic field. The sun can possess a steady field only if the following conditions are met: (1) the field is symmetric around the axis of rotation, (2) the lines of force lie in surfaces symmetric about the axis, and (3) these surfaces rotate with constant angular velocity (so-called isotachial surfaces). This is the law of isorotation (Ferraro, 1937), that is, ω is constant along a line of force.

The law may be derived in the following manner (Cowling, 1957). We start with the equation (1.50) that describes the change in the magnetic field,

$$\frac{\partial \mathbf{B}}{\partial t} = \nabla \times (\mathbf{v} \times \mathbf{B}) + \frac{c^2}{4\pi\sigma} \nabla^2 \mathbf{B} .$$

Considering only an infinitely conducting gas and remembering that $\mathbf{v}$ and $\mathbf{B}$ are divergence free, we reduce Equation (1.50) to

$$\partial \mathbf{B}/\partial t = (\mathbf{B} \cdot \nabla)\mathbf{v} - (\mathbf{v} \cdot \nabla)\mathbf{B} . \tag{5.68}$$

We introduce cylindrical coordinates r, ϕ, z, where the z-axis is the axis of rotation. Since $v = \omega r$, Equation (5.68) may be written

$$\frac{\partial B_r}{\partial t} = -\omega \frac{\partial B_r}{\partial \phi} , \qquad \frac{\partial B_\phi}{\partial t} = r\left(B_r \frac{\partial \omega}{\partial r} + B_z \frac{\partial \omega}{\partial z} \right) - \omega \frac{\partial B_\phi}{\partial \phi} ,$$

$$\frac{\partial B_z}{\partial t} = -\omega \frac{\partial B_z}{\partial \phi} \tag{5.69}$$

For a steady field, $\partial \mathbf{B}/\partial t = 0$, we find $B_r \neq B_r(\phi)$, and $B_z \neq B_z(\phi)$, whence $B_\phi \neq B_\phi(\phi)$—since $\mathbf{B}$ is divergence free. Equation (5.69) then shows that

$$(\mathbf{B} \cdot \nabla)\omega = 0 . \tag{5.70}$$

This is the equation for an isotach—a surface of constant angular velocity—which is the condition that ω should be constant along a line of force.

By breakdown of the condition of isorotation, the initially poloidal field will become increasingly distorted, developing toroidal components. Let us suppose that a steady state of rotation is disturbed by an azimuthal displacement symmetric around the axis of rotation. The distortion in the magnetic field will lead to a restoring force, and a disturbance is propagated along the lines of force. This disturbance can be considered a torsional hydromagnetic wave. The equations for such waves may be deduced from Equation (1.50) for the change in $\mathbf{B}$ and Equation (1.33a) for the change in $\mathbf{v}$ (i.e., the equation of motion). Let the motion be composed of the undisturbed part due to the undisturbed angular velocity ω_0 and a perturbation due to an increment ω'

in the angular velocity. Similarly, $\mathbf{B}$ is the sum of the undisturbed field $\mathbf{B_0}$ and the azimuthal disturbance field $\mathbf{B'}$. Equation (1.53a)—which is taken in the simplified form (5.69)—then to first-order in $\mathbf{B'}$ and ω' will give

$$\partial B'_\phi/\partial t = r(\mathbf{B_0} \cdot \nabla)\omega' . \tag{5.71}$$

The equation of motion

$$\rho \frac{d\mathbf{v}}{dt} = -\nabla p + \rho \mathbf{g} + \frac{1}{4\pi} (\nabla \times \mathbf{B'}) \times \mathbf{B}$$

reduces for the ϕ-component to

$$4\pi \rho r^2(\partial \omega'/\partial t) = (\mathbf{B_0} \cdot \nabla)r B'_\phi . \tag{5.72}$$

Equations (5.71) and (5.72) are the equations for the torsional hydromagnetic waves set up when isorotation breaks down.

If the isotachial surfaces cut more deeply into the sun than do the magnetic lines of force, then these lines will be drawn out in longitude, and we will get a toroidal field. The degree of amplification of this field will be a function of the latitude ϕ_0.

(b) AMPLIFICATION OF A GENERAL FIELD — A number of authors have considered the possibility of letting the differential rotation distort an existing dipolar field and amplify a thereby created azimuthal component of the field. Cowling (1953) noted that if the undisturbed field $\mathbf{B_0}$ in meridian planes is twisted through an angle α, an azimuthal field $\mathbf{B_1} = \mathbf{B_0} \tan \alpha$ is produced. The angle α is given by $\alpha = d/D$, where D is the distance (in latitude) over which ω varies and d is the relative displacement of the field lines at a distance D apart. Taking $D = \frac{1}{10}R_\odot$ and $\mathbf{B_0} = 25$ gauss, we find with Cowling that to get a field $\mathbf{B_1} = 3000$ gauss (as observed in larger sunspots), one needs $d = 12R_\odot$. This could, for example, be accomplished by a differential rotation of the order of 0.05 km/sec acting for $5\frac{1}{2}$ years. We know today that $\mathbf{B_0}$ is not 25 gauss; if it exists at all, it is probably one order of magnitude smaller. But the basic idea of creating a toroidal field by this mechanism retains its interesting aspects, and it has been investigated in detail by Bullard (1949, 1955) and Elsasser (1956).

To use the concept of field distortion outlined above, we must consider a shallow magnetic field configuration (Babcock, 1961). For the magnetic lines of force to be drawn out in the appropriate direction, the lines must not cut so deeply into the sun as the isotachs. Then the submerged part of the lines will be drawn out in an east–west direction as a consequence of the hydrodynamic flow brought about by the nonuniform rotation. On each side of the equator we get a fairly tightly wound spiral, and this toroidal field will steadily increase in amplitude as the differential rotation continues to tighten the spiral.

Babcock extended this idea to a theory of the 22 year sunspot cycle. We shall treat this problem in Section 5.3.5. Here we only give an account of that part of the work that pertains to the amplification and redistribution of the general field. Babcock used Equation (5.67) for the differential rotation, and he assumed the shallow poloidal field to be given by

$$B(\phi_0) = B(0) \sec \phi_0, \qquad -30 \deg < \phi_0 < +30 \deg, \qquad (5.73)$$

where $B(0)$, the field at the equator, was taken to be 5 gauss.

Let the process of winding up the lines of force start t_1 years before a given sunspot minimum of the 11 year cycle. At the time of sunspot minimum, the field will have been amplified to a critical value $B_{\text{crit}}(\phi_0)$, so that the first spots of the new cycle will appear at a critical latitude ϕ_{crit}. As the nonuniform rotation continues to draw out the field lines, the differential advance in longitude t_2 years after minimum will be given by

$$\theta = \theta_0(t_1 + t_2) \sin^2 \phi. \qquad (5.74)$$

The angle α between the lines of force and the meridian will increase from 0 (at time $-t_1$ when the field is purely poloidal) to a value given by $\tan \alpha = (d\theta/d\phi_0) \cos \phi_0$. Babcock neglected the factor $\cos \phi_0$ in this relation, which is equivalent to ignoring the shrinking of small circles on a sphere as one goes away from the equator (Kopecký, 1963). One may now deduce that the intensity of the magnetic field in latitude ϕ_0 t_2 years after minimum is given by

$$B_\phi = 2\theta_0(t_1 + t_2)B_0 \sin \phi \cos \phi. \qquad (5.75)$$

Babcock postulated that the spots will be formed at the critical latitude when the field B_ϕ has been amplified to a critical value.

(c) BIERMANN'S THEORY — This mechanism for creating magnetic fields (Biermann, 1950) was developed for conditions in stellar interiors. If we want to use it for sunspots, an additional special transport to the solar surface of the created flux tubes must again be incorporated. We shall return to this in Section 5.3.4.

The theory depends on currents created due to the sun's nonuniform rotation. These currents will produce an azimuthal field, directed in opposite senses in the two hemispheres. When parts of the azimuthal flux tubes are carried to the surface, sunspots may be formed.

Biermann's treatment of the problem needs an equation for the electric currents, $\mathbf{j} = ne\mathbf{v}$, where $n = n_e = n_i$ is the number density and $\mathbf{v}$ is the diffusion velocity, $\mathbf{v} = \mathbf{v}_i - \mathbf{v}_e$, of the electrons through the ion gas. Here

v_i and v_e are the macroscopic velocities of the components of the simple binary gas mixture considered. The expression for v is given by Equation (1.86), and Biermann writes it in the form

$$\mathbf{v} = -\frac{D_{ie}}{kT}\left[\frac{1}{2n}\nabla p - m_e\left(\frac{\mathbf{F}_e}{m_e} - \frac{\mathbf{F}_i}{m_i}\right)\right] - D_T\nabla(\ln T),$$

where $p = p_e + p_i = 2nkT$, and $\mathbf{F}_i$ and $\mathbf{F}_e$ are the external forces acting on the particles (electric fields, radiation pressure, etc.). The pressure gradient and the other forces leading to diffusion can be considered an electromotive force,

$$e\mathbf{E}_e = \frac{1}{2n}\nabla p - \frac{1}{2}\frac{D_T}{D_{ie}}k\nabla T. \tag{5.76}$$

If the force $(1/2n)\nabla p$ can be derived from a potential, we see that the surfaces of constant pressure and of constant temperature coincide. In that case, the radiation pressure will also be curl free, and a state where no current flows will be realized, due to the setting up of an electrostatic field $\mathbf{E}'$

$$-e\mathbf{E}' = \frac{1}{2n}\nabla p_{rad} - \frac{1}{2}\frac{D_T}{D_{ie}}k\nabla T.$$

This will be accomplished automatically by a very slight charge separation.

On the other hand, the vector field $\mathbf{E}_e$ may contain a part that is not curl free. In that case, one cannot find an electric field $\mathbf{E}'$ that will compensate this part. Electric currents will flow, generating magnetic fields. For a stationary case, we find

$$\nabla \cdot \mathbf{j} = \nabla \cdot [\sigma(\mathbf{E}_e + \mathbf{E}')] = 0, \tag{5.77a}$$

where

$$\nabla \times \mathbf{E}' = 0. \tag{5.77b}$$

Furthermore, $\sigma = (2e^2/kT)D_{ie}$, and we obtain a magnetic field given by

$$\nabla \times \mathbf{B} = (4\pi/c)\mathbf{j}.$$

The electric field $\mathbf{E}'' = \mathbf{E}_e + \mathbf{E}'$ is determined if $\mathbf{E}_e$ and σ are known. Biermann then showed that in stellar interiors ($\sigma \approx 10^{17}$), very small fields $\mathbf{E}''$ will lead to important magnetic field strengths. He defined the effective acceleration g'' by $e\mathbf{E}'' = m_0 g''$, where $m_0 = \frac{1}{2}(m_i + m_e) \approx \frac{1}{2}m_i$, and put $g'' = 1$ cm/sec^2. Then, $\mathbf{E}'' \approx 10^{-15}$ e.s.u., and for a rotation of $10^{-10.5}$ cm^{-1}, the field $\mathbf{B}$ becomes ≈ 1000 gauss.

Schlüter (see Biermann, 1950) has calculated the magnetic field to be expected when the angular velocity has the form

$$\boldsymbol{\omega} = \boldsymbol{\omega}_0 \sqrt{(r/R)^j}, \tag{5.78}$$

where j is an arbitrary parameter, except that it has to be greater than -5 to ensure finite rotational energy. The condition for equilibrium (neglecting radiation pressure and thermal diffusion) is

$$\frac{\nabla p}{n(m_{\mathrm{i}} + m_{\mathrm{e}})} = \mathbf{g} + \boldsymbol{\omega} \times (\boldsymbol{\omega} \times \mathbf{r}) = \mathbf{g} + \left(\frac{r}{R}\right)^j \boldsymbol{\omega}_0 \times (\boldsymbol{\omega}_0 \times \mathbf{r}). \tag{5.79}$$

Using Equations (5.78) and (5.79), we find that the equations of the problem, Equations (5.76), (5.77a), and (5.77b), take the form

$$\mathbf{j} = \sigma(\mathbf{E}_{\mathrm{e}} + \mathbf{E}'),$$

$$e\mathbf{E}_{\mathrm{e}} = \frac{1}{2n}\nabla p = m\mathbf{g} + \frac{1}{2}m_{\mathrm{i}}\left(\frac{r}{R}\right)^j \boldsymbol{\omega}_0 \times (\boldsymbol{\omega}_0 \times \mathbf{r}),$$

$$\nabla \cdot \mathbf{j} = 0,$$

$$\nabla \times \mathbf{E}' = 0.$$

Schlüter made the simplifying assumption that the electric conductivity is constant, $\sigma = \sigma_0$ for $r < R$ and $\sigma = 0$ for $r > R$. Furthermore, $\mathbf{E}_{\mathrm{e}}$ was expressed as $\mathbf{E}_{\mathrm{e}} = \mathbf{E}'' + \mathbf{E}_1$, where $\nabla \cdot \mathbf{E}'' = 0$ and $\nabla \times \mathbf{E}_1 = 0$. Also, we obtain

$$\nabla \times \mathbf{E}'' = (m_{\mathrm{i}}/2e)\nabla \times [\boldsymbol{\omega} \times (\boldsymbol{\omega} \times \mathbf{r})], \qquad \nabla \times \mathbf{g} = 0,$$

and we find for $\mathbf{E}''$ the solution

$$\mathbf{E}'' = \frac{m_{\mathrm{i}}}{2e}\frac{1}{j+5}\left(\frac{r}{R}\right)^j \left[(j+3)\boldsymbol{\omega} \cdot (\boldsymbol{\omega} \cdot \mathbf{r}) - j\frac{\mathbf{r} \cdot (\boldsymbol{\omega} \cdot \mathbf{r})^2}{r^2} - \omega^2 \mathbf{r}\right]. \tag{5.80}$$

The condition $\nabla \cdot \mathbf{j}_1 = 0$ can be satisfied in the interior by putting $\mathbf{E}' = -\mathbf{E}_1$, but $\mathbf{j}_1$ will not be divergence free on the surface. Schlüter therefore required the normal component of $\mathbf{E}' + \mathbf{E}_{\mathrm{e}}$ to vanish at the surface and wrote

$$\mathbf{E}' = \mathbf{E}_2 - \mathbf{E}_1, \qquad \text{that is,} \qquad \mathbf{E}' + \mathbf{E}_{\mathrm{e}} = \mathbf{E}_2 + \mathbf{E}'',$$

$$\nabla \times \mathbf{E}_2 = 0,$$

$$\nabla \cdot \mathbf{E}_2 = 0 \qquad \text{for} \qquad r \leq R,$$

$$r\mathbf{E}_2 + r\mathbf{E}'' = 0 \qquad \text{for} \qquad r = R. \tag{5.81}$$

The only solution of (5.80) and (5.81) is then

$$E_2 = \frac{m_{\mathrm{i}}}{2e}\frac{1}{j+5}\{3\boldsymbol{\omega} \cdot (\boldsymbol{\omega} \cdot \mathbf{r}) - \omega^2 \mathbf{r}\}, \qquad r < R.$$

The current density then becomes

$$\mathbf{j} = \sigma_0(\mathbf{E'} + \mathbf{E_e}) = \sigma_0(\mathbf{E_2} + \mathbf{E''}) = \frac{\sigma_0 m_i}{2e} \frac{1}{j+5}\left(1 - \left(\frac{r}{R}\right)^j\right)[3\boldsymbol{\omega}(\boldsymbol{\omega} \cdot \mathbf{r}) - \omega^2 \mathbf{r}]$$

$$- \frac{\sigma_0 m_i}{2e} \frac{j}{j+5}\left(\frac{r}{R}\right)^j\left[\boldsymbol{\omega} \cdot (\boldsymbol{\omega} \cdot \mathbf{r}) - \frac{\mathbf{r} \cdot (\boldsymbol{\omega} \cdot \mathbf{r})^2}{r^2}\right].$$

$$(5.82)$$

From this we find the field $\mathbf{B}$, using the equations and conditions

$$\nabla \cdot \mathbf{B} = 0, \quad \nabla \times \mathbf{B} = 4\pi \mathbf{j}/c \quad \text{for } r < R; \quad \sigma\nabla \times \mathbf{B} = 0 \quad \text{for } r > R.$$

The result is

$$\mathbf{B} = 4\pi\sigma \frac{m_i}{2ec}\frac{j+5}{j}\left[1 - \left(\frac{r}{R}\right)^j\right](\boldsymbol{\omega} \times \mathbf{r}) \cdot (\boldsymbol{\omega} \cdot \mathbf{r}) \quad \text{for} \quad r < R, \quad (5.83)$$

$$\mathbf{B} = 0 \quad \text{for} \quad r > R.$$

The magnetic lines of force are circles around the axis of rotation parallel to the equator. Numerical values may be obtained by putting $\sigma = 10^{17}$ e.s.u., $\omega = 14$ deg/day $= 2.83 \times 10^{-6}$ sec^{-1}, whence we find

$$B = \frac{1.41 \times 10^3}{j+5}\left(\frac{r}{R}\right)^2\left[1 - \left(\frac{r}{R}\right)^j\right]\sin 2\phi \text{ gauss}.$$

For a toroidal field created halfway between center and surface ($r/R = 0.5$) we have the following values at $\phi = 45$ deg, computed by Schlüter for different values of j (see Table 5.11).

TABLE 5.11   Angular velocity, ω, and magnetic field, B, at $r = \frac{1}{2}R$, $\phi = 45$ deg due to nonuniform rotation ($j = 0$ corresponds to uniform rotation) (courtesy Biermann, 1950, Table 1, p. 68)

j	ω, deg/day	B, gauss
-3	112	-1230
-2	56	-352
-1	28	-88
0	14	0
1	7	$+29$
2	3.5	$+38$

5.3.3.2. *Effects of hydromagnetic waves from the core*

Since Alfvén (1943b) discovered the existence of hydromagnetic waves, some attempts have been made to explain sunspots as due to the effects of such waves emerging from the solar interior. The most pretentious of these is the theory due to Alfvén (1943b, 1945a, 1945b). Another approach was taken by Walén (1944, 1947).

(a) ALFVÉN'S WHIRL-RING THEORY — This theory is based on a series of assumptions, among which are:

(1) The sun has a general magnetic field pervading the whole sun.

(2) Whirl-rings are generated in unstable regions in the sun's core.

(3) The whirl-rings travel to the surface along the field lines of the general field as hydromagnetic waves.

(4) As the hydromagnetic waves reach the surface, they generate the sunspot magnetic field.

In addition to these, further assumptions are necessary to explain the sunspot cycle, and we shall return to this in Section 5.3.5.

Any of the last three assumptions mentioned above raises important questions concerning the behavior of hydromagnetic waves in the sun. It is, however, unlikely that they can be answered in a way favorable to the sunspot theory. Nevertheless, the importance of Alfvén's pioneering work on hydromagnetic waves in solar physics is not easily overestimated. Even though the applications of such waves to the sunspot theory are rather speculative, we shall here treat the main aspects of the theory.

Alfvén starts out by postulating that there are isolated regions of the solar convection core which are unstable and give rise to hydromagnetic waves in the form of whirl-rings. In these, the material motion $\mathbf{v}$ and the (perturbation) magnetic field $\mathbf{b}$ are directed along the torus, i.e., like the motion of a tire turning around its axle. The ring is transmitted along a field line of the general field $\mathbf{B}_0$ with a velocity $\mathbf{V}_A = \pm\mathbf{B}_0/(4\pi\rho)^{1/2}$, where the minus sign applies to a ring in which the velocity $\mathbf{v}$ is parallel to the field $\mathbf{b}$, the plus sign to a ring where $\mathbf{b}$ and $\mathbf{v}$ are antiparallel. One may therefore have whirl-rings transmitted to both the northern and the southern hemisphere by postulating formation in the core of both types of whirl-rings. According to Walén (1944), the disturbance field $\mathbf{b}$ and the velocity $\mathbf{v}$ are related by the expression $\mathbf{v} = \mathbf{b}/(4\pi\rho)^{1/2}$ if the electric conductivity is infinite. Then $\frac{1}{2}\rho v^2 = b^2/8\pi$, which means that the kinetic energy of the ring equals its magnetostatic energy. Consequently, the magnetostatic pull of the lines of force counterbalances the centrifugal force due to the curvature of the ring.

An initial hydrodynamic whirl will produce two hydromagnetic whirls, one moving in the $+\mathbf{B}_0$ direction, the other in the $-\mathbf{B}_0$ direction. Let us consider a whirl moving as a wave in the positive $\mathbf{B}_0$ direction and let it increase its velocity by Δv in a small time interval Δt. This is equivalent to adding a new whirl to the initial wave, and the new whirl will be transmitted in the positive $\mathbf{B}_0$ direction as well as in the negative $\mathbf{B}_0$ direction. Hence, every wave gives rise to what Alfvén calls a "recoil" wave in the opposite direction. The recoil whirl will have the same direction of rotation as the initial whirl and therefore the opposite sense of magnetic field. This can, in due time, be used to account for the different polarities of sunspots in the two hemispheres.

Alfvén assumes the sun to possess a general magnetic field of dipolar nature, except for the core, where the field is homogeneous. Once the whirl rings are formed in the core, they will travel out along the field lines and approach the surface at latitudes that can be predicted when that part of the core which gives rise to the whirls is specified. Hence, to reproduce the well-observed sunspot zones, only very restricted parts of the core can be unstable enough to produce whirls. This possibility is not obvious in reality.

The rings will hit the photospheric layers and be reflected. During this phase, two sections of the torus intersect the surface, and Alfvén identifies them with a bipolar sunspot group. The field will have opposite polarities in the two spots, but no treatment has ever been given to show that a hydromagnetic wave during its reflection can actually generate a continuous strong field above the surface (Cowling, 1955). In Section 5.3.5 we shall return to those aspects of Alfvén's theory that deal with the cyclic nature of the sunspot phenomenon.

(b) WALÉN'S TORSIONAL THEORY — Walén (1947) tried to explain sunspot magnetic fields by torsional oscillations of the sun. The idea has been further analyzed and evaluated by Cowling (1955).

The first part of the theory is concerned with the generation and propagation of torsional hydromagnetic waves. The magnetic lines of force in the sun's core are assumed to be tangled together because of convective motions. This will give the core a certain rigidity, and it is assumed to rotate more or less as a rigid body. We note that this is a different picture than that proposed by Alfvén, where the field in the convective core is homogeneous. Walén further supposed that from time to time sudden outbursts of strong convective motions take place in the core. To conserve angular momentum during the convection, the angular velocity at the boundary of the core must decrease. This will induce hydromagnetic waves of a torsional character, and these waves will be transmitted to the photosphere along the—assumed— general magnetic field of the sun. The equations for the waves are (5.71) and (5.72). These apply even when the disturbance field $\mathbf{B}'$ is large compared with the undisturbed field $\mathbf{B_0}$. Consequently, Walén supposes that the torsional oscillations can produce a large azimuthal field from an initially small poloidal field.

In this theory, the hydromagnetic waves are generated by convulsions in the core, built up to a "breaking point" by inhibition of convection due to rotation. This inhibition leads to an unstable temperature gradient, until at last the instability breaks through—at intervals of about 22 years—to account for the sunspot cycle.

The next question is how to concentrate the disturbance field into a tight bundle that will create the even larger sunspot field as it breaks through the surface. With Walén we go back to the conditions reigning in a frozen-in field configuration (infinite electric conductivity). Considering the cross-section A of a magnetic tube of force, we notice that the flux BA of the tube must remain constant as it is carried around by the material motions. The mass within a section of the tube of length L is $\rho L A$ and must also remain constant, whence $\mathbf{B}$ is found to be proportional to ρL. As the tube now rises to the surface, Walén believes that ρ will decrease much more than L will increase, and the field $\mathbf{B}$ will therefore decrease. If this is true, there may be strong flux tubes below the surface and still we may see only very weak fields above it. Even though the effects of a finite conductivity will limit the validity of Walén's argument, it points to an interesting effect of density changes on the field. Assuming for the moment the argument to be valid, we find that the torsional wave from the core will finally travel below, and close to, the photosphere. As Cowling points out, the field lines are then in a tight bundle which forms a girdle around the sun, one in each hemisphere. When parts of this bundle break through the photosphere, two regions of opposite polarities will be formed, which are to be identified with a bipolar sunspot group.

5.3.3.3. *The role of prominences*

A very different way of using the general magnetic field of the sun in a sunspot theory is due to Menzel (1950). He assumes prominences initially to be supported against gravity by the general magnetic field. As more and more prominence material collects in the prominences, they will ultimately bend the lines of force of the field down to the photosphere. Menzel now assumes that the field lines—in this bending process—will crowd together and form the sunspot magnetic field. To justify this idea, he uses an equation for the field $\mathbf{B}$ (under the condition of infinite electric conductivity) first deduced by Walén:

$$\frac{d}{dt}\left(\frac{\mathbf{B}}{\rho}\right) = \left(\frac{\mathbf{B}}{\rho} \cdot \nabla\right)\mathbf{v}. \tag{5.84}$$

(This equation may be derived from Equation (1.53) by combining it with the equation of continuity (1.29) (for density ρ instead of particle density n) and with the condition $\nabla \cdot \mathbf{B} = 0$.) The influx of gas into the prominence is given by the velocity $\mathbf{v}$ and will lead to a certain enhancement of $\mathbf{B}$. But the enormous degree of convergence of the lines of force required casts serious doubt on Menzel's mechanism.

5.3.3.4. *The role of convective motions*

An interesting attempt to use the convective motions in subphotospheric layers to produce strong localized magnetic fields from a faint general field is due to Weiss (1964a). He assumes that the general magnetic field is confined to discrete ropes of flux throughout the convective zone. Measurements of magnetic fields in the photosphere support this view, since there the fields are confined to more or less discrete regions (see Section 5.1). Weiss argues that since there is no reason for assuming any motion in the radiatively stable part of the sun, it is very unlikely that the magnetic fields can penetrate into that part. On the other hand, the horizontal scale of the bipolar magnetic regions is probably similar to the depth of the convection zone. The magnetic fields are therefore assumed to extend throughout this layer, i.e., to a depth of perhaps 100,000 km. Unlike the situation in Alfvén's and Walén's theories, we here need an amplifying mechanism that operates in the convection zone only. Weiss suggests that the effect of convection on a weak magnetic field is to produce flux ropes of the observed strength. The convection is assumed to be more or less cellular, even though turbulence is expected, and the convection velocities can be estimated. All energy transport is taken as by convection (while actually 10 to 15% may be radiatively transported) so that the convective heat flux is given by $F = E/c_p\rho$, where E is the energy flux. Weiss (1964b) shows that the vertical velocity v_z is

$$v_z \approx (g \, dF/T)^{1/3}.$$

In the photosphere F is about 2×10^8 cm $°\text{K}$ sec^{-1}, and in the convection zone $F = 3 \times 10^4$. This gives convection velocities of 4 km/sec and 0.2 km/sec for the photosphere and convection zone, respectively. The interaction of these motions with the magnetic field will then produce the strong flux tubes. Weiss' argument goes as follows: The kinetic energy density is about 10^6 ergs/cm^3. He assumes the mean poloidal field to be about 1 gauss and the toroidal field 10 gauss. Then, the magnetic energy density corresponding to a uniform field would be only about 4 ergs/cm^3, and the convective motions would completely dominate the fields. Thus, the flux will be concentrated into tubes where the magnetic energy density is about 10^6 ergs/cm^3 so that they can withstand the convection. The corresponding field strengths will be $B = (8\pi 10^6)^{1/2} \approx 5000$ gauss. If such a flux tube is carried to the surface and breaks through the photosphere, a bipolar sunspot group will be formed.

A consequence of Weiss' argument is that the sunspots are very shallow, only affecting the topmost part of the convection zone. To see this in the framework of the present theory, we write the condition for hydrostatic equilibrium of the tube with its surroundings in the form

$$p_1 + p_m = p_0, \qquad (5.85)$$

where p_1 is the gas pressure in the tube, p_0 the pressure of its surroundings, and p_m the equivalent magnetic pressure $B^2/8\pi$. We now evaluate the field B_1 for which the magnetic pressure exceeds, for example, $\frac{1}{8}$ of the total pressure. Then we find that it is only in the photosphere that B_1 is less than the critical field B_0, which is the field that will establish equipartition with convection at a given depth (see Table 5.12). The spot will exist only in a

TABLE 5.12   Magnetic fields inhibiting convection, after Weiss

h, km	p_m/p_0	ΔT, °K	B_0, gauss	B_1, gauss
-300	0.28	1900	600	420
-430	0.12	1200	1000	970
-1000	0.074	1000	1500	2000
-2000	0.016	320	2000	5600
-5000	0.002	70	2500	20000

region where $B_0 > B_1$, beneath which convection will be suppressed. The depth of the spot in Weiss' model is only about 500 km. The exact value of this depth of course will depend on the assumed value for the ratio p_m/p_0, but the value 500 km corresponding to the choice $p_m/p_0 = \frac{1}{8}$ is indicative of the model.

5.3.4. Transport of Flux Tubes to the Surface

A number of the sunspot theories described in Section 5.3.3 depend on the transport of magnetic flux tubes from the sun's interior to the surface. It was shown independently by Jensen (1955) and Parker (1955) that a magnetic flux tube in an electrically conducting plasma is buoyant and will tend to rise. This "magnetic buoyancy" seems to ensure the soundness of the assumption that magnetic flux tubes created in the solar interior will be transported to the surface, where they are supposed to produce the sunspots,

Let us consider a horizontal magnetic flux tube in a plasma in thermal equilibrium with its surroundings. The results to be obtained do not critically depend on the assumption of thermal equilibrium, however. The case of a flux tube with an adiabatic interior has been treated by Parker, but yields nothing essentially new for this discussion. Hydrostatic equilibrium requires Equation (5.85) to hold, namely $p_0 = p_1 + p_m$ (see Section 5.3.3.4). Since p_m is always positive, $p_1 < p_0$, and since the temperature of the plasma is assumed to be the same inside and outside the tube, $\rho_1 < \rho_0$. Consequently, the tube acts like a bubble and will tend to rise.

With Parker, we consider a section of length L of a flux tube whose cross-section is A. Let the section be clamped at both ends. Then the buoyant force per unit length of the flux tube is $gA(\rho_0 - \rho_1)$. If the tube shall be able to rise, the buoyant force must exceed the tension at the ends of the length which will try to hold the length in place, whence

$$Lg(\rho_0 - \rho_1)A \geq 2AB^2/8\pi. \tag{5.86}$$

Since we may write for the gas pressure $p = kT\rho/m$, Equation (5.85) takes the form

$$\rho_0 = \rho_1 + mB^2/8\pi kT, \tag{5.87}$$

and Equation (5.86) takes the form

$$L > 2kT/mg. \tag{5.88}$$

Hence, so long as we consider lengths of tubes exceeding twice the scale height of the plasma, Equation (5.88) shows that the magnetic buoyancy will be effective. The buoyant force per unit volume is given by

$$F = \frac{mg}{kT} \cdot \frac{B^2}{8\pi}.$$

Since the density within the tube can never be less than zero, Equation (5.87) may—as shown by Jensen—be used to find an approximate expression for the upper limit to the magnetic field. Let us rewrite Equation (5.87) as

$$\rho_1 = \rho_0 - \frac{mB^2}{8\pi kT} = \frac{m}{kT(p_0 - B^2/8\pi)}.$$

The condition $\rho_1 \geq 0$ then gives

$$B_c \leq (8\pi p_0)^{1/2}. \tag{5.89}$$

We can get an idea of the order of magnitude of this maximum field by applying Equation (5.89) to the central region of the sun. The central pressure of the homogeneous stellar model used by Chandrasekhar and Fermi (1953) is

$$p_c = 1.33 \times 10^{15} M_*^2 / R_*^4 \quad \text{dynes/cm}^2,$$

where M_* and R_* are, respectively, the mass and radius of the star in solar units. The corresponding limit B_c becomes

$$B_c = 1.83 \times 10^8 M_* / R_*^2 \quad \text{gauss}. \tag{5.90}$$

5.3.5. Theories of the Sunspot Cycle

We have considered the possibility that magnetic tubes of force may exist in subphotospheric layers and on occasion may be transported to the surface—where they produce sunspots. Several authors have started with such a picture and tried to envisage how large-scale motions of the flux tubes might be used to account for the 22 year sunspot cycle. In his theory, Bjerknes (1926) (see Section 5.3.2.1) believed the magnetic field to be caused by the vortex motions of the plasma, and he accordingly assumed the existence of vortex rings instead of magnetic flux tubes in the sun.

This type of theory (Bjerknes, 1926; Allen, 1960) requires the existence of large-scale meridional circulation. The general theory of meridional motions in the presence of nonuniform rotation of a plasma is very complicated. In the theories of the sunspot cycle, the motions are simply postulated and then used to move the tubes of force (or vortex rings) around in the desired way.

Other theories do not require meridional circulation. In that case, however, they will depend on some other general property of the solar plasma, like the existence of a general poloidal magnetic field (Alfvén, 1945a, 1945b; Babcock, 1961).

5.3.5.1. *Theories depending on meridional circulation*

(a) BJERKNES' THEORY — Bjerknes (1926) assumed that there are two vortex rings in each hemisphere (see Figure 5.6a). The vortex motions have opposite directions in these rings to account for the change of polarity in alternate cycles. One vortex is supposed to travel—carried by the meridional currents—from about 35 deg latitude toward the equator just below the photosphere, which explains the equatorward drift of the sunspot zone. Simultaneously, the other vortex ring—which has given rise to the previous sunspot cycle—returns in deeper layers to the higher latitudes carried by the same circulation (Figure 5.6b).

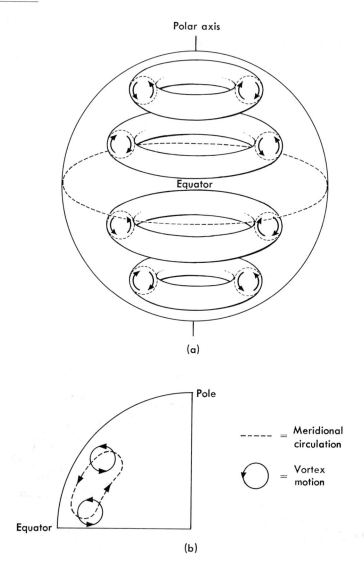

(a)

(b)

FIGURE 5.6. The vortex rings in Bjerknes' theory of sunspots (after Bjerknes, 1926)

Whereas Bjerknes' theory of the spot magnetic field is untenable (Section 5.3.2.1), his work on the cyclic nature of the phenomenon has had lasting value. It is not obvious that one can find circulatory motions in the sun that will carry flux tubes at the right speed to account for the 22 year cycle, but the idea still stimulates research in this field.

(b) ALLEN'S THEORY — Allen's work (1960) may be considered an extension of Bjerknes' idea. The vortex rings are replaced by magnetic flux tubes which are transported by meridional currents, much as in Bjerknes' theory. In addition, Allen's theory requires a poleward surface current carrying magnetic regions to the poles, where they account for a seemingly general field of the sun. This field will change polarity roughly every 11 years since the polarity of the flux tubes carried to the poles alternates. The surface poleward currents return to middle latitudes at greater depths.

Allen also tries to explain the nonuniform rotation of the sun as an equatorial acceleration due to the coupling between spots (i.e., between flux tubes) in the northern and southern hemisphere. The leading spots in bipolar groups are forced nearer to the equator than the following spots due to repulsion from the nearer pole or by attraction to the leading spots of groups in the other hemisphere. The result of these forces, according to Allen, would be to cause the observed inclination of the bipolar groups. When the leading spots coupled in the northern and southern hemispheres disappear, the interconnecting magnetic tubes will submerge. A subsurface magnetic tension will then be built up between the interacting flux tubes, and this tension will cause an equatorial acceleration. No quantitative arguments are given to show that the forces mentioned will produce the required effects.

5.3.5.2. *Theories depending on a general magnetic field*

Of the two theories we shall consider in this Section, one (Alfvén, 1943b) requires a general field pervading the whole sun. In addition, it requires that disturbances be produced periodically in the sun's core. These disturbances are transported to the surface along the field lines. The other theory (Babcock, 1961) requires a shallow magnetic field. Differential rotation will then wind up the field lines until the toroidal field created reaches a certain value in the sunspot zone. For the first part of both these theories, we refer to Section 5.3.3.

(a) ALFVÉN'S THEORY — Of the hydromagnetic waves that are sent out as whirl-rings from the core, those which reach the surface at latitudes of about 40 deg have shorter paths to travel than those which reach the surface closer to the equator. If therefore two sets of waves start at the same time, the set reaching latitude 40 deg arrives first. This is Alfvén's (1943b) explanation of why any sunspot cycle starts at moderate latitudes and why the sunspot zone progresses toward the equator as the cycle advances. To account for the observed progression time, the hydromagnetic waves must travel along lines of force of a general poloidal field whose strength at the surface at the equator is about 25 gauss. This is much stronger than the observed "general" field of the sun. However, arguments like Walén's (see Section 5.3.3.2) indicate that even though only small fields are seen above the photosphere, much stronger fields may exist below it.

The polarities observed in bipolar spots during any one cycle are explained by postulating that all whirl-rings in one hemisphere whirl in the same direction and that those in the other hemisphere whirl in the opposite sense. To explain the alteration of polarities in consecutive cycles, Alfvén resorted to a complicated set of assumptions. The rings are supposed to be generated in two active regions in the core, one north and one south of the equatorial plane. A "recoil" ring is generated and sent to the southern active region each time a ring is generated in the northern active region and transported to the northern hemisphere. The recoil ring is amplified in the southern active region and forms a new ring which travels to the surface while a new recoil ring is formed. This last ring travels to the northern active region, and the process is repeated. Alfvén postulated that it takes 11 years for a ring to travel from one active region to the other, thereby accounting for the 11 year cycle.

No convincing argument has been given to explain why the convective core should exhibit such an extraordinarily unstable behavior.

(b) BABCOCK'S THEORY — We have seen that as the nonuniform rotation draws out the general field lines, the differential advance in longitude, θ, can be computed. It is given by Equation (5.74). The corresponding field strength t_2 years after minimum—on the assumption that the winding up started t_1 years before minimum—is given by Equation (5.75), namely

$$B_\phi = 2\theta_0(t_1 + t_2)B_0 \sin \phi \cos \phi.$$

At the beginning of the cycle, the intensity of this field attains, at latitude of about 30 deg, a critical value, B_{crit}, which is favorable for the formation of sunspots. This field is then ($t_2 = 0$) :

$$B_{\text{crit}} = 2\theta_0 t_1 B_0. \tag{5.91}$$

Combining (5.75) and (5.91), we find

$$\sin \phi \cos \phi = \frac{t_1\sqrt{3}}{4(t_1 + t_2)}. \tag{5.92}$$

Babcock (1961) assumes that the process of winding up the field lines begins $t_1 = 3$ years before a minimum. Equation (5.92) then gives

$$\sin \phi \cos \phi = \text{const}/(t_2 + 3),$$

which is the mathematical expression for Spörer's law and gives the progression of the sunspot zone toward the equator as a function of the time t_2 after minimum.

So far we have described what Babcock calls stages 1 and 2 of his theory, namely the initial dipolar field (for times $t < t_1$) and the amplification period (from t_1 years before minimum to t_2 years after). We now come to stage 3, the formation of dipolar magnetic regions and sunspots. Parts of the created toroidal flux ropes will be carried to the surface by magnetic buoyancy. When they break through the photosphere, they will form bipolar regions that may be identified with sunspots whenever the fields are strong enough to partly inhibit convection. The flux ropes rising to the surface in the northern hemisphere will all give rise to bipolar regions of the same polarity, which is opposite to that of the bipolar regions formed in the southern hemisphere. Hence this accounts for the law of sunspot polarity. We have already seen in stage 2 that the sunspot migration toward the equator (Spörer's law) can be reproduced.

Finally, stage 4 deals with the breakup of bipolar regions and the transport of the follower spots toward the poles. It is interesting to note that a decade ago Babcock and Babcock (1955) were already thinking along the lines of this stage 4. They considered the polar magnetic field as the result of a poleward migration of the f-portions of disintegrating bipolar regions. This part of Babcock's theory is seen to depend on the existence of meridional currents and on the assumption that the rising magnetic lines of force of the migrating bipolar regions will sever and reconnect in the proper manner. As more and more bipolar regions form and vanish, the initial dipole field is first neutralized by the poleward drift of the f-parts and then succeeded by a new dipolarlike field of the opposite polarity. After this, the whole cycle—stages 1 through 4—is repeated with all magnetic polarities reversed from the previous cycle.

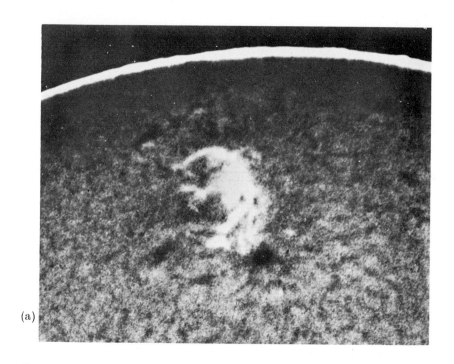

(a)

Two examples of flares photographed at the Climax Station of the High Altitude Observatory: (a) 22 October, 1963, 1435 U.T., (b) 23 October, 1962, 1711 U.T.

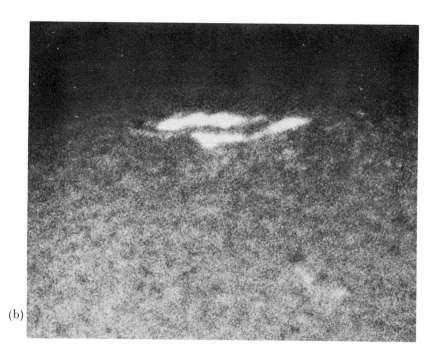

(b)

Flares | 6

The signs of solar activity considered thus far, i.e., plages and sunspots, have been defined in terms of their observed magnetic fields. These fields are strong compared to any observable field connected with the quiet, nonactive, solar atmosphere. Observations of the remaining manifestations of solar activity, namely flares, prominences, and coronal condensations, do not readily yield magnetic fields greatly in excess of quiet sun conditions. Yet, in all probability, the effects of magnetic fields on the formation and development of these phenomena are of prime importance.

We shall repeatedly find in the next chapters that what we call flares and what we call prominences are often intimately connected. To treat these two aspects of solar activity separately may therefore seem somewhat artificial. Likewise, the connection between some types of prominences and coronal condensations is very close. When we also treat these phenomena separately, it is mainly for historical reasons and expediency in organizing the material. However, when it is more convenient, we shall treat them simultaneously in any of the three chapters.

6.1. *Observations*

The flare, as it is observed spectroscopically, occurs much higher in the solar atmosphere than sunspots. It is basically a chromospheric phenomenon, as its French name, éruption chromosphérique, implies. Often it reaches up into the corona proper.

Only very rarely are flares observed in integrated, white, light. Detection of monochromatic radiation from flares is the common way to identify them. This radiation may fall in the X-ray, UV, or radio parts of the spectrum, but generally is in the visible part and for the most part is observed by using the Hα line (6563 Å). The characteristic brightening of this line is often used as a definition of flares. Particle emission from some flares is observed, but this aspect of the phenomenon, although very important, is still known only in a rudimentary way.

When observed at the limb, against the dark sky background, the typical flare spectrum exhibits a multitude of emission lines from hydrogen, neutral and ionized helium, and many neutral and singly ionized metal atoms and ions. Superficially, some prominences are characterized by the same kind of spectrum when seen on the limb. (We shall later see how detailed studies indicate differences between flare and "flarelike" prominence spectra.) The similarities between spectra of flares and many prominences when observed on the limb do not carry over into disk observations. Disk flares give spectra not unlike limb spectra, even though all emission lines are generally considerably fainter. Prominences, on the other hand, always appear dark, on the disk, as brought out in the familiar Hα—or Ca II, K—spectroheliograms (see Figure 2.2).

6.1.1. The Optical Flare—Classifications, Incidence

Spectroscopically, a flare on the disk is a temporary appearance of a strong emission within some dark Fraunhofer lines. In the case of great flares, the emission excess inside the Hα line, for instance, may be several times the intensity of the adjacent continuous solar spectrum. On a spectroheliogram or a Lyot filtergram, a flare is observed as a brightening of parts of the plage in the active region in question. The area covered by the flare brightening may be several times 10^9 km^2. Flares smaller than about 3×10^8 km^2 are called subflares.

The area of the flare is the primary basis of the classification. It is measured as the projected area in terms of the unit 1 square degree heliographic at the center of the disk, and the measurements are made at the time of maximum brightness:

1 degree heliographic = 1/360 of the solar circumference = 12,500 km.

The projected area is generally corrected for foreshortening and expressed in millionths of the visible hemisphere or, more recently (IAU Rep., 1964) in millionths of the disk:

1 millionth of the hemisphere = 1/48.5 (=0.0206) square degree,

1 millionth of the disk = 1/97 (=0.0103) square degree,

1 square degree = 1.476×10^8 km^2 of solar surface.

For a number of years, the corrected area at the time of maximum brightness has been used to assign to a flare an *importance* classification (IAU

TABLE 6.1   Importance classification of flares

Importance class	Corrected area	
	In square degrees	In millionths of hemisphere
1 −	<2.06	<100
1	2.06–5.15	100–250
2	5.15–12.4	250–600
3	12.4–24.7	600–1200
3 +	>24.7	>1200

Trans., 1955) according to the following limits (see Table 6.1). Categories 1+ and 2+ were introduced for flares that have the appropriate areas for classes 1 and 2, respectively, but whose intensity, line width, or duration is greater than that for normal flares in their area classes.

A new dual form for importance classification has recently been adopted (IAU Rep., 1964). It is recommended that subflares be identified by the letter S rather than by 1− and that the number 4 replace 3+ in the area importance classification. The new importance evaluation for a flare will consist of two elements, a number and a letter. The number will describe the area essentially as before. The letter will indicate whether the intensity of the flare is faint (f), normal (n), or brilliant (b) for its respective class (see Table 6.2).

For flares more than 65 deg from the center of the disk, no reliable value of "corrected" area can be given. The new dual form recommends that the apparent area of flares not more than 65 deg from the center of the disk be corrected for foreshortening, as in the past, by applying the cosine law.

The determination of the brightness of a flare is quite difficult, and it

TABLE 6.2   Dual importance classification

Corrected area	Relative intensity evaluation		
Square degrees	Faint (f)	Normal (n)	Brilliant (b)
<2.06	S f	S n	S b
2.06–5.15	1 f	1 n	1 b
5.15–12.4	2 f	2 n	2 b
12.4–24.7	3 f	3 n	3 b
>24.7	4 f	4 n	4 b

depends on the instrument used. The brightness measurements do not refer to the central intensity of the profile of the line observed, but rather to the integral of the emission in the line profile over the bandwidth of the instrument. Furthermore, the maximum intensity of a flare may occur only within a small fraction of the total area and before or after the time of the maximum extension of the flare. For these and other reasons, the validity of intensity measurements is often questionable.

The light curve (intensity vs. time) of a flare characteristically shows a rapid rise (lasting from a few to several minutes) to maximum brightness, followed by a considerably slower decline to the preflare value. (Great flares may last two to three hours, for instance.) A similar behavior is found if we plot the time dependence of the flare area. Individual flares, however, show a great diversity in both brightness and duration. The smallest subflares, microflares, are difficult to distinguish from the plage background, and there is hardly a lower limit to their lifetimes. The greatest flares seem to last about three hours and reach peak intensities in the center of $H\alpha$ of two or three times the intensity of the continuous emission outside the line.

Nearly all flares are found close to sunspots and are often seen as brightenings of the pre-existing plages. Waldmeier (1938b) showed that, in relation to latitude, flares and sunspots have nearly identical distributions. Such simple facts may be taken as indications that flares are the result of the play of magnetic fields.

The concept of flare incidence (the ratio of the observed number of flares during a given period to the net hours of actual observation time during the period) has been used as an index of solar activity (Waldmeier, 1938b; Behr and Siedentopf, 1952). As is to be expected, there exists a strong positive correlation between this index and the occurrence of sunspots as measured, for instance, by the Wolf number (H. Smith, 1962a). There are some indications that the flare incidence increases with spot area, but the correlation is not strong (Giovanelli, 1939; Bell and Glazer, 1959). However, of greater value for a physical understanding of the flare phenomenon is a comparison of the flare incidence with the type of spot group in which the flares occur. One finds that the more magnetically complex the spot group is, the greater is the flare incidence (Richardson, 1939; Giovanelli, 1939). According to Bell and Glazer, the percentage of α, β, and γ groups (see Section 5.1.5) that produce 10 or more flares is 1.5, 5, and 46, respectively. This seems to indicate that it is not the strength of the magnetic field alone that determines the probability of a flare occurring. The configuration of the field may be of equal, or greater, importance. It is also worth noting that the flare incidence is considerably greater in the first half of a group's lifetime than in the last half, with a maximum during the phase before maximum area (Giovanelli, 1939; Witte, 1951). This is generally the time when changes in the sunspot magnetic field are most pronounced.

6.1.2. Flare Morphology

As stated by Smith and Smith (1963) in their excellent book on flares, the morphology of the phenomenon offers important clues to its physical character. In this section we shall discuss some aspects of the structure and development of flare regions which we believe are particularly important for later theoretical interpretations. The treatment in general follows the outline in the book by Smith and Smith, even though the emphasis will often be different.

6.1.2.1. Development

We have seen in Section 4.2 that plages show a granulation-like fine structure. Hα spectroheliograms of the quiet chromosphere show a more or less roundish bright fine-structure—the *mottles*. Similar features also make up part of the plage fine structure, but the Hα plage consists primarily of *fibrilles*. These are longer and thinner than the mottles. Discovered by Hale (1908a, 1908b) the fibrilles are also called chromospheric *striation* (Ellison, McKenna and Reid, 1960a, 1960b). The word *whirl* is used to describe a common configuration of the fibrilles and bears some resemblance to the cyclonic shape.

Most flares start as small localized brightenings of a plage, often along the fibrille structure. Then the flaring fibrilles seem to swell and merge with one another. Often the brightest parts preserve a very elongated shape, likened, by some authors, to ropes or kinked ribbons. These changes may all occur in a period of a few minutes, called the *flash phase*. The brightest parts of the flare at maximum, and also generally during the declining phase, are still the ropes or ribbons, but small bright *nodules* are also common. The latter show a characteristic Hα profile (see Section 6.1.3) and are called *moustaches* (Severny, 1957).

At maximum development, great flares often partially extend over the penumbra and umbra of the associated sunspot. Part of the flare may therefore occur close to where the sunspot magnetic field has its maximum strength, and this configuration has been correlated with the ejection of matter from flares (see Section 6.1.7).

6.1.2.2. Sympathetic flares

With more than one active region visible on the sun, flares may occur more or less simultaneously in different locations on the disk. Richardson (1936, 1951) studied flare data from Mount Wilson for the period 1937 to 1951 and found that there are more flares occurring nearly simultaneously than can be accounted for under the assumption of random occurrence of flares. He concluded that flares may brighten in response to some stimulus generated by another flare in progress in a different active region. Such flares are called sympathetic. Richardson's conclusion could not be confirmed by statistical investigations by Waldmeier (1958), Fritzová (1959) and H. Smith (1962b), but by studying single cases, Becker (1958), and especially S. Smith (1965), showed the reality of the phenomenon. S. Smith actually observed the disturbance propagate from a flare and interact with a filament that resulted in the second flare.

That many flares generate some kind of stimulus which affects distant prominences is another story. We shall return to these interactions in Sections 7.4 and 7.5.

6.1.2.3. *Homologous flares*

It is often observed that a flare is brightening in exactly the same position and showing the same geometrical outline as a previous flare in that region. This repetitive character was discovered by Waldmeier (1938b), and flares showing this behavior are called homologous (Ellison, McKenna, and Reid, 1960a, 1960b). Detailed studies of this phenomenon are due to Dodson–Prince and Hedeman (1949) and H. Smith (1962c). The homologous character of flares has an important bearing on the question of their generation. If a magnetic field is involved, it shows that the field configuration often is not seriously affected by the occurrence of a flare or that the field regains its previous character after the flare disappears. We shall return to this in Section 6.1.4.

6.1.2.4. *Some characteristics of great flares*

The *nimbus* is a rare aspect of great flares (Ellison, McKenna, and Reid, 1960a, 1961a). It consists of a dark halo forming around a flare at the time of maximum phase. The brightness of the Hα disk is diminished up to 5% over a roughly circular area of radius about 150,000 km. Ellison, McKenna and Reid studied five cases of flares with nimbus and found that they all involved importance-4 flares, which ejected cosmic ray particles and emitted a continuous spectrum of radio waves.

We also owe to Ellison, McKenna and Reid (1960a, 1960b) the discovery that great flares may affect the fibrille structure in the neighboring more quiet chromosphere; the brightness contrast between the fibrilles and the darker portions becomes significantly less. This may extend over large areas (several times 10^{10} km^2) and may last for several hours, after which the fibrille structure recovers and attains its former sharpness and contrast.

6.1.2.5. *The three-dimensional flare*

Statistical studies of the distribution of flares on the disk and observations of flares at the limb permit us to draw conclusions regarding the actual shape of flares. One of the most common forms is the roundish mound of more or less uniform brightness. It develops as the plage swells and brightens simultaneously. The heights of these mounds range from a few thousand to more than 50,000 km.

Another common shape is the conical flare. Here we find a range from small subflares less than 2000 km high to large structures reaching heights in excess of 30,000 km. These flares have an average height-to-base ratio of 3 to 1. At times the cone is degenerated into a cylindrical structure.

The third major group is made up of loop-shaped flares. The loop structure is also important in prominence studies, and to avoid confusion later, we shall here elaborate on the flare loop. Following Smith and Smith (1963), we notice that flares acquire loops in three characteristic ways, always in an upward sense.

(1) A surgelike excrescence can protrude from the chromosphere, extending along a curved trajectory to come back to its point of origin.

(2) The whole loop may appear from a point in the chromosphere, increasing in diameter to a maximum of 5000 to 40,000 km, growing with a velocity of between 20 and 100 km/sec.

(3) A solid swelling can become transparent at the center, leaving its outline visible as a loop.

The majority of flares, sometime during their lifetime, will be fairly well described by one of these three major shapes. However, there are many flares that defy any simple classification scheme, and they can only be designated as irregular.

The analyses of flare heights are difficult because of the necessary corrections that must be applied (observations are incomplete for flares with areas smaller than about 20 millionths of the hemisphere; limb darkening favors faint flares, etc.). According to Warwick and Wood (1959) 25 % of flares have heights exceeding 10,000 km. Giovanelli and McCabe (1958a) derived a mean height of 7300 km, excluding all flares smaller than 20 millionths.

6.1.3. Spectral Characteristics

The wealth of spectral lines observed in emission in some limb flares is quite remarkable. In the visible part, the spectrum is not unlike that observed in many active prominences, and without additional information it may even be difficult to decide what kind of object one is observing. This ambiguity, as stated in the introduction, is not present for disk work.

As examples of earlier spectral observations of flares, we mention the works of d'Azambuja (1939), Richardson and Minkowski (1939), and Allen

(1940). Allen lists 116 lines between 3920 and 6680 Å. Later spectrographic work on flares, either studies of selected lines or line identification lists, includes papers by Ellison (1946), Richardson (1950), Suemoto (1951), Švestka (1951a, 1951b, 1951c, 1951d, 1951e, 1951f, 1952, 1957, 1960, 1961, 1962a, 1962b, 1963), Severny (1954a), Severny and Mustel (1955), Zirin (1957), Kazachevskaya and Severny (1958), Jefferies, Smith and Smith (1959), and E. Smith (1962).

6.1.3.1. *Hydrogen emission*

The best observed line is undoubtedly Hα, and there exists an extensive literature on its behavior in flares. The observed intensity in this line ranges from an insignificant filling in of the Fraunhofer absorption line of the quiet disk in the case of small flares to central intensities reaching 300% of the local continuum near the line. The half-width of the line may be several Å. It is customary not to use the width at half intensity but to define the line widths as the separation between the two points of the profile where it merges visually with the normal profile of the quiet disk. Often the flare profile is much wider than the absorption line of the background disk, and in that case the width is defined as the interval between the 105% brightness level. Using this definition, we find widths as great as 20 Å or more.

There is a loose correlation between line width and importance of the flare. Roughly speaking the line widths are 3, 5, and 10 Å for flares of importance 1, 2, and 3, respectively. Since large flares at least conceivably may change the physical conditions of deeper layers, we do not know the background absorption line well. Hence the true shape of disk flare profiles is uncertain. To go correctly from observations to flare models and thence to theoretical interpretations requires solution of transfer problems that for the time being are beyond our capabilities.

The emergent intensity I_λ from a disk flare may be written

$$I_\lambda = I_B \, e^{-\tau\lambda} + S_\lambda(\tau_\lambda)(1 - e^{-\tau\lambda}), \tag{6.1}$$

where I_B is the controversial background intensity, τ_λ the total optical thickness, and S_λ the source function in the flare. Depending on how S_λ varies with optical depth, we may arrive at different models for the flare.

Observations of flares at the limb are not beset with the same difficulties and seem easier to interpret. In this case, we observe the flare against the dark sky background. However, the lower part of limb flares is often hidden by, or at least affected by, the chromosphere, and this may introduce additional complications. Besides, the source function will still be an unknown function of optical depth.

The Hα profile does not in general show a Gaussian shape. In the cases when it is approximately Gaussian, its half-width, from Equation (1.110a), may be written

$$\Delta\lambda_D = (\lambda/c)\sqrt{2kT/m}. \tag{6.2}$$

The "broadening temperature" is often very high, and may not be the kinetic temperature of the plasma, since part of the broadening may be due to "microturbulence."

In some flares the Hα profile possesses more pronounced wings than the error curve. In others—mainly great flares—the profile shows central self-reversal. The self-reversal may indicate strong self-absorption—the optical depth certainly is often very large—but it is equally probable that the shape is dictated by the behavior of the source function in the flare (Jefferies and Thomas, 1958, 1959; Švestka, 1960, 1961, 1962a, 1962b).

Disk flares generally reveal profiles centered at the wavelength of the laboratory line center. At most, small displacements and asymmetries are involved. Limb flares, on the other hand, often show significant Doppler shifts or large irregularities which imply considerable mass motions of parts of the flare. This same kind of behavior is also found in many active prominences seen on the limb.

The behavior of the other Balmer lines in flares is similar to that of Hα. The line width as well as the central intensity decrease with increasing principal quantum number. However, the Balmer decrement often behaves very irregularly in great flares (E. Smith, 1962). As a general rule, H_{11} or H_{12} is the highest member of the Balmer series that can be seen in flares at the center of the disk, while good limb observations may reveal H_{26} to H_{28}.

The Balmer continuum is very difficult to see in disk flares (Kazachevskaya and Severny, 1958; Michard, 1959). In limb flares the same continuum is quite pronounced (Dunn, Jefferies, and Orrall, 1960; Jefferies and Orrall, 1961a, 1961b). If one makes the assumption that the continuous emission observed in flares—and in prominences—is due entirely to hydrogen and to scattering of photospheric radiation by free electrons, one may use the observations to deduce the physical conditions of the flare plasma. Studies along these lines have been carried out by Zanstra (1950), who gives the expressions for the different emissions (Balmer continuum, higher continua, free–free emission and electron scattering), Redman and Zanstra (1952), Orrall and Athay (1957), and Jefferies and Orrall (1961a). The specific formulas for the continuous emissions at 3646 Å, the head of the Balmer series, may be written per wavelength unit $d\lambda = 1$ cm, in units of ergs cm^{-3} sec^{-1} sr^{-1} (sr = steradian).

Free–free emission

$$\epsilon_{\rm ff} = 1.23 \times 10^{-19}\, n_{\rm p} n_{\rm e} T_{\rm e}^{-1/2}\, e^{-3.94\times 10^4/T_{\rm e}} \tag{6.3}$$

Free–bound emission

$$\epsilon_{\infty,n} = 3.89 \times 10^{-14} \, n_{\mathrm{p}} n_{\mathrm{e}} T_{\mathrm{e}}^{-3/2} \, e^{[(15.79\times10^4)/n_{\mathrm{e}} T_{\mathrm{e}}]-[(3.96\times10^4)/T_{\mathrm{e}}]} \qquad (6.4a)$$

Specifically, the Balmer continuum, $n = 2$

$$\epsilon_{\infty,2} = 4.87 \times 10^{-14} \, n_{\mathrm{p}} n_{\mathrm{e}} T_{\mathrm{e}}^{-3/2} \qquad (6.4b)$$

Electron scattering

$$\epsilon_{\mathrm{es}} = 2.82 \times 10^{-11} \, n_{\mathrm{e}} \qquad (6.5)$$

H^- emission

$$\epsilon_{\mathrm{H}^-} = B(T_{\mathrm{e}}) k_{\mathrm{H}^-}(\lambda, \, T_{\mathrm{e}}) k T_{\mathrm{e}} n_{\mathrm{e}} n_0 \qquad (6.6)$$

In these formulas n_{p} and n_{e} are the proton and electron number densities, respectively, n_0 is the number density of neutral hydrogen atoms, $B(T_{\mathrm{e}})$ is the Planck function, and k_{H^-} is the absorption coefficient of the H^- ion. The first three formulas result from the use of Cillié's (1932) expression for the number of electrons captured by protons into the nth quantum level per cm³ per second, namely

$$n_{\mathrm{p}} n_{\mathrm{e}} \alpha_{\mathrm{pe}} = 3.29 \times 10^{-6} \, n_{\mathrm{p}} n_{\mathrm{e}} T_{\mathrm{e}}^{-3/2} \frac{Z^4}{n^3} \, e^{(\chi_n/kT_{\mathrm{e}})} [-E_{\mathrm{i}}(-\chi_n/kT_{\mathrm{e}})],$$

where $Z = 1$ is the charge of the nucleus (proton), χ_n is the excitation potential of the nth bound level, E_{i} is the exponential integral and α_{pe} is the recombination coefficient. This expression results from integrating the basic Equation (1.98) as explained in Section 1.4.1. The formula for the electron scattering is obtained from the basic Equation (1.103) by taking proper account of limb darkening (Zanstra, 1950; Zirin, 1964).

The contribution due to the negative hydrogen ion is of importance only for $T_{\mathrm{e}} < 10,000\,°\mathrm{K}$. For such temperatures $k_{\mathrm{H}^-}(\lambda, \, T_{\mathrm{e}})$ is given by (Chandrasekhar and Breen, 1946)

$$k_{\mathrm{H}^-}(3646, \, T_{\mathrm{e}}) = 3.80 \times 10^{-28} \, e^{2.58\times10^4/T_{\mathrm{e}}}.$$

We shall see later (Section 6.2) that it is convenient to analyze the continuous emission in terms of the ratio R (Orrall and Athay, 1957; Jefferies and Orrall, 1961a):

$$R = \frac{\text{Balmer continuum at } 3646\ \mathring{A}}{\text{All other continua at } 3646\ \mathring{A}}, \qquad \text{namely,}$$

$$R = \frac{\epsilon_{\infty,2}}{\epsilon_{\mathrm{ff}} + \displaystyle\sum_{n=3}^{\infty} \epsilon_{\infty,n} + \epsilon_{\mathrm{es}} + \epsilon_{\mathrm{H}^-}}. \qquad (6.7)$$

Substituting into Equation (6.7) the expressions for the different contributions, Equations (6.3) through (6.6), we find a quadratic expression for n_e. Only for T_e greater than a certain lower limit do real values of n_e exist. This lower limit on T_e depends on n_0. Then R will approach a limited value R_∞ as n_e increases and an upper limit on T_e thereby is also established.

Jefferies and Orrall (1961b) have shown that if one extrapolates the emission from 3646 Å to 3639 Å and to 3699 Å the ratio R may be written

$$R = \frac{\epsilon(3639) - \epsilon(3699)}{\epsilon(3699)} \, , \tag{6.8a}$$

since $\epsilon(3639) = \epsilon_{H^-} + \epsilon_{es} + \epsilon_{ff} + \sum_{n=3}^{\infty} \epsilon_{\infty,n}$ and $\epsilon(3639) - \epsilon(3699) = \epsilon_{\infty,2}$. If the emissions were constant throughout the flare or prominence, R could be deduced from the observed intensities, I:

$$R = \frac{I(3639) - I(3699)}{I(3699)} \, . \tag{6.8b}$$

In most cases, however, the observed intensity is a complicated integral over the emission ϵ.

6.1.3.2. Moustaches

Ellerman (1917) observed very thin short-lived emission wings on hydrogen lines in active regions, and the phenomenon has been known as Ellerman's "solar hydrogen bombs." Extensive work in this field has been undertaken by Severny (1956, 1957), who refers to the spectral characteristics as moustaches. They have also been observed by Lyot (1944), who called them "petit points" and by McMath, Mohler, and Dodson (1960).

The moustaches have their origin in small bright grains with diameters of a few hundred kilometers. Severny describes moustaches as very thin (perpendicular to dispersion) but wide (along the direction of dispersion) emission wings emerging from normal Fraunhofer lines. Sometimes the emission is seen on only one side of the line, at other times the moustache extends in both directions. Continuous emission generally occurs together with moustaches. In the Balmer lines (up to about H_{10}), and in the Ca II, K and H lines, the moustaches may be traced for 10 to 15 Å from the line center. Less extensive moustaches are seen in some iron and titanium lines and in the Mg I, b-group. For strong lines the moustaches are generally not seen in the line center, in weak lines they fill in the cores. There is a pronounced asymmetry in most moustaches in that the blue wing is broader and brighter than the red wing. The brightness of moustaches as well as their lifetimes seem to be similar to those of ordinary flares. They also have a tendency to recur at the same locations (Michard, 1961).

Many metal lines in moustache spectra are as broad as the hydrogen lines and this has been taken as evidence that mass motions—not Stark effect or radiation damping—are at work. If the moustaches are explosive outbursts of matter (Severny, 1957), the velocities involved are of the order of 1000 km/sec.

6.1.3.3. *Metal emission*

A number of different metal lines are influenced by flares, but none more strongly than the Ca II, K and H lines. While Švestka, Kopecký, and Blaha (1961) found a loose correlation between the width of the K and H lines and the width of Hα in some flares, there are also flares whose K and H lines are much narrower than Hα (Jefferies, Smith and Smith, 1959; Švestka, 1961). When one bears in mind how complex the interpretation of the K and H lines is for the quiet chromosphere (Jefferies and Thomas, 1960), it is not surprising that our understanding of the Ca II flare emission is quite rudimentary.

Lines of neutral and singly ionized iron are generally quite conspicuous in flare spectra (Allen, 1940). In addition, one finds represented Na I, Mg I, Mg II, Al I, Si I, Si II, Ca I, Sc II, Ti II, V II, Cr I, Cr II, Mn I, Co I, Ni I, Sr II, Ba II, Y II (Smith and Smith, 1963; Zirin, 1957). As we shall see in the next Chapter, most of the same lines are also seen in many active prominences. There are, however, finer details that may be used to distinguish the different limb events.

The development of the flare spectrum with time has been studied by Stepanyan (1963), who found that the emission in the fainter metal lines lags behind that of the strongest metal lines (Ca II, K and H) and of the hydrogen and helium lines. The lines belonging to the rare earths attain maximum intensity latest of all. Since weak metal lines, and especially the lines of the rare earths, are formed lower in the atmosphere than hydrogen, etc., Stepanyan's observation indicates that an exciting agent is propagated down into photospheric layers from the flare region above.

6.1.3.4. *Helium lines*

One of the most characteristic features of flare (and active prominence) spectra is the presence of strong and broad lines of neutral and ionized helium. The excitation of helium in flares, or almost anywhere in the solar atmosphere at that, confronts us with a most interesting and very complex problem. To appreciate the different aspects of the question, we shall first consider the energy-level diagram of helium and make some remarks on the ways in which different levels may be excited. Referring to Figure 6.1, we see that some of the lines used in flare and prominence studies come from orthohelium (the triplet series) and some from parahelium (the singlet series). We note further that the ground configuration lies extremely low, 20 eV below the next lowest. The metastable 2^3S state acts as a sort of ground level for the triplet series.

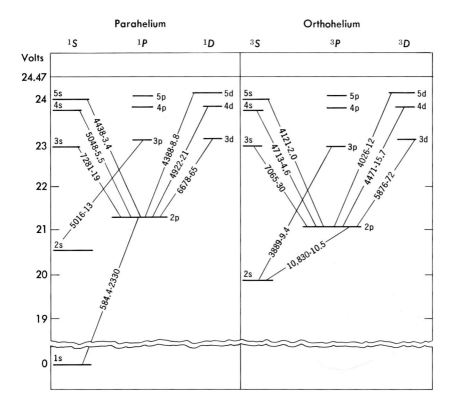

FIGURE 6.1.   Energy level diagram of helium (He I)

Since radiative processes involving changes in multiplicity are forbidden, the 2^3S state is populated by collisions. Of the collision rates for intersystem transitions leading to excitation of the 2^3S state, that from the ground state (1^1S) is well known (Massey and Moiseiwitsch, 1954). For quantum numbers $n > 2$, absorption of photospheric radiation is the dominant excitation process in the triplet series. The 6000 °K radiation cannot to any extent remove electrons from the ground state to excite the singlet levels. Here we must rely on collisions. In this way the 2^1P state is excited, and subsequent absorption of photospheric radiation can excite the higher levels of the S and D series.

The resonance line of He I, 584 Å, is observable only with airborne
equipment and little is known of its behavior in flares. Since the 2^3S level
is metastable, the infrared line $2^3S - 2^3P$, at 10,830 Å may be considered
a pseudoresonance line for the triplet structure. We easily resolve the faint
blue component at 10,829.04 Å, while the two stronger red components at
10,830.25 Å and 10,830.34 Å remain unresolved. The theoretical intensity
ratios for small optical depth are 10,830.34:10,830.25:10,829.04 = 5:3:1.
It is convenient for the following discussion to introduce the intensity ratio

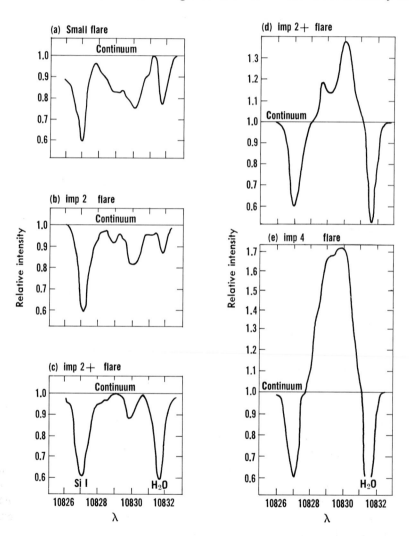

FIGURE 6.2.   Profiles of the He I, 10830 line in disk flares

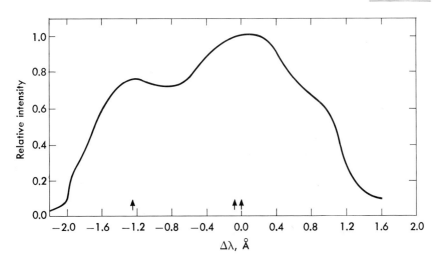

FIGURE 6.3.   The profile of the He I, 10830 line in a limb flare

q = intensity of blue component/intensity of red components, which then theoretically should be $\frac{1}{8}$.

Outside the solar disk, the line always shows up in emission, both in the chromosphere and in flares and prominences. The q-ratio is always greater than $\frac{1}{8}$, except in some quiescent prominences (Tandberg-Hanssen, 1960, 1962). On the disk, the line is reported in emission in only a few great flares (Richardson and Minkowski, 1939; Tandberg-Hanssen, Curtis and Watson, 1959), and the q-ratio is again considerably greater than $\frac{1}{8}$. In smaller flares we see an absorption line, and there seems to be a "critical importance" (about $2+$) which a flare has to reach before the line will show up in emission. We note that the line from plage areas is Gaussian, i.e., the q-ratio is close to $\frac{1}{8}$ (see also Mohler and Goldberg, 1956; Namba, 1960, 1963).

In Figure 6.2 are shown some line profiles from disk flares; the 10,830 line as well as the adjacent Si I line, 10,827 and the H_2O line, 10,832 (terrestrial). In going from a small flare in Figure 6.2a to greater flares in Figure 6.2b and c, we notice how the absorption in the He I line becomes less and less. Figure 6.2c is from the outer part of an importance $2+$ flare, and the emission has already started to fill in the line. Figure 6.2d is from the central part of the same importance $2+$ flare, and here the emission is fairly strong. Finally, Figure 6.2e shows the impressive profile of an importance 4 flare. The profile of an importance $1+$ flare observed at the limb is portrayed in Figure 6.3. The blue component is seen to be very pronounced, indicating a q-ratio in excess of $\frac{1}{2}$.

The 2^3P–3^3D line at 5876 Å—the well-known D_3 line—shows a behavior in flares similar to the 10,830 line. For flares of importance 2 or less, it is always in absorption, and in greater flares it shows up in emission (Smith and Smith, 1963).

A number of other helium lines, from the triplet as well as from the singlet series, are observed both in limb flares and in disk flares. Of special interest is the observed ratio between corresponding triplet and singlet lines, like 5876 and 6678, 4471 and 4922, 7065 and 7281, 4713 and 5048, etc. In thermodynamic equilibrium the ratio should be given by the ratio of the statistical weights involved, that is, 3:1 (disregarding the Boltzmann factor because of the small difference in excitation potentials). The observed chromospheric ratio is about 30:1, and this is generally explained as due to a radiation leak in the singlet structure (the 2^1P level connects to the ground level) which is not available to orthohelium. While the triplet/singlet ratio is still large in quiescent prominences, it reaches values approaching the theoretical value in active prominences and flares (Jefferies, Smith and Smith, 1959; Steshenko and Khokhlova, 1960).

Another way to study the excitation conditions in helium is to observe the ratio between corresponding lines of the series 2^3P-n^3S and 2^3P-n^3D, for instance 4471 and 4713. If we have a pure recombination spectrum, the intensities of 4471 and 4713 would be proportional to the statistical weights, that is, $\frac{15}{3} = 5$. This is the lowest value we can normally have for this intensity ratio. Under conditions of photo-excitation (by photospheric radiation) of the triplet series, the above value should be multiplied by the ratio of the transition probabilities, that is, $I(4471)/I(4713) = \frac{15}{3} \times 15.7/4.6 = 17$. The chromospheric value is 13.7 (Athay and Menzel, 1956). Few observations are available for flares, but indications are that the value of the ratio is low, smaller than 5 (Zirin, 1957; Jefferies, Smith and Smith, 1959). In prominences it ranges from values around 5 to more than 20 (see Section 7.1).

Ionized helium is represented in flare and active prominence spectra on the limb by the lines 4684 $(4 \rightarrow 3)$, 5411 $(7 \rightarrow 4)$, and 4541 $(9 \rightarrow 4)$. The parentheses indicate the level transitions involved. The lines are very broad, corresponding to broadening temperatures of several hundred thousand degrees. In disk spectra only the strongest line, 4686 Å, is easily visible, and its profile gives a broadening temperature of 30,000–50,000 °K. We shall return to the interpretation of these line width observations in Section 6.2.

According to Zirin (1961a, 1964), the intensity ratios of the He II lines in limb flares and active prominences are roughly 4684:5411:4541 = 10:5:1. If the lines are optically thin, and they most certainly are, the intensity ratios should be given by $n(4)A(4 \rightarrow 3)h\nu_{43}:n(7)A(7 \rightarrow 4)h_{74}: n(9)A(9 \rightarrow 4)h\nu_{94} \approx 75:4:1$, where $n(u)$ is the number density of atoms in the uth level $(u = 4, 7, \text{or } 9)$ and $A(u \rightarrow l)$ is the Einstein probability of spontaneous emission from an upper level u to a lower level l. Zirin showed that the observed intensity ratios may be accounted for if the lines are formed in a pure recombination spectrum. In such a capture spectrum the intensity of each line depends only on the number of recombinations and direct cascade to the upper level of the line. A recombination spectrum will occur whenever the probability of exciting levels $u > 3$ from the ground level of He II is less than the probability of a recombination to He I. Taking into account Burgess' (1964) calculations of dielectronic recombination, we can show with Zirin that the recombination rate to He I exceeds the probability of exciting the $u = 4$ level for all temperatures below $180,000°K$. Hence, whenever the temperature is less than $180,000\ °K$, the He II spectrum is a recombination spectrum. Such a dynamic spectrum seems to imply a nonstationary model for the He II ion. It may be part of a plasma going through a process of rapid cooling. Again, we postpone a more detailed discussion of these implications to Section 6.2.

6.1.3.5. Classifications

The different states of the solar plasma (chromosphere, corona, flares, active prominences, quiescent prominences) give different kinds of line spectra. It would therefore seem reasonable to classify the different objects

TABLE 6.3   Waldmeier's classification

Class	Criterion
I	$b_3 < b_4$
II	$b_3 = b_4$
III	$b_4 < b_3 \leq b_2$
IV	$b_2 < b_3 \leq b_1$
V	$b_1 < b_3$

according to their spectra. One may then hope to find criteria whereby, for instance, flares may be distinguished.

A classification along these lines was introduced by Waldmeier (1949b, 1951, 1961b) using the b-lines (Mg I, 5184, 5173, 5167 and Fe II, 5169). Such a comparison of an ionized metal line with neutral metal lines of different relative intensities gives an impression of the degree of excitation in the plasma. It leads to a spectrographic distinction between active prominences and flares seen at the limb. Table 6.3 gives the criteria of Waldmeier's classification, where b_i represents the intensity of the b_i line. Flares generally fall in classes IV and V.

Another classification of the solar atmospheric objects was given by Zirin and Tandberg-Hanssen (1960) (see Table 6.4). The philosophy behind this classification is based on a picture of flares and prominences as being

TABLE 6.4   The Zirin–Tandberg-Hanssen classification

Class	Criteria	Objects
I	He I, 4026 $\ll$ Sr II, 4078 He I, 4713 $\ll$ Ti II, 4572 He II, 4686 $\ll$ He I, 4713	Low chromosphere
II	He I, 4026 $\approx$ Sr II, 4078 He I, 4713 $\approx$ Ti II, 4572 He II, 4686 $\ll$ He I, 4713	Middle chromosphere ($h \approx 1500$ km) Quiescent prominences
III	He I, 4026 $\gg$ Sr II, 4078	High chromosphere, i.e., spicules
	He I, 4713 $\gg$ Ti II, 4572 He II, 4686 $\approx$ He I, 4713	Active prominences Flares
IV	Presence of Fe X, 6374, Fe XIV, 5303, Ca XIII, 4086 or Ca XV, 5694	Coronal enhancements and condensations

built up of different regions. Some regions are fairly cool ($\sim 10^4$ °K) with strong hydrogen and metal line emission, while the helium emission is weak. Others are composed of a rather hot plasma (several times 10^4 °K), with strong helium and faint metal line emission. A comparison between the "classification lines" gives a measure of which regions dominate a given object. This, then, is the simple classification of Table 6.4, where the criteria refer to the intensity of the lines mentioned. It is seen that both active prominences and flares fall in the same class III, according to this table. The classification shows that both types of objects are spectroscopically very active, exhibiting high-excitation conditions. While this emphasizes the fact that it is often difficult to decide whether a given object is a limb flare or a very active, brilliant prominence, it also shows that the simple classification is unable to cope with such subtleties.

In order to try to remedy this, certain metal lines that behave differently in flares and in active prominences have been introduced as classification criteria (Tandberg-Hanssen, 1963). It turns out that Fe II lines which are generally faint in active prominences attain considerable strength in flares. The reverse holds true for Ba II lines, and especially for Ti II lines. Introducing the ratio between the intensity of the Fe II line, 4584 and Ti II, 4572, $M = I(\text{Fe II}, 4584)/I(\text{Ti II}, 4572)$, we can classify an active limb event as a flare if $M \geq 1$ and as a prominence if $M < 1$. We shall return to this classification in more detail in Chapter 7.

6.1.4. Magnetic Field Configurations

There are conflicting reports in the literature as to if and how magnetic fields in active regions change when a flare is produced. Also, there is controversy as to the location of flares relative to the magnetic field. Evidence has been presented (Severny, 1958a; Bumba, 1958; Evans, 1959; Bruzek, 1960) that flares occur near or along neutral points of lines in the magnetic field configuration. A neutral line is here to be taken as the line that divides two regions of opposite polarities as seen in the longitudinal component by a magnetograph (see Section 2.2). Severny and Evans also report that the field alters significantly as the flare appears. On the other hand, Howard and Babcock (1960), and Michard, Mouradain, and Semel (1961) found no evidence of small magnetic changes in photospheric levels during flare occurrences. A possible reorientation of strong fields, however, could not have been detected by the instruments used by these authors (Howard and Severny, 1963). According to Severny; a strong gradient of the field, in addition to the presence of neutral points, is required for a flare to appear. After the flare, the gradient is much flatter and there is a positive correlation between the gradient before the flare and the importance of the flare (Gopasyuk, Ogir, Severny and Shaposhnikova, 1962). Gradients of the longitudinal component that are 0.05 to 0.1 gauss/km before a flare are reduced to values of approximately 0.01 to 0.02 gauss/km after the flare.

Some neutral points disappear, as do separate "magnetic hills" (isogauss closed contours, Severny, 1960). Furthermore, magnetic hills may be shifted in location during a flare (Gopasyuk, 1961). There is also evidence of a shift in the position of the neighboring sunspots (Gopasyuk, 1962). As the flare develops, the sunspots are seen to shift in a direction generally toward the flare knots, and these shifts may attain a distance of 20,000 km. Observations like these suggest a strong coupling between the magnetic field and the very flare phenomenon. We shall return to this in Sections 6.2 and 6.3.

From the observed shifts of spots and magnetic hills, the change of magnetic energy, ΔW, may be estimated on the assumption that the shifts are due to a compression effect resulting from the transformation of magnetic energy to thermal energy of the flare. Let us consider with Gopasyuk (1961) a volume V in the plasma pervaded by a magnetic field B, and let us assume that the region initially is in equilibrium with its surroundings. Then, see Equation (5.85),

$$p_\mathrm{i} + B^2/8\pi = p_0 \, .$$

The magnetic energy in the volume V is

$$E_\mathrm{m} = (B^2/8\pi) \cdot V \, . \tag{6.9}$$

Since the compression is assumed to result from the destruction of the magnetic field, we find that the internal (heat) energy of the plasma increases by the amount

$$E_i = p'_m V/(\gamma - 1). \qquad (6.10)$$

If a total conversion of magnetic energy into thermal energy takes place, $E_i = E_m$, and from Equations (6.9) and (6.10) we find the corresponding pressure

$$p'_m = (\gamma - 1)(B^2/8\pi). \qquad (6.11)$$

The total pressure in the volume V after the transformation of magnetic energy to thermal energy is, by Equation (6.11),

$$p'_m + p_i = (\gamma - 1)(B^2/8\pi) + p_i < p_0$$

since $\gamma \approx \frac{5}{3}$. Thus, the conversion of energy leads to a decrease in the pressure inside the volume V, which contracts under the action of the external pressure. The work done is $p_e \, dV \approx \Delta W$, where the volume element $dV = 2\pi r \, \Delta r h$. Gopasyuk assumes the region to be cylindrical with initial radius $r = 4 \times 10^9$ cm, displacement $\Delta r = 10^9$ cm, and height $h = 5 \times 10^8$ cm. A pressure $p_e = 10^4$ bars (corresponding to a field $B = 500$ gauss) then gives a value of about 10^{32} ergs for the work done, ΔW.

6.1.5. Radio Emission

Solar radio astronomy was heralded in 1942 when Hey (1946), as a member of the Operational Research Group in England, made his report of the pioneer observations of the February flare and hinted at a correlation between intense, highly variable radio noise in the meter band and solar flares. The word *burst* is used to describe these abrupt fairly short-lived increases in the radiation.

It turns out that different types of radio bursts originate in flares. Type II bursts, or slow-drift bursts, are one of the most conspicuous of all radio-astronomical events. They are a fairly uncommon phenomenon, requiring the occurrence of a great flare. By studying their dynamic spectra (see Section 2.3.2), we find that the bursts at different wavelengths (corresponding to different heights of generation above the flare) are being excited by an agent traveling away from the flare at a velocity of the order of 1000 km/sec. The central frequency ν drifts with a speed

$$d\nu/dt \approx -0.2 \text{ Mc/sec}^2, \qquad (6.12)$$

(i.e., toward lower frequencies). In many cases the radiation takes place on two center frequencies in the ratio 2:1. This may be explained by a nonlinear emission process, which in addition to the fundamental frequency, also excites the first harmonic. These bursts are of a nonthermal character, since one would need extremely high temperatures to account for them in terms of thermal radiation. For especially large type II bursts, the sun would have to radiate at a blackbody temperature of more than 10^{13} °K .

Type III bursts (or fast-drift bursts) are often observed prior to the recording of a type II burst. These fast-drift bursts are very short-lived and have a dynamic spectrum corresponding to a frequency drift

$$dv/dt \approx -20 \text{ Mc/sec}^2 . \tag{6.13}$$

Also in these bursts, one can at times see the higher harmonics. The drift velocity (6.13) may on occasion decrease numerically, become zero, and then increase again. This will give rise to a so-called inverted U-burst, a name derived from the shape of the dynamic spectrum. It indicates that the propagation direction of the exciting agent changes and points down into the sun again. The velocity of whatever excites the bursts reaches values of the order of 10^5 km/sec.

The bandwidth of bursts of types II and III is fairly narrow—a few to several megacycles. One of the most important radiations associated with flares is the type IV burst, which has a continuous spectrum, covering the whole observed frequency range (several octaves). This type of burst often follows after a type II burst similarly as a type III burst often is followed by another type of continuous radiation, a type V burst. In a simplified and idealized case, we therefore have the following sequence of events. Nearly simultaneously with the flare, there are several short type III bursts followed by a type V continuum. Several minutes later a type II burst occurs and is succeeded by a type IV continuum. The spectrum of type V bursts is not as well studied as that of type IV. The emission is probably stronger on low frequencies, thereby distinguishing it from the type IV continuum. Further- more, a type V burst only lasts several minutes, while a type IV continuum may be observed for hours or even days.

The type IV continuous emission at cm- and dm-wavelengths (type IVμA, for microwave burst) tends to start first, often nearly simultaneously with the flash phase of the flare. The radiation is partly circularly polarized and is emitted from regions in the corona just above the flare. As this part of the burst attains maximum strength, the radiation is gradually extended to meter wavelengths (type IVmA). This is the burst that was first recog- nized as a continuous type of solar radio burst (Boischot, 1958), and it is this part of the type IV phenomenon which is often preceded by a type II burst. The source of the type IVmA is very large (several hundred thousand kilometers across) and moves in the corona with velocities of the order of

1000 km/sec. When a great flare is followed by a strong type IVmA burst, another phase of the radiation at meter wavelengths often follows, the type IVmB. This burst is distinguished from type IVmA by its high directivity of emission and its ordinary sense of polarization as compared to the extraordinary mode of type IVmA bursts. Its source is fairly small and remains fixed in the corona, at heights of roughly 200,000 km.

There is some uncertainty as to whether flares can be held responsible for the only type of nonthermal solar radio bursts not mentioned here, the type I, or noise-storm radiation. This radiation is highly circularly polarized, indicating the influence of strong magnetic fields and a close association with sunspots. Dodson-Prince (1958) and Fokker (1960) found evidence that some noise storms are caused by flares, but according to Swarup, Stone, and Maxwell (1960) the correlation is not statistically significant.

6.1.6. Flares and X Rays

A number of experiments with airborne equipment (balloons, rockets, and satellites) have provided us with a fair knowledge of X-ray emission from flares (Peterson and Winckler, 1959; Chubb, Friedman, and Kreplin, 1960, 1961; Vette and Casal, 1961; Yefremov, Podmoshensky, Yefimov, and Lebedev, 1961, 1963; Anderson and Winckler, 1962; Culhane, Willmore, Pounds, and Sanford, 1964). The equipment (Section 2.4) was used to record parts of the extreme ultraviolet (EUV) spectrum, 20 to 100 Å as well as X rays, $\lambda < 20$ Å.

The main results are that X rays and EUV radiation are enhanced during a flare, and the increases last at least during the time the flare brightness increases. It is further of great interest that the shorter the wavelength, the greater the increase in the X-ray production. This means that not only do the X-ray and EUV-radiations intensify during a flare, but there is also a considerable hardening of the X-ray spectrum. Many of the X-ray experiments have also included monitoring of the hydrogen Lyα line (1216 Å). Comparing the Lyα and the X-ray data, we get further information on the hardening of the spectrum. The Lyα radiation is only slightly increased (10%), while the X-ray flux below 10 Å, for instance, may be increased by a factor of 10 or more.

Not only large disk flares but also bright surges and small flares seen at the limb seem to give substantial increases in X-ray emission. Furthermore, there is evidence (Vinogradov and Eryushev, 1963) that X-ray bursts may occur without any optical flare activity. This should be kept in mind when a complete flare model is considered.

To begin a discussion of X-ray emission from different kinds of flares, we note that many small flares and subflares do not produce observable X rays at all. The observed X-ray flux at wavelengths greater than a few Å from somewhat more intense flares is equivalent to a gray-body radiation at a temperature of a few million degrees Kelvin (Elwert, 1961). X-ray flares in which this thermal emission characteristic occurs alone, or strongly dominates, appear to be fairly common (Acton, 1964). For such flares, the X-ray increase at longer wavelengths may be quite significant, but they produce very little nonthermal radio emission of the types discussed in Section 6.1.5.

Turning to the hard X-ray emission from flares, we find that this radiation requires temperatures of many million degrees to be accounted for as thermal radiation (see de Jager, 1960). The X-ray emission may be due to nonthermal processes which seem to be mainly associated with flares having a distinct explosive or flash phase (Dodson-Prince and Hedeman, 1964a). In addition, such flares will generate significant amounts of thermal radiation, but it is important to note that the production of hard X rays may occur independently of the enhancement of softer (thermal) radiation. The most "active" flares so far as X-ray production is concerned are also those that produce strong type IV radio bursts and often emit energetic solar proton streams (see Section 6.1.7).

Information on the spectra of flare X rays may be derived indirectly by studying their ionizing effects on the upper atmosphere of the earth. The density of the atmosphere decreases exponentially with height, and the penetrating power of the X rays increases with the photon energy. Because of this, photons of a given energy will have their ionizing effects (called sudden ionospheric disturbances) restricted to a fairly thin layer in the earth's ionosphere. It is outside the scope of this book to consider in detail how a study of these disturbances can be used to infer the nature of the X rays. We only mention for reference that by measuring the amount of ionization at different heights, we obtain a crude idea of the spectrum of the incident X rays. The most important varieties of sudden ionospheric disturbances used in such studies are briefly mentioned below.

(1) Short wave fade-out (SWF, the Mögel-Dellinger effect). A sharp decrease in the field strength of a distant short-wave transmitter.

(2) Sudden cosmic noise absorption (SCNA). A decrease in the intensity of the galactic radio noise signal.

(3) Sudden enhancement of atmospherics (SEA). An increase in the signal strength of atmospherics.

(4) Sudden phase anomaly (SPA). A change in the phase between the ground wave from a frequency standard and the reflected sky wave.

(5) Sudden frequency deviation (SFD). A shift in the frequency of the sky wave signal from a short wave transmitter.

(6) Solar flare effect (SFE, magnetic crochet). An excursion of the magnetogram trace from its normal quiet day variation.

Several attempts have been made to specify the conditions necessary to produce a flare that will emit hard X rays, particle emission, and nonthermal radio bursts (Ellison, McKenna and Reid, 1961b, 1962; Dodson-Prince and Hedeman, 1961; Martres and Pick, 1962; Le Squeren, 1963; Malville, 1964; Severny, 1963). In the most extreme cases the emitted particles are energetic enough to penetrate the entire terrestrial atmosphere. Roughly a dozen such "cosmic ray flares" have been examined in detail. About the only conclusion generally agreed on is that the flares occur in complex magnetic sunspot groups, i.e., magnetic classification $\beta\gamma$. Ellison, McKenna, and Reid claim that such flares develop as two parallel filaments, one over the umbrae of the main spots of north polarity, the other over the spots of south polarity. However, Severny's studies do not confirm this.

6.1.7. Particle Ejection

Few observations in the realm of solar activity surpass in importance the ones leading to the realization that matter sometimes is ejected from flare regions. The ability of the sun to eject energetic particles was discovered by Forbush (1946), and the arrival of this solar component of cosmic rays at the earth has been studied in detail over the last decade. We now know that the cosmic ray particles ejected from flares are primarily protons with a steep spectrum of energies, ranging from less than 10^7 eV to several times 10^9 eV. Small amounts of α-particles and heavier nuclei are also present.

These solar cosmic ray events must be detected as increases in the particle intensity, I, over and above the general galactic cosmic ray background, I_G. We define the intensity as the number of particles per steradian per second (particles sec^{-1} sr^{-1}) crossing unit area perpendicular to their motion. Roughly speaking, $I_G \approx 4$ particles cm^{-2} sec^{-1} for the energy range of interest (see for instance Webber, 1964), and the integrated energy spectrum of the galactic protons (number of protons with energy, E, greater than a certain value E_0) is well represented by (Winckler, 1961),

$$'I_G(E > E_0) = 0.3/(1 + E^{3/2}) \quad \text{particles cm}^{-2} \text{ sec}^{-1} \text{ sr}^{-1},$$

where E is in units of 10^6 eV. This expression holds for $\sim 5 \times 10^8$ eV $> E > \sim 2 \times 10^{10}$ eV.

6.1.7.1. The intensity–time profile

An ideal cosmic-ray event will have a set of more or less different intensity–time profiles corresponding to the different energies involved. Each profile may be characterized by an onset-delay time, t_0, a rise time, t_r, and a decay time, t_d. The onset-delay time is defined as the time interval from the maximum of the visible flare intensity to the arrival of the first particles at the earth. It is strongly energy-dependent, being shorter the more energetic the particles are.

More specifically, in the rare ground-level events (GLE) the arrival of high-energy particles (energy above 10^9 eV) at the earth is recorded within a few minutes of the time of maximum brightness of the flare, while in the polar cap absorption (PCA) events the arrival of particles with energies in the range 10^7 to 10^9 eV is recorded within a few hours after the flare maximum. Only 10 times during the period 1942–1961 have flares emitted

TABLE 6.5   Particle ejection from the sun

Emitting region	Ejecta	Energy per particle, eV	Velocity of protons, km/sec	Terrestrial effect	Onset-delay time
Flares	Individual particles	$>10^9$	relativistic	Ground level event	Few minutes
		10^7–10^9	$\sim 4 \times 10^4$–4×10^5	Polar cap absorption	Few hours
		$<10^7$	$<4 \times 10^4$	Not observed	
Flares	Plasma	10^3–10^5	1000–2000	Geomagnetic storm	1–2 days
Plages	Cloud	$\sim 10^3$	~ 500	Geomagnetic disturbance. "Gust" of solar wind	Several days
Quiet corona		$<10^3$	200–400	Solar wind	$> \sim 5$ days

relativistic protons that were observed as GLE. For comparison, about 10 times a year there is a flare which emits sufficiently large quantities of nonrelativistic protons in the energy range 10^7 to 10^9 eV, so that their ionization effects can be detected as PCA events. Flares undoubtedly emit large quantities of particles with energies below 10^7 eV, but it has not been possible to detect them in the presence of the higher energy particles. There is, in addition, some doubt as to whether such low-energy particles can disentangle themselves from the solar field and escape into space (Parker, 1963). Finally, 1 or 2 days after a flare, a geomagnetic storm may occur, indicating the arrival at the earth of "clouds" of particles, plasma clouds, with particle energies of the order of 10^3 to 10^5 eV.

In addition to these flare-initiated corpuscular emissions, one also observes slower low-energy plasma clouds (particle energy about 10^3 eV) emitted from plage areas. These particles arrive at the earth many days after they were emitted from the plage and may be considered as an increased activity of the solar wind. In Section 3.3.2 we saw that the sun also emits particles continuously, regardless of the presence of activity. This quiet solar wind component of the particle emission forms the low-energy end of the spectrum (see Table 6.5).

The rise time is defined as the time interval from the first arrival at the earth of particles of a given energy to the time of maximum intensity of these particles. This time is also strongly energy-dependent, the higher energies reaching maximum intensity first.

An examination of the rise-time characteristics for a number of events reveals that the increase in the integrated solar particle intensity may be closely approximated by (Malitson and Webber, 1963)

$$I(E > E_0, t) = I(E > E_0, 0)\, e^{-t/t_r} \quad \text{particles cm}^{-2} \text{ sec}^{-1} \text{ sr}^{-1}, \quad (6.14)$$

where $I(E > E_0, t)$ is the intensity of the particles with energies greater than some energy E_0 at time t; $t = 0$ is the time of maximum intensity, and t is measured from the time of maximum intensity *back* to the time of the flare.

The decay time also is often defined in terms of an assumed exponential variation of the intensity of the particles. The intensity at time t *after* the maximum is then given by

$$I(E > E_0, t) = I(E > E_0, 0)\, e^{-t/t_d} \quad \text{particles cm}^{-2} \text{ sec}^{-1} \text{ sr}^{-1}. \quad (6.15a)$$

Interpretations in terms of power laws have also been used, that is,

$$I(E > E_0, t) = \frac{I(E > E_0, 0)}{t^n}. \quad (6.15b)$$

The decay time is a function of energy and changes often with time. Typically, it ranges from a value of a few hours for high-energy particles to values of 2 or 3 days for low–energy particles.

6.1.7.2. *The energy spectrum*

Because of the energy- and time-dependence of all the parameters involved in the intensity–time characteristics of flare particles, it is obvious that there is no unique energy spectrum for any one event. The spectrum measured in a single event will therefore depend on both the specific time in the event and the energy range of the measurements. Each of the methods of detection (see Section 2.5) may cover only a very narrow energy interval or it may be a measurement of intensity integrated over energy, that is, for $E > E_0$. By the total integrated intensity, we understand the time integral of $I(E > E_0, t)$,

$$J(E > E_0) = \int_{-\infty}^{\infty} I(E > E_0)\, dt \quad \text{particles cm}^{-2} \text{ sr}^{-1}. \quad (6.16)$$

Using Equations (6.14), (6.15) and (6.16), we can write for the total integrated intensity in an event

$$J(E > E_0) = \int_{-\infty}^{0} I(E > E_0, 0)\, e^{-t/t_r}\, dt + \int_{0}^{+\infty} I(E > E_0, 0)\, e^{-t/t_d}\, dt$$

$$= (t_r + t_d) I(E > E_0). \tag{6.17}$$

It has been the practice to define a differential energy spectrum—existing in the energy region above a certain energy E (generally taken as 3×10^7 eV)—as that measured at the time when the integrated intensity of these particles is a maximum. Furthermore, it is customary to represent this spectrum in the form

$$dI(E)/dE = \text{const}/E^n \quad \text{particles cm}^{-2}\ \text{sec}^{-1}\ \text{sr}^{-1}, \tag{6.18a}$$

where n is a constant. For different events, n generally lies between 3 and 6. The specific time in the event when Equation (6.18a) holds will also vary. Before this time, n may be much less than 3 (that is, the spectrum is flatter), particularly at low energies. Afterward n may be greater than 6, particularly for high energies. Similarly, an integrated energy spectrum may be defined by

$$dI(E > E_0)/dE = \text{const}/E^n \quad \text{particles cm}^{-2}\ \text{sec}^{-1}\ \text{sr}^{-1}. \tag{6.18b}$$

Defining the rigidity P of a particle by the equation

$$P = pc/Z, \tag{6.19}$$

where p is the momentum of the particle and Z its electric charge, we may also introduce a differential rigidity spectrum, generally given in the form

$$dI(P)/dP = \text{const}/P^{-\gamma} \quad \text{particles cm}^{-2}\ \text{sec}^{-1}\ \text{sr}^{-1}, \tag{6.20}$$

where γ is assumed to be a constant. The corresponding integrated rigidity spectrum may also be used, $I(P > P_0)$ particles cm^{-2} sec^{-1} sr^{-1}.

For large events $I(E \approx 10^8$ eV) may reach values of several hundred particles cm^{-2} sec^{-1} sr^{-1}, and the differential rigidity spectrum may vary as P^{-4} to P^{-7} (that is, $4 < \gamma < 7$).

6.1.7.3. *Charge composition*

Of great theoretical significance is the observation that cosmic-ray particles heavier than protons are accelerated in flares (Ney and Stein, 1962; Fichtel and Guss, 1961; Biswas, Freier, and Stein, 1962). It is found (Webber, 1964) that the α-particles and the heavier nuclei have the same exponential rigidity spectrum as the protons in an event, that is, γ is the same.

A thorough study of cosmic rays from the November 12, 1960 solar flare has been undertaken by Biswas, Fichtel, and Guss (1962). They found that the relative numbers of α-particles, light nuclei, medium ($6 \leq Z \leq 9$) nuclei, and heavy ($Z \geq 10$) nuclei in this case were approximately in the ratios $700: < 0.1 : 10 : 1$. This is similar to the composition of the solar atmosphere but quite different from that of galactic cosmic rays.

Energetic electrons (10^7 to 10^8 eV) have been observed in cosmic rays (Earl, 1961; Meyer and Vogt, 1962), but it is not known whether they are of solar or galactic origin (Cline, Ludwig, and McDonald, 1964).

6.2. *Models*

In the first part of this chapter we discussed the pertinent observational data on flares. Before we can treat the different theories and hypotheses set forth to explain the complex flare phenomenon, it may be helpful to consider some flare models, often primitive, that are more or less directly derivable from the observations. We shall, however, first look at the energies involved.

6.2.1. Energy Considerations

In the undisturbed chromosphere the thermal energy density, given by $\approx nkT$, is of the order of 10^{-2} ergs cm^{-3}, and in the photosphere it reaches values of 1 to 10 ergs cm^{-3}. We also recall that the flux of emergent radiant energy from the photosphere is 6×10^{10} ergs cm^{-2} sec^{-1}.

By comparison, it is quite difficult to estimate the total radiation output from a flare. In principle, one should only have to integrate over the entire electromagnetic spectrum. In practice this is not easily accomplished because the flare is very faint compared with the disk except in the strong emission lines. Estimates range from 10^{30} or 10^{31} ergs for class 2 flares (Billings and Roberts, 1953; Warwick, 1962) to values in excess of 10^{32} ergs for flares of importance 3 and 4 (Parker, 1957a; Ellison, 1963).

The volume of a large flare is probably 10^{28} to 10^{29} cm^3, so that the radiant energy released by the flare plasma is of the order of 10^3 ergs cm^{-3}. This is seen to be several orders of magnitude greater than the thermal energy density of the undisturbed surrounding plasma.

Besides the energy expended by the flare as radiation, there is also the acceleration of particles to consider. Meyer, Parker, and Simpson (1956) estimated the kinetic energy emitted by the great flare of February 23, 1956 in protons with energies greater than 2×10^9 eV at 3×10^{30} ergs. This was, however, an exceptional case. Most events give rise to steep energy spectra so that most of the particle energy is near the lowest observed energy. The peak flux of protons above 3×10^8 eV is probably about 10^4 protons cm^{-2} sec^{-1} (Malitson and Webber, 1963), which implies a particle density of the order of 3×10^{-6} cm^{-3} and a total energy density of 1.6×10^{-10} ergs cm^{-3}. If we assume with Parker (1963) that the particles at the time of peak intensity at earth occupy about 1 cubic astronomical unit, we find the energy of solar protons above 3×10^8 eV to be of the order of 10^{30} ergs. In addition, we have the particles expelled with smaller velocities ($\sim$1500 km/sec, see Table 6.1) which are responsible for the geomagnetic storms. These particles form blast waves (Parker, 1961, 1962, 1963) of density about 30 particles/cm^3. The blast wave is probably not less than 0.1 astronomical unit thick and occupies at least 1 steradian as seen from the sun. Combining these data, we find a total energy $\sim$$10^{32}$ ergs associated with the particle ejection (see also de Jager, 1960, 1963; and Warwick, 1962).

In summary, we may conclude that the total energy expenditure in a large flare is of the order of 10^{32} ergs, or 10^{29} ergs/sec, since the lifetime is about 1000 sec. The area of a large flare may be taken as 10^{19} cm^2, indicating a mean flux of 10^{10} ergs cm^{-2} sec^{-1} through the flare area.

The question now is to find where this energy comes from. As we shall see in Section 6.3, several sources have been considered, including thermonuclear reactions, electric discharges, and magnetic fields. By way of illustration, we note that in terms of magnetic energy 1000 ergs/cm^3 (the radiant energy released by the flare plasma) is equivalent to the destruction of a field of about 150 gauss. Using another estimate, we find that 10^{32} ergs is equivalent to the complete annihilation of a 500 gauss field occupying a volume of 10^{28} cm^3.

6.2.2. The Optical Flare

The emission from limb flares and active prominences in the Balmer continuum has been extensively studied by Jefferies and Orrall (1961a, 1961b). They have used a simple geometrical model of a flare (a series of concentric cylindrical shells, with emission constant within each shell) and employed Equation (6.8b) as described in Section 6.1.3.1. The main result of their study is a model where the hydrogen emission comes from a plasma of temperature about 10,000 °K in the central part of the (cylindrical) flare. The temperature increases slowly with distance from the axis, so that most of the region emitting the hydrogen radiation is at a temperature below 15,000 °K (i.e., out to about 20,000 km from the axis). The value of the electron density in this same region falls an order of magnitude from a few times 10^{11} cm^{-3} in the center. Outside this cool hydrogen cylinder, there is an unobserved transition region where the temperature increases to coronal values of several 10^6 °K. These variations of temperature and density call for a gas pressure significantly higher in the central parts of the flare than 20,000 km from the axis. The high central pressure is connected with the explosive character of many flares. According to Polupan and Yakovlin (1965), the hydrogen emission is well represented by a model in which $n_e = 2 \times 10^{12}$ cm^{-3} and $T = 7500$ °K.

It is unlikely that the strong He I, and especially He II, emission found in flares can be accounted for with the temperatures quoted for the hydrogen emission. In addition, lines of ionized helium are decidedly broader than the He I lines, and this fact leads one to consider a model for flares—and for active prominences—where lines from different stages of ionization come from different parts of the flare plasma (Sobolev, 1958; Jefferies, Smith and Smith, 1959; Tandberg-Hanssen and Zirin, 1959). This is referred to as the multitemperature model (Smith and Smith, 1963), but the different degree of line broadening in the different regions of the plasma may be due to different microscopic ("turbulent") motions as well as to different temperature regimes. Goldberg-Rogozinskaya (1965) studied the line emission from both neutral and ionized helium and concluded that a flare model with $n_e = 10^{10}$ cm^{-3} would fit the data, provided that the He I radiation was excited in a plasma of temperature around 30,000 °K and the He II emission in a plasma of temperature around 50,000 °K. According to Zirker (1959), He III begins to be more abundant than He II for $T_e > \approx 50{,}000$ °K, while He I is more abundant than He II for $T_e < \approx 20{,}000$ °K.

The profiles of most He I lines of small and intermediate intensity are well represented by Gaussian profiles. However, emission from the 10,830 Å line frequently indicates self-absorption. We may write the intensity of an emission line observed in a limb flare (or prominence) in the form

$$I(\lambda) = \int_0^{\tau(\lambda)} S[\lambda, \tau(\lambda)] \, e^{-\tau(\lambda)} \, d\tau(\lambda), \qquad (6.21)$$

where $S[\lambda, \tau(\lambda)]$ is the source function [see Equation (1.72)], and $\tau(\lambda)$ is the optical depth [see Equation (1.70)]. In the simple case where the source function is constant with depth, $S[\lambda, \tau(\lambda)] = S_0$, Equation (6.21) is easily integrated and yields the following expression for the profile:

$$\frac{I(\lambda)}{I_0} = \frac{1 - e^{-\tau(\lambda)}}{1 - e^{-\tau_0}} \qquad (6.22)$$

where a subscript 0 refers to the line center. The He I, 10,830 line is a triplet (see Section 6.1.3.4) and the optical depth takes the form

$$\tau(\lambda) = \tau_0(r_1)\{e^{-(\Delta\lambda/\Delta\lambda_D)^2} + \tfrac{3}{5} \, e^{-[(\Delta\lambda+0.09)/\Delta\lambda_D]^2} + \tfrac{1}{5} \, e^{-[(\Delta\lambda+1.26)/\Delta\lambda_D]^2}\}, \qquad (6.23)$$

where r_1, r_2, and b refer to the two red and the blue components, respectively, and where the wavelengths are measured in Å. We have included only the effect of Doppler broadening in Equation (6.23), since damping (Johnson, 1960), Zeeman effect (Namba, 1963), and Stark broadening (Tandberg-Hanssen, 1960) are all negligible.

The approximation of a constant source function leads to theoretical profiles in fair agreement with those observed in emission from the quiet chromosphere and many quiescent prominences. However, the profiles from flares cannot be approximated this way. Švestka (1960, 1961) found for strong hydrogen lines in flares that a linear dependence of the source function on optical depth

$$S[\lambda, \tau(\lambda)] = S_0[1 + \beta\,\tau(\lambda)] \qquad (6.24a)$$

gives a satisfactory fit. The constant β is negative, indicating a source function decreasing with optical depth.

If we try to simulate the He I, 10,830 profile in flares with Equation (6.24a), we find that we are unable to do so. But good agreement may be obtained with a source function of the form (Tandberg-Hanssen, 1962)

$$S[\lambda, \tau(\lambda)] = S_0[\text{const} + \beta(\lambda)\tau(\lambda)], \qquad (6.24b)$$

provided that the function $\beta(\lambda)$ is negative, in agreement with Švestka's result, and provided that $\beta(\lambda)$ corresponds to the case where the optical depth is small in the line center while observations of the wings give information from deeper layers of the flare. With a functional dependence $|\beta(\lambda)| = 1 - \tau(\lambda)/\tau_0$, one finds profiles like the ones portrayed in Figure 6.4 (p. 270). These profiles should be compared with the observed profile shown in Figure 6.3.

6.2.3. The X-ray Flare

6.2.3.1. *Thermal models*

Attempts have been made to construct models of flares that would give the observed amount of X-ray emission without violating the requirements set by data on optical or radio radiation. Acton (1964) has derived models for those flares that mainly produce soft X rays which may be accounted for as thermal radiation. The radio emission from such flares is very weak.

First, an electron temperature is assumed or derived from the X-ray observations. The source region is assumed to be isothermal, and then one may compute the expected X-ray flux. This flux, due to free–free transitions (bremsstrahlung), free–bound transitions (recombination), and bound–bound transitions (line emission) in the different atomic and ionic species present, has been considered in the case of X-ray plages (see Section 4.2.4). Acton

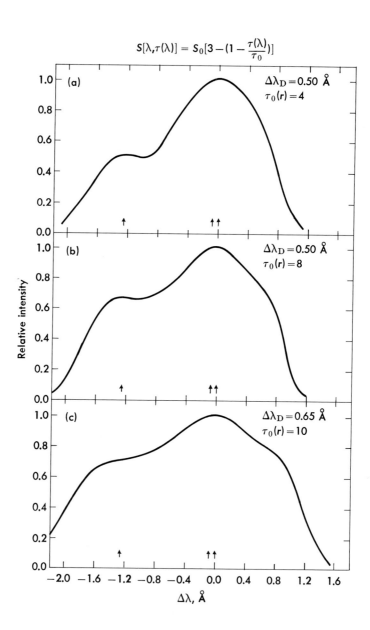

$$S[\lambda,\tau(\lambda)] = S_0[3-(1-\frac{\tau(\lambda)}{\tau_0})]$$

FIGURE 6.4.   Calculated He I, 10830 profiles

gives the flux in the region $\lambda < 14$ Å as a function of the square of the electron density integrated over the emitting volume, i.e., as a function of the parameter $S \equiv \int n_{\mathrm{e}}^2 \, dV$ already defined by Equation (4.13). Under the assumption that the source region is optically thick, one then determines the maximum surface area which it can have and still remain undetectable at radio wavelengths. (For instance, a signal-strength change greater than 10^{-19} ergs cm^{-2} sec^{-1}(c/sec)$^{-1}$ at $\lambda = 10$ cm should be detectable.) The volume is now computed by assuming a simple geometrical shape of the X-ray flare. Finally, for a uniform density one obtains the electron density of the region, and this completes the model.

Acton assigned to the peak flux intensity from a "thermal X-ray flare" the value 1.5×10^{-2} ergs cm^{-2} sec^{-1}. A volume of 8×10^{27} cm^3 will then give an electron density of 9×10^{10} cm^{-3} for a temperature of 2.3×10^6 °K, while a volume of 4×10^{27} cm^3 results, for a 4×10^6 °K plasma, in an electron density of 7×10^{10} cm^{-3}.

The main feature of the models is that the X-ray observations demand regions, at least as large as the optical flare, whose electron temperature is in excess of 2×10^6 °K and where the electron density is larger than about 5×10^{10} cm^{-3}. This is a radically different picture from that presented by the optical flare.

6.2.3.2. *Nonthermal X-ray emission processes and resulting models*

Going to more intense flares that in addition to thermal X rays also produce hard nonthermal X rays, we find that they generally emit nonthermal radio bursts and eject cosmic-ray particles. A model for such a hot flare plasma must include the acceleration of protons into regions where nonthermal electrons can produce the required X rays. By nonthermal electrons, we merely mean electrons whose energy distribution is not Maxwellian at a given temperature and may be anisotropic in velocity space. We shall now consider some X-ray emission processes that may be of interest in flares.

(a) BREMSSTRAHLUNG — This process has been considered in connection with the thermal X-ray emission from flares in Section 6.2.3.1, and the appropriate formula when the electrons have a Maxwellian energy distribution is given in Section 4.2.4. Under nonthermal conditions, the electron distribution function is not Maxwellian. If an electron stream is generated in the flare, the radiation, in a first approximation, will be due to the interaction of mono-energetic electrons. This case has been treated by Acton (1964), who considered electrons with an energy of 1.5×10^4 eV. Equation (4.14) for the bremsstrahlung emissivity then takes the form

$$\epsilon_{\mathrm{ff}}(E_1, \nu) = n_i n_{\mathrm{e}}^{\mathrm{nt}} \frac{4\sqrt{2}\, h\pi}{c^2} \sqrt{\frac{mE_2}{E_1^2}}\, v_1 \nu^3 k'_{\mathrm{ff}} \quad \text{ergs cm}^{-3} \text{ sec}^{-1} \text{ (c/sec)}^{-1}, \quad (6.25)$$

where nt stands for nonthermal, E_1 and E_2 are the energies of the electrons before and after the interaction with the nuclei n_i, and v_1 is the velocity of the nonthermal electrons n_e^{nt} before collisions. Instead of the expression (1.100) for the absorption coefficient k_{ff}, the nonrelativistic Born-Elwert absorption coefficient k'_{ff} (Koch and Motz, 1959) was used.

The expected X-ray emission from these mono-energetic electrons may be expressed in terms of a parameter $S^{nt} = n_i n_e^{nt} \, dV$, where n_i is the combined density of atom and ions in the emitting volume V. The nonthermal bremsstrahlung spectrum in Figure 4.7 (curve c) taken from Acton's work is derived for electrons with energy 1.5×10^4 eV in a gas composed of 87% hydrogen and 13% helium by number. From the curves in Figure 4.7, one may determine a rough model of large flares that produce a significant number of X-ray quanta below, say, 2 Å. The flux of such X rays at the earth is calculated to be

$$F^{nt}(\lambda < 2 \text{ Å}, E_e = 1.5 \times 10^4 \text{ eV}) \approx 2.5 \times 10^{-52} S^{nt} \quad \text{ergs cm}^{-2} \text{ sec}^{-1},$$

while observations indicate values between 10^{-5} and 10^{-4} ergs cm^{-2} sec^{-1}. Taking an observed value of 5×10^{-4} ergs cm^{-2} sec^{-1}, we find $S^{nt} = 2 \times 10^{47}$ cm^{-3}. If we have volume $V = 10^{28}$ cm^3 and the density $n_i = 5 \times 10^{12}$ cm^{-3}, we find the density of 15 keV electrons in the flare to be $n_e^{nt} = 4 \times 10^6$ cm^{-3}. This implies that only one in every 10^6 electrons takes part in the nonthermal acceleration process.

(b) FLUORESCENCE RADIATION — If an atom or ion with atomic number Z collides with a sufficiently energetic electron, the encounter may result in the removal of an inner electron, usually a K-shell electron. As a result of this, an outer electron jumps to fill the K-shell and an X-ray photon, $h\nu_Z$, is emitted (fluorescence radiation) unless the energy is carried away by an outer electron being expelled from the atom (the Auger process). The ratio of the probability for the occurrence of fluorescence radiation to the probability of inducing an Auger process is called the K fluorescence yield, $W(Z)$, and depends on the atom involved. The yield increases with atomic number, from small to large values: $W(Z) = 0.02$ for $Z = 11$ (Na), to $W(Z) = 0.83$ for $Z = 48$ (Cd) (Bergström, 1955). The emissivity is given by

$$\epsilon(K\text{-line}, Z) = n_Z W(Z) \, h\nu_Z \int_{E_{min}}^{\infty} n_e(E) v_e Q(E) \, dE, \quad \text{ergs cm}^{-3} \text{ sec}^{-1}, \quad (6.26)$$

where n_Z = the number density of atoms of atomic number Z, $Q(E)$ = the K-shell ionization cross section, E_{min} = minimum energy necessary for electrons to ionize K-shell, and $n_e(E)$ = number density of electrons with energies in the range E to $E + dE$. Calculations show (Acton, 1964) that K-fluorescence radiation accounts for only a small part of the radiation from thermal regions. For temperatures of 2 to $4 \times 10^6\ {}^\circ\mathrm{K}$, the fluorescence radiation from iron for example is between 5 and 10 times smaller than the free–free emission from an electron–proton plasma. However, certain emission lines should show up in the spectrum (see Figure 4.7).

(c) SYNCHROTRON RADIATION (MAGNETIC BREMSSTRAHLUNG) — Synchrotron radiation has been suggested as a source of X-ray emission from flares by Severny (1958b), and the process has been studied by Stein and Ney (1963). Kruse, Marshall, and Platt (1956) tried to account for radio-noise outbursts from flares by synchrotron radiation, and extensive calculations along these lines are due to Takakura (1960).

The synchrotron emission, in which many harmonics are emitted, is the relativistic form of gyroradiation. The latter is due to the acceleration of charged particles in a magnetic field, whereby radiation is emitted at the gyro frequency or Larmor frequency, Equation (1.15). According to Schwinger (1949), the power emitted by a high-energy electron is given by

$$P(\omega) = \frac{3\sqrt{3}\, e^3 B_\perp}{mc^2} \frac{\omega}{\omega_c} \int_{\omega/\omega_c}^{\infty} K_{5/3}(x)\, dx \quad \text{ergs sec}^{-1} \text{ (c/sec)}^{-1}, \quad (6.27)$$

where m is the rest mass, $B_\perp = B \sin\theta$, and θ is the angle between the velocity and the magnetic field B. Furthermore, ω_c is a critical frequency given by

$$\omega_c = \frac{3eB_\perp}{2mc} \left(\frac{E}{mc^2}\right)^2 \propto B_\perp E^2, \quad (6.28)$$

where E is the energy of the electron. The spectrum (6.27) exists for $\omega > \omega_c$, having a maximum near $\omega = 0.3\omega_c$. The total power is

$$P = \int_0^{\infty} P(\omega)\, d\omega = \frac{2e^4 B_\perp^2}{3m^2 c^3} \left(\frac{E}{mc^2}\right)^2 \propto B_\perp^2 E^2. \quad (6.29)$$

The radiation is totally polarized with the electric vector parallel to the radius of curvature of the orbit. Furthermore, the radiation is concentrated in a cone whose axis coincides with the velocity of the electron.

Guseinov (1963) argues that X-ray photons generated by the synchrotron process may be of importance in flares, while Stein and Ney (1963) and Acton (1964) rule it out on the ground that it requires electrons of improbably high energies. For instance, to observe 3 Å radiation ($\nu = 10^{18}$ c/sec), one needs for $B_\perp \approx 10^3$ gauss energies $E \approx 10^7\, mc^2$ in the case of $\omega = 10\omega_c$. There is no evidence that electrons with energies much above 10^{10} eV are accelerated in the solar atmosphere.

(d) THE INVERSE COMPTON EFFECT — Gordon (1960) and Shklovsky (1964) have advocated the view that the inverse Compton effect is a possible cause of X-ray bursts from flares. Involved in the process is a scattering interaction between a relativistic electron and a low-energy (optical) photon. The electron loses energy and an X-ray photon is produced. The optical photon takes up an energy given by (Ginzburg and Syrovatskii, 1964)

$$\Delta E \approx \bar{\epsilon}(E/mc^2)^2 , \tag{6.30}$$

where E is the electron energy and $\bar{\epsilon}$ is the mean energy of the photons.

With Zheleznyakov (1965), from Equation (6.30) we can compute the necessary energy E of the relativistic electron to give X-ray quanta about 1 Å, or energy, for example, of 3.5×10^3 eV. For $\bar{\epsilon}$ we take the energy of optical quanta in the photosphere, namely $\bar{\epsilon} \approx 3$ eV. This leads to $E \approx 2 \times 10^8$ eV.

The "Compton energy loss" by a relativistic electron is given by (Ginzburg and Syrovatskii, 1964),

$$dE/dt \approx 2 \times 10^{-14} q(E/mc^2)^2 \quad \text{ergs/sec} , \tag{6.31}$$

where q is the energy density of the low-energy photons in ergs. The total number of high-energy electrons, N_e^C, necessary to give the observed X-ray flux has been estimated by Zheleznyakov. Assuming that the density of the optical photons is $q = 5$ ergs/cm^3, we find $N_e^C = \int_V n_e^C \, dV \approx 4 \times 10^{30}$ electrons. We have here used an observed flux of hard X rays at the earth of about 2.2×10^{-5} ergs cm^{-2} sec^{-1}. If we further assume that the linear dimensions of the region in which the hard X rays are generated are equal to the diameter of the source of radio bursts at 3 cm, that is, 2×10^{10} cm (Kundu,1959, 1961),the density of relativistic electrons sufficient to produce the observed flux is about 0.5 cm^{-3}.

Acton (1964) points out a serious difficulty in accepting the inverse Compton effect as a major contributor to the X-ray flux from flares. If we accept the values for E ($\approx 2 \times 10^8$ eV) and N_e^C($\approx 4 \times 10^{30}$ cm^{-3}) above—and they seem reasonable—it is easy to show that the bremsstrahlung to be expected from such a cloud of relativistic electrons is much greater than what is observed. Anderson and Winckler (1962) observed an X-ray flux in the spectral interval 5×10^7 eV to 1.5×10^8 eV of 6 photons cm^{-2} sec^{-1}, while Acton concludes that the flux to be expected should be about 230 photons cm^{-2} sec^{-1}.

(e) DIELECTRONIC RECOMBINATION — Many atoms and ions have what is called auto-ionizing states, discrete energy levels in the continuum, i.e., levels whose energy is greater than the first ionization limit. The atom or ion in question may find itself in one of these states by either: (1) radiative absorption (Madden and Codling, 1963, 1964), (2) collisional excitation (Simpson, Mielczarek and Cooper, 1964), or (3) radiationless recombination.

The auto-ionizing states are generally short-lived and decay spontaneously by one of the following processes:

(1) A radiationless auto-ionization transition, wherein an electron is ejected from the atom carrying away the excess energy,

(2) A two-electron radiative transition wherein a single, high-energy, photon is emitted,

(3) A single electron radiative transition resulting in the emission of a photon of lower energy and leaving the atom in an excited state.

Radiationless recombination is the inverse of auto-ionization and is due to the capture of a free electron in such a way that the energy of recombination is used to excite a bound electron. If the recombined atom or ion stabilizes itself by a radiative transition, the whole process is referred to as dielectronic recombination. According to Burgess (1964), the dielectronic recombination rate may, under certain conditions, greatly exceed the rate of radiative recombination. However, one does not know enough about the processes involved to evaluate properly the possible importance of this source of continuous emission for the X-ray region. In this connection, Acton (1964) points to the heliumlike ions C V, N VI, O VII and Ne IX as likely candidates for solar X-ray emission at wavelengths in the region 5- to 20-Å. This is because in heliumlike ions, radiative decay of auto-ionizing states by two-electron transitions seems to be an important process (Cooper, Fano, and Prats, 1963). For the time being, we can only draw attention to the possibility of this source of solar X-ray emission.

6.2.4. The Radio Flare

The diversity of the radio emission observed from flares makes it unlikely that a single mechanism can account for all the radio bursts. As a consequence, one finds in the literature at least three different processes treated as probable, or at least possible, sources for the nonthermal radio emission. They are described in the following three paragraphs.

6.2.4.1. *Bremsstrahlung from fast nonthermal electrons*

This mechanism has already been discussed as a source for X-ray emission.

6.2.4.2. *Gyro- and synchrotron radiation*

This process also has been considered as a possible X-ray source.

6.2.4.3. *Plasma waves*

We shall now discuss this possibility. The plasma wave mechanism is an indirect one. A stream of particles, generally considered to be electrons, excite a plasma wave [see Equation (1.149)]. A partial conversion of this longitudinal plasma wave into transverse electromagnetic waves must then take place for observable radio emission to escape the sun. Assuming for the time being that electron streams capable of exciting plasma waves exist near flares, we must find ways of converting the plasma waves. Several suggestions have been made.

(a) MODE COUPLING — Ginzburg and Zheleznyakov (1959) suggested that the transformation from plasma waves to electromagnetic waves may take place where the dispersion curves of the two wave modes come fairly close together. The interaction occurs in the vicinity of the plasma frequency, ω_p, when large-scale inhomogeneities of density or magnetic field are present (Gershman, Ginzburg, and Denisov, 1957).

In a uniform plasma, the four possible wave modes (see Section 1.5) corresponding to the different dispersion curves are independent. If the plasma is nonuniform, interactions arise between these waves in regions where the different modes have phase velocities, V_ϕ, very close to each other. In the presence of a magnetic field, the probability of coupling is enhanced for longitudinal propagation, and the radiation can be transformed to the ordinary electromagnetic mode [Equation (1.140)] from a longitudinal wave with a similar phase velocity ($V_\phi > c$). Such a wave is the electron plasma wave [Equation (1.150)].

This method has been invoked by Denisse (1960) to explain the type IV mB bursts. An evaluation of this, and other transformation mechanisms, is due to Wild, Smerd, and Weiss (1963).

(b) SCATTERING ON INHOMOGENEITIES — This transformation mechanism was also proposed by Ginzburg and Zheleznyakov (1958). The plasma waves are supposed to undergo scattering on density fluctuations in the plasma. The fluctuations have two components: one, the fluctuations due to the thermal motions of the ions, and two, the space-charge fluctuations due to the electrons. Since the first type of fluctuation is more or less neutral, the interaction may be considered a Rayleigh scattering process. It takes place at the plasma frequency, and the resulting intensity of the radiation is

$$I_1 = \frac{n_e V e^4}{6 m^2 c^3} E_0^2 \frac{v_{\text{th}}}{v_0} , \qquad (6.32)$$

where V is the volume of the scattering region, E_0 the amplitude of the electric vector, v_{th} the thermal velocity of the electrons, and v_0 the velocity of the electron stream exciting the plasma wave. The efficiency of energy conversion in the solar corona is estimated to be about 3×10^{-6}.

The scattering by the electron space-charge fluctuations results in a scattered wave of frequency about $2\omega_p$. The reason for this is that the fluctuations themselves are plasma waves. Let a plasma wave of frequency ω be scattered off a wave component ω_{th} of the fluctuations in the thermal plasma. The two waves will combine, and the frequency of the scattered wave is $\omega_s = \omega + \omega_{\text{th}}$. This interaction is called combination scattering. Plasma waves can exist only at frequencies near ω_p, whence both ω and ω_{th} will have values near ω_p.

The intensity of the scattered wave is

$$I_2 = \frac{n_e V e^4}{\sqrt{3}\ m^2 c^3}\ E_0^2\ \frac{v_{\text{th}}^2}{v_0^2}\ . \tag{6.33}$$

Reasonable values of the parameters involved in Equations (6.32) and (6.33) lead to intensity ratios I_1/I_2 in accordance with observations of type III bursts (Wild, Smerd, and Weiss, 1963). Ginzburg and Zheleznyakov have proposed the scattering by electron space-charge fluctuations as an explanation of the observed harmonics of types II and III radio bursts, the fundamentals being attributed to the Rayleigh scattering (see also Akhiezer, Prokhoda, and Sitenko, 1957).

(c) SCATTERING BY FREE ELECTRONS — Altschuler (1964) and Oster and Altschuler (1964) consider the electromagnetic radiation generated by a plasma wave scattered by electrons belonging to the "background plasma," i.e., electrons not partaking in the plasma perturbation. Charged particles traversing a plasma at speeds less than the mean thermal speed of the plasma electrons will be shielded by their respective Debye clouds (see Section 1.1). If, however, the particles exceed the mean electron speed, they excite plasma waves in their wake (analogous to a Čerenkov cone). Coaxial cones of positive and negative charge density move outward as a plasma wave.

Altschuler and Oster calculate the "bremsstrahlung" radiation which is emitted when the Coulomb field of the streaming charges, together with the fields of their plasma disturbances, accelerate the plasma electrons. This is equivalent to the scattering of the Čerenkov plasma waves by free electrons. When the streaming particles move slower than the mean particle speed, the ordinary bremsstrahlung spectrum is obtained. At higher velocities, the plasma Čerenkov cone causes an enhancement of the electromagnetic radiation close to (but higher than) the electron plasma frequency. Altschuler proposes this mechanism as an explanation of the type III bursts.

All the three emission processes (bremsstrahlung, synchrotron radiation, and plasma oscillation) that may be invoked to explain the observed types of radio bursts from flares require the existence of high-energy particles in the flare region. Furthermore, some of the observed radiation is circularly polarized and strongly implies the existence of significant magnetic fields in parts of the flare. We are consequently led to models of the radio flare the main characteristics of which are:

(1) Regions where particles are accelerated to high energies, i.e., energies much in excess of the thermal energy, kT, corresponding to any reasonable temperature,

(2) Regions where magnetic fields dominate the motions of a large fraction of the charged particles. These regions may, or may not, be the same as those where the acceleration mechanism takes place.

The existence of high-energy particles seems to be essential in the generation of radio bursts, whence we conclude that models of radio-flares and of particle flares are intimately connected. Consequently, we shall now discuss the particle flare before we present some tentative models of the combined radio-particle flare phenomenon.

6.2.5. The Particle Flare

For many years the nearly mysterious flare phenomenon has been observed and discussed mainly in regard to its visual effects. It now emerges that the optical flare—interesting as it undoubtedly is—may possibly be regarded as a more or less accidental by-product, or a superficial manifestation, of a more deep-seated disturbance or instability. Given the existence of fast-moving particles and magnetic fields, we are forced to view the optically more conspicuous manifestations in a new light.

The observations (see Section 6.1.7) reveal that particles of all energies up to about 10^{11} eV are ejected from flare regions. High-energy ($>10^9$ eV) protons produce secondary cosmic-ray events at ground level (GLE), protons of lower energy (10^7–10^9 eV) are responsible for ionospheric polar cap absorption (PCA) effects, and clouds or streams of magnetic storm and auroral particles have energies less than about 10^6 eV.

How and where these particles are accelerated is a subject for Section 6.3, as is the nature of the magnetic fields. Here we shall consider some capabilities of models in which the presence of particles and fields is granted.

6.2.5.1. *Magnetic trapping of particles*

To explain aspects of the radio-flare effects as well as time-delays at the earth of high-energy particles from flares, the suggestion has been made that some of the ejected particles are trapped by magnetic fields and temporarily stored in the corona (Stepanyan and Vladimirskii, 1961; Wild, 1962; Weiss and Stewart, 1965; Schatzman, 1965).

Stepanyan and Vladimirskii pointed out that if we consider particles with energy $E = 10^8$ to 10^9 eV, the radius of gyration λ_B [see Equation (1.11)] is much less than the characteristic dimension L of the magnetic field involved, whether this be the nearby sunspot field or the general field of the sun. This means that both types of magnetic field are adequate to trap the particles. For this statement to hold true, the characteristic length of the sunspot field (of strength several gauss) was taken to be $L = 10^{10}$ cm, while for the general field $L \approx 2 \times 10^{11}$ cm.

The maximum possible density of trapped fast particles is given by the magnetic energy density, $B^2/8\pi$. For $B \approx 5$ gauss, $E = 10^8$ eV, $L = 10^{10}$ cm, about 10^4 particles/cm³ may be trapped. Assuming a volume V of the "particle flare," equal to 10^{30} cm³, we arrive at a total number of trapped particles of approximately 10^{34}.

The question arises as to how long particles can exist with these high energies in different layers of the solar atmosphere. Considering for simplicity an electron-proton plasma, we find that the $\approx 10^8$ eV protons lose energy mainly through collisions with electrons, even though losses due to proton–proton encounters are also involved. The energy lost by a proton with nonrelativistic energy E ($E < 10^9$ eV) in a plasma with electron density n_e is given by (see Stepanyan and Vladimirskii, 1961)

$$\frac{dE}{dt} = -1.52 \times 10^{-8} n_e \frac{c}{v} + \left(42 - \frac{1}{2} \ln n_e + \ln \frac{1}{2} \frac{v^2}{c^2} \right) \quad \text{eV/sec}.$$

This gives a lifetime against collisions of $t = E/(dE/dt)$ which decreases from about 5×10^6 sec for a 10^6 eV proton to about 5×10^2 sec for a 10^9 eV proton.

In addition to the energy lost by collisions, the lifetime will also be affected by the diffusion of particles out of the region. We are interested in the drift of a particle of mass m, electric charge q, moving with a velocity whose component parallel to the (inhomogeneous) magnetic field $\mathbf{B}$ is $v_{\parallel}$ and whose component perpendicular to the magnetic field is $v_{\perp}$. Let us first consider a magnetic field whose lines of force are everywhere parallel to a given direction but whose strength changes perpendicular to this direction. The drift velocity v'_D can be found to first order in $v'_D/v_{\perp}$, as shown by Alfvén (1950),

$$v'_D = \frac{\lambda_B \nabla_{\perp} B}{2B} v_{\perp}, \tag{6.34}$$

where $\nabla_{\perp} B$ is the gradient of the scalar B in the plane perpendicular to $\mathbf{B}$.

Next, let us consider a magnetic field whose lines of force are curved with a constant radius of curvature R. As shown by Spitzer (1956), this leads to a drift

$$v''_D = \frac{1}{R} \frac{v_{\parallel}^2}{\omega_B}. \tag{6.35}$$

Here we shall consider only the two drifts given by Equations (6.34) and (6.35), but remember that particle drifts may be caused also by an electric field or by the gravitational field if there is a component of these fields perpendicular to the magnetic field. Furthermore, a time variation of the magnetic field will produce a drift (see Schatzman, 1965).

Due to these drifts, a charged particle trapped in a magnetic field may escape. Using the characteristic length $L = 10^{10}$ cm adopted above and considering the magnetic field as that of a dipole formed by a bipolar sunspot group, we find, with Stepanyan and Vladimirskii a diffusion velocity,

$$v_D = v_D' + v_D'' = \frac{\nabla_\perp B}{B} \frac{1}{\omega_B} \left(\frac{1}{2} v_\perp^2 + v_\parallel^2 \right) \approx 10^6 \quad \text{cm/sec} .$$

The lifetime of a particle in the active region is therefore about 10^4 sec.

6.2.5.2. Particle-induced radiation and radio models

The realization that nonthermal particles form an essential part of the flare has led to a new fruitful approach to the whole flare problem. It is clear that the existence of such particles provides means of accounting for excess electromagnetic radiation by any of several mechanisms: bremsstrahlung, gyro- and synchrotron radiation and plasma waves. Most aspects of relevance to these processes have been considered in previous sections. Now we shall briefly treat a specific facet of plasma waves, the phenomenon of "two-stream instability." The model is discussed in this section because it presupposes the existence of streams of particles in the flare region.

Let us first note that electrons which are sufficiently well separated will act independently and that the radiation from them (through the Čerenkov effect) will be incoherent. This case is probably not of importance in flares. But when the electrons form streams, they will radiate coherently; such emission is proportional to the square of the number of particles and coherent emission is achieved (Bohm and Gross, 1949a, 1949b). In these coherent plasma waves the electrons will tend to bunch together around the peaks of the wave. Considering waves traveling along an electron stream, we find that the waves tend to trap the electrons in the potential wells of the wave. The trapping is brought about by the electrostatic forces created. One of two things may now happen. If there is an excess of electrons streaming slightly slower than the phase velocity, V_ϕ, of the plasma wave, the electrons will take energy from the wave which then is damped (Landau damping). On the other hand, if there is an excess of electrons slightly faster than V_ϕ, kinetic energy will be fed into the wave from the electrons, and the wave is amplified. Haeff (1949) considered the excitation of plasma waves by this mechanism, when two particle streams interact, to account for nonthermal radio bursts.

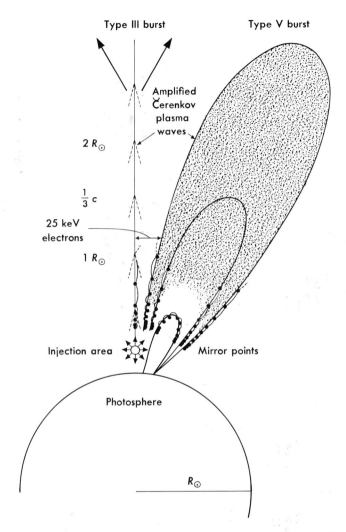

Type III burst   Type V burst

Amplified
Čerenkov
plasma
waves

$2\,R_\odot$

$\frac{1}{3}\,c$

25 keV
electrons

$1\,R_\odot$

Injection area   Mirror points

Photosphere

$R_\odot$

FIGURE 6.5.   Model of radio flare according to Weiss and Stewart
(courtesy A. A. Weiss and R. T. Stewart, 1965)

A number of models have been proposed to account for the emission of the
different types of radio waves from a flare region. For details, we refer to
the comprehensive study by Kundu (1965). Figure 6.5 pictures the physical
state of a flare at the time when type III and type V bursts are generated,
according to Weiss and Stewart (1965). Their model is based on a magnetic
field configuration resulting from a bipolar source. High-energy electrons
(velocity $\approx \frac{1}{3}c$) are ejected from the flare, travel rapidly outward without

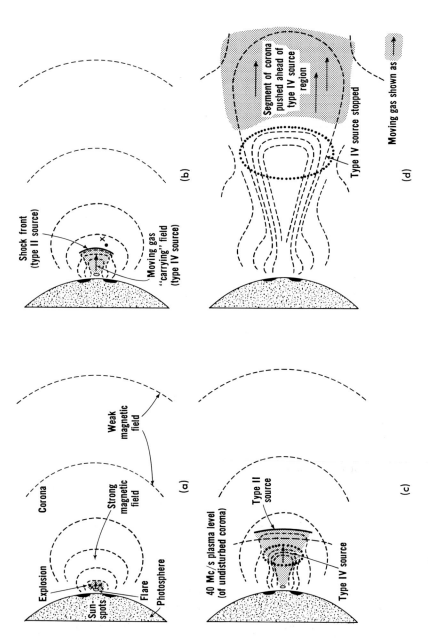

FIGURE 6.6. Model of radio flare according to McLean (courtesy D. J. McLean, 1959)

being seriously affected by the field, and are responsible for Čerenkov plasma waves. These waves—after conversion to electromagnetic radiation—are identified with type III bursts. Other fast electrons are assumed to be trapped in the magnetic field configuration above the optical flare for 1 minute or longer. During this time, the electrons oscillate between the magnetic mirror points in the field and are supposed to produce the broadband type V bursts.

Models for type II and IV bursts also have been proposed in which the same kind of magnetic field configuration as above has been assumed. McLean (1959) considered a model in which a shock front results from an initial flare "explosion" and excites the type II burst. A moving cloud of plasma follows the shock front and carries the magnetic field along, i.e., stretches the field lines of the bipolar region. The electrons in this cloud produce the type IV burst by synchrotron radiation (see Figure 6.6). In his work, McLean builds on previous studies by Denisse and Boischot (Boischot, 1958), who proposed synchrotron radiation for type IV bursts, by Westfold (1957), who considered plasma oscillations resulting from the passage of a shock front, and by Wild, Murray and Rowe (1954), who proposed that type II bursts are produced by plasma oscillations [see also Tidman's (1965) model].

Uchida (1960) advocated a model in which both type II and type III bursts are due to plasma oscillations. In the case of type II bursts, the oscillations are generated by hydromagnetic shocks, through charge separation, while it takes the free streaming motion of individual high-velocity particles to excite the plasma waves of type III bursts. Uchida dismisses ordinary gas-dynamic shocks as a possible exciting mechanism for type II bursts, since even for particles with velocity $\approx 10^8$ cm/sec, the mean free path in the corona is so long, $\approx 10^{11}$ cm, that the particles cannot participate in the wave motions (Schatzman, 1949). When a magnetic field is present, the particles will gyrate around the magnetic lines of force and motions perpendicular to the field lines necessarily become wavelike, unless the kinetic energy density of the motions exceeds the magnetic energy density. Uchida starts with the jump conditions in the presence of a magnetic field, Equations (1.169), (1.170) and (1.171), and proceeds to calculate the dissipation in the shock. He suggests that the charge separation created in the front will excite the plasma oscillations.

The models mentioned so far have relied on a simple magnetic field configuration above a bipolar sunspot group. In several electromagnetic theories of flares, the total flare energy is made available from a pair of bipolar sunspot groups (the Sweet mechanism, see Section 6.3). Anticipating these theories, we present in Figure 6.7 (p. 284) a schematic model of a radio particle flare that relies on this kind of field configuration. It is due to Wild (1962, 1963), de Jager (1963), and Fokker (1963) [see also Kundu (1965)].

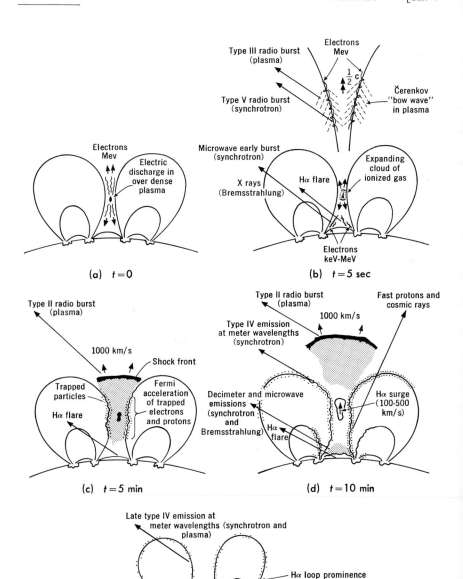

FIGURE 6.7. Model of radio and particle flare according to Wild (courtesy J. P. Wild, 1962)

At time $t = 0$, high-energy particles are ejected into the plasma near the site of the optical flare. Several seconds later (Figure 6.7a), some fast electrons give type III bursts by plasma oscillations, while others produce type V bursts by synchrotron radiation. Both these radiations take place at considerable heights since the electrons responsible have traveled approximately a solar radius outward. Lower down, less energetic electrons produce X rays by bremsstrahlung. Figure 6.7b pictures the situation at $t \approx 5$ min. A shock front is moving out from the flare region at a speed of approximately 1000 km/sec, exciting plasma oscillations and thereby giving rise to type II bursts. Trapped particles in the plasma behind the front are accelerated in the magnetic field and will in due time (Figure 6.7c) at $t \approx 10$ min, give rise to the different phases of the type IV continuum by synchrotron radiation. Some protons are accelerated to subrelativistic and relativistic velocities and escape as cosmic rays. The shock front continues out into space and gives rise to geomagnetic storms.

6.3. *Theoretical Interpretations*

6.3.1. Introduction

We have seen in Section 6.2.1 that the amount of energy used up in a great flare display is of the order of 10^{32} ergs. One of the first tasks of any flare theory is to account for this impressive energy, and there are two obvious possibilities to explore, namely:

(1) The energy is produced *in situ*. Nearly all theories in this category rely on the conversion of magnetic energy of local magnetic fields. However, there are also theories that attempt to use gravitational potential energy as an alternative or complementary form of storage of energy or electric fields that can build up discharges to sufficient energy.

(2) The energy is produced and released somewhere else and is transported to the flare region. Two different points of view seem possible; either the energy comes from the above-lying corona or it comes from subphotospheric layers. No theory advocating the former point of view has been proposed. If the energy comes from subphotospheric layers, one may consider the flare as a manifestation of the transport of the energy to the chromospheric regions where some parts of the flare phenomenon are observed. The transport may be accomplished by either high-energy particles or some form of radiation.

Besides the question of the flare energy, one of the most important aspects of the flare phenomenon is the nature of the acceleration mechanism of high-energy particles. Several methods have been suggested, and also here most of them rely on a magnetic field. The question of where the acceleration takes place in the sun, whether it is in the neighborhood of the optical flare or in regions remote from it, is of considerable importance. Direct observations have been indecisive, leaving this problem to what may be deduced from the different theories.

Because of the dual function of the magnetic field (that is, both supplying the general heating of the flare region and being responsible for the selective acceleration of particles), it might be best to consider these two aspects of flare theories more or less simultaneously. However, many of the flare theories were conceived of as theories for the optical flare only, i.e., they considered mainly or exclusively the heating problem. We shall therefore divide the rest of this chapter in such a way that the origin of the flare energy and the acceleration mechanism are treated separately, with deviation occurring from this scheme whenever useful for the presentation.

6.3.2. Origin of the Flare Energy; Local Sources

In this section we shall treat theories that generally rely on some sort of storage of the energy in or near the region where the optical flare phenomenon occurs. The source is not local in the sense that the energy originally can be found in the chromosphere. For example, when magnetic sources are considered, the energy is stored in the chromosphere but it may be fed into this region from subphotospheric layers by the magnetic field of sunspots.

6.3.2.1. *Theories relying on magnetic fields*

The theories that derive the flare energy from a magnetic field are closely linked with the problem of how fast magnetic lines of force can be annihilated, reconnected, or diffused in a plasma. Since Cowling's (1945) pioneering work on the diffusion of magnetic field lines, it has been realized that the time-scales involved in converting magnetic energy into kinetic, or heat, energy by resistive diffusion are very considerable in most astrophysical cases. The decay time of a field due to this type of diffusion is given by Equation (1.52):

$$\tau_{\text{diff}} = 4\pi\sigma L^2/c^2 ,$$

where L is a characteristic length and σ is the electric conductivity.

We now use the information on the electric conductivity in Chapter 1, Equations (1.19) and (1.20), denote the electron–ion collision frequency by ν_c, and find

$$\tau_{\text{diff}} = 4\pi n_e e^2 L^2/c^2 m_e \nu_c \tag{6.36a}$$

or

$$\tau_{\text{diff}} \propto L^2 T^{3/2}. \tag{6.36b}$$

The long time scale at high temperatures and for large structures is the chief difficulty in many of the theories in this category.

However, there are several effects which will speed up the destruction of the magnetic field beyond the rather slow rate defined by resistive diffusion, and we now proceed to discuss them, partly following the excellent review by Parker (1963).

(a) AMBIPOLAR DIFFUSION — The changes in the magnetic field are described by the hydromagnetic equation for the field $\mathbf{B}$ carried by a conducting ionized component of the plasma, namely by Equation (1.50):

$$\frac{\partial \mathbf{B}}{\partial t} = \nabla \times (\mathbf{v} \times \mathbf{B}) + \frac{c^2}{4\pi\sigma} \nabla^2 \mathbf{B}.$$

In this equation, $\mathbf{v}$ is the velocity of the ionized component of the plasma. If $\mathbf{v} = 0$, the above equation reduces to the diffusion Equation (1.51) and we retrieve the basic means for reconnection of magnetic lines of force: the electric resistivity of the plasma.

If we have a partially ionized plasma where the number density, n_a, of the neutral atoms is greater than the number density of the electrons, n_e, and ions, n_i, the field $\mathbf{B}$ still will be carried by only the ionized component. One may then consider the neutral atoms as forming another fluid. Let its velocity be $\mathbf{u}$. Under such conditions the phenomenon of ambipolar diffusion is at play. The physical essence of ambipolar diffusion is simply that the magnetic field moves with the electrically conducting ionized component, whose motion relative to the dominant neutral component is impeded by the friction due to collisions of the ions with the neutral atoms (Parker, 1963). The frictional force is given approximately by $n_i(m_i\nu_i + m_e\nu_e)(\mathbf{u} - \mathbf{v})$, where ν_i and ν_e are, respectively, the ion and electron collision frequencies with the neutral atoms. In addition, Maxwell stresses, $(\nabla \times \mathbf{B}) \times \mathbf{B}$, also will act on the ionized component, leading to an equation of motion for the ionized component

$$n_i m_i \frac{d\mathbf{v}}{dt} = -\nabla p_i + \frac{1}{4\pi} (\nabla \times \mathbf{B}) \times \mathbf{B} - n_i m_i \nu_i (\mathbf{u} - \mathbf{v}), \tag{6.37}$$

where the term $m_e\nu_e$ has been neglected compared to $m_i\nu_i$. If the scale considered is sufficiently large that the friction maintains $\mathbf{u}$ of the same order as $\mathbf{v}$, we find, following Parker (1963), that the inertial term in Equation (6.37) may be neglected since $n_i \ll n_a$. Equations (1.50) and

(6.37) then give Parker's equation for the field,

$$\frac{\partial \mathbf{B}}{\partial t} - \nabla \times (\mathbf{u} \times \mathbf{B}) - \frac{c^2}{4\pi\sigma} \nabla^2 \mathbf{B}$$

$$= \nabla \times \left\{ \frac{1}{n_i m_i \nu_i} \left[-\nabla p \times \mathbf{B} + \frac{1}{4\pi} \left[(\nabla \times \mathbf{B}) \times \mathbf{B} \right] \times \mathbf{B} \right] \right\}. \quad (6.38)$$

A similar expression was obtained by Cowling (1957), who considered the effect of diffusion in terms of an equivalent electric field.

The dissipation of the energy in the magnetic field, brought about by the mechanism that **B** diffuses through the neutral gas toward equilibrium of the Maxwell stresses, is given by the right-hand side of Equation (6.38). By dimensional analysis, the extra terms in Equation (6.38) give the time of relaxation of the field,

$$\tau_{\text{amb diff}} = L^2 n_i m_i \nu_i / B^2 . \quad (6.39a)$$

Remembering that the collision frequency $\nu_i = v_i^{\text{th}}/\lambda_i$, where v_i^{th} is the ion thermal velocity and λ_i the corresponding mean free path, and using the relation $\lambda_i = 1/n_a a_i$, where a_i is the collision cross section, we find

$$\tau_{\text{amb diff}} = L^2 n_i a_i v_i^{\text{th}} / V_A^2 , \quad (6.39b)$$

where $V_A = B/(4\pi n_i m_i)^{1/2}$, see Equation (1.14).

The diffusion time for ambipolar diffusion may be compared with the corresponding time for resistive diffusion, Equation (6.36), which—for a partially ionized plasma—should be changed to

$$\tau_{\text{diff}} = \frac{4\pi n_e e^2 L^2}{c^2 m_e (\nu_e + \nu_c)} \propto L^2 T^{3/2} \left(1 + \frac{\nu_e}{\nu_c} \right)^{-1} . \quad (6.40)$$

Since this expression is nearly independent of the gas density, while Equation (6.39a) shows that the diffusion time for ambipolar diffusion varies as $n_i n_a$, one concludes that ambipolar diffusion will be much more rapid than resistive diffusion in regions of very low density.

In their theory of flares, Gold and Hoyle (1960) maintained that the application of ambipolar diffusion leads to a characteristic time of field annihilation of 10^2 sec, in good agreement with observations. However, Parker (1963) showed that the favorable agreement found by Gold and Hoyle is due to the use of erroneous values of the density. It seems as if the only hope for ambipolar diffusion to play an important role in the flare phenomenon is that the effective characteristic length L is at least two orders of magnitude smaller than the over-all value of 10^4 km characterizing the whole flare or active region. We return to Gold and Hoyle's work in Section 6.3.2.1c.

(b) SWEET'S MECHANISM — Few ideas in the search for a mechanism to speed up the annihilation of magnetic fields have proved more stimulating than one proposed by Sweet (1958). The basic principle involves two oppositely directed fields that are pushed against each other, thereby interdiffusing in times small compared to the decay time for resistive diffusion over distances characterizing the sunspot configuration. We shall treat Sweet's mechanism as it may operate in sunspot regions, partly following Parker (1957b, 1963).

Let us consider two bipolar sunspot groups (Figure 6.8a, p. 290). If the spot groups move toward each other, the lines of force will be pressed together in a neutral plane $N–N$, and they will be distorted (see Figure 6.8b). Finally, the lines of force will reconnect as shown in Figure 6.8c. The reason why Sweet's mechanism works, i.e., why two oppositely directed fields interdiffuse more rapidly than Equation (1.52) would indicate when the fields are pressed together, is that the field vanishes on the neutral surface between the two field regions. The entire compressive stress then falls on the plasma, which responds by flowing out of the region along the lines of force. Consequently, the two oppositely directed magnetic fields approach each other more and more closely. In a region of very high electric conductivity, this motion is initially given by Equation (1.50), which is well approximated by Equation (1.53):

$$\partial \mathbf{B}/\partial t = \nabla \times (\mathbf{v} \times \mathbf{B}).$$

However, the gradient of the magnetic field across the neutral plane $N–N$ will increase until the diffusion term, $(c^2/4\pi\sigma)\nabla^2\mathbf{B}$, in Equation (1.50) becomes of comparable importance as the dynamic term, $\nabla \times (\mathbf{v} \times \mathbf{B})$. When this happens, the two oppositely directed fields interdiffuse with a velocity determined by the rapidity with which plasma can escape from between the fields in the neutral plane.

Let l be the characteristic length of the field gradient across the plane $N–N$. This length is several orders of magnitude smaller than the characteristic length L of the sunspot field configuration. The decay time of the field in the steep gradient region is given by

$$\tau_{\text{Sweet}} = 4\pi l^2 \sigma/c^2, \tag{6.41}$$

while without Sweet's mechanism, the diffusion time is

$$\tau_{\text{diff}} = 4\pi\sigma L^2/c^2 = (L/l)^2 \tau_{\text{Sweet}}.$$

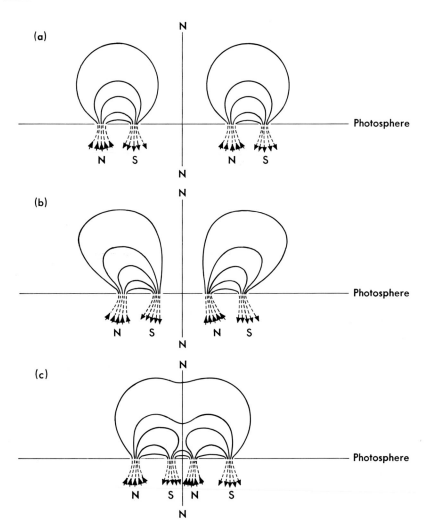

FIGURE 6.8.   Annihilation of magnetic fields by Sweet's mechanism
(after Parker, 1957b)

The velocity with which the two fields will interdiffuse, the merging
velocity v_m, is determined by the three conservation principles, conservation
of mass, momentum and energy, and from the principle of diffusion of magnetic fields. Mass is carried into the region of the neutral surface of length L
at the velocity v_m and is expelled from this region of width l at a velocity
$v_{\exp}$. The conservation of mass then leads to the equation $v_m L = v_{\exp} l$ for
incompressible flow, and to the equation $n_0 v_m L = n_1 v_{\exp} l$ for the more
realistic case of compressible flow. The quantities n_0 and n_1 are, respectively,

the number density of the gas before and after compression in the neutral region. The thermal pressure of the compressed gas must balance the external magnetic pressure under stationary conditions, that is, $n_1 kT = B_0^2/8\pi$. The two other conservation laws show that v_{exp} is of the order of the Alfvén velocity: $V_A = B_0/(4\pi n_1 m)^{1/2}$, and the diffusion of the fields gives for the velocity $v_m = l/\tau_{Sweet} = c^2/4\pi l\sigma$. Combining these equations, we find the order-of-magnitude estimates

$$v_m = c(n_1 V_A/4\pi n_0 \sigma L)^{1/2} \tag{6.42}$$

and

$$l = (n_0 c^2 L/4\pi n_1 \sigma V_A)^{1/2} ; \tag{6.43}$$

see also Hoyle and Wickramasinghe (1961).

If we substitute $L = 10^4 \,\text{km}$, $n_0 = 10^{11} \,\text{cm}^{-3}$, $T = 10^4 \,°\text{K}$, and $B_0 = 150$ gauss, there results $n_1 \approx 10^{15} \,\text{cm}^{-3}$ and $\dot{\tau}_{\text{total diss}} = L/v_m \approx 40 \,\text{hr}$. Parker (1963) concluded that unless the effective characteristic length is much smaller than L, it is not possible to dissipate the magnetic field energy fast enough in a stationary flow to account for the flare.

In the picture of Sweet's mechanism given above, the nature of the forces pushing the fields together is rather obscure. Of the theoretical approaches to the flare problem mentioned in the following subsections, some may be regarded primarily as attempts to find physical conditions that inevitably will bring oppositely directed magnetic flux tubes together. They may all be regarded as versions of the Sweet mechanism.

Of special interest is the problem of the stability of the plasma caught between two magnetic fields. A stationary state may be established, and the plasma and the magnetic field may then flow toward the neutral surface at such a speed that the field is dissipated and the plasma is simultaneously expelled from the region. This is the rather slowly working case treated above. However, it may be that the flow toward the neutral surface does not lead to pressure equilibrium and to a stationary state. The plasma then experiences a collapse toward the neutral surface under nonstationary conditions, and the rate of field annihilation may be greatly increased.

Perhaps the most promising development regarding "improvements" of the Sweet mechanism is due to Petschek (1964). In re-examining Sweet's mechanism, Petschek pointed out that the conversion of magnetic energy to plasma energy is greatly speeded up if one includes the effect of the hydromagnetic waves generated near the interface between the two merging magnetic fields. If these two fields are strictly antiparallel, interdiffusion is the only mechanism by which annihilation will take place, and the merging velocity is given by Equations (6.41) and (6.42) as shown above. But if the fields are not strictly antiparallel, reconnection of nearly antiparallel field lines will occur. The kinks or bends in the field lines that are thereby created are to be considered as hydromagnetic waves that propagate away from the reconnecting region, thus reducing the magnetic energy at the interface. The Alfvén speed, Equation (1.146), is independent of electric conductivity and hence is the rate at which magnetic energy is converted to plasma energy by this mechanism. Petschek showed that, in a steady flow situation, both the diffusion and the wave propagation mechanism are important and that this leads to a much more rapid rate of annihilation and reconnection of the field lines in a high conductivity plasma than is obtained when the wave propagation mechanism is overlooked.

(c) THE EFFECT OF TURBULENCE — Wentzel (1963a, 1964) has argued that magnetic flux tubes of opposite polarities may be brought together in a very efficient way for dissipation of the magnetic energy by turbulent motions. The idea of invoking turbulence is a promising approach since hydromagnetic turbulence is to be expected under a variety of conditions in the active sun. If the collapse toward the neutral plane in the Sweet mechanism exceeds a critical speed, inhomogeneities will permit the plasma to carry the field lines with it, the magnetic field will be twisted, and turbulence may be set up. Oppositely directed magnetic fields will be pushed together at a large number of eddy boundaries, thereby permitting a high rate of dissipation. On the other hand, we have seen, from Equations (1.63) and (1.64), that turbulence can amplify a magnetic field under favorable conditions. There will therefore be a competition between the amplifying and dissipative forces, and dissipation will be helped by lowering the value of the electric conductivity, as is done by ambipolar diffusion, and by having a very large number of eddy boundaries in contact at any one time.

If L_t is the eddy size, v_t the eddy velocity, then the contact of boundaries lasts for a time $\tau_t = L_t/v_t$, and this will limit dissipation to a skin depth l_t given by $\tau_t = 4\pi\sigma l_t^2/c^2$. The total time of dissipation, $\tau_{\text{turb diss}}$ is τ_t multiplied by the number of boundary skin layers in an eddy, which is approximately L_t/l_t. Hence, we have

$$\tau_{\text{turb diss}} = \frac{4\pi\sigma l_t^2}{c^2}\frac{L_t}{l_t} = \sqrt{\frac{4\pi\sigma L_t^3}{c^2 v_t}}. \tag{6.44}$$

For $v_t = 200$ km/sec, a decay time of 10^3 sec requires $L_t \approx 40$ km. Whether such subtelescopic dimensions are involved in the flare phenomenon still remains unsolved. However, Hirayama (1961) and Suemoto, Hiei and Hirayama (1962) argue that their flare observations can be internally reconciled only by a model in which the fine structure has a characteristic length of about 10 km.

(d) PLASMA INSTABILITIES — There are a number of instability effects associated with the collapse toward the neutral surface in the Sweet mechanism, and some of these effects may greatly enhance the dissipation of magnetic field energy.

CASE 1: Runaway electrons

When in the foregoing we have considered the magnetic field as the energy reservoir, we have tacitly understood that the transformation of the magnetic energy leads to a general heating of the plasma, and this appearance of excess kinetic energy is identified with the flare. However, at times there may be involved in the transformation of magnetic energy a mechanism which selects a small minority of charged particles. These particles, mainly electrons, will then receive a large fraction of the available energy and we are faced with an acceleration mechanism. Different acceleration mechanisms will be treated in Section 6.3.4, but we want to emphasize here the often close connection with general flare theories.

Also, when we consider the magnetic field as providing the extra energy, we must remember that this process requires an intermediate step. Magnetic fields do not accelerate charges. An electric field is necessary, and the particles acquire their energy directly from the electric field. This, in turn, draws energy from the magnetic field.

Let us consider electrons moving in an electric field. They will acquire energy from the field between collisions. The interchange of energy with ions during collisions is slow, and this leads to an electron energy far in excess of the thermal energy of the ions, i.e., the electron temperature increases relative to the ion temperature. But since the Coulomb collision frequency decreases with increasing electron temperature, the energy loss suffered by electrons during collisions will be further reduced and the electrons may extract more energy from the electric field. Under certain conditions, the electron energy will increase without limit. This is referred to as the phenomenon of "runaway electrons" and, as seen above, is due to the decreasing effect of Coulomb collisions with increasing electron velocity.

Cowling (1953) showed that, provided the accelerating electric field $\mathbf{E}$ is parallel to the magnetic field and provided $\mathbf{E}$ is sufficiently large, runaway electrons will be created. Cowling followed Giovanelli's (1947, 1948) argument that the mean loss of energy of an electron per elastic collision with ion is roughly $(2m_e/m_i)(W_e - W_i)$, where W_e and W_i are the mean energies of electrons and ions, respectively. Since the electric field does work on the electron at a rate $e\mathbf{E} \cdot \mathbf{v}$, where $\mathbf{v}$ is the mean velocity of the accelerated electrons through the plasma, the rate of change of electron energy is given by

$$\frac{dW_e}{dt} = -e\mathbf{E} \cdot \mathbf{v} - \frac{2m_e v}{m_i}(W_e - W_i),$$

where ν is the collision frequency. When $\mathbf{E}$ is parallel to the magnetic field $\mathbf{v} = -e\mathbf{E}/\nu m_e$. The collision frequency is proportional to $T^{-3/2}$, and with Cowling we put $\nu = \alpha n_i W_e^{-3/2}$ since the temperature is determined by the electron energy. This leads to the equation

$$\frac{dW_e}{dt} = \frac{2m_e\nu}{m_i}\left[W_i - W_e + \frac{m_i e^2 W_e^3 E^2}{2m_e^2 \alpha^2 n_i^2}\right],\qquad(6.45)$$

and the condition for runaway electrons is

$$E > 2\sqrt{2}m_e\alpha n_i/3\sqrt{3}e W_i\sqrt{m_i}.\qquad(6.46)$$

Considering a pure hydrogen plasma whose protons have thermal energies corresponding to $\approx 6000\ ^\circ$K, we find from the inequality (6.46) that the condition for runaway electrons may be written $E > 5 \times 10^{-17}\ n_i$ stat volt cm^{-1}, a value first given by Giovanelli. The obvious question, whether such fields can be built up in the solar atmosphere, will be considered in Section 6.3.2.1e.

Parker (1963) expressed the condition for runaway electrons in terms of the electron conduction velocity, v_e, relative to the electron thermal velocity, v_e^{th}, assuming that runaway electrons will be produced when the conduction velocity equals or exceeds the thermal velocity. The conduction velocity is related to the current density $\mathbf{j}$, see Equation (1.27b), and $\mathbf{j} = (c/4\pi)\nabla \times \mathbf{B}$. Let us apply the picture used in treating Sweet's mechanism, where the gradient of the magnetic field is related to the characteristic length by Equation (6.43). We then have $n_e v_e e = cB/4\pi l$. The thermal velocity is $v_e^{\text{th}} = (3kT/m_e)^{1/2}$, and the Alfvén velocity V_A in Equation (6.43), which is really the velocity with which the plasma is expelled from the transition region defining l, is essentially the speed of sound in this region, or the electron thermal velocity. Using these expressions for the velocities and putting $\sigma = 10^7 T^{3/2}$, we find the condition for runaway electrons to read

$$v_e > v_e^{\text{th}}\frac{6T}{(n_0 L)^{1/2}}.\qquad(6.47)$$

According to Parker, the inequality (6.47) precludes the application of runaway electrons in flare theories since the ratio v_e/v_e^{th} is several orders of magnitude smaller than unity in the chromosphere and corona.

CASE 2: The hydrodynamic instability

Parker (1963) has looked at hydrodynamic instabilities that may occur in the thin transition region between two merging magnetic fields in the Sweet mechanism. Let the plasma be expelled from between the magnetic fields in the y-direction, which is also the direction of the lines of force of the two oppositely directed magnetic fields. Unstable transverse waves may now arise in the transition region, which we take to lie in the y,z plane and which is of thickness l. If the wave vector is in the plane of the transition region, i.e., in the z-direction, waves of large amplitudes, s, will exchange magnetic flux between opposite sides of the transition region. This may lead to enhanced diffusion of the fields since the transition layer is stretched and annihilation takes place on a larger surface. If the wavelength, λ, of the wave is large compared to the thickness l, the diffusion is effective over a layer stretched by a factor $(1 + s^2/\lambda^2)^{1/2}$.

CASE 3: Pinch effect

This plasma instability takes place when the stresses of the magnetic field of an electric current are strong enough to compress the plasma, against the gas pressure, and cause a contraction of the field and plasma in the vicinity of the current. Severny (1958a, 1958c) and Gold and Hoyle (1960) have considered the possibility that flares may be explained as a consequence of the pinch effect, which would lead to a cataclysmic collapse of the plasma in the magnetically neutral surface. If the stresses of the magnetic field start to exceed the gas pressure, the magnetic pressure around the neutral surface increases with compression more rapidly than the counteracting gas pressure, and the collapse goes on with ever-increasing velocity.

Severny and Shabansky (1960, 1961) have studied three stages of the collapse toward the neutral plane: (1) an initial compression of the plasma, (2) formation of shock waves, (3) an expansion of the plasma and collisions of shocks with themselves.

The initial compression is due to the pinch effect, and two possible magnetic configurations promoting the instability are considered: (1) a force-free field in which the instability occurs spontaneously, (2) a bipolar sunspot field which changes rapidly enough to trigger the instability.

Considering (1), we find that magnetic fields in the chromosphere are essentially force-free because there are no forces except magnetic stresses which can balance them and the field configuration must reach equilibrium under the action of these stresses alone (Severny, 1964). This is brought out by comparing the gas pressure in the chromosphere, $p_g \approx 1$ dyne/cm², with the magnetic pressure resulting from a 100-gauss field, that is, $B^2/8\pi \approx$ 400 dyne/cm². An arbitrary change in the field outside the neutral point or plane will in general make it impossible for the chromospheric field to adjust itself to a new equilibrium at the neutral point. This inability of the field may lead to instability near the neutral plane.

In (2), Severny (1962b) considered the instability as caused by a change in the magnetic field of sunspots, assumed to form a dipole. If equilibrium exists on isopotential surfaces, one has $B^2/8\pi + p_g = \text{const}$. Then condensations must form near a neutral point where $B = 0$, and an increase in the field strength around the condensation will cause it to increase.

As the collapse proceeds, the velocity of compression will eventually exceed the local velocity of sound (about 20 km/sec in a flare), and shock waves will be generated. It is assumed that the time of growth of the external field is small compared to the time it takes for the field to penetrate into the condensation (the skin time). In other words, the field acts like a piston compressing the plasma in the neutral plane. The shocks will form on each side of the neutral plane and converge toward this surface. Under such conditions the shock front is not hydromagnetic, moving ahead of the region of strong field which moves with the main mass of the plasma behind the shock.

Finally, the shocks will collide and be reflected in the neutral plane, the fronts of the reflected shocks will move in the contracting gas, and a hot $(T \approx 3 \times 10^{7\circ} \text{ K})$ and dense $(n_e \approx 10^{14} \text{ cm}^{-3})$ plasma may be formed behind the fronts. The pressure gradients will then cause the surrounding plasma to expand. Matter between converging shocks may be pushed out very rapidly with its own magnetic field, giving rise to surges (see Chapter 7).

In this theory, the magnetic energy is first converted to kinetic energy of motion in the collapse, and the resulting shocks convert kinetic energy into heat, radiation, and corpuscular energy. Severny proposes that in the hot regions behind the reflected shocks, thermonuclear reactions may occur. We shall return to this possibility in Section 6.3.3.

From the jump-conditions, Equations (1.157) to (1.160), one may compute the increase in density and temperature due to the passage of the shock fronts, which are taken to be nonhydromagnetic, see also Shabansky (1961). Let a subscript 1 refer to the undisturbed plasma in front of the shock and a subscript 2 to the plasma behind the shock front, i.e., to the flare plasma. Then we have

$$\frac{p_2}{p_1} = \frac{2U_1^2}{\gamma + 1} \frac{p_2}{p_1}, \tag{6.48}$$

$$\frac{T_2}{T_1} = \frac{\gamma - 1}{\gamma + 1} \frac{p_2}{p_1}, \tag{6.49}$$

$$u = \frac{2U_1}{\gamma + 1}, \tag{6.50}$$

where U_1 is the velocity of the front relative to the plasma and u is the velocity of medium 2 relative to medium 1. Observations indicate that

$$U_1 - u = U_1 \frac{\gamma - 1}{\gamma + 1} = \frac{1}{4} U_1$$

may be of the order of 5×10^7 cm/sec. Then we have $U_1 = 2 \times 10^8$ cm/sec and, for $T_1 = 10^4$ °K, Equations (6.48) and (6.49) give $T_2 \approx 3 \times 10^7$ °K. At such temperatures thermonuclear reactions become of importance.

The high-temperature region around a neutral point is found to be only about 10 km thick, and the time from initial collapse to reflection at the neutral point is only 3 seconds. Severny has pointed out that Ly_α radiation from the region should diffuse slowly, thereby lengthening the development and area of the optical flare.

We mentioned in Section 6.3.2.1a that Gold and Hoyle used the increased dissipation of magnetic energy by ambipolar diffusion to account for the flare phenomenon. Their theory could have been discussed in more detail under the heading of ambipolar diffusion, since it relies heavily on that mechanism. However, we prefer to discuss the theory in this section since other aspects of it rely on the pinch effect in force-free magnetic configurations.

According to Gold and Hoyle, the magnetic energy is stored in filamentary arched structures that reach up into the chromosphere and have their "feet" anchored in the photosphere. One may think of these arches as bundles of lines of force of a magnetic field that emerge from subphotospheric layers at one foot and re-enter at the other. In this way, field strengths of the order of 100 gauss may be maintained in the chromosphere for long periods of time. The anchoring makes possible field configurations which are force-free in the chromosphere but not in the subphotospheric layers. Consequently, the relatively high magnetic energy density in the chromosphere will not lead to explosions, and below the photosphere the kinetic energy density will dominate anyway. The problem is then mainly to find a process whereby magnetic energy can be fed into the chromosphere along the arches from subphotospheric regions. Gold and Hoyle point out that if the energy stored in the arches is to be dissipated in the chromosphere, it must be associated with currents flowing there. The strong field in the chromospheric arches must be force-free, whence the currents must flow along the lines of force. This means that one must postulate motions in the photosphere that can generate electric currents along the lines of force. The generation of such currents is equivalent to generating a field with the structure of a twisted arch. The nonuniform motion in the photosphere that can send the current along the arch is therefore the motion that will twist up the initial arch. Gold and Hoyle considered a horizontal rotation in the photosphere around each foot of the arch in the same direction as the basic type of motion that generates force-free, but not current-free, fields in the chromosphere.

The energy stored in a force-free twisted magnetic field may be calculated from the condition for a force-free field:

$$\mathbf{B} \times (\nabla \times \mathbf{B}) = 0 \qquad (6.51)$$

and from suitable assumptions regarding the twisting, namely, see Gold and Hoyle (1960):

(1) all points of a line of force are at the same distance r from the axis, i.e., the radial component of the magnetic field vanishes, $B_r = 0$;

(2) all lines of force have the same number of turns, N, about the axis;

(3) the field does not depend on the azimuthal coordinate ϕ, about the axis, nor on the coordinate z along the axis, that is,

$$\frac{\partial B_\phi}{\partial \phi} = \frac{\partial B_\phi}{\partial z} = 0 , \qquad \frac{\partial B_z}{\partial \phi} = \frac{\partial B_z}{\partial z} = 0 .$$

If L is the length of the filament and θ the angle that a line of force makes with the planes normal to the axis, it follows that

$$\cot \theta = 2\pi (N/L) r . \tag{6.52}$$

The r-component of Equation (6.51) gives

$$d \ln B / dr = -\cos^2 \theta / r . \tag{6.53}$$

The flux through a normal section of the filament is

$$F = 2\pi \int_0^R B_z r \, dr , \tag{6.54}$$

where R is the radius of the filament. Eliminating θ between equations (6.52) and (6.53), we find

$$B = \frac{4\pi (N/L)^2 F}{\ln (1 + 4\pi^2 (N/L)^2 R^2) \sqrt{1 + 4\pi^2 (N/L)^2 r^2}} . \tag{6.55}$$

Now we have $B_\phi = B \cos \theta$ and $B_z = B \sin \theta$, which may be written as

$$B_\phi = \frac{8\pi^2 (N/L)^3 r F}{\ln (1 + 4\pi^2 (N/L)^2 R^2)(1 + 4\pi^2 (N/L)^2 r^2)} \tag{6.56}$$

and

$$B_z = \frac{4\pi (N/L)^2 F}{\ln (1 + 4\pi^2 (N/L)^2 R^2)(1 + 4\pi^2 (N/L)^2 r^2)} . \tag{6.57}$$

The total magnetic energy per unit length is given by

$$W(B) = \frac{1}{4} \int_0^R B^2 r \, dr = \frac{1}{2} \frac{F^2 (N/L)^2}{\ln (1 + 4\pi^2 (N/L)^2 R^2)} , \tag{6.58}$$

and the energy per unit length of the axial component is

$$W(B_\phi) = \tfrac{1}{4} \int_0^R B_\phi r \, dr \,,$$

while that of the longitudinal component is

$$W(B_z) = \tfrac{1}{4} \int_0^R B_z r^2 \, dr \,.$$

On the axis, we see that $B_\phi = 0$ [see Equation (6.56)]. For $r \to \infty$, B_z goes to zero as $1/r^2$ [see Equation (6.57)], while B_ϕ decreases as $1/r$. Hence, the magnetic field is essentially longitudinal near the axis and becomes more and more azimuthal at distances away from it.

The flare phenomenon is now to be identified with the sudden release of the stored magnetic energy as heat, Equation (6.58). This could conceivably be brought about in two ways: (a) the release is due to the onset of an inherent instability in the twisted field, or (b) the release is due to the interaction with an outside agency, not a mere triggering.

Even though Gold and Hoyle rejected the first possibility since they could not find any suitable instability to trigger the release, it should be emphasized that our knowledge of plasma instabilities is still quite rudimentary, and the possibility probably still deserves attention.

Gold and Hoyle consider the release of energy to be due to the interaction of two filaments. The two filaments will touch each other along a line and they are supposed to have the same sense in the axial field component and opposite senses in the longitudinal components. In other words, the lines of force are right-handed spirals in one filament and left-handed spirals in the other. Interpenetration of the filaments tends to augment the axial component and to annihilate the longitudinal component, leaving conditions suitable for the pinch effect to operate. The gas densities are fairly low, and ambipolar diffusion is supposed to be important. According to Gold and Hoyle, the diffusion time can be brought down to about 10^2 seconds. The process depends on a continued low degree of ionization since otherwise ambipolar diffusion loses its importance.

(e) THE DISCHARGE THEORY — The possibility of electric discharges in the solar atmosphere has been considered by a number of authors (Alfvén, 1940; Giovanelli, 1946, 1947, 1948; Hoyle, 1949; Dungey, 1953a, 1958b; and others). Giovanelli suggested that the changing magnetic field around sunspots would induce electric fields (according to Faraday's law) and that the fields would build up to values large enough to accelerate charged particles efficiently enough to cause runaway electrons. The discharges thereby created are identified with flares. There are a number of attractive aspects in this theory as we shall presently see, but it also meets with some severe difficulties.

Giovanelli's discharge mechanism is the one discussed in Section 6.3.2.1d (Case 1) where we have given the conditions for runaway electrons. The theory for this phenomenon is on a sound basis, and no difficulty for the flare theory should result from it. The difficulty is rather to account properly for the required electric field which, according to the inequality (6.46), must be of the order of $5 \times 10^{-17} n_i$ stat volt cm^{-1}, where n_i is the proton number density. Let us compare the growing magnetic field of a sunspot with a continuously oscillating magnetic dipole in a homogeneous isotropic medium of uniform conductivity (Giovanelli, 1947). The electromagnetic field set up around the dipole is given by Stratton (1941) and may be written as

$$E = \text{Im}\left[k_1^2 \frac{\mu}{\epsilon'} \left(\frac{1}{r} + \frac{i}{k_1 r^2} \right) A e^{-i(\omega t - k_1 r)} \right], \tag{6.59}$$

$$B = \text{Im}\left[\left(\frac{1}{r^3} - \frac{i k_1}{r^2} - \frac{k_1^2}{r} \right) A e^{-i(\omega t - k_1 r)} \right], \tag{6.60}$$

where ω is the frequency and A is the amplitude of the magnitude moment of the dipole, μ is the permeability of the plasma, $\epsilon' = \epsilon - i(4\pi\sigma/\omega)$ is the complex dielectric constant [see Equation (1.44)], $k_1 = (\epsilon\mu\omega^2 - i4\pi\omega\mu\sigma)^{1/2}$, and r is the distance from the dipole. The frequency ω is very small, that is, 10^{-6} to 10^{-5} sec^{-1} for typical sunspot growth times. Giovanelli showed that for the magnetic field to penetrate to distances from the sunspot where flares are found, say 3.5×10^9 cm, in the time of growth of a sunspot of 2.8×10^5 sec, σ must not exceed about 10^8 sec^{-1}. However, in the absence of a magnetic field, the conductivity of the chromospheric plasma is of the order of 10^{13} sec^{-1}. The way out of this difficulty, as found by Giovanelli, proceeds in several steps. Note first that perpendicular to the magnetic field the conductivity, $\sigma_\perp$, may be small enough to permit the field to propagate rapidly. Equation (1.24) gives the expression for $\sigma_\perp$, which is reduced by a factor of $1 + e^2 B^2/m_e^2 v_c^2$ relative to the field-free case. But the induced electric field is perpendicular to the magnetic field, and since $\sigma_\perp$ is small the induced currents are small. Consequently, even though the electromagnetic field given by Equations (6.59) and (6.60) may propagate rapidly enough, the currents cannot build up to values large enough for discharges.

The next step is based on the realization that the induced electric field must not necessarily be perpendicular to the inducing magnetic field because, in addition to this magnetic field, there will also be the contributions of magnetic fields of neighboring spots and perhaps even a general magnetic field of the sun. The induced electric field will then have a component along the magnetic field in the direction of high conductivity, and strong currents may be set up, provided that one can find closed paths for them. This is not easy because the field must be force-free and the currents must therefore follow the magnetic lines of force. Giovanelli showed that this final step can be accomplished by letting the currents flow through neutral points in the magnetic field configuration, and these points assume a vital role in the discharge theory.

Some of the details concerning Giovanelli's neutral points depend on the existence of a general magnetic field of the sun of the order of 25 gauss. We know today that such a field does not exist, but other aspects of the theory lead to interesting results. The neutral point discharge gives for example a flare path which may point out from a sunspot in a fashion closely resembling the outline of observed flares.

Hoyle (1949) modified Giovanelli's theory by supposing that not all electrons in the flare plasma acquire runaway energies, but only a fraction of them. Consider an electron moving with high velocity. Its collision frequency may be so far reduced that between successive collisions it can acquire from the electric field an energy as great as its initial energy. This means that if the electric field is too small to give all the electrons runaway energies, a few may still be so accelerated, and they will constitute the discharge.

Cowling (1953) has criticized the discharge theory and has tried to show that it leads to unreasonable results. Let us follow one of his objections in some detail. First we note that the electric field required to explain a flare may be estimated from energy considerations. The total rate of emission of energy in a flare per cm^2 surface is about 1% of the sun's continuous radiation, or 6×10^8 ergs cm^{-2} sec^{-1}. Now, the total rate of energy generation in a discharge is $E_{eff}I$ ergs cm^{-2} sec^{-1}, where E_{eff} is the effective electric field and I is the current integrated over all heights in the flare. Here I is supposed to be in the same direction as E_{eff}. From the equation $\nabla \times \mathbf{B} = (4\pi/c)\mathbf{j}$, we find for I the order of magnitude estimate $\Delta B/4\pi$, where ΔB is the change in B through the flare thickness. Taking $\Delta B = 1000$ gauss, we find $I \approx 2.4 \times 10^{12}$ cgs (centimeter-gram-second). Thus, to obtain a rate of emission of 6×10^8 ergs cm^{-2} sec^{-1}, one needs an $E_{eff} \approx 3 \times 10^{-4}$ cgs. On the other hand, the permissible current density can be estimated from the equation $(4\pi/c)j = |\nabla \times \mathbf{B}| \approx \Delta B/L$, where L is the thickness of the flare layer. Again, taking $\Delta B = 1000$ gauss and assuming L to be 1000 km, we find $j \approx 2 \times 10^4$ cgs. The conductivity is about 10^{13} sec^{-1}, giving $E_{eff} \approx 2 \times 10^{-9}$ cgs, not 3×10^{-4}. This discrepancy points to the serious weakness found in most theories involving electric discharges in the solar atmosphere, namely their inability to account convincingly for the generation of strong electric fields.

Other objections raised by Cowling, for instance that self-induction effects will prevent the building up of the electric field (by Lenz's law), have been countered by Dungey (1958a), who has contributed significantly to the theory of discharges.

The question of the role of discharges in flares is still highly controversial, but whatever the outcome may be, Alfvén and Giovanelli have pointed the way to a possible different approach in solar physics research. Discharge theories have many attractive features, but one must remember that the problems encountered in establishing electric fields in highly conducting plasmas are of a vastly different nature than those found in dealing with neutral gases.

6.3.2.2. Nonmagnetic energy sources

(a) BRUCE'S DISCHARGE THEORY — In a series of papers, Bruce (see for instance Bruce, 1963, for detailed references) has put forth the view that flares and prominences are the result of electric discharges in the solar atmosphere. The application to flares and prominences is only one of many considered by Bruce in an imaginative attempt to introduce electric discharges as a universal mechanism operating nearly everywhere and explaining a variety of phenomena from small-scale transients in planetary atmospheres to variable stars and galactic structure (Bruce, 1944). The theory falls into four major parts:

(1) The building-up of cosmic atmospheric electric fields;

(2) The breakdown of these fields in electric discharges;

(3) The gathering of atmospheric matter along the discharge channels;

(4) The production of jets of hot gas as a result of the preceding processes.

Here we shall mainly consider the first point, since Bruce is probably right in advocating that the others will follow more or less automatically if the first step can be accomplished.

In variance with Giovanelli's theory, Bruce does not consider the electric field to be produced as a result of a varying magnetic field. In the first version of the theory, which he later abandoned, the discharges are supposed to occur in the electric field set up by the emission of highly charged ions from nuclear reactions in the sun's interior.

In later papers, Bruce relies on another mechanism to set up the electric fields. If solid particles are present in the atmosphere considered, they will be subjected to collisions. Bruce builds on work by Shaw (1926) and shows that asymmetries in the collision processes will tend to give the solid particles electric charges, some positive and some negative. The oppositely charged dust particles will separate and set up an electric field. This field will grow until the gas breaks down in a discharge. The electric current flowing will generate a magnetic field, and the pinch effect can cause matter to accumulate along the discharge. This accumulation of hot gas is to be identified with prominences and flares.

Bruce has also applied this idea to the phenomenon of long-period variable stars. In this case the surface temperature is low, less than 3000 °K, and an appreciable amount of solid particles may be present. Under such conditions, Bruce's theory offers an interesting approach, as it does for various phenomena in planetary atmospheres. However, in the solar chromosphere where most flares and prominences occur, and even more in the corona where some flares and prominences occur, it is not likely that one can rely on a sufficient density of dust particles for Bruce's mechanism to work. Even if one could, electrons and protons would probably neutralize the electrified particles in times small compared to the time required to set up any appreciable electric field.

(b) GRAVITATIONAL POTENTIAL ENERGY — In Section 6.3.2.1d we considered a series of plasma instabilities that could lead to the destruction of magnetic fields imbedded in the plasma. Under certain conditions, there are also gravitational instabilities of a plasma that may be of importance in connection with flares. Let us follow Coppi's (1964) treatment and consider a plasma layer threaded by a horizontal magnetic field under gravity. The equilibrium magnetic field is assumed to be properly sheared, so that the system is stable in the absence of dissipation. Furthermore, let all equilibrium quantities be functions of the vertical coordinate, z, only. The equations governing the problem are (1.29), (1.33), (1.35), (1.37), (1.38), (1.40) and (1.46), which we write in the form

$$\frac{\partial \rho}{\partial t} + \nabla \cdot (\rho \mathbf{v}) = 0 \,,$$

$$\rho \frac{d\mathbf{v}}{dt} = -\nabla p - \frac{1}{c} \mathbf{j} \times \mathbf{B} - \rho \nabla \Phi \,,$$

$$\frac{\rho^\gamma}{\gamma - 1} \frac{d}{dt} (p \rho^{-\gamma}) = \nabla \cdot (K \nabla T) + \frac{j^2}{\sigma} \,,$$

$$\nabla \times \mathbf{B} = \frac{4\pi}{c} \mathbf{j} \,,$$

$$\nabla \times \mathbf{E} = -\frac{1}{c} \frac{\partial \mathbf{B}}{\partial t} \,,$$

$$\nabla \cdot \mathbf{B} = 0 \,,$$

$$\mathbf{j} = \sigma \left(\mathbf{E} + \frac{\mathbf{v}}{c} \times \mathbf{B} \right) \,.$$

The only equilibrium condition for the described model is of the form

$$\mathbf{B} \cdot \frac{d\mathbf{B}}{dz} = \frac{\rho \, d\Phi}{dz} - T \frac{d\rho}{dz} \, .$$

If the system is perturbed about the equilibrium, instabilities may develop. Let the displacement brought about by the perturbation be d and let us look for solutions of the form $d(r, t) = d(z) \exp [i(\omega t - \mathbf{k} \cdot \mathbf{r})]$ where $\mathbf{k}$ is the wave vector. The electric field, $E_{\parallel}$, parallel to the lines of force of the magnetic field will tend to decouple the plasma motions and the magnetic field lines, thereby opposing the electric field, $E_{\perp}$, perpendicular to the magnetic field, which tends to prevent motions of the plasma across the field lines. Then, unless the magnetic field is sufficiently sheared, the system will be unstable against gravitational modes. Without going into details, we find with Coppi that when the magnetic pressure $p_m = B^2/8\pi$ is much greater than the gas pressure, instability will occur when

$$g \left| \frac{d\rho}{dz} \right| > \frac{p}{p_m} \left(\frac{\mathbf{k}}{k} \cdot \frac{d\mathbf{B}}{dz} \right)^2 f \left(\frac{\sigma_{\parallel}}{\sigma_{\perp}} \right) , \qquad (6.61)$$

where $f(\sigma_{\parallel}/\sigma_{\perp})$ is a finite positive function of the electric conductivities and may be found by a variational method.

Sturrock and Coppi (1964, 1965) have used this kind of instability in an attempt to account for the flash phase of flares, arguing that the theories which rely solely on the destruction of magnetic fields run into severe difficulties when trying to explain homologous flares (see Section 6.1.2.3). In the present theory the preflare is thought of as a dense layer of cool gas of thickness L, supported by a magnetic field that is becoming more and more compressed as plasma accumulates in the preflare and weighs down the field lines. The magnetic field has, as mentioned, nonzero shear, and the accumulation of plasma represents a storage of energy, not only in magnetic form but in gravitational form as well. The storage will continue until the configuration becomes unstable, see inequality (6.61). The gravitational energy is then suddenly released, and the magnetic field will return to its previous unstressed state. In this mechanism the magnetic field is not annihilated and the field lines may once again partake in the storage process. Consequently, the phenomenon of homologous flares becomes a natural occurrence in this theory.

The growth time of the instability is roughly $t = L/V_A$, where V_A is the Alfvén velocity. With $L \approx 3000$ km, $n_e \approx 10^{14}$ cm^{-3}, and $B \approx 300$ gauss, we find with Sturrock and Coppi a growth time of about 100 seconds, which is in good agreement with observations of the flash phase.

The idea of using gravitational instabilities has several attractive features. For example, we have seen how the phenomenon of homologous flares—so difficult to incorporate in many theories—finds a natural explanation. Also, even though a new form of energy storage is introduced, the magnetic field still plays a vital part in the theory. Hence, this work does not fall in the category where one tries to explain flares without invoking the—always present—magnetic field. Recently, Sturrock (1966a) has used the tearing-mode instability (Sturrock, 1966b) to explain the acceleration of particles during the flash phase of flares.

(c) KINETIC ENERGY OF PROMINENCE MOTION — In a short but thought-provoking paper, Roberts and Billings (1955a, 1955b) considered the kinetic energy associated with the motion of surge prominences as the source of flares. In active regions surge prominences are seen to be shot up from photospheric or low chromospheric layers (for details on prominences, see Chapter 7). The kinetic energy involved is of the order of 10^{32} ergs for a surge of diameter 30,000 km moving up to heights of 70,000 km with a velocity of about 300 km/sec. We have previously seen that the energy expended in a large flare display is of the same order of magnitude. Roberts and Billings suggest that in many cases the kinetic energy is converted to potential energy as the surge moves up against the solar gravitational field. Ultimately the surge will stop and fall back, in accordance with observations. However, in other cases there may be a magnetic field above the surge of such con-figuration that the prominence is trapped by it. Remember that the surge plasma will be restrained from moving across (i.e., perpendicular to) the lines of force of the magnetic field. A sudden compression of the surge plasma will occur, and we may expect an explosive conversion of the kinetic energy to heat, a process to be identified with the flash phase of the optical flare. An adiabatic compression along these lines should lead to a temperature rise of the order of 10^6 °K, yielding a plasma 1000 times more dense than the surge, that is, $n_e \approx 10^{13}$ cm^{-3}.

The theory links the flare phenomenon to an important and often over-looked observation, namely the motion of large clouds of plasma more or less simultaneously with the flare. A difficulty encountered by the theory is the high magnetic field required to stop the surge prominence. By equating the change in momentum effected by 1 cm² of the magnetic field barrier per second to the lateral pressure, $B^2/8\pi$, exerted by that barrier, we find, with Roberts and Billings, a field of about 500 gauss. This is probably more than can reasonably be expected at coronal or high chromospheric heights. However, a smaller field will constitute a yielding barrier, and even though the conversion of kinetic energy will not be so sudden and not be complete, it may still be possible to raise the temperature sufficiently to produce flare-like conditions.

6.3.3. Origin of the Flare Energy; Nonlocal Sources

In this section we shall treat flare theories that rely on an energy supply in deep photospheric or subphotospheric layers. These theories prescribe a method by which some of the deep-seated energy may be transported to chromospheric levels, and they consider the optical flare to be the manifestation of the arrival of this energy in the chromosphere. From an energy consideration, the theories are on a very solid basis; they have at their disposal an essentially unlimited supply: the energy of the turbulent motions in the convection zone. The response of the chromospheric plasma to the arrival of the energy also seems to give predictable effects in accord with observations, even though this needs further elucidation. The main problem is to explain the mode of energy transport. In many respects, the problem is similar to that of accounting for the heating of plages, only on a much grander scale.

6.3.3.1. *Transport by high-energy particles*

Warwick (1962) has drawn attention to the importance of the particle flare, which often is considered a byproduct of the—in some respects—more spectacular optical flare. His thesis is that "instead of producing particle radiation, flares may be a result of the generation of fast particles in some other part of the sun." In Section 6.1 we have stressed the importance of the particle aspect of flares, and Warwick has made a significant contribution in pointing to the particles as possibly being the primary concern of any flare theory. He assumes the particles to be accelerated in subphotospheric magnetic fields to subrelativistic and relativistic velocities. In this respect, magnetic fields also play a crucial role in his model, which emphasizes the "fields and particles" picture relative to more conventional approaches.

A question that immediately poses itself concerning this theory is whether the high-energy particles have mean free paths of sufficient length to account for the transport. Following Warwick, we may state that the source of the particles can be no farther away than the distance in which protons up to as much as 3×10^8 eV would be stopped by ionization processes. The relation between the vertical range, h, of a 3×10^8 eV proton and its velocity, v, in a neutral hydrogen gas is (see Mott and Massey, 1949):

$$dh = - \frac{m_p m_e v^3}{4\pi e^4} \frac{dv}{n \ln (2m_e v^2/I)}, \qquad (6.62)$$

where I is the ionization energy of hydrogen and n the number density, given by $n = n_0 \, e^{-h/H}$, where H is the scale height of photospheric gases, that is, ≈ 110 km, and $n_0 \approx 10^{16}$ cm^{-3}. To integrate Equation (6.62) from the initial velocity $v_0 \approx 0.8c$ to zero at height h_1, we assume that above h_1 there is a distance less than H where the atmosphere has the same density as at h_1. For $h > h_1$, Warwick assumes a negligible density. Integration of (6.62) then gives

$$He^{-h_1/H} = \frac{m_p m_e v_0^4}{16\pi e^4 n_0 \ln (2m_e v_0^2/I)} \approx 1.8 \times 10^9 \quad \text{cm}$$

or $h_1 \approx 480$ km, which is the greatest depth from which protons of energy 3×10^8 eV can emerge from the photosphere.

Beyond these considerations, the theory has not been developed significantly. The acceleration mechanism by which one gets high-energy particles must involve the (turbulent) magnetic field in deep photospheric regions. We have seen in Section 1.1.4 that turbulence may amplify magnetic fields embedded in the turbulent plasma, but it is not obvious that this will lead to acceleration of charged particles in the field. We shall return to the general problem concerning acceleration mechanisms in Section 6.3.4.

The present theory runs into difficulties when it tries to explain the optical flare. The high-energy particles that escape from the photosphere are believed to be guided along suitable magnetic lines of force until they are stopped in the chromosphere, where the optical flare takes place. It is difficult to visualize how sufficient material can be brought to the flare region in the short time required to cause an increase in density by a factor of 1000 relative to the surroundings without leaving observable traces in the photosphere. It seems as if the theory, which offers some very interesting suggestions concerning the often neglected particle flare, must be modified to account for the more conventional aspects of the flare phenomenon.

6.3.3.2. Transport by hydromagnetic waves

We have seen in Chapter 4 that Piddington (1956) proposed a mechanism by which one can heat the atmosphere above plages. The energy source is the subphotospheric turbulence, the transport of energy is accomplished by hydromagnetic disturbances, and the new mechanism accounts for the dissipation of the energy by the interaction with the neutral component of the atmosphere. The theory is reviewed in Section 4.2.4 and emphasizes the fundamental importance of active regions in the heating of the corona.

Piddington (1958) has also proposed that the extra heating responsible for flares may be caused by a variant of the same theory. He considered the hydromagnetic disturbances that may travel up the more or less cylindrical bundle of lines of force of the sunspot magnetic field, B_0. If B_p is the perturbation magnetic field associated with the wave, then the Poynting flux of energy is

$$P = \frac{1}{8\pi} B_p^2 V_A = \frac{1}{8\pi} B_0 B_p v,$$

where v is the velocity of the gas perturbation given by $v = (B_p/B_0)V_A$ and $V_A = B_0/(4\pi\rho)^{1/2}$. The total flux in a tube of cross section A is $\int_A P \, dA$. Piddington reasoned that in a uniformly expanding flux tube, $B_p V_A = \text{const}$ since $\int B_0 \, dA = \text{const}$. Hence $v \propto \rho^{-1/4}$, which shows that the disturbance grows as it rises into more and more teneous regions of the atmosphere.

Let us examine this growing perturbation in the case where it emerges from a depth of 20,000 km. When it comes to the photosphere it has experienced a density drop of about 10^3 and the velocity has increased by a factor of about $10^{3/4} \approx 6$, that is, an initial disturbance of 0.1 km/sec has grown to 0.6 km/sec. Taking $B_0 = 2000$ gauss, we find, with Piddington $B_p \approx 70$ gauss and a Poynting flux $P \approx 3 \times 10^8$ ergs cm^{-2} sec^{-1}. When this flow of energy is being absorbed by the Piddington mechanism, the temperature should rise very considerably, and this may be used to explain "hot spots" in the corona above active regions (see Chapter 8).

Piddington has speculated that if hydromagnetic waves with perturbation velocities of 10 km/sec arrive at the photosphere, the effects may be vastly more violent, and might lead to flare conditions. No details are available, but Piddington predicts a very abrupt and intense heating, emission of X rays, violent mass motions of the flare plasma, and acceleration of particles. In this case, perturbation velocities should reach values of about 10^3 km/sec in chromospheric levels, and the perturbation magnetic field in the photosphere already should be 1000 gauss.

It is difficult to evaluate these more cataclysmic predictions of Piddington's theory. So long as we stay with the conditions describing plage regions, it seems that the theory offers the most promising attempt to explain active regions in general. It is not so obvious that conditions exist that are conducive to the flare development described by Piddington. However, until more detailed calculations become available, it is premature to try to pass final judgement on the theory.

6.3.4. Acceleration of Particles

Of the greatest importance for flare models is their ability to include a mechanism for the acceleration of charged particles. Several mechanisms have been proposed, and we shall now give an account of them.

6.3.4.1. Acceleration due to a magnetic field

We have repeatedly seen how magnetic fields play a major, probably dominant, role in most aspects of solar activity discussed so far. It is therefore natural that most acceleration mechanisms also rely on the action of a magnetic field as the accelerating agent, through an intermediary electric field. Parker (1958b) has discussed different mechanisms and showed that they all reduce to the basic process of the so-called Fermi mechanism. However, several years before Fermi (1949, 1954) published his far-reaching theory for particle acceleration, Swann (1933) had considered the effects of a changing magnetic sunspot field and showed that acceleration would occur. The principle is similar to that applied in betatrons, and it is referred to both as the Swann mechanism and as betatron acceleration.

In many respects, the two mechanisms are the same process. The coupling of the particle with the magnetic field takes place in one of two ways. If the interaction results in an increase of the component of the momentum perpendicular to the field we speak of betatron acceleration; if the result is an increase in the component parallel to the field, we have Fermi acceleration (see Hayakawa, Nishimura, Obayashi and Sato, 1964).

(a) SWANN'S MECHANISM — Swann's (1933) mechanism may be considered an application of Faraday's law, which states that in the presence of a time-dependent magnetic field, an electromotive force is induced in a conductor. In a closed loop where dl is an element of arc length bounding an open surface A through which there is a field $\mathbf{B}$, the induced electric field $\mathbf{E}$ satisfies the equation

$$\int_l \mathbf{E} \cdot dl = -\frac{1}{c}\frac{d}{dt}\int_A \mathbf{B} \cdot \frac{d}{A},$$

where we have integrated Equation (1.38) using Stokes' theorem.

Electrically charged particles, of charge Ze, will be accelerated in the electric field as they experience the force $Ze\mathbf{E}$. This is the force that in betatrons accelerates electrons ($Z = 1$) to velocities close to the velocity of light.

Swann computed the energy gain of a charged particle to be expected under conditions of increasing sunspot fields. From the Hamiltonian equations for the case of a sunspot with axial symmetry in cylindrical coordinates (r, θ, z), he derived the expression for the Hamiltonian $\mathscr{H}$, for the derivative

$$\frac{d\mathscr{H}}{dt} = -\frac{e^2}{\mathscr{H}}\left[\frac{r_0 U_0}{r} - U_\theta\right]\frac{\partial U_\theta}{\partial t}$$

and for

$$\frac{d\mathscr{H}^2}{dt} = 2e^2\left[U_\theta - \frac{r_0 U_0}{r}\right]\frac{\partial U_\theta}{\partial t},$$

where U_θ is the θ-component of the vector potential ($U_r = U_z = 0$), and a subscript zero refers to values at the initial instant. Now $\mathscr{H} = mc^2 + W_{\mathrm{kin}}$, where W_{kin} is the kinetic energy of the particle of mass m, whence

$$\frac{1}{2}\frac{d}{dt}[W_{\text{kin}} + mc^2]^2 = e^2\left[U_\theta - \frac{r_0 U_\theta}{r}\right]\frac{\partial U_\theta}{\partial t}\,.$$

The kinetic energy is seen to increase so long as $rU_\theta \geq r_0 U_0$, a condition that in essence means that $|E| > |B_z|$. The condition is satisfied initially, and Swann concluded that it will be valid long enough for electrons to acquire energies of the order of 10^{10} eV.

Riddiford and Butler (1952) computed the acceleration of protons in a field growing linearly with time ($B = \alpha t$) using relativistic equations. They concluded that sunspot fields should be able to accelerate protons to energies of the order of 10^{12} eV.

Both Dungey (1958b) and Parker (1958b) have objected to the use of the Swann mechanism in sunspots and reject this acceleration mechanism. Again, the difficulty lies with the very high electric conductivity of the solar plasma. Riddiford and Butler's computations were done for a vacuum where $\sigma = 0$. However, in sunspots $\sigma \approx 10^9$ sec^{-1} and $\mathbf{E} \approx -(1/c)\mathbf{v} \times \mathbf{B}$, where $\mathbf{v}$ is the material velocity. Hence, $E < B$ and the necessary condition for the kinetic energy to grow is not fulfilled.

(b) FERMI'S MECHANISM — We shall discuss Fermi's (1949, 1954) mechanism in terms of the magnetic moment of the accelerated particle. The magnetic moment μ_B of a charged particle is given as the ratio between the energy associated with the motion perpendicular to the magnetic field $\mathbf{B}$ and this field, that is,

$$\mu_B = \tfrac{1}{2}mw_\perp^2/B\,.$$

If $\mathbf{B}$ varies slowly in time and space, μ_B will be nearly constant and an approximate integral of the motion; it is an adiabatic invariant.

We consider now what happens to a charged particle in a slowly varying magnetic field. Let $\mathbf{B}$ be along the z-axis and denote by θ the angle between this axis and the velocity vector $\mathbf{w}$, the so-called pitch-angle. Then $w_\perp/|w| = \sin\theta$. Furthermore, let θ_0 be the initial value of θ, where $\mathbf{B}$ equals $\mathbf{B}_0$. If $\mathbf{B}$ increases, the constancy of μ_B implies that $w_\perp^2$ increases proportionally to $|\mathbf{B}|$ or

$$\sin^2\theta/\sin^2\theta_0 = B/B_0\,. \tag{6.63}$$

As $B/B_0 \to 1/\sin^2\theta_0$, all the energy of the particle is transformed into transverse kinetic energy. The velocity parallel to the field lines, $w_\parallel$, goes to zero and the particle is reflected. Let B_{max} be the maximum value of the magnetic field. Then, from Equation (6.63), we see that all particles for which $\sin^2 \theta_0 > B_0/B_{\max}$ will be reflected from this region, which is called a "magnetic mirror."

If the mirrors are moving, they reflect the particles and cause a gain or loss in particle energy according to whether the collision is in a head-on or over-taking direction. If the particles find themselves between two approaching mirrors, there will be a tendency for a net gain in energy, head-on collisions being more common. This is the essence of the Fermi (1949, 1954) accelera-tion, see also Spitzer (1956) and Parker (1958b).

We have previously emphasized that the acceleration of charged particles requires an electric field. Instead of treating the Fermi acceleration in terms of the magnetic moment, the intervention of an induced electric field could have been brought out by taking a different approach. For instance, re-member that the electric field is of the form $\mathbf{E} = -(1/c)\mathbf{v} \times \mathbf{B}$, and insert this into the equation of motion for the particle to be accelerated. One then sees how the electric field determines the rate of gain of particle energy $d/dt \, (\tfrac{1}{2}mw^2)$, which is obtained from the equation of motion.

A problem with the Fermi mechanism is that the particles in the long run will experience nearly as many decelerations as accelerations. This makes the net rate of acceleration quite small. Parker tried to remedy this by proposing that the particles are accelerated between shocks which cross each other. Wentzel (1963b) elaborated this idea and showed that the shocks need not be strong to accomplish significant acceleration. It seems today that a mechanism relying on acceleration in shocks furnishes the most promising avenue toward an understanding of high-energy particles from solar flares, see also Schatzman (1963), Severny (1964).

Let us follow Wentzel's argument for particles with pitch angle, θ, and velocity, w, much greater than the velocity of the mirrors, i.e., of the reflecting magnetic fields, which is the velocity of the hydromagnetic shock, V_{sh}. The maximum magnetic field in the shock is B_{sh}, and we consider shocks moving a curved magnetic line of force along which the undisturbed magnetic field is B_0. Particles will be reflected from the shock when the pitch angle is greater than a critical value θ_c given by

$$\sin^2 \theta_c = B_0/B_{\mathrm{sh}}.$$

Let the plane shock intersect the curved lines of force in two points which define a trap for particles ahead of the shock, trapped between the front and the magnetic field lines (concave toward the shock front). As the shock moves across the field lines, the two points of intersection move together, the trap becomes shorter, and the particles are accelerated. The particles will escape the trap before the points of intersection have moved completely together and the energy of the particles has been increased by a factor $\sin^2 \theta / \sin^2 \theta_c$. Neglecting decelerations and assuming an initially isotropic distribution of pitch angles, we find with Wentzel that the ratio of final to initial energy, averaged over all particles in the trapping region, is

$$\frac{\overline{W}}{W_0} = \int_{\theta_c}^{\pi/2} \frac{\sin^2 \theta}{\sin^2 \theta_c} \cdot \sin \theta \, d\theta + (1 - \cos \theta_c) = 1 + \frac{2 \cos^3 \theta_c}{3 \sin^2 \theta_0} \cdot \quad (6.64)$$

Wentzel established two conditions for efficient acceleration: (1) the particle velocity must exceed the shock velocity, $w > V_{sh}$, and (2) collisions with other particles can be neglected. Takakura (1961) considered the Fermi acceleration brought about after several head-on collisions with oppositely moving wavefronts of ordinary Alfvén waves. He concluded that thermal electrons easily may attain subrelativistic velocities (0.6 to 0.8c). However, only electrons in the tail of the Maxwellian velocity distribution have thermal velocities greater than the wave velocity, whence the bulk of electrons corresponding to the mean thermal velocity will not be accelerated.

(c) THE "MELON-SEED EFFECT" — An interesting suggestion concerning the acceleration of aggregates of charged particles, plasma clouds, has been made by Schlüter (1957a). He assumes that the matter to be ejected is not magnetized and therefore moves easily between the magnetic lines of force, "punching holes in the field." The plasma clouds behave like diamagnetic bodies and they are accelerated by the Maxwell tensions of the magnetic field. This is referred to as the melon-seed effect. It is made possible by the very high electric conductivity supposed to prevail in the plasma clouds. The force acting on them is given by $\nabla \ln B^2$, where B is the magnitude of the field in the absence of the unmagnetized clouds.

If operative, this mechanism might provide a means of explaining the surge-like ejections observed at times of flares. However, not enough is known about the magnetic field associated with these objects to make any final evaluation.

6.3.4.2. *Thermonuclear acceleration*

We have seen that some form of the Fermi acceleration may provide the most promising mechanism for the acceleration of high-energy particles. However, one difficulty is that in order to prove efficient, the process requires the particles initially injected into the accelerating region to have larger than mean thermal velocities. Severny and Shabansky (1961) have suggested that such velocities are achieved by thermonuclear reactions in the hot regions associated with the passage of shock waves. This part of the flare, where the thermonuclear reactions take place, will then serve as an injector of particles that already have energies of the order of 10^6 to 10^7 eV. These energies are sufficiently high for further acceleration to take place in the Fermi mechanism (Shabansky, 1961).

For the thermonuclear pre-acceleration to take place, a certain abundance of deuterium, H_1^2, is required (Severny and Stepanov, 1956). Observations are unclear on this point, but, following Severny and Shabansky, we find the following reactions of importance provided the ratio H_1^2/H_1^1 is sufficiently high (i.e., of the order 5×10^{-4}):

$$H_1^2 + H_1^2 \rightarrow H_1^3 + H_1^1. \tag{6.65}$$

The proton, H_1^1, is given off with a kinetic energy of 3×10^6 eV. Instead of giving tritium, H_1^3, by relation (6.65), we may also get an isotope of helium, He_2^3, and a neutron, n_0^1 :

$$H_1^2 + H_1^2 \rightarrow He_2^3 + n_0^1.$$

The helium nucleus created may now react with deuterium and give

$$He_2^3 + H_1^2 \rightarrow He_2^4 + H_1^1, \tag{6.66}$$

where the proton carries away 1.45×10^7 eV.

In conclusion, we emphasize that thermonuclear reactions *per se* are not sufficient to give the high-energy cosmic-ray particles observed from flares. These reactions are conceived of as only providing the extra injection energy so valuable for an efficient use of other acceleration mechanisms of the Fermi type.

A quiescent prominence seen in Hα photographed at the Climax Station of the High Altitude Observatory on 25 July, 1951.

Prominences | 7

7.1. *Introduction, Historical Remarks*

In the previous chapter on flares we treated several aspects that pertain to active prominences also. Some flare-associated objects (loops, certain surges, etc.) may be considered as parts of flares or as prominences, and the distinction between them may at times be difficult to make. We shall develop some criteria by which prominences may be distinguished from similar prominencelike flares, but as long as our physical understanding of active prominences is not complete, there will always be an ambiguity. Instead of trying to make a unique definition of prominences at this time (which at best would be debatable), we shall try to let their nature become clear through a discussion of several, very different, aspects of their behavior as revealed by observations.

In addition, one finds in the literature statements to the effect that the physics of flares and prominences is of the same kind (Kiepenheuer, 1965), and attempts have been made (Sturrock and Coppi, 1964) to construct models and theories embracing both the flare and the prominence phenomenon. However, we shall see that there are so many differences between a flare display and a prominence that caution should be exercised when dealing with them simultaneously. This pertains particularly to flares and quiescent prominences, but there are also distinctive differences between flares and many flarelike active prominences (Smith and Smith, 1963).

For example, an important parameter in the discussion of flares and prominences is the lifetimes involved. The lifetimes characterizing some active prominences, e.g., several hours, are not unlike the lifetimes of large flares. On the other hand, the most stable quiescent prominences exist more or less unchanged for months on end. This fact is but an indication of the diversity of prominences, which may not form such a homogeneous class of objects in the realm of solar activity as do flares. From several points of view, many active prominences behave much more like flares than like quiescent prominences.

In discussing the observations and appearance of sunspots and flares, the two major manifestations of solar activity encountered so far, we have repeatedly relied on the excellent recent books by Bray and Loughhead (1964) and Smith and Smith (1963). One can refer to these for historical material and many observational details. When we now embark on the study of prominences, the situation is somewhat different in that there is in existence no book on the subject comparable to the ones for sunspots and for flares, even though good reference articles exist (see, for example, de Jager, 1959). Consequently, we start this chapter with a brief historical review, and we may in the section on observations at times go into a little more detail than we have done in previous chapters.

In his truly remarkable book *Le Soleil*, Secchi (1875–77) began his chapter on prominences with the following statement: "The phenomenon of prominences is now so well known by everybody that it may seem unnecessary to retrace the history of their discovery." It is interesting to note that ninety years later this "well-known phenomenon" still poses some of the most puzzling questions in solar activity.

Prominences have been observed regularly during total eclipses since 1842, but sporadic reports go back to the Middle Ages. They are mentioned in medieval Russian chronicles (see Vyssotsky, 1949) and described by Muratori (see Secchi, 1875), who in 1239 observed the corona during a total eclipse and reported "a burning hole" in it. This burning hole in all probability was a prominence. During the eclipse of May 2, 1733, Vassenius (1733) observed three or four prominences from Gothenburg, Sweden, and gave a more scientific description of them. He called the prominences "red flames" and considered them clouds in the lunar atmosphere. A report of the Swedish observations, edited by Celsius (1735), shows that other observers agreed with Vassenius' description (see also Grant, 1852). Another observation, made by Ulloa (1779) (see also Young, 1896) during the eclipse of 1778, of what probably was an active prominence was attributed to a hole in the moon.

These observations were subsequently forgotten, and during the eclipse of July 8, 1842 in France and Italy, Bailey, Airy, Struve and Schidlofscky, Arago, and others were all taken by surprise when they rediscovered prominences. In fact, they were so amazed that hardly any reliable account of what they really saw is available. As a consequence, their descriptions of the shape of prominences were so vague that they could not prevent other observers in the following years from believing that prominences were mountains on the sun. For detailed references, see Grant (1852). The next eclipse observations, made in Norway and Sweden in 1851, led, by contrast, to uniform interpretations and conclusions. Both Airy and Carrington agreed on what they had observed and ruled out the possibility (due to their forms) that prominences could be mountains; they had to be solar cloud formations (see Secchi, 1875–77; Young, 1896).

Photography was introduced in eclipse observations at the total eclipse in Spain in 1860 (Secchi, 1875), and the prominence forms could then be adequately studied. On August 18, 1868, spectrographic methods were employed at the eclipse in India and Malacca to study the "chemistry of prominences" (Secchi, 1868; de la Rue, 1868). It was found that the spectrum of prominences consisted of bright lines, and from then on prominences were considered to be glowing masses of gas. One of the lines observed, at 5876 Å (the D_3-line), was not known to be emitted from any terrestrial atom and was therefore ascribed to a specific solar element, called helium (after helios, the Greek Sun god).

An interesting development followed immediately after the eclipse. Janssen (1868) realized that many of the emission lines were so brilliant that they should be visible without an eclipse. The next day he placed the slit of the spectrograph outside the limb of the sun's image and observed prominence emission lines in full daylight. Independently and simultaneously, the same kind of observation was reported by Lockyer (1868a, 1868b), who with Huggins had tried to accomplish this for some time. Since then, regular observations of prominences have been carried out regardless of eclipses, but for more than 60 years the special conditions made eclipse observations of prominences superior and they continued to be of great importance.

The spectrographic efforts were continued by Harkness and Young (see Young, 1896) in America during the eclipse of 1869, when the first coronal line was also discovered. At this time, Huggins (1869) realized that if one opened the spectroscope slit, one obtained a series of monochromatic images of the prominence, corresponding to the emission lines observed with a normal slit, and that the complex forms of prominences could by this method be better studied (see Figures 7.1 and 7.2, pp. 318 and 319).

Systematic photometric measurements of spectral lines in prominences were first performed on the eclipse data of August 30, 1905. They were published in an important investigation by Schwarzschild (1906).

Observations during the many later eclipses, as well as the limb observations performed outside eclipses, gradually added to our knowledge about the shapes, dimensions, distribution on the sun, spectrum, movements, and changes of prominences, see for instance Pettit (1919, 1925, 1932), Davidson and Stratton (1927), Pannekoek and Doorn (1930), Mitchell (1935), McMath and Pettit (1937, 1938). In addition, when spectroheliographs became available in the 1890's, prominences could be studied on the disk as absorption features, generally referred to as *filaments* (see Deslandres, 1910; Hale and Ellerman, 1903; L. and M. d'Azambuja, 1948).

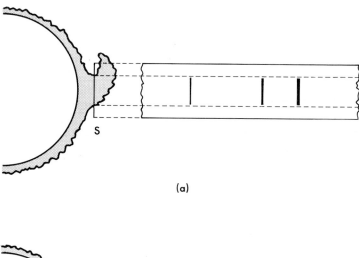

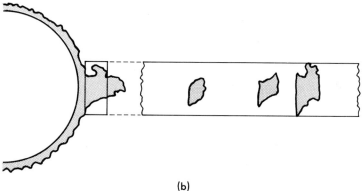

FIGURE 7.1.   Spectrographic observations of prominences: (a) emission
line spectrum, (b) spectrum with a widened slit (courtesy G. Abetti, 1963)

Finally, with Lyot's invention of the coronagraph, it became possible to observe limb prominences at any time nearly as thoroughly as during eclipses
(Lyot, 1936, 1939).

Among the first to undertake regular observations of prominences were
Secchi and Respighi in Rome, and the first crude classification is due to
Secchi (1875–1877), see also Young (1896). Secchi divided prominences into
quiescent and eruptive objects, thereby describing their activity as manifested by the degree of prominence motion. We have repeatedly referred to
the two main classes of prominences as quiescent and active, and even though
our scheme as we shall presently see is also based on spectroscopic differences,
it coincides well with Secchi's original classification, which was mainly based
on dynamic properties.

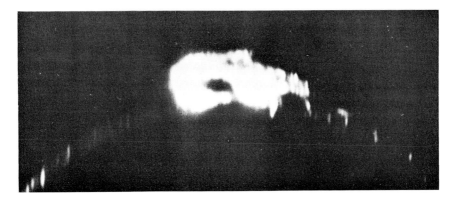

H I 6563 (Hα)

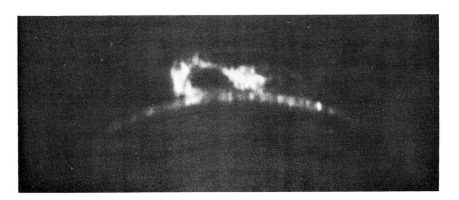

H I 4861 (Hβ)

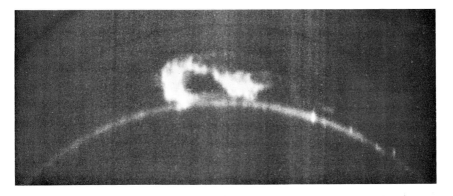

He I 5876 (D₃)

FIGURE 7.2.   Prominence observed with a slitless spectrograph

We stressed in Chapter 3 the importance of spicules for the understanding of the quiet sun. In most respects, spicules can be considered as small prominences. Dynamically they are active, but they are essential to the quiet chromosphere, forming the "burning prairie" referred to earlier. We shall return to their relationship to the prominence phenomenon in the next section.

7.2. *Observations*

In the introduction to this chapter we have mentioned a number of observations concerning prominences, and a picture of these objects is beginning to emerge. It is clear that prominences may take on very different forms, their lifetimes may range from minutes to many months, and the degree of dynamic activity varies greatly from one prominence to another. It would seem natural to try to classify prominences using some of these, or other, characteristics, and we have seen that Secchi (1875–1877) divided them into quiescent and active (he called the latter eruptive) prominences. Secchi further subdivided the quiescent and the active prominences into subclasses (clouds, filaments, stems, plumes, horns and cyclones, flames, jets, sheafs, spikes—see also Young, 1896). It is often difficult to maintain the distinction between these subgroups, but the main two-class arrangement is of lasting value.

By a quiescent prominence we understand a fairly long-lived (days to months) object that changes form only slowly. By contrast, an active prominence is one that is dynamically active and changes its form significantly in hours. Often, the whole visible display is over in minutes or hours.

There are also significant differences in the spectra from quiescent and from active prominences (see Section 7.2.2). Secchi was aware of this, and because of the many metal lines he observed in active prominences, he also called them metallic prominences.

7.2.1. Classifications according to Topography and Motions

7.2.1.1. *Pettit's classification*

For many years, the most widely known and used classification was that due to Pettit (1932, 1936, 1943, 1950). He divided the prominences into five classes, as shown in Table 7.1.

Pettit found that classes 1 and 2 are closely related; at times prominences show both phases simultaneously or pass from the active to the eruptive state. Class 4 contains fairly small objects, averaging about 12,000 km in diameter and 50,000 km in height.

TABLE 7.1   Pettit's classification

Class	Name	Description
1	Active	Material seems to be streaming into nearby active center (like sunspots).
2	Eruptive	The whole prominence ascends with uniform velocity (of several hundred km/sec often). The velocity may at times suddenly increase.
3	Sunspot	These are found near sunspots and take the shape of "water in a fountain" or loops.
4	Tornado	A vertical spiral structure gives these prominences the appearance of a closely wound rope or whirling column. A rare type.
5	Quiescent	Large prominence masses which show only minor changes over periods of hours or days.

No prominence is really quiescent, but the changes with time are much slower for those we call quiescent than for any other class. As we shall see later, however, they may go through some active phases in their lifetimes (prominence activation). Quiescent prominences generally take the form of enormous sheets standing vertically in the solar atmosphere. These sheets are about 200,000 km long and 50,000 km high, but their thickness is only 5000 to 10,000 km.

7.2.1.2. Newton's classification

As a result of their spectroheliographic work, Hale (Hale and Ellerman, 1903) and Deslandres (1910) early realized that the dark filaments seen in absorption on the disk (also called dark flocculi or dark markings) are nothing more than prominences seen against the bright photosphere. However, further progress along these lines was hampered by two drawbacks of the spectroheliograph; (1) it takes a fairly long time to complete a spectroheliogram and get ready for the next one, and (2) if the prominence exhibits a substantial radial motion (in Pettit's case more than 30 km/sec), the Doppler effect will throw the line outside the second slit, and the observation will be lost (see Section 2.1.1). Hale (1929, 1930, 1931a, 1931b) remedied both these drawbacks in constructing the spectrohelioscope. The observation is here made visually, and the line (generally Hα) is kept on the second slit by a lineshifter, whose position directly gives the radial velocity.

Newton (1934, 1935) used this spectrohelioscope technique in a study of filaments and derived from such observations a prominence classification (see Table 7.2, p. 322).

TABLE 7.2   Newton's classification

Class	Description
I	Prominences that avoid the neighborhood of sunspots (but not the whole sunspot zone). Long well-defined filaments lasting several days.
II	Prominences that are associated with sunspots or with the plage areas. Generally smaller than objects of class I. Lifetimes of the order of minutes or hours.

(a)	(b)
Prominences that show large radial velocities and occur after the appearance of a localized emission (a so-called bright flocculus).	Prominences originally of class I that become activated by the sudden appearance of an emission object. The emission remains more or less stationary, but it gives the filament a large radial velocity.

Newton's class II comprises different types of active prominences (Pettit's classes 1, 2, 3, and 4). Furthermore, class IIb describes an interesting flare-prominence relationship to which we shall return in Section 7.4. The objects of class I are identical to Pettit's quiescent prominences.

7.2.1.3. *The Menzel-Evans classification*

An important distinction between different kinds of prominences was introduced by Menzel and Evans (1953), who classify prominences according to whether they originate from above, i.e., in the corona, or from below. Also, as has been done previously, they distinguish between those prominences that are associated with sunspots and those that are not. The further subdivision is pictorial, based on the shapes of the prominences. Table 7.3 summarizes this two-dimensional classification.

The letter following each type of prominence is the designation given by Menzel and Evans. For example, loops are referred to by the symbols ASl and spicules by the designation BNs.

7.2.1.4. *de Jager's classification*

In his scheme, de Jager (1959) divides prominences into two main groups, quiescent and moving prominences. The subdivision is apparently inspired by Pettit's classification (see Table 7.4).

TABLE 7.3   The Menzel-Evans classification

| | | Place of origin | |
		From above, A	From below, B
	Associated with sunspots, S	Rain, a Funnels, b Loops, l	Surges, s Puffs, p
Relation to sunspots	Not associated with sunspots, N	Coronal rain, a Tree trunks, b Trees, c Hedgerows, d Suspended clouds, f Mounds, m	Spicules, s

TABLE 7.4   de Jager's classification

Class I. Quiescent prominences
    (a) Normal prominences (low to medium latitudes)
    (b) Polar prominences (high latitudes)

Class II. Moving prominences
    (a) Active prominences
    (b) Eruptive prominences
    (c) Spot prominences
    (d) Surges
    (e) Spicules

Class Ia corresponds to Pettit's quiescent prominences (class 5), while de Jager's classes IIa and IIb cover Pettit's classes 1 and 2, respectively. The important prominence types, surges and spicules, are explicitly classified, as they are in the Menzel-Evans classification. de Jager draws attention to those quiescent prominences that are found in polar regions (class Ib). We shall return to them later.

7.2.1.5. Severny's classification

Severny (1950, 1959b) and Severny and Khokhlova (1953) argued that to arrive at a classification with any physical significance, prominences must

TABLE 7.5   Severny's classification

Class	Name	Description
I	Eruptive	Quiescent prominences becoming eruptive. Rare, 5 to 10% of all cases. Outward motions with velocities of several hundred km/sec, at times exceeding the velocity of escape.
II	Electromagnetic	Electromagnetic prominences. The knots or condensations making up the prominences exhibit motions along definite curved trajectories. Velocities range from several tens to a few hundred km/sec. About 50% of all prominences belong here.
III	Irregular	Prominences with irregular, random, motions of individual knots.

be characterized mainly by their motions. Table 7.5 gives the characteristics of Severny's three classes.

Class II corresponds to sunspot prominences in the Menzel-Evans classification, and class III encompasses normal quiescent prominences. It is apparent from this—as has been noted before—that the word quiescent must be taken in a relative sense only.

7.2.2. The Spectra of Limb Prominences

We stated in Chapter 6 that some active prominences and flares give spectra that show a wealth of emission lines. Special mention was made of the many helium lines. When spectra are obtained of dense (brilliant) quiescent prominences, the resulting list of emission lines is just as impressive. Numerous metal lines show up even though these prominences are generally not of the active type in which Secchi (1875–1877) found so many metal lines that he called them metallic prominences. The abundance of metals is not different from what it is in other prominences, but the excitation conditions are conducive to the strong emission of metal lines, relative to hydrogen, and especially to helium lines.

We shall generally avoid the term metallic prominence both because it hardly has any physical meaning and to avoid confusion, since the term has also been used by Ananthakrishnan and Madhavan Nayar (1953) to characterize "small intense, very active short-lived prominences that exhibit emission lines of H, He, Mg, Na, Fe II, Cr, etc."

Many of the metal lines we are going to discuss in the following sections will show up in prominences of very different types, provided that the prominence plasma is dense enough (that is, the prominence looks bright enough) to give sufficient intensity in the lines. As we shall see, prominences are often so dense that the strongest lines are optically thick. On the other hand, all prominences are invisible on the disk in white light. Hence, even though we often see a distinct continuous spectrum in bright limb prominences, these objects are all optically thin for continuous radiation.

Spectra of prominences have been studied by a series of authors, including Grotrian (1931a), Richardson (1950), Conway (1952), Severny (1954b), Haupt (1955), Ivanov-Kholodny (1955, 1958), Zuikov (1955), ten Bruggencate and Elste (1958), Sobolev (1958), Jefferies and Orrall (1958, 1961a, 1961b, 1961c, 1962), Tandberg-Hanssen and Zirin (1959), Zirin and Tandberg-Hanssen (1960), Zirin (1959), Tandberg-Hanssen (1959, 1963, 1964), Bratiichuk (1961), Rigutti and Russo (1961), Shin-Huei (1961), Morozhenko (1963), Yakovkin and Zel'dina (1963, 1964).

7.2.2.1. Hydrogen emission

The hydrogen lines are invariably among the strongest emission lines observed in limb prominences of all types. The early Balmer lines are often self-absorbed and even higher members may be affected in dense objects. We mentioned in Chapter 6 that, as a general rule, in flares, both the half-width and the central intensity of the hydrogen lines decrease with increasing principal quantum number, n, but there are often irregularities in the Balmer decrement. In prominences, the Balmer decrement behaves normally in the sense that the intensity decreases monotonically toward higher members (with increasing values of n). The detailed variation of the half-width with n depends on the kind of prominence observed. In some prominences, $\Delta\lambda_D/\lambda$ is approximately constant, which at first sight might indicate negligible self-absorption. As shown by Jefferies and Orrall (1958), this is not the case; in fact, the constancy of $\Delta\lambda_D/\lambda$ with n is rather an indication that not only are the earlier Balmer lines self-absorbed, but also later members are strongly affected. If the source function had been constant with depth in the prominence, a significant drop in the value of $\Delta\lambda_D/\lambda$ from one line to the next higher would indicate that self-absorption had lost its importance. There is, however, no reason to believe that the source function as a rule is constant. A simple interpretation of the half-widths is therefore not immediately obvious.

The Balmer decrements for a number of prominences are given in Tables 7.6 and 7.7 (pp. 326 and 327), together with the decrement in some flares and in the chromosphere. The intensities of the early Balmer lines are shown in Table 7.6 and clearly reveal the effect of self-absorption. The decrement is very flat for flares (Smith and Smith, 1963) and also for the chromosphere (Thomas and Athay, 1961). In some dense prominences, the decrement may

TABLE 7.6   Balmer decrement of early Balmer lines in prominences and flares

Line		Yakovkin and Zel'dina (1964)	Shin-Huei (1961)		Zuikov (1955)		Bratiichuk (1961)	
λ, Å	n		7	9	1945 eclipse	1952 eclipse	1955 a	1955 b
6563	3	4.4	6.8	24.0	43.0	47.0	24.0	10.4
4861	4	2.1	2.0	5.6	9.0	6.2	4.5	2.8
4340	5	1.1	1.2	3.3	2.8	2.9	1.9	1.6
4101	6	1.0	1.0	1.0	1.0	1.0	1.0	1.0
3970	7	0.62	0.92	0.78				

Line		Ivanov-Kholodny (1958)		Smith and Smith (1963)				Thomas and Athay (1961)
						Disk flare		Chromo-
λ, Å	n	1	2	Preflare	Flash	Maximum	Post flare	sphere
6563	3	11.6	28.3	1.4	1.6	1.5	2.0	4.1
4861	4	3.1	5.0	1.1	1.4	1.8	1.7	2.7
4340	5	1.7	1.83	1.0	1.7	1.5	1.3	1.9
4101	6	1.0	1.0	1.0	1.0	1.0	1.0	1.0
3970	7	0.68		0.71	0.95	0.80	0.71	

be as flat as in the chromosphere, but in most prominences the effects of self-absorption are much less. Shin-Huei (1961) considers self-absorption negligible in most prominences for Balmer lines later than about H_δ. For comparison, Thomas and Athay (1961) deduced that self-absorption must be taken into account in studies of the chromosphere up to $n = 20$.

Note the abnormal behavior of the decrement in the flare reported by Smith and Smith (1963). During the flash phase, H_γ and, during the maximum phase, H_β, were stronger than H_α.

Table 7.7 portrays the Balmer decrement in prominences for later Balmer lines, again compared with the decrement in some flarelike objects (Jefferies and Orrall, 1961a, 1961b) and in the chromosphere. We find that in large quiescent prominences the observed decrement is not unlike the chromospheric decrement. We also note that the decrement changes rapidly in very active objects. The flare-loop refers to a flaring-up of great loops and the decrement is at times very flat. The spray is a surgelike object; its decrement became more "prominencelike" in the spectrum of 1732 UT compared with what it was shortly before.

TABLE 7.7   Balmer decrement of later Balmer lines in prominences and flares

Line λ, Å	n	Jefferies and Orrall (1962) Quiescent prominence	Tandberg-Hanssen Quiescent prominences April 18, 1962	Tandberg-Hanssen March 30, 1964	Shin-Huei (1961) 7	Shin-Huei (1961) 9	Yakovkin and Zel'dina (1964)	Jefferies and Orrall (1961b) Flare(loop) 1820UT	1822UT	Jefferies and Orrall (1961a) Spray 1730UT	1732UT	Thomas and Athay (1961) Chromosphere
4101	6				6.2	10.0	8.3					5.5
3970	7				5.7	7.8	5.2					
3889	8		3.2		1.9	2.9	3.4					3.3
3835	9		1.8	1.9	1.5	1.4	2.0					1.8
3798	10	1.23	1.0	1.5	1.6	1.0	1.5					1.2
3771	11	1.0	0.75	1.0	1.0	1.0	1.0	1.0	1.0	1.0	1.0	1.0
3750	12	0.91	0.50	0.83	0.6	0.7	0.9	0.95	0.83	0.78	0.86	0.79
3734	13	0.76	0.44	0.72	0.7	0.7	0.8	1.0	0.66	0.78	0.71	0.68
3722	14	0.69	0.32	0.41				0.89	0.51		0.49	0.47
3712	15	0.53	0.31	0.34				0.73	0.48	0.46	0.31	0.37
3704	16	0.46	0.28	0.33				0.61	0.38		0.29	0.33
3697	17	0.41		0.29				0.60	0.33	0.42	0.22	0.25
3692	18			0.11				0.46	0.29	0.30	0.19	0.23
3687	19	0.31						0.37	0.21	0.26	0.13	0.21
3683	20	0.26						0.29	0.21	0.23	0.12	0.20

In several branches of astrophysics (excitation in planetary nebulae and in stars with extended atmospheres, to mention a few) the observed Balmer decrement is compared with that expected under different conditions (recombination spectra or spectra resulting from radiative excitation, the plasma being more or less opaque to radiation in the lines). From such comparisons one may deduce important information on the interaction of the radiation field with the plasma in question and even derive values for T_e and n_e. The same method has been used in the study of prominences (Vyazanitsyn, 1947; Shin-Huei, 1961; Yakovkin and Zel'dina, 1964). These authors conclude that the hydrogen lines in prominences are excited by photospheric radiation, with the possibility that recombination emission may be important for the later Balmer lines. Divergent conclusions are drawn from studies of the cause of hydrogen ionization. Both photo-ionization and collisional ionization have been advocated.

This use of the Balmer decrement assumes that the observed lines are free from self-absorption or that the effects of self-absorption can be reliably removed from the observed data. Our discussion of the Balmer lines, both their half-widths and their central intensities, shows that not only is the effect difficult to ascertain in any given case, but self-absorption evidently effects different prominences to very different degrees.

However, we can draw some conclusions regarding the physical state of the emitting prominence plasma. In those cases where the line profiles are Gaussian, we may make the assumption that the lines are broadened by thermal motions at temperature T and by processes leading to the same shape of the profiles, i.e., microturbulent motions, v_t. The observed Doppler width is related to the parameters T and v_t by the following equation [see Equation (1.110b)]:

$$\frac{\Delta\lambda_D}{\lambda} = \frac{1}{c}\sqrt{\frac{2kT}{m} + v_t^2} \, . \tag{7.1}$$

In quiescent prominences we observe for H_δ (4101 Å) half-widths, $\Delta\lambda$ (that is, width at half intensity), of about 0.20 Å, which corresponds to a Doppler half-width $\Delta\lambda_D = \Delta\lambda/2\sqrt{\ln 2} = 0.12$ Å. Table 7.8 shows what temperatures and velocities are compatible with a given value of $\Delta\lambda_D/\lambda$ according to Equation (7.1).

TABLE 7.8   Temperatures and broadening velocities
for hydrogen lines, $\Delta\lambda_D/\lambda = 3.33 \times 10^{-5}$

v_t, km/sec	0	2	4	6	8	10
T, °K	6000	5750	5000	3900	2150	0

Because of the dependence of $\Delta\lambda_D$ on mass, we see that all heavier atoms are less sensitive to thermal broadening, and for the metals we find that this broadening is negligible for any reasonable temperature. Profiles of hydrogen lines, on the other hand, give for quiescent prominences a fairly narrow allowable range for the temperature and set a useful upper limit, which for most prominences lies between 5000 and 10,000°K. In praxis, the difficulty is again that the hydrogen lines are often self-absorbed and thereby additionally broadened.

In many active prominences, like surges, the hydrogen lines are very broad, with Gaussian profiles often corresponding to values of $\Delta\lambda_D/\lambda$ between 1×10^{-4} and 2×10^{-4}. The higher value would give a broadening temperature in excess of 2×10^5 °K, which is not a reasonable temperature. On the other hand, it would take a turbulent velocity $v_t \approx 60$ km/sec to account for this amount of broadening. Other profiles are quite irregular, showing the effects of "macroturbulence," i.e., different parts of the prominence are moving with different velocities relative to the observer.

From this discussion, it seems to follow that the hydrogen line emission in quiescent prominences (which here is the same as prominences with narrow emission lines) comes from a plasma of temperature several thousand degrees below 10^4 °K. In active prominences, the hydrogen plasma may not be very much hotter. Jefferies and Orrall (1961b) suggest temperatures of 10^4 °K to maybe 2×10^4 °K. The extra broadening of the lines must be due to some nonthermal source, like microturbulence, geometric effects, Stark-broadening, and so on. By geometric effects, we mean a superposition mechanism, whereby a broad line can be built up by summing over several narrow lines. Jefferies and Orrall (1961a) showed that broad Gaussian-looking lines could be thought of as a sum of narrow Gaussian lines separated by a certain amount (for example, one Doppler half-width). This would mean that the prominence emission was made up of contributions from several small parts of the prominence plasma, each part moving with a different radial velocity relative to the observer.

The Stark effect is certainly of importance as a broadening mechanism in higher Balmer lines. However, up to about H_9 the wings of the Balmer lines are not significantly affected by Stark broadening. It is probable that most of the extra line broadening in active prominences like surges is due to random mass motions. Similar results seem to hold for flares (Suemoto and Hiei, 1959). However, in many loops the hydrogen line profiles have much more extended wings than in other prominences. Jefferies and Orrall (1965a) have attributed this to the effect of a jetlike streaming of matter along the loops (see Section 7.3.3.3b).

The spectra of many dense prominences reveal a continuous radiation which appears as a bright bead in the position where the line emission is also most intense. The intensity of the continuum varies with wavelength and increases near the Balmer limit. We have seen in Section 6.1.3.1 how measurements of this continuum may be used to derive temperature estimates of the emitting gas using Equation (6.8b). Jefferies and Orrall (1961c) found for quiescent prominences that the electron temperature is at least 12,000 °K. This is definitely higher than the value deduced from studies of the hydrogen lines. The discrepancy raises the questions of departures from LTE and whether the line and continuous radiations come from different parts of the plasma. We shall shortly return to this interesting problem.

The Balmer emission may give information not only on the temperature of the emitting prominence and flare plasma but also on the electron densities involved. Using the Balmer lines, we determine the electron density, n_e, from the Stark effect (the confluence of the lines for large values of the principal quantum number, n) and observing the continuous emission around the Balmer jump, we may also compute n_e. Jefferies and Orrall (1962) have used the second method, employing Equation (6.8b), as for flares, and find $n_e \approx 10^{11}$ cm^{-3} or slightly less. This value is smaller than what other authors derive using the method of the Stark effect.

The latter method is based on the fact that the interionic Stark effect will influence the wings of higher Balmer lines so that they become different from purely Doppler-broadened lines. As we go to large values of n, the lines tend to coalesce and can no longer be resolved. The higher the electron density, the more pronounced is this effect and the fewer are the lines that can be distinguished. This, then, gives us two methods by which to judge the electron density. From a study of observed prominence profiles, Ivanov-Kholodny (1959) deduced a density, $n_e \approx 10^{12}$ cm^{-3}. The measurements are difficult since it is only in the far wings, where the intensity has dropped to less than ten percent of the central intensity, that the Stark profile and the Doppler profile differ significantly.

The other version of the Stark-effect method leads to the following relation, named after Inglis and Teller (1939), between the electron density, n_e, and the quantum number n_{max} of the last resolvable line

$$\log n_e = 22.96 - 7.5 \log n_{max}. \tag{7.2}$$

Estimates based on formula (7.2) give $n_e \approx 10^{12}$ cm^{-3} (Ivanov-Kholodny, 1955, 1959), but it should be borne in mind that this is an upper limit since the difficulties experienced in observing the higher Balmer lines may prevent detection of lines corresponding to $n > 30$ ($n_e = 10^{12}$ cm^{-3} corresponds to $n_{max} = 29$).

In a reevaluation of the Stark effect in prominence Balmer lines, Hirayama (1963) concluded that n_e should be near 10^{11} cm^{-3}. For comparison, estimates of the Stark effect on Balmer lines in flares lead to values of n_e about an order of magnitude higher than for prominences.

7.2.2.2. *Metal lines*

In spectra of dense prominences, one finds lines emitted by a large number of metal atoms and singly ionized ions. At times the spectra are so rich that many multiplets, including intrinsically faint satellite lines, are completely recorded. Both active and quiescent prominences may give such rich line spectra, but there are distinctive spectroscopic differences between active and quiescent objects.

Figure 7.3 (p. 332) is a reproduction of some spectral regions of the dense quiescent prominence of March 26, 1960. For a complete list of all the emission lines observed in these very rich spectra, see Tandberg-Hanssen (1964), which may serve as an atlas of prominence emission lines.

The difference between spectra of active and quiescent prominences, as far as metal lines are concerned, is illustrated in Figure 7.4 (p. 334) for the prominences of March 23, 1958. Many of the same lines are present in both objects, but they are invariably broader in the spectra of the active prominence. Furthermore, many metal lines that are absent or very weak in the spectra of active prominences show up with considerable strength in quiescent prominence spectra. The term "metallic" prominence as a synonym for dynamically active prominences may therefore cause confusion in an already unclear situation. Let us, for instance, consider the spectral region 5350 through 5500 Å. Spectra of active prominences and flares will here show significant emission only in the lines Mg I, 5528 and He II, 5411, and in some Fe I and Fe II lines. The emission from quiescent prominences is, on the other hand, characterized by lines of the same Fe I and Fe II multiplets and lines of Cr I, Ti II and, above all, Sc II. It is worth noting that the Sc II emission completely dominates the spectral region around 5600 Å (Tandberg-Hanssen, 1964).

Consequently, one of the main spectral characteristics of quiescent prominences is the moderate-to-strong emission in lines of Sc II, the numerous Ti II lines, and lines of Y II. The Sc II and Y II lines are faint in most active prominences and flares. The great richness of prominence Ti II lines is evident from Table 7.9 (p. 336), where we present a systematic list of all the Ti II lines observed in the quiescent prominence of March 26, 1960.

Lines of neutral and ionized iron are present in nearly all flare and prominence spectra, but while they often dominate the flare spectrum, their intensity is superseded by Ti II lines in prominences. This relative increase in intensity of iron lines in flares was found several years ago by Allen (1940) and was also noticed by Waldmeier (1949b), and it has been used as a classification criterion to distinguish between flares and active prominences (see Section 7.2.4).

It is interesting to contrast some of our spectra of quiescent prominences with Allen's flare observations (1940) and with the observations of Richardson

26 MARCH 1960

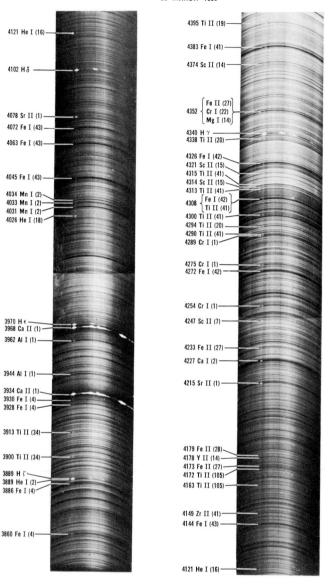

(a)

FIGURE 7.3.   Reproduction of spectra of a dense quiescent prominence, March 26, 1960. (a) Region: 3855 Å to 4400 Å; (b) region: 4320 Å to 4865 Å

26 MARCH 1960

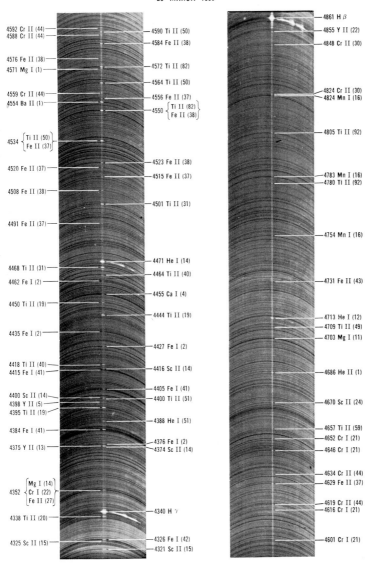

4592 Cr II (44) —
4588 Cr II (44) —

4576 Fe II (38) —
4571 Mg I (1) —

4559 Cr II (44) —
4554 Ba II (1) —

4534 $\left\{ \begin{array}{l} \text{Ti II (50)} \\ \text{Fe II (37)} \end{array} \right\}$

4520 Fe II (37) —

4508 Fe II (38) —

4491 Fe II (37) —

4468 Ti II (31) —
4462 Fe I (2) —

4450 Ti II (19) —

4435 Fe I (2) —

4418 Ti II (40) —
4415 Fe I (41) —

4400 Sc II (14) —
4398 Y II (5) —
4395 Ti II (19) —

4384 Fe I (41) —
4375 Y II (13) —

4352 $\left\{ \begin{array}{l} \text{Mg I (14)} \\ \text{Cr I (22)} \\ \text{Fe II (27)} \end{array} \right\}$

4338 Ti II (20) —

4325 Sc II (15) —

— 4590 Ti II (50)
— 4584 Fe II (38)

— 4572 Ti II (82)

— 4564 Ti II (50)

— 4556 Fe II (37)
— 4550 $\left\{ \begin{array}{l} \text{Ti II (82)} \\ \text{Fe II (38)} \end{array} \right\}$

— 4523 Fe II (38)
— 4515 Fe II (37)

— 4501 Ti II (31)

— 4471 He I (14)
— 4464 Ti II (40)

— 4455 Ca I (4)

— 4444 Ti II (19)

— 4427 Fe I (2)

— 4416 Sc II (14)

— 4405 Fe I (41)
— 4400 Ti II (51)

— 4388 He I (51)

— 4376 Fe I (2)
— 4374 Sc II (14)

— 4340 H γ

— 4326 Fe I (42)
— 4321 Sc II (15)

— 4861 H β
— 4855 Y II (22)

— 4848 Cr II (30)

— 4824 Cr II (30)
— 4824 Mn I (16)

— 4805 Ti II (92)

— 4783 Mn I (16)
— 4780 Ti II (92)

— 4754 Mn I (16)

— 4731 Fe II (43)

— 4713 He I (12)
— 4709 Ti II (49)
— 4703 Mg I (11)

— 4686 He II (1)

— 4670 Sc II (24)

— 4657 Ti II (59)
— 4652 Cr I (21)
— 4646 Cr I (21)

— 4634 Cr II (44)
— 4629 Fe II (37)

— 4619 Cr II (44)
— 4616 Cr I (21)

— 4601 Cr I (21)

(b)

23 MARCH 1958 (1448 U.T.)

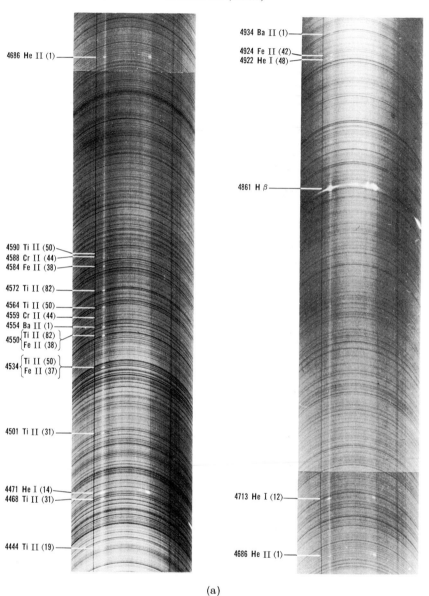

(a)

FIGURE 7.4. Comparison between spectra of a quiescent and an active
prominence, March 23, 1958. (a) Region: 4400 Å to 4940 Å.
(b) region: 3885 Å to 4150 Å

23 MARCH 1958 (1519 U.T.)

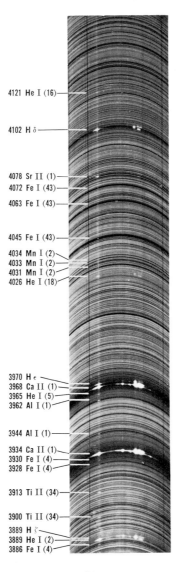

4121 He I (16)

4102 H δ

4078 Sr II (1)
4072 Fe I (43)
4063 Fe I (43)

4045 Fe I (43)
4034 Mn I (2)
4033 Mn I (2)
4031 Mn I (2)
4026 He I (18)

3970 H ε
3968 Ca II (1)
3965 He I (5)
3962 Al I (1)

3944 Al I (1)

3934 Ca II (1)
3930 Fe I (4)
3928 Fe I (4)

3913 Ti II (34)

3900 Ti II (34)

3889 H ζ
3889 He I (2)
3886 Fe I (4)

(b)

TABLE 7.9   Lines of Ti II in the prominence spectra of March 26, 1960 (central intensity I_0 in 10^{-6} of photospheric radiation)

Multiplet		λ	I_0	Multiplet		λ	I_0
11	a^2F–z^4G^0	3987.6	Faint			4563.8	515
		3982.0	Faint			4590.0	80
		4025.1	Faint	51	a^2P–z^4D^0	4399.8	120
		4012.4	65			4394.0	Faint
19	a^2D–z^2F^0	4395.0	1040			4418.3	Faint
		4443.8	440			4407.7	Faint
		4450.5	65	59	b^4P–z^2F^0	4657.2	Faint
20	a^2D–z^2D^0	4294.1	310			4719.5	Faint
		4337.4	210	61	b^4P–z^4D^0	4395.8	Faint
21	a^2D–z^4D^0	4161.5	Faint			4398.3	?
30	a^2G–z^4F^0	4545.1	Faint			4411.9	Faint
31	a^2G–z^2F^0	4468.5	820			4391.0	Faint
		4501.3	370	69	b^2D–z^2F^0	5381.0	25
		4444.6	15			5418.8	20
34	a^2G–z^2G^0	3900.5	305	70	b^2D–z^2D^0	5188.7	Faint
		3913.5	255			5154.1	Faint
40	a^4P–z^2D^0	4417.7	125	82	a^2H–z^2G^0	4549.6	640
		4464.4	35			4572.0	635
41	a^4P–z^4D^0	4300.0	475			4529.5	Faint
		4290.2	270	86	b^2G–z^2G^0	5185.9	Faint
		4301.9	130	87	b^2G–y^2F^0	4028.3	Faint
		4312.9	180	92	b^2P–z^2S^0	4805.1	95
		4307.9	325			4780.0	55
		4315.0	110	93	b^2P–y^2D^0	4374.8	215
		4330.7	Faint	94	b^2P–z^2P^0	4316.8	Faint
		4321.0	Faint	104	b^2F–y^2G^0	4386.8	Faint
48	a^2P–z^4F^0	4764.5	Faint	105	b^2F–x^2D^0	4163.6	35
		4763.8	Faint			4171.9	55
49	a^2P–z^2F^0	4708.7	25	115	c^2D–x^2F^0	4488.3	?
50	a^2P–z^2D^0	4534.0	560			4411.1	Faint

(1950) and of Jefferies, Smith and Smith (1959). For example, we see no emission between the two lines 3900 and 3913 Å of Ti II in the quiescent prominence spectra, whereas both Richardson and Jefferies, Smith and Smith observed the line 3906 Å of Si I of moderate intensity, the two Ti II lines being faint. Also, between 4144 and 4200 Å Richardson and Jefferies, Smith and Smith observed only Fe I and Fe II lines and the line 4167 Å of Mg I, while the spectra of quiescent prominences show the strongest emission in Ti II and Y II.

With the outstanding exception of iron lines, we seem to find that the metal line emission is often richer and more diversified in quiescent prominences than in more active objects. It is possible that other elements of the iron group, i.e., cobalt and nickel, follow more closely the pattern of iron, see Ellison (1946).

Among the strongest metal lines found in the spectra of prominences are the lines of the Ca II resonance doublet, the K-line at 3934 Å and the H-line at 3968 Å. Often—nearly as a rule—these lines are self-absorbed in dense prominences. However, in faint prominences and in the outer more tenuous parts of dense prominences, the lines are emitted under optically thin conditions. (The ratio between the intensities of the K- and H-lines is close to 2.0, and the value of $\Delta\lambda_D/\lambda$ corresponds to the value of this ratio for the infrared lines from the same ion, at 8500 Å.) The value of $\Delta\lambda_D/\lambda$ for the

TABLE 7.10   Temperatures and broadening velocities for Ca II lines,
$\Delta\lambda_D/\lambda = 2.87 \times 10^{-5}$

v_t, km/sec	0	6	8	8.3	8.4	8.5	8.6
T, °K	1.8×10^5	9.1×10^4	2.4×10^4	1.2×10^4	7200	3600	0

Ca II lines in quiescent prominences is of the order 2.5×10^{-5}. Using Equation (7.1), we can find the temperatures and turbulent velocities compatible with such profiles; see Table 7.10 for an example. Furthermore, the table is presented here to illustrate the fact that temperature broadening is negligible, most of the half-width being due to motions.

The data in Tables 7.8 and 7.10 pertain to the same prominence. If thermal broadening and microturbulence are the only significant contributors to the broadening of the lines involved, we must conclude that either the temperature of the emitting gas is less than 2000 °K or the calcium and the hydrogen emission come from different parts of the prominence. We have seen that the hydrogen emission probably comes from a plasma whose temperature is between 5000 and 10,000 °K, in active prominences somewhat more. This discussion therefore points to the possibility of a multicomponent prominence model. We shall return to this concept in more detail when discussing helium emission.

7.2.2.3. *Helium emission*

Of the greatest interest for our understanding of the physics of prominences is the fact that most prominence spectra show significant emission in lines of neutral, and often also ionized, helium. In spectra of quiescent prominences the lines of ionized helium are weak, but they show up with considerable intensity in active prominences and in flares; at times they exceed the intensity of neutral lines. This fact in itself points to a high degree of excitation of the emitting plasma and is of great importance for classification purposes, as seen in Section 7.2.4.

Lines of orthohelium (the triplet series) as well as lines of parahelium (the singlet series) are present in prominence spectra (see Figure 6.1). As mentioned in Section 6.1.3.4, the ratio between the intensities of corresponding lines in the triplet and in the singlet series should be close to $3:1$ in

TABLE 7.11   He I triplet/singlet line intensity ratios in some prominences

Lines compared	Date	Time (UT)	GH	Ratio	Type of prominence
(a) The ratio $\dfrac{I(7065)}{I(7281)}$	June 18, 1964	1611	3	>54	Quiescent
	Nov. 8, 1964	1910	2	40	Quiescent
	Jan. 17, 1965	1729	3–4	128	Quiescent
(b) The ratio $\dfrac{I(5876)}{I(6678)}$	Oct. 12, 1964	1442	2–3	16	Semiactive
	Dec. 5, 1964	1754	4–5	27	Quiescent
	Jan. 16, 1965	2217–2221	3–4	>14	Quiescent
(c) The ratio $\dfrac{I(4471)}{I(4922)}$	Dec. 19, 1956	1831–1903	2–5	3	Active
	Dec. 14, 1957	1530–1909	6–10	7	Active
	Aug. 2, 1958	2201	8–11	2	Active
	Sept. 10, 1958	1354–1535	4–8	11	Semiactive
	Sept. 16, 1958	2253	4	15	Quiescent
	May 13, 1963	1412–1544	2–5	11	Semiactive
	Sept. 26, 1963	1456	13–14	5	Active
	Jan. 16, 1965	2053	2–4	31	Quiescent

thermodynamic equilibrium. In quiescent prominences, the ratio is much larger, 20 or 30 to 1, but the value decreases as the degree of activity of the prominence increases. For very active prominences and for flares the ratio approaches the value 3. This is not an indication that such objects are in thermodynamic equilibrium, but it shows that the mode of excitation of these lines changes from quiescent to active objects. In Table 7.11 we show some triplet:singlet intensity ratios for a number of prominences with a different degree of activity.

There are two effects to be noted in Table 7.11. First, as mentioned above, the triplet/singlet line intensity ratio is larger for quiescent than for active objects. Second, the difference between the ratios in quiescent and in active prominences becomes smaller as we go to lines that originate closer to the continuum. This is presumably due to the fact that the radiation in the continuum is very close to local thermodynamic equilibrium.

In Section 6.1.3.4 the discussion of the ratio between corresponding lines of the series 2^3P-n^3D and 2^3P-n^3S (the D/S ratio) in flares showed that helium may exhibit a recombination spectrum. This should give a value of the ratio determined by the statistical weights of the upper levels involved, that is, $5:1$. In active prominences we find at times this same small value,

TABLE 7.12   He I D/S line intensity ratios in some prominences

Lines compared	Date	Time (UT)	GH	Ratio	Type of prominence
(a) The ratio	Nov. 22, 1956	2109	7	11	Quiescent
$I(4471)$	Dec. 19, 1956	1831–1903	1–5	5	Active
$\overline{I(4713)}$	Dec. 14, 1957	1530–1909	6–10	6	Active
	Aug. 2, 1958	2201	8–11	3	Active
	Sept. 10, 1958	1354–1535	4–8	5	Semiactive
	Sept. 16, 1958	2253	4	8	Quiescent
	Nov. 17, 1959	1706	4–6	13	Quiescent
	Mar. 24, 1960	1726	9–10	21	Quiescent
	Mar. 26, 1960	1734	15–17	16	Quiescent
	Nov. 18, 1960	2030	14–17	9	Semiactive
	Nov. 10, 1961	1955	10	11	Semiactive
	May 13, 1963	1412–1544	2–5	6	Semiactive
	Sept. 26, 1963	1456	13–14	5	Active
	Jan. 16, 1965	2053	3–4	18	Quiescent
(b) The ratio	Dec. 14, 1957	1800–lower	3–5	14	Quiescent
$I(4026)$	Dec. 14, 1957	1800–upper	3–5	13	Active
$\overline{I(4121)}$	Mar. 23, 1958	1419–1519 upper	2–5	7	Quiescent
	Mar. 23, 1958	1519–lower	3	5	Active
	Mar. 26, 1960	2026	5–6	9	Quiescent
	July 29, 1962	1502	3–5	9	Quiescent
	Feb. 19, 1965	2148	3–7	12	Quiescent

while quiescent prominences generally reveal a larger ratio, not unlike what should be expected under conditions of photoexcitation—by photospheric radiation.

Table 7.12 portrays the behavior of the D/S ratio in some prominences of different degree of activity. We conclude that in very active prominences the helium emission can be explained by a recombination spectrum, as for flares, while quiescent prominences give conditions conducive to photo-excitation of helium.

The pseudoresonance line of the triplet series, at 10,830 Å, is often self-absorbed in dense prominences. Profiles apparently free from self-absorption show Doppler half-widths between 0.3 and 0.4 Å, corresponding to broadening velocities of approximately 10 km/sec or a broadening temperature of 20,000 °K. Corresponding values of the half-width are found for other He I lines in quiescent prominences. Active prominences, and flares, show considerably broader lines corresponding to higher temperatures and/or larger motions.

The spectroscopic studies discussed so far have shown that active prominences and quiescent prominences are subject to quite different physical conditions. In many respects, active prominences are more like flares than

TABLE 7.13   Doppler half-widths ($\Delta\lambda_D$ in Å) and intensities ($I_0\,\Delta\lambda_D$ in relative units) of some helium lines as a function of height in (a) a surge and (b) a loop prominence

(a)

Height, km	He I				He II	
	4922		4713		4686	
	$\Delta\lambda_D$	$I_0\,\Delta\lambda_D$	$\Delta\lambda_D$	$I_0\,\Delta\lambda_D$	$\Delta\lambda_D$	$I_0\,\Delta\lambda_D$
8000	0.90	1.00	0.92	1.00	1.40	1.00
12500	0.98	0.79	0.97	0.73	1.27	1.03
17000	0.79	0.59	0.77	0.32		
21500	0.77	0.61	0.82	0.43	1.08	0.44
25000	0.77	0.26				

(b)

Height, km	He I, 4026						He II, 4686			
	$\Delta\lambda_D$			$I_0\,\Delta\lambda_D$			$\Delta\lambda_D$		$I_0\,\Delta\lambda_D$	
	Blue	Center	Red	Blue	Center	Red	Blue	Center	Blue	Center
17,000	0.52		0.33	1.00		0.47	0.62		1.00	
21,000	0.54		0.34	1.04		0.42	0.81		0.82	
25,000	0.68		0.45	0.79		0.41	0.73		1.08	
29,000		0.68			0.43		0.88		0.82	
34,000		0.71			0.28			0.66		0.70
38,000								0.74		0.54

"Blue" and "red" refer to the two "legs" of the loop, the lines from which are Doppler-displaced in opposite directions. "Center" refers to the top part of the loop.

like quiescent prominences. Also, dynamically speaking, this distinction often holds true. However, there are also differences between active prominences and flares, and we shall return to this in Section 7.2.4.

The variation of the helium emission with height in prominences can be used to bring out differences between different kinds of prominences. In particular, we shall now draw on such data to show that there are two different classes of objects among active prominences.

Table 7.13 indicates how the observed half-width and intensity varied with height in a surge (part a of Table 7.13) and in a loop (part b). Studies of the dynamics of prominences (Section 7.2.1) show that surges are examples of prominences that originate from below; they are, so to speak, shot up into the corona, while loops exemplify objects that form at coronal heights and in which matter is often seen to stream down toward the chromosphere and photosphere. The intensity of the helium emission lines remains fairly constant as we go up the loop into coronal regions, whereas in the surge the emission fades rapidly as we follow the surge upward into the corona. This fading with increasing distance from the limb is caused both by a decrease in the width, $\Delta \lambda_D$, and by a decrease in central intensity, I_0. On the other hand, the more nearly constant value of $I_0 \, \Delta \lambda_D$ in the loop is brought about as a result of two opposing effects, namely a decrease in the central intensity (as for the surge and due to decreasing density with height) combined with a general increase in half-width.

A change in $\Delta \lambda_D$ may be intepreted as a change in either temperature or microturbulence. The surge is thus "less active" in its upper parts than at its base, as if the plasma "relaxed" after being shot out. The loop, on the other hand, seems to be decidedly more active near its top. It is more intimately connected with the hot coronal plasma. This important distinction was recognized by Menzel and Evans (1953) in their dynamic classification of prominences (see Table 7.3).

7.2.3. The Multicomponent Model of Prominences

For a number of prominences we have good data on lines of both hydrogen and metals (for example from Ca II, Fe I, Fe II, Ti II, etc.) as well as lines from helium (neutral and ionized). At times it is possible, using Equation (7.1), to find one reasonable value for T and one for v_t that will satisfy both hydrogen and a set of metal line data, as if the two different kinds of emission came from the same volume elements of the prominences. However, as indicated in the previous section, this is not always the case. Furthermore, when we then add the information gained from the He I and He II data, the pair of values T and v_t that satisfied the hydrogen and metal lines do not fit the helium data. Consequently, the *shapes* of spectral lines give strong evidence for a multicomponent model of prominences. Similar arguments have been used by several authors to advocate this idea (Jefferies and Orrall, 1958; Sobolev, 1958; Orrall, 1962).

On rare occasions, Doppler *displacements* can furnish the most direct evidence that helium and metal lines, for instance, come from different regions. As an example, we shall discuss the surge of November 18, 1960.

18 NOVEMBER 1960

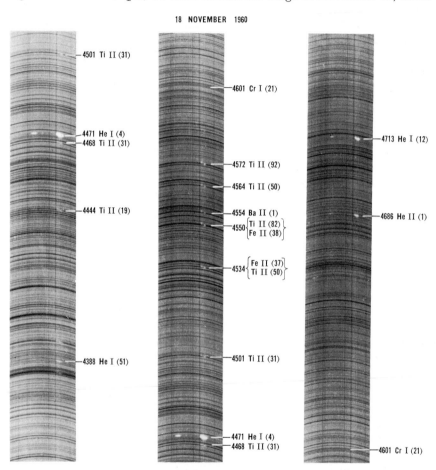

FIGURE 7.5.   Doppler motion in surge spectra, November 18, 1960

The surge was apparently triggered by a flare (see Section 7.4.4.2a) and consisted of several "subsurges." Spectra reveal two sets of emission features, *A* and *B*, clearly separated in the metal lines, but not in the helium lines, Figure 7.5. The metal lines from region *A* display strong Doppler motions (toward longer wavelengths) which decrease with height and are not paralleled by the neutral or ionized helium lines.

The surge thus consisted of at least two parts, and we measured the velocity at right angles to the line of sight (from the H_α patrol films) and the line-of-sight velocity (from the Doppler-displaced lines). The composite picture thus obtained is that of a surge shot out from a flare at a velocity greater than 200 km/sec. One part, B, started out in a direction perpendicular to the line of sight. Part A started out in a direction partly away from the observer making an angle of approximately 70 deg with the line of sight (Doppler motions corresponding to some 50 km/sec). It then curved toward the earth until it flowed out in a direction perpendicular to the line of sight.

Let $\lambda(A)$ and $\lambda(B)$ be the observed wavelengths of any line in the spectra of part A and B, respectively. Defining $\delta\lambda = |\lambda(A) - \lambda(B)|$, we find the following characteristic Doppler displacements for different lines (see Table 7.14, where $v = c\, \delta\lambda/\lambda$).

TABLE 7.14   Doppler displacements of lines from part A relative to part B in the surge of November 18, 1960

Line	$\delta\lambda$, Å	v, km/sec	Ion	Mean v, km/sec
He II, 4686	0.08	5.1	He II	5
He I, 4388	0.01	0.7		
4471	0.09	6.0	He I	5.5
4713	0.19	12.0		
Ti II, 4550	0.78	51		
4572	0.80	53	Metals	50
Ba II, 4554	0.71	47		

The difference between the $\delta\lambda$ value for the He II line and the mean value of $\delta\lambda$ for the He I emission is not significant, but the scatter within the He I data may be. Even though a value of 5 km/sec is approaching the noise level, it may be that the data indicate a situation where different helium lines are excited preferentially in different parts of the surges. One may tend to shy away from such a conclusion that would carry the idea of a multi-component model to its extreme. However, there is other evidence that different helium lines are not all excited in the same part of prominences. For example, the width of the intrinsically strong lines 4026 Å and 4471 Å is often less than the width of the lines 4713 Å and 4922 Å (Zirin and Tandberg-Hanssen, 1960).

Whatever the outcome of the "helium-region" may be, there is no doubt about the reality of the great difference in the $\delta\lambda$ values between the helium lines and the metal lines. We must conclude that the surge is built up of regions where the physical conditions differ from one region to another.

What we have called region A of the surge consists of at least two subsurges. In the first, the excitation conditions are such that helium emission dominates, and in the other they favor emission from singly ionized metal ions.

There are at least two ways to explain why the excitation conditions are such that the metal lines do not show up in the region between position angles A and B, namely (1) the temperature is too high, and (2) the density is too low. Careful tracings of the spectra show that the He II emission (4686 Å) comes mainly from the region between position angles A and B. This, in itself, points strongly to a high temperature of that plasma. Furthermore, the intensity of the He I lines is stronger from the region between A and B than from position A, indicating that the density of that region is quite high compared to the density in part A. If this picture is correct, the absence of the Ti II, Fe II, and Ba II emission lines from the region between A and B should be due to the high temperature there.

7.2.4. Spectral Classifications

The rich and strong line emission from limb flares and prominences has prompted several attempts at a spectral classification of such objects. We have already mentioned Secchi's (1875–77) pioneering work in this field. In later years, considerable research has been done by Waldmeier (1949b, 1951, 1961b).

7.2.4.1. *Waldmeier's classification*

Waldmeier (1951) used the b-lines of Mg I (b_1 at 5184 Å, b_2 at 5173 Å and b_4 at 5167 Å) and compared their intensity with that of b_3 of Fe II at 5169 Å (see Table 6.3). In Chapter 6, we noted that while flares generally fall in classes IV and V, different prominences belong to Waldmeier's classes I, II, or III.

7.2.4.2. *The Zirin and Tandberg-Hanssen classification*

The philosophy behind this classification is based on the multicomponent model of flares and prominences (Zirin and Tandberg-Hanssen, 1960; Tandberg-Hanssen, 1963). The classification is presented in Table 6.4, where the criteria refer to the intensity of the lines mentioned.

This scheme furnishes a convenient way of cataloging different aspects of solar atmospheric activity and of comparing them with the chromosphere (the quiet sun). However, as mentioned in Chapter 6, it lumps together flares and active prominences. While this again shows that active prominences in some respects are more like flares than like quiescent prominences, it also brings out the fact that it takes "finer" criteria, like Waldmeier's, to distinguish between active objects. We found that the distinction can be made by using lines of ionized iron, which are strong in flares, and comparing them with lines characteristic of prominences. We have also seen that Ti II lines abound in quiescent prominences, and it turns out that in active prominences they are also stronger than many iron lines. Mean relative values of lines of some Fe II and some Ti II multiplets and of the resonance line of Ba II in flares, in active prominences and in quiescent prominences, are given in Table 7.15.

TABLE 7.15   Relative intensities of lines of Fe II and Ti II as well as Ba II in spectra of flares and of prominences

| | | Intensity | | |
Line, Å	Ion and multiplet	Flares	Active prominences	Quiescent prominences
4584	Fe II, 38	10	1	4.5
4508	38	3	0	1
4629	37	5	0	0.5
4555	37	4.5	0	0.5
4572	Ti II, 82	3.5	10	10
4564	50	3	9	10.5
4534	50	4	9	10
4501	31	2	5	10
4554	Ba II, 1	1	5	10.5

The table reveals that in prominences the Ti II emission (and that of Ba II) is decidedly stronger than the Fe II emission, whereas in flares the intensity of the Fe II lines equals or exceeds the intensity of the Ti II lines. The intensity ratio between a suitably chosen Fe II line and a Ti II (or Ba II) line should give a useful criterion to distinguish between flares and active prominences. Since the other "classification lines" in the blue–green region of the spectrum lie around 4600 Å, we choose the 4584 Å line of Fe II (multiplet 38) together with the line 4572 Å of Ti II (multiplet 82). The ratio $M = I(\text{Fe II}, 4584)/I(\text{Ti II}, 4572)$ will then classify an active limb event as a prominence when $M < 1$ and as a flare if $M \geq 1$.

7.2.5. Magnetic Fields

The very shape of many active prominences seen on the limb has led several authors to infer that magnetic fields play a major role in the physics of such objects. In some cases, attempts have been made (Correll, Hazen and Bahng, 1956; Correll and Roberts, 1958) to deduce the configurations of the magnetic fields involved. Field lines resulting from magnetic dipoles buried in the photosphere seem to approximate the outline of the fine structure of many prominences fairly well. H. D. and H. W. Babcock (1955) were the first to point out that quiescent prominences seen on the disk (i.e., filaments) tend to fall more or less along the neutral line between the two opposite polarities in bipolar magnetic regions, see also Stepanov (1958b) and Howard (1959). L. and M. d'Azambuja (1948) found that filaments, in the earlier stages of their lives, generally occur poleward of the bipolar group.

Actual measurements of the magnetic field strength in prominences proper became possible with the adaption of the magnetograph (see Chapter 2) to use with prominence lines, see Zirin (1961b), Zirin and Severny (1961), Ioschpa (1962, 1963), Rust (1966a, 1966b). The observed field is a lower limit since the instrument is operated in such a way that it is sensitive to the longitudinal component only. Estimates of the magnetic field strength in prominences can also be made from a study of the linear polarization of prominence lines, for example H_α (Warwick and Hyder, 1965; Hyder, 1964, 1965b). The results are consistent with magnetograph data.

7.2.5.1. *Quiescent prominences*

Let us first consider the magnetograph measurements of quiescent prominences. Both Ioschpa and Zirin found that the field must be smaller than 50 gauss, but further details were not available. Rust found the field to be of the order of 2 to 10 gauss as a general rule. In some instances, the same prominence was observed at successive limb passages and the field remained quite constant with time. The polarity changed from the east limb observation to the west limb and back again in the next east limb observation, and so forth. When we combine this information with Babcock's observation of the field on either side of a filament, we arrive at a picture of the structure of the magnetic field relative to quiescent prominences, as shown schematically in Figure 7.6. Part (a) of the figure is a view from above indicating magnetic plages of different polarities (+ and −) and the field lines between them. In Figure 7.6b, we look edge-on at the prominence and see the lines of force rising from the plage on one side of the filament and descending on the other side. We shall return to what may happen to the lines of force within the prominence in Section 7.3. Also, we shall find that magnetic fields of the configuration and strength indicated above seem to lead to plausible models for quiescent prominences.

7.2.5.2. *Active prominences*

We now turn our attention to active prominences. We have mentioned before the important subdivision that often has to be made when dealing with active prominences, namely (1) prominences that originate, like condensations, in the corona, and (2) prominences that are "shot up" from

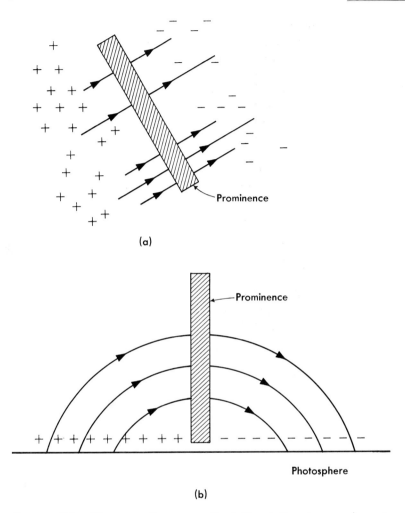

FIGURE 7.6.   Diagram of a magnetic field relative to a quiescent prominence

chromospheric or photospheric levels as if due to explosions of some kind. Loops are examples of the first type; surges represent the other.

Both Ioschpa and Zirin have measured the magnetic field in prominences of the explosion type and the field strength seems to be of the order of 100 to 200 gauss. Since the prominence plasma is highly conductive, one would expect the magnetic field to be carried out with the mass motions from photospheric levels. Surges occur in active regions near sunspots, and the observed prominence field is probably related to the plage and spot fields.

There is no clear-cut reference in the literature to direct measurements of magnetic fields in prominences of the condensation type. At the heights where they first occur, one would not expect to find fields as strong as those reported for some surges. Hyder's (1964) measurements of polarization of H_α indicate field strengths of about 60 to 80 gauss. Marshall (1957) computed the field B_h, to be expected at a height $h = 50,000$ km from a sunspot magnetic field. She assumed the field to be a dipole, took $B_0 = 3500$ gauss as the central umbral field, and assigned a value of 50,000 km to the distance between the two spots of the bipolar group. This leads to a field $B_h = 3$ gauss, which is much smaller than the fields found in surges but large enough to ensure dominence of the magnetic energy over kinetic energy in the ambient corona at 50,000 km.

The actual sunspot field may not be of a dipolar nature, but this is often considered a sufficient approximation. To find an upper limit to the field from a strong sunspot group, one can calculate the fields to be expected from monopole sources (Harvey, 1966), since the field strength then falls off only as $1/r^2$ while it falls off as $1/r^3$ for dipole sources. The actual case may be intermediate between these two models (see Roka, 1950). We find that Marshall's value of 3 gauss at 50,000 km may perhaps be increased an order of magnitude, but fields of several hundred gauss should be excluded, unless processes involving compression or twisting of magnetic fields take place at coronal heights. It is therefore of great importance to actually observe the field in some high loop prominences.

7.3. Models

7.3.1. General Remarks

The foregoing discussion shows that different types of prominences probably reveal very different physical conditions, and it is quite unlikely that they can be described by one and the same model. In this respect, the term prominence is a catch-all that covers a variety of phenomena. It is probable—nearly obvious—that different physical processes are at work in the different types of prominences. We shall return to these more profound questions in Sections 7.4 and 7.5, while here we discuss some models that each can account for at least some observational facts (line-intensities, shapes, magnetic fields etc). In analogy with Chapter 5, we shall first consider those models that ignore the presence of magnetic fields and can be considered successful if they describe the temperature and density of prominences and perhaps say something about their shape. Since magnetic fields seem to play a decisive role in the physics of many (probably all) types of prominences, these models cannot claim to be complete. However, they may be of great help in promoting our understanding of the physics involved in the formation and development of these objects.

It is often difficult to decide which investigations should be considered in developing a prominence model and which should not. Some studies are naturally more complete than others and describe or predict more parameters. For these reasons, the treatment in Sections 7.3.2. and 7.3.3 is not exhaustive. Nevertheless, we hope that the major different approaches to the construction of prominence models are adequately covered.

The models that endeavour to describe quiescent prominences generally consider such objects to be in quasi-equilibrium (except, of course, during periods of activation, see Section 7.4). If, therefore, magnetic fields are neglected, one must assume pressure equilibrium at any given height. Since quiescent prominences reach high up in the corona, the restriction

$$n_{\text{prom}} T_{\text{prom}} \approx n_{\text{cor}} T_{\text{cor}} \qquad (7.3)$$

must hold at all heights. Density determination in prominences is a difficult problem, but we have seen that the temperature must be close to $10^4\,^\circ\text{K}$, with an uncertainty less than a factor 1.5, in the hydrogen plasma. As an example, this gives the value $n_{\text{prom}} = 10^{10}\,\text{cm}^{-3}$ at a height where $n_{\text{cor}} = 10^8\,\text{cm}^{-3}$ and $T_{\text{cor}} = 10^6\,^\circ\text{K}$. If one finds significantly higher values of n_{prom}, this implies that the model is in some sort of dynamic equilibrium.

If a magnetic field B_{prom} threads the prominence plasma, Equation (7.3) may no longer hold. On the other hand, the left-hand side cannot simply be replaced by $n_{\text{prom}} T_{\text{prom}} + B_{\text{prom}}^2/8\pi k$, since this assumes a magnetic field with no twist, and in actual cases the tension of the magnetic lines of force, $(\mathbf{B}_{\text{prom}} \cdot \nabla)\mathbf{B}_{\text{prom}}$, may partly cancel the $B_{\text{prom}}^2/8\pi$ term. We will return to a further discussion of this in Section 7.3.3.

The models that describe active prominences have to do with objects that are far removed from equilibrium in the sense of the word used so far. Even for many prominences that seem to retain their shape for several hours, observations show that material is constantly being fed into the structure and the prominence is furthermore seen to lose material, possibly at the other end. Consequently, models of active prominences must allow for this transient behavior of the prominence plasma; i.e., we shall need dynamic models.

Of great importance for the following discussion is the question whether prominences consist of a more or less homogeneous plasma or whether they are made up of fine-structure elements in a "filamentary model." Unfortunately, ground-based observations cannot give information about dimensions smaller than about 1 sec of arc, or about 700 km. We do see details down to this limit, and there is no reason to believe that smaller dimensions do not exist. Analyses of the observed line emission from prominences can give the product nL, where n is the number density of atoms and L is the length of the emitting (or absorbing) column. A knowledge of the ionization conditions then gives $n_e L = N_e$, where n_e is the electron number density. *A priori*, the column may be more or less homogeneous, that is, n_e is fairly constant along L, or only a fraction, α, of the length L corresponds to regions of prominence material. In the latter case, to get the same value of N_e as for a homogeneous plasma, n_e must take on larger values. While de Jager (1959) in his model assumed $\alpha = 1$ and found a homogeneous prominence plasma with $n_e = 2 \times 10^{10}$ cm^{-3}, Ivanov-Kholodny (1959) deduced $\alpha = 0.01$, which means that the prominence is made up of thin (100 km) threads of high density, $n_e = 10^{12}$ cm^{-3}. Other models are intermediate between these extremes.

The models must also allow for the fact that active prominences emit spectral lines corresponding to an impressive range in excitation conditions. We concluded in Section 7.2.3. that to do this we are forced to use multicomponent models. This means that the temperature and/or turbulent velocities are different in different fine-structure elements; this leads us to models where the helium emission comes from hot parts of the threads, while the emission in lines from metal ions comes from cooler elements. However, we notice that Hirayama (1963) presents a model which consists of individual threads but where lines of very different excitation are all emitted from elements at the same temperature. In our terminology this is therefore not a multicomponent prominence model, even though it is a filamentary model.

7.3.2. Quiescent Prominences

7.3.2.1. *Models in which the magnetic field is accidental*

(a) DE JAGER'S MODEL — In his resumé of prominences, de Jager (1959) summarized the physical conditions in quiescent prominences as given in Table 7.16. De Jager relied mainly on studies of hydrogen line profiles that were corrected for self-absorption (Conway, 1952) and that were compared with profiles of lines from heavier elements to determine a possible effect of microturbulence. This is a difficult procedure, and the quoted kinetic temperature is probably too high.

TABLE 7.16   de Jager's model

T_e, °K	T_{ex}		v_t, km/sec	n_e, cm^{-3}	α
	$\chi \approx 3$ eV	$\chi \approx 10$ eV			
1.5×10^4	4×10^3	1.5×10^4	4 to 10	2×10^{10}	1.0

The electron density, which refers to a homogeneous model, was determined from the total emission in the lines using a curve-of-growth technique. The validity of this procedure in prominences is debatable, but the value of $N_e = 1.2 \times 10^{19}$ cm^{-2} implied by de Jager for observations along the shortest dimension ($L \approx 6 \times 10^8$ cm) of quiescent prominences seems reasonable.

(b) IVANOV-KHOLODNY'S MODEL — Ivanov-Kholodny (1959) determined the kinetic temperature from the half-width of prominence lines and arrived at a value of $T_e \approx 7500$ °K. The electron density was found from an analysis of the Stark effect (both in the line profile and on the total number of hydrogen lines visible) and led to $n_e \approx 10^{12}$ cm^{-3}. The model is summarized in Table 7.17.

TABLE 7.17   Ivanov-Kholodny's model

T_e, °K	n_e, cm^{-3}	v_t, km/sec	α
6×10^3 to 9×10^3	10^{12}	6	<0.1

He further concluded that prominences consist of fine threads that only fill a small fraction of the space occupied by the prominence as a whole, that is, $\alpha \ll 1$. To show this, he determined the two quantities $n_e^2 L$ and $n_e L = N_e$. A value for the first quantity can be deduced following a method due to Unsöld (1938, 1947) that converts the observed line intensity to $n_e^2 L$ by means of Saha's formula. According to Ivanov-Kholodny, the result is $n_e^2 L = 10^{30}$ cm^{-5}. The quantity N_e was found from the expression for the continuous radiation in prominences I_{prom} when it is assumed due to photospheric radiation, I_{ph}, scattered by electrons:

$$I_{\text{prom}} = W \sigma_e n_e L I_{\text{ph}},$$

where σ_e is the Thomson scattering cross section, Equation (1.103), and $W \approx 0.2$ is the geometrical dilution factor. The adopted value $I_{\text{prom}}/I_{\text{ph}} = 10^{-6}$ gives $N_e = 10^{19}$ cm^{-2}. The two values for $n_e^2 L$ and N_e lead to a mean electron density, $\overline{n_e} = 10^{11}$ cm^{-3}. But the value $n_e = 10^{12}$ cm^{-3} from the Stark effect analysis indicates, together with $n_e L = 10^{19}$ cm^{-2}, that the effective width of the threads is only 10^7 cm $= 100$ km, which gives a rather extreme filamentary model.

In Section 7.2 we saw that the use of the Stark effect to analyze prominence lines may be precarious, and it is likely that the value $n_e = 10^{12}$ cm^{-3} is an overestimation. Furthermore, the condition $n_e = 10^{12}$ cm^{-3} would lead to a value for $n_{\text{prom}} T_{\text{prom}}$ in Equation (7.3) that could not be balanced by the coronal pressure, and instabilities would occur in a static model. We shall return to this problem in Section 7.5.

(c) HIRAYAMA'S MODEL — Hirayama (1963, 1964) constructed a model using Equation (7.1) to determine the temperature and turbulent velocity from hydrogen, helium, and metal lines. This is not a multicomponent prominence model—Equation (7.1) can then not be used—but Hirayama showed that the prominences have a filamentary structure, the dimensions of the individual threads being of the order of 2000 to 3000 km ($\alpha = 0.3$). After having determined n_e from the Stark effect, Hirayama obtained this result using the same technique employed by Ivanov-Kholodny. Hirayama found $n_e^2 L = 10^{30.4}$ cm^{-5} and assumed the over-all thickness of prominences to be 10^9 cm. The model is portrayed in Table 7.18. Kawaguchi (1964, 1965)

TABLE 7.18   Hirayama's model

T_e, °K	T_{ex}		n_e, cm^{-3}	t_v, km/sec	α
	H$_\alpha$	He I triplet			
4.5×10^3 to 8×10^3	4.2×10^3	5×10^3	10^{11}	6	0.3

studied the effect of the ultraviolet radiation from the chromosphere–corona region on the excitation of the prominence material and expressed views of prominence models in agreement with Hirayama.

(d) JEFFERIES AND ORRALL'S MODEL — Jefferies and Orrall (1963) realized the necessity of having regions of different temperatures to account for the observed emission in the Balmer lines and in the Balmer continuum (see Section 7.2). Theirs is consequently a genuine multicomponent model. They did not include the helium emission in their model, but Jefferies and Orrall (1961c) were among the first to point to the necessity of having different parts of a prominence emit the hydrogen and the helium radiation.

In principle, the temperature in this model may be distributed across the prominence in either of two ways: (1) The material is everywhere arranged in unresolvable threads, similar to the models discussed in (b) and (c), or (2) The temperature and density have a smooth distribution over the prominence; for example, the temperature increases with the radial distance from the axis of a cylindrical model.

The observations of quiescent prominences seem to favor the first of these alternatives. The conditions in the threads are such that the Balmer lines are mainly emitted in their central parts, where $T_e \approx 6000$°K and $n_e \approx 10^{10}$ cm^{-3}. The authors further assumed the model to be isobaric, that is, $(2n_e + n_H)T = $ const. By specifying the degree of ionization of the hydrogen plasma (for $T > 10^4$ °K, ionization may be considered complete and $2n_e T = $ const), we find with Jefferies and Orrall (1961c, 1963) the variation of electron density with temperature in the assumed model as given in Table 7.19.

TABLE 7.19   Jefferies and Orrall's model

T_e ,°K	5×10^3	6.3×10^3	7.5×10^3	1.0×10^4
n_e , cm^{-3}	8.1×10^9	1.7×10^{10}	4.5×10^{10}	5.0×10^{10}

The continuous emission comes from the outer parts of the threads, where the temperature has increased to 10,000 to 12,000 °K, but only a small fraction of the prominence plasma is at temperatures above 15,000 °K. This small fraction, the "coating" of the threads, is responsible for the helium emission, and in it the temperature rapidly increases to coronal values.

7.3.2.2. Models including magnetic fields

(a) FORMULATION OF THE MAGNETOHYDROSTATIC PROBLEM — The basic idea in the models invoking magnetic fields is that the prominence material is supported against gravity by the stresses exerted by the magnetic field. The models describe the prominence material in mechanical equilibrium under the combined actions of gas pressure, gravity, and the Lorentz force. Waldmeier (1955) showed that the radiation pressure can be neglected and so can the centrifugal force due to the sun's rotation (the corresponding acceleration is only of the order of 1 cm/sec^2, while the gravitational acceleration is about 10^4 cm/sec^2).

The first quantitative attempt at showing that coronal magnetic fields can support quiescent prominences in a static equilibrium model was made by Menzel (Bhatnagar, Krook, and Menzel, 1951). Other formulations of the problem are due to Dungey (1953b) and Kippenhahn and Schlüter (1957). We shall here partly follow Brown's (1958) treatment to show the interrelation between the different formulations.

From the equation of motion (1.33), we find the magnetohydrostatic equations

$$\nabla p - \rho \mathbf{g} - (1/c)\mathbf{j} \times \mathbf{B} = 0$$

or

$$\nabla p - \rho \mathbf{g} - (1/4\pi)(\nabla \times \mathbf{B}) \times \mathbf{B} = 0 \qquad (7.4)$$

and

$$\nabla \cdot \mathbf{B} = 0 . \qquad (7.5)$$

Following Menzel, we consider a two-dimensional case, $B_x = 0$, and take p, ρ, and $\mathbf{B}$ independent of x. The coordinate x is horizontal, along the vertical prominence sheet, y is perpendicular to the sheet, and z is vertical. Furthermore, the acceleration due to gravity is constant and the atmosphere is isothermal, that is,

$$p = g\rho H_0, \tag{7.6}$$

where H_0 is the scale height, neglecting the magnetic field. From Equation (7.5), we find for this two-dimensional case that

$$B_y = -\partial F/\partial z, \qquad B_z = \partial F/\partial y, \tag{7.7}$$

where F is a scalar function. Equation (7.4) may now be written

$$\nabla p - \rho \mathbf{g} = -(1/4\pi)(\nabla^2 F)\nabla F. \tag{7.8}$$

Equations (7.6) and (7.8) combine to give

$$\nabla[pe^{z/H_0}] = -(1/4\pi)[\nabla^2 F e^{z/H_0}]\nabla F. \tag{7.9}$$

This shows that pe^{z/H_0} is a function of F, $p(F)$, and that

$$\nabla[p(F)] = -(1/4\pi)\nabla^2 F e^{z/H_0}.$$

Consequently, $\nabla^2 F e^{z/H_0}$ is also a function of F, and the scalar function must satisfy the equation

$$\nabla^2 F = \phi(F)e^{z/H_0}, \tag{7.10}$$

where $\phi(F)$ is some arbitrary function of F.

With Brown, we consider Equation (7.10) as the basic equation for static equilibrium in the simplified two-dimensional case. Any function F that is a solution of Equation (7.10) gives a possible model for the field (7.7). The corresponding pressure distribution will be given by

$$p = -(1/4\pi)e^{-z/H_0}\int \phi(F)\,dF. \tag{7.11}$$

(b) MENZEL'S MODEL — Menzel (Bhatnagar, Krook, and Menzel, 1951) used Equations (7.6) and (7.8) and remarked that the latter is separable if the function $p(F)$ has the form $p_1(y)e^{-z/H}$ and if F can be written $F = F_1(y)e^{-z/2H}$. This is equivalent to having

$$\phi(F) = A F^{(1-2H/H_0)}, \tag{7.12}$$

where A is a constant, and it leads to the following differential equation for F_1:

$$\frac{d^2 F_1}{dy^2} + \frac{F_1}{4H^2} = A F_1^{(1-2H/H_0)}. \tag{7.13}$$

If we put $H/H_0 = q + 1 > 1$, Equation (7.13) can readily be integrated:

$$\left(\frac{dF_1}{dy}\right)^2 + \frac{F_1^2}{4H^2} = C - \frac{A}{qF_1^{2q}} \,,$$

where C is a constant.

The lines of force are supposed to be horizontal $(dF_1/dy = 0)$ at their intersections with the plane $y = 0$, that is, with the prominence sheet. Further, inserting $F_1(0) = F_1(y = 0)$ we find

$$B^2 e^{z/H} = \left(\frac{dF_1}{dy}\right)^2 + \frac{F_1^2}{4H^2} = \frac{[F_1(0)]^2}{4H^2} + \frac{A}{q}[[F_1(0)]^{-2q} - F_1^{-2q}], \quad (7.14)$$

and the corresponding pressure is

$$p = \frac{A}{8\pi q} F_1^{-2q} e^{-z/H} \,. \tag{7.15}$$

Let r be the ratio of gas and magnetic pressures, that is,

$$r = 4H^2 A/q[F_1(0)]^{2q+2} \,.$$

Then the function F_1 satisfies the equation

$$4H^2\left(\frac{dF_1}{dy}\right)^2 = [F_1(0)]^2(1 + r) - F_1^2 - r[F_1(0)]^2\left(\frac{F_1(0)}{F_1}\right)^{2q} , \tag{7.16}$$

and the pressure can be written as

$$p = \frac{r[F_1(0)]^2}{32\pi H^2}\left(\frac{F_1(0)}{F_1}\right)^{2q} e^{-z/H} \,. \tag{7.17}$$

Equation (7.16) must normally be solved numerically, but general physical properties may be inferred without solving it. The lines of force, $F = \text{const}$, form a set of parallel curves that can be described by the equation

$$F_1 = e^{(z-z_0)/2H} ,$$

where z_0 is a constant that varies from one line to another. If $rq > 1$, F_1 has a minimum at $y = 0$. This means that the lines of force are bowed to a minimum height at $y = 0$ (see Figure 7.7) and, further, that the pressure— Equation (7.16)—has a maximum there. One may consequently consider the lines of force as bowed down at $y = 0$ by a local excess of matter (see Cowling, 1957). Menzel's model gives a rough picture of how prominence material is denser and causes a slight sag of the lines of force in the plane $y = 0$.

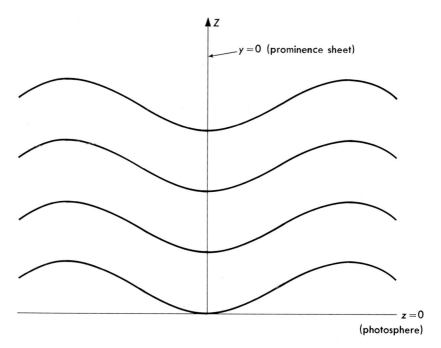

FIGURE 7.7.   The supporting magnetic field in Menzel's model

(c) DUNGEY'S MODEL — Chronologically next in line is a model due to Dungey (1953b). In the framework of Equation (7.10), the simplest example of solutions derived by Dungey is found by taking $\phi(F) = \text{const} = A$. Then

$$F = F_2 + AH_0^2 e^{-z/H_0} \qquad (7.18)$$

is a solution, where F_2 is any harmonic function. The special type of solution given by Dungey is

$$F_2 = 1 + e^{-z/H_0} - 2e^{-z/2H_0} \cos (y/2H_0). \qquad (7.19)$$

The lines of force determined by $F = \text{const}$ are closed loops for $F < 1$ and infinite wavy lines for $F > 1$ (see Figure 7.8).

Dungey derived a relationship between the gas pressure and the magnetic pressure by considering the current density $\mathbf{j}$, which has only an x-component,

$$j_x = -\frac{c}{4\pi}\left[\frac{\partial^2 F}{\partial y^2} + \frac{\partial^2 F}{\partial z^2}\right], \qquad (7.20)$$

and by using Equation (7.14). The relation is

$$\frac{d}{dF}\left[e^{z/H}\left(p + \frac{B^2}{8\pi}\right)\right] = -\frac{B^2}{4\pi F}\,e^{z/H}. \tag{7.21}$$

In Dungey's model, the magnetic field is assumed to be zero except between two closed loops, $F = a$ and $F = b$, so that the pressure outside the outer loop $F = a$ is not affected by the field. Inside the loop $F = a$, the pressure is lower than outside, while inside the loop $F = b$, the pressure is greater than outside $F = a$ at the same height. By redistributing the matter inside $F = a$ (the prominence), the magnetic field may ensure that a narrow horizontal filament floats in equilibrium, surrounded by matter of much smaller density.

The model was criticized by Cowling (1957), who drew attention to the fact that Dungey's solution implies currents running in opposite directions

FIGURE 7.8. The supporting magnetic field in Dungey's model (courtesy J. W. Dungey, 1953b)

near $F = a$ and $F = b$; this hardly seems likely. Furthermore, it is difficult to conceive of arguments in favor of a situation where the currents flow in the cool prominence material surrounded by the hotter corona.

(d) KIPPENHAHN AND SCHLÜTER'S MODEL — Probably the most successful model for the support of quiescent prominences is that due to Kippenhahn and Schlüter (1957). Referring again to Equation (7.10), we see that their model is based on solutions corresponding to the case

$$\phi(F) = Ce^{F/AH_0}. \tag{7.22}$$

Here A and C are constants, and the trial solution has the form $F = Az + F_3(y)$. We then obtain an equation for $F_3(y)$ that can be integrated directly.

Kippenhahn and Schlüter actually combined Equations (7.4) and (7.6), given in the form $p = (R/\mu)\rho T$, in the two-dimensional case—Equation (7.7)—with the condition of a constant temperature and derived the following equation for the field:

$$B_y\left[\frac{\partial^2 B_z}{\partial y^2} + \frac{\partial^2 B_z}{\partial z^2}\right] - B_z\left[\frac{\partial^2 B_y}{\partial y^2} + \frac{\partial^2 B_y}{\partial z^2}\right] + \frac{B_z}{H_0}\left[\frac{\partial B_z}{\partial y} - \frac{\partial B_y}{\partial z}\right] = 0. \tag{7.23}$$

The y-component of (7.4) then gives the following expression for the density distribution $\rho(y, z)$:

$$\frac{R}{\mu}T\frac{\partial \rho}{\partial y} = -\frac{B_z}{4\pi}\left[\frac{\partial B_z}{\partial y} - \frac{\partial B_y}{\partial z}\right]. \tag{7.24}$$

We shall briefly discuss their arguments and simplify Equations (7.23) and (7.24). In a thin prominence, B_y will vary little with y, and it is safe to take B_y completely independent of the y-coordinate. Because of (7.5), B_z will not depend on z, and we let it be a function of y alone. Furthermore, we assume that B_y is not a function of height, that is, $B_y = $ const. Equation (7.23) then reduces to

$$\frac{\partial^2 B_z}{\partial y^2} + \frac{B_z}{H_0 B_y}\frac{\partial B_z}{\partial y} = 0. \tag{7.25}$$

The boundary condition at $y = 0$ is $B_z = 0$ and, for $y \to \infty$, we have $B_z = B_z(\infty)$, where $B_z(\infty)/B_y > 0$. With this condition, Equation (7.25) yields the solution

$$B_z = B_z(\infty)\tanh\left[\frac{B_z(\infty)}{B_y}\frac{y}{2H}\right]. \tag{7.26}$$

The density distribution (7.24) becomes

$$\frac{R}{\mu}T\frac{\partial \rho}{\partial y} = -\frac{1}{8\pi}\frac{\partial B_z}{\partial y}.$$

The solution of this equation with the boundary condition lim $\rho \to 0$ as $y \to \infty$ is

$$\frac{R}{\mu}\,\rho T = -\,\frac{1}{4\pi}\,B_z^2(\infty)\left[\tanh^2\left(\frac{B_z(\infty)}{B_y}\,\frac{y}{2H}\right) - 1\right]. \qquad (7.27)$$

Figures 7.9 and 7.10 show, respectively, the magnetic lines of force in the yz-plane on either side of the prominence sheet ($y = 0$) and the distribution of density as a function of y.

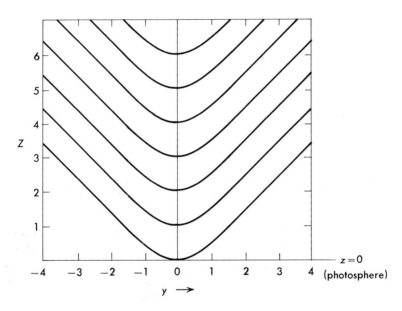

FIGURE 7.9.   The supporting magnetic field in the model of Kippenhahn and Schlüter (courtesy R. Kippenhahn and A. Schlüter, 1957)

Kippenhahn and Schlüter analyzed the electric currents responsible for the magnetic field by considering Ohm's law—Equation (1.34)—in a form given by Schlüter (1950) and made applicable to the present simplified case,

$$\mathbf{E} + \frac{1}{c}\,\mathbf{v} \times \mathbf{B} = \frac{1}{en_ec}\,\mathbf{j} \times \mathbf{B} + \mathbf{j}/\sigma. \qquad (7.28)$$

This equation holds in the prominence as well as in the corona. In the latter, the field must be force-free, and hence there is no significant component of the current perpendicular to the field. We assume the coronal material to be at rest. Then $\mathbf{E}$ has no component perpendicular to $\mathbf{B}$, because of Equation (7.28). Symmetry considerations then show that the component of $\mathbf{E}$ in the

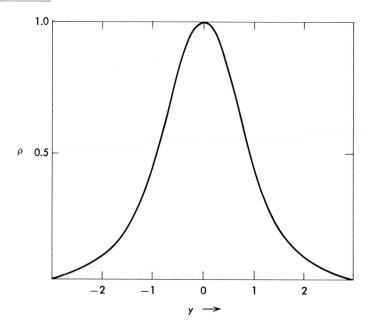

FIGURE 7.10.   The density distribution in the model of Kippenhahn
and Schlüter (courtesy R. Kippenhahn and A. Schlüter, 1957)

direction of the filament, E_x, must vanish and, finally, because of the steady-state condition, **E** is curl-free and there can be no E_x-component within the filament. Consequently, the equilibrium condition $(1/c)\mathbf{j} \times \mathbf{B} = \rho\mathbf{g}$ gives the current that determines the mass velocity, and this velocity can be found from Equation (7.28). We find a vertical velocity component

$$v_z = \rho g c^2 / \sigma B^2, \qquad (7.29)$$

which, for the following values of the parameters $\rho = 10^{-14}\ g/cm^3$, $g = 10^{4.4}$ cm/sec², $B_x = B_y = 1$ gauss, and $\sigma = 10^{13}\ sec^{-1}$, yields $v_z \approx 0.03$ cm/sec. Similarly, the horizontal component of v is given by $v_x = \rho g c / e n_e B \approx 3$ cm/sec.

(e) COMMENTS ON STATIC VS. DYNAMIC MODELS — Mass motions can be observed in most quiescent prominences. This indicates that even though the over-all shape of filaments remains constant with time, the material at any point in the prominence may be in motion. If this is so, the static models considered can only describe prominences to a first—but probably reasonable—approximation. Besides, the models that rely on spectroscopic data to derive the physical parameters of the prominence plasma may not be particularly vulnerable to mild nonstatic conditions.

In some respects, Kippenhahn and Schlüter (1957) took the first step toward a dynamic interpretation of prominences in their paper on the magnetohydrostatic model. They realized that the electric conductivity σ is not infinite and that the prominence plasma will slowly slip through the lines of force of the supporting magnetic field. The vertical velocity due to ambipolar diffusion is small compared to the thermal velocity of the plasma particles, and the mass loss out of the "bottom" of the filament was shown to be small compared to the mass that may be considered condensing onto the filament from the surrounding corona. With the densities and velocities quoted by Kippenhahn and Schlüter, their static model will not be significantly affected. However, it seems clear that for prominences in which the activity is more pronounced, the semistatic conditions should be replaced by dynamic models.

In a dynamic model, material must continuously be fed into the prominence from the surrounding corona or from the chromosphere or photosphere below. The former case is referred to as a condensation, and various aspects of the physics of this process have been discussed in the literature. Some attempts have also been made to account for the mass balance in quiescent prominences in terms of models where material is brought up from below. This becomes a more serious concern for active prominences, and we shall return to the different views when dealing with active prominences in the next section.

7.3.3. Active Prominences

7.3.3.1. *Introductory remarks*

No model has been worked out in detail for active prominences with the same sophistication used for quiescent prominences. The reason for this is obvious from the remarks of the previous section so far as the support mechanism is concerned: the equilibrium must be described by a more complicated dynamic model. However, when we consider the excitation conditions in the active prominences, we are on somewhat safer ground. The presence in the spectra of lines of neutral and singly ionized metals and of lines of He II strongly suggests a multicomponent model (see Section 7.2.3). Reasonable confidence can also be put in density and temperature determinations for the cooler regions of the multicomponent models. It is more difficult to ascertain the conditions in the hotter regions, whence comes the He II radiation. It is probable that these regions in loops that form after large flares present us with the hottest prominence plasmas found in the solar atmosphere. The outer parts of such loops are adjacent to very hot coronal condensations (see Chapter 8).

Turning to the type of prominences that are "shot up" from below, often from flares, we find that the "active" regions of such prominences are characterized by very broad emission lines. However, it is difficult to determine whether the width is caused mainly by temperature or by chaotic mass motions. The emission line profiles do not show great wings, indicating that Stark broadening is not of prime importance. This sets an upper limit to the electron density, which probably is significantly less than 10^{12} cm^{-3}.

The active filaments seen in absorption in active regions, especially during flare activity, present a puzzling problem. They are probably very dense, and the word filament—which implies a quiescent prominence—is so misleading that a new designation should be given to them. We shall return to these objects in Section 7.4.

7.3.3.2. Condensing prominences

(a) CONDENSATION AS A THERMAL INSTABILITY — A number of authors have advocated the view that many types of prominences form from material condensing out of the corona (Kiepenheuer, 1951, 1953b, 1959; Kleczek, 1957, 1958; Lüst and Zirin, 1960; Menzel and Doherty, 1963). No model is available to describe the initial phase of the condensation process, but it has often been supposed that a simple thermal instability would result in the formation of the prominence: if some part of the coronal plasma became cooler (or denser), it would radiate more. Hence, it would continue to cool and would rapidly condense. This simple picture has been treated by Kleczek (1957). We shall briefly follow his arguments.

The conservation of energy per cm^3 of the coronal plasma that ultimately becomes a prominence may be written as

$$dE/dt = G_{\text{comp}} + G_{\text{rad}} - L_{\text{rad}}, \qquad (7.30)$$

where E, the internal energy, is mainly the kinetic energy $E_{\text{kin}} = \frac{3}{2}nkT \approx 3n_e\,kT$. The ionization energy and the excitation energy are both significantly smaller. Kleczek considered isobaric cooling, which demands $dE/dt = 0$. Here G_{comp} is the heat gained by compression, G_{rad} the heat gained by radiative absorption, while L_{rad} denotes the heat loss due to radiation from the plasma. He argued further that the heating by radiation is of little importance, at least in the initial stages of condensation, and put $G_{\text{rad}} = 0$. This leads to a simplified equation for the energy conservation:

$$G_{\text{comp}} = L_{\text{rad}}; \qquad (7.31)$$

that is, in isobaric cooling the emitted energy is supplied by compression. Now, we have

$$G_{\text{comp}} = \frac{p}{n} \cdot \frac{dn}{dt} = \frac{p}{T} \cdot \frac{dT}{dt}, \qquad (7.32)$$

while L_{rad} is made up of three components: a loss due to free–free radiation, another caused by free–bound radiation, and finally a loss due to line emission,

$$L_{\text{rad}} = L_{\text{ff}} + L_{\text{fb}} + L_{\text{bb}}.$$

Kleczek used Elwert's (1954) determinations of the radiation processes. The radiation loss due to free–free emission is proportional to $n_e^2 T^{1/2}$ and also follows from Equation (6.3), while radiation losses involving transitions from bound levels are proportional to $n_e^2 T^{-1/2}$, whence we have

$$L_{\text{rad}} = n_e^2 \left[a T^{1/2} + \frac{b + c}{T^{1/2}} \right]. \tag{7.33}$$

The coefficients a, b, and c give the contributions due to free–free, free–bound, and bound–bound radiation, respectively. Equations (7.31), (7.32), and (7.33) give

$$\frac{dT}{dt} = -\frac{p}{4k^2 T} \left[a T^{1/2} + \frac{b + c}{T^{1/2}} \right]. \tag{7.34}$$

Assuming that the pressure remains constant, we can determine the time of condensation from Equation (7.34), which yields

$$t_{\text{cond}} = \text{const} \, \frac{k^2}{p} \int_{T_1}^{T_2} \frac{T^{3/2}}{T + \text{const}} \, dT. \tag{7.35}$$

According to Kleczek, the time t_{cond} turns out to be of the order of 10^7 sec for values of the constants corresponding to conditions that describe condensation from a coronal plasma ($T_c \approx 10^6 \, °\text{K}$, $n_c \approx 10^8 \, \text{cm}^{-3}$). From this picture, one might possibly explain the condensation of quiescent prominences by isobaric cooling. But the time scale is much too long to be applicable to active prominences.

(b) KLECZEK'S MODEL — Kleczek (1958) realized that the simple thermal instability would not produce the rapid condensation necessary to explain the formation of active prominences. Since the energy loss by radiation is proportional to n^2, he argued that if one could first compress the coronal plasma, the subsequent cooling time might be short enough so that the theory of isobaric cooling could be applicable. In Kleczek's model, it is hot coronal regions that are being formed and that thereafter cool, and we shall now outline the physics of the compression phase.

If the compression is very rapid, the radiation loss will be small and the process will be quasi-adiabatic,

$$n^{1-\gamma} k T = \text{const} \qquad \text{or} \qquad T = \text{const} \, n^{2/3}.$$

This may be written in differential form,

$$dT = \tfrac{2}{3} T/n \, dn \,. \tag{7.36}$$

Kleczek determined the constant by inserting values of n and T for the initial condition of the plasma, $n_c = 10^8 \text{ cm}^{-3}$ and $T_c = 10^6 \text{ °K}$. Then, $T = \sqrt[3]{100 n^2}$. Since the pressure changes approximately as $n^{5/3}$, we find $p \approx T^{5/2}$. In the limiting case of adiabatic compression, the time $t \approx 0$.

On the other hand, if the compresssion is quasi-isothermal, $T = T_c = 10^6 \text{ °K}$. The change in energy is $dE = \tfrac{3}{2} nk \, dT + \tfrac{3}{2} kT \, dn$. In isothermal compression, the energy $\tfrac{3}{2} nk \, dT$ is radiated away, and this is given by Equation (7.33). To find an expression for dT, Kleczek considered the isothermal compression as a series of infinitely small adiabatic changes. The corresponding increments dT are then emitted as radiation according to

$$\frac{3}{2} nk \, dT = n_e^2 \left[a T^{1/2} + \frac{b + c}{T^{1/2}} \right] . \tag{7.37}$$

Equations (7.36) and (7.37) give

$$dt = \frac{kT}{n_e^2 [a T^{1/2} + (b + c) T^{-1/2}]} \, dn \,.$$

Inserting the values $a = 2 \times 10^{-27}$, $b = 3 \times 10^{-21}$, and $c = 2 \times 10^{-20}$ corresponding to a million degree corona, we find with Kleczek for a pressure increase of a factor of 100:

$$t \approx 2 \times 10^{13} \int_{10^8}^{10^{10}} dn/n^2 \simeq 2 \times 10^5 \quad \text{sec} \,.$$

This estimate shows that isothermal compression is too slow, and the model calls for compression intermediate between the extremely fast adiabatic and the too-slow isothermal compressions.

(c) LÜST AND ZIRIN'S MODEL — Kleczek's model requires a strong initial compression ($n \approx 10^{11} \text{ cm}^{-3}$) to produce the subsequent rapid cooling. However, Lüst and Zirin (1960) pointed out that prominences condense out of a plasma that already is hotter than normal ($T_c \geq 2 \times 10^6 \text{ °K}$). If one simply compressed such a plasma, the temperature would probably become much too high before the cooling started. To remedy this defect in the model, they considered how thermal conduction may influence the condensation process. They assumed that an element of coronal plasma of temperature T_c and density n_c, permeated by a strong magnetic field, is subjected to a strong uniform compression perpendicular to the magnetic field according to the equation

$$n = n_c + \alpha t, \tag{7.38}$$

where t denotes time. The equation governing the change of temperature may be written

$$dT/dt = G_{\text{comp}} - L_{\text{cond}} - L_{\text{rad}}, \tag{7.39}$$

where G_{comp} is the amount of heat gained per particle by compression, L_{cond} is the heat loss per particle by conduction, and L_{rad} the heat loss due to radiation. Equation (7.39) may be compared with the corresponding equation used by Kleczek (7.30). Note that the terms G_{comp} and L_{rad} are not identical in the two equations in that Lüst and Zirin give the amount of heat per particle, not per unit volume. If the collision times for the particles are short, the ratio of specific heats may be taken as $\gamma = \frac{5}{3}$, and we find

$$G_{\text{comp}} = 2k\alpha T_c/3(n_c^2 n)^{1/3}. \tag{7.40}$$

The magnetic field will prevent heat conduction across the lines of force, whence heat is only conducted out of the element of plasma in the direction of the field. The expression for the loss per particle can be found from Spitzer's (1956) work and is

$$L_{\text{cond}} = \text{const } T^{5/2} \frac{\Delta T}{nL^2}. \tag{7.41}$$

Lüst and Zirin approximated the radiation losses by the following expressions:

$$L_{\text{ff}} = \text{const } n T^{1/2} \tag{7.42}$$

and

$$L_{\text{fb}} + L_{\text{bb}} = \alpha t \left(\text{const} + \frac{\text{const}}{T} \right), \tag{7.43}$$

where $L_{\text{rad}} = L_{\text{ff}} + L_{\text{fb}} + L_{\text{bb}}$, as before. Inserting Equations (7.38), (7.40), (7.41), (7.42), and (7.43) in (7.39), we arrive at an equation that may be integrated for a number of starting values of n_c and T_c, using α as a parameter. Lüst and Zirin found that the temperature will first increase to a maximum, T_{max}, at a time, t_{max}, due to the initial compression, after which the increased internal energy is radiated and conducted away and the cooling proceeds. The cooling time, t_{cool}, may be defined as the time it takes for the plasma to cool to a temperature $T < 2 \times 10^5\,°\text{K}$. The higher the compression rate, α, the faster the initial temperature increases, but the

TABLE 7.20   Lüst and Zirin's model

T_e,°K	n_e, cm^{-3}	α, n_c/sec	T_{max},°K	t_{max}, sec	t_{cool}, sec
		10^{-4}	1.005×10^6	6×10^2	10^5
10^6	10^9	10^{-3}	1.12×10^6	2.6×10^3	1.4×10^4
		10^{-2}	1.65×10^6	1.9×10^3	5.7×10^3
		10^{-4}	1.03×10^6	1.5×10^3	7×10^3
10^6	10^{10}	10^{-3}	1.24×10^6	9×10^2	3×10^3
		10^{-2}	2.26×10^6	6×10^2	1.6×10^3
		10^{-4}	2.03×10^6	7×10^2	1.7×10^4
2×10^6	10^{10}	10^{-3}	2.15×10^6	5×10^2	4.8×10^3
		10^{-2}	3.16×10^6	6×10^2	2.1×10^3

subsequent cooling is also faster. Results for a number of assumed values of α, n_c, and T_c are shown in Table 7.20.

We find that in most cases the cooling takes place in a few hours, which is the time scale necessary to form active prominences. The model does not provide any explanation for the forces responsible for the compression, but it is assumed that they are of magnetic nature.

7.3.3.3. *Injection mechanisms for prominences*

(a) PROMINENCES AS "INJECTIONS" OR "EXPLOSIONS" — We have mentioned that the prominences that are seen to shoot up from below may resemble explosions and therefore probably reveal a very different type of phenomenon than condensations. No model involving any detail is available to describe the explosions, but magnetic fields and thermonuclear reactions near the surface (Gopasyuk, 1960) have been mentioned as possible causes. The word explosion may convey the picture of too violent a condition when we think of a certain well-organized motion in prominences that originate from below. Well-directed surges are possibly due to a more gentle injection mechanism than that which the chaotic motions resulting from explosions generally imply. A unidirectional acceleration mechanism may have to be sought when we deal with the more organized prominence motions. However, in the presence of a strong magnetic field, it is conceivable that an initially chaotic motion may become sufficiently organized as the plasma travels out along specific configurations of the magnetic lines of force.

The concept of injection from below has been used in a different way to account for prominences that seem to condense out of the corona. Jefferies and Orrall (1965b) have argued that neither is there enough coronal material available to condense into a loop prominence, nor could the coronal plasma,

even if sufficiently abundant, condense across the strong magnetic field lines
to form the loop system. On this basis, they proposed that loop prominences
are formed by matter coming up from below in an injection mechanism.
Let us first consider the arguments against condensation as given by Jefferies
and Orrall.

CASE 1: Mass requirements

In principle, one can determine the density, n_e, and the velocity, v_p,
of the prominence material in the loops, as well as the diameter of the loops,
and thereby estimate the total mass flux to the photosphere or chromosphere.
Jefferies and Orrall assumed $n_e = 10^{11}$ cm^{-3}, $v_p = 100$ km/sec, and arrived
at a value in excess of 10^{16} gm for the total mass flow, M, during the lifetime
of the loops. Similar estimates have been made by Kleczek (1964), who
found values of $M = 2 \times 10^{15}$ gm, $M = 10^{15}$ gm, and $M = 2.3 \times 10^{16}$ gm
for three different loop systems. Now, loop prominence systems occur in
coronal condensations (see Chapter 8), and according to Waldmeier and
Müller's (1950) model of such condensations, their total mass is of the order
of 10^{15} gm. From this, Jefferies and Orrall argued that there is not enough
matter available for large loops to form, and they proposed the injection
mechanism. From this picture, the loop prominences are seen to be not
condensations but injections, and one may ask also whether other types that
are generally thought of as condensations only give the impression of condensing while in reality they originate from below. Whatever the answer
to this might be, one should still remember that those types that seem to
originate from above do so in the sense that material first becomes visible
in the corona, whence it streams down. Hence, in theories implying injection
from below, we also find differences in the physical state of the injected
plasma. For instance, in surges the material is at a temperature and in
a degree of ionization such that it emits in the visible part of the spectrum
(as a not-too-hot gas) on its way up, in other words, the plasma is thermalized
during its entire lifetime in the chromosphere. As we shall see shortly, this is
not so for loops in Jefferies and Orrall's model.

CASE 2: Motions across the magnetic lines of force

There is reason to believe that matter—in addition to the permanent
coronal condensations—is available to partake in the formation of loop
prominences (see Section 7.4). Whether this is enough to account for the
total mass, $M \approx 10^{16}$ gm, required is not known, and even if it were, Jefferies
and Orrall argued that the difficulty of transporting the plasma across the
magnetic field lines still remains. It is, however, hardly possible to evaluate
this objection before we gain further insight into the mechanism of certain
plasma instabilities that might change the picture significantly. We will

here mention only the hydromagnetic instability (Bishop, 1966; Jeffrey and Taniuti, 1966), which accomplishes an interchange in position between plasma and magnetic field. Therefore, if a dense coronal condensation is adjacent to a magnetic flux tube, it is conceivable that the instability might lead to the formation of a dense knot of plasma in the field and that the loop might grow out of this knot.

(b) JEFFERIES AND ORRALL'S MODEL — The basic idea in this model (Jefferies and Orrall, 1965a) is that the mass of loop prominences is fed into the system in the form of energetic protons at the bottom of the loops. The particles follow the magnetic lines of force until they give up their ordered motion by Coulomb collisions with the ambient gas. This thermalization process is supposed to take place mainly near the top of the loops. In so doing, the particles create a dense hot region, and as its density increases, more and more energetic particles can be trapped. Ultimately, this hot region becomes so dense that it explodes, and matter will stream out along the magnetic lines of force and flow down the two legs of the loops. The expanding plasma will cool enough to be visible in H_α and other optical radiations.

Jefferies and Orrall's model has a number of attractive features, and we shall consider it in some detail. As the particles become thermalized they produce heat, much of which will be lost by radiation. An estimate of the net radiant energy loss, E_{rad}, can be made by using an expression for an optically thin solar plasma derived by Orrall and Zirker (1961) and valid over a wide range of temperatures. In cgs units we have:

$$\Delta E \approx 2 \times 10^{-23} n_e^2. \tag{7.44}$$

The total energy loss from the whole loop system due to radiation is then

$$E_{rad} = \frac{\Delta E}{n_e} \frac{M}{m_H} t_{loop}, \tag{7.45}$$

where t_{loop} is the lifetime of an individual loop in the system. Also, $t_{loop} \approx 10^3$ sec and $M/m_H = 6 \times 10^{39}$ cm^{-3} for a total mass $M = 10^{16}$ gm. Equations (7.44) and (7.45) give

$$E_{rad} = 2 \times 10^{20} n_e. \tag{7.46}$$

The electron density is difficult to estimate. It is probably greater than 10^{11} cm^{-3}, which means that the total radiative loss is several times 10^{31} ergs. The model implies that there is energy balance between the radiative loss and the kinetic energy, E_{kin}, delivered to the loop by the fast particles, that is, $E_{\rm rad} = E_{\rm kin}$. If all the particles have the same initial velocity, v, the kinetic energy is $E_{\rm kin} = \frac{1}{2}Mv^2$ and

$$v^2 = 20n_e t_{\rm loop}. \tag{7.47}$$

Jefferies and Orrall assumed $n_e = 5 \times 10^{11}$ cm^{-3} and concluded that the energy balance of this type of active object can be maintained by particles with velocities 10^8 cm/sec, or energy about 10^4 eV.

In their treatment of the actual injection mechanism for the energetic particles, Jefferies and Orrall rely on the concept of particle storage in magnetic fields (see Section 6.3). The particles are assumed to be generated during those flares that probably always occur prior to loops, and the following steps can be recognized in the loop model.

(1) The particles are stored in the sunspot magnetic field overlying the coronal condensation.

(2) Some of these particles drift into those loops of the sunspot magnetic fields that are wholly contained in the coronal condensation, where the density is much higher than in the ambient corona.

(3) Particles with the right energy (between 10^3 and 10^4 eV) will be thermalized near the top of the loop. Eventually the temperature and density of this region rise sharply, $T > 10^7$ °K, $n_e > 10^{11}$ cm^{-3}.

(4) The hot dense region will explode to produce a sporadic condensation (see Chapter 8) and the loops subsequently will be seen in H$_\alpha$, and the cooled prominence material will flow down into the photosphere.

The model does not provide the mechanism by which high-energy particles are accelerated, but rather refers to the flare model proposed by Wild, Smerd, and Weiss (1963) which gives particle generation as treated in Chapter 6.

As the cooled prominence material flows down into the photosphere, it emits a spectrum the lines of which should reveal characteristic profiles. For instance, the wings of H$_\alpha$ should be quite pronounced and be different from Stark-broadened lines. We have seen in Section 7.2.2.1 that such profiles are actually observed in loops.

Jefferies and Orrall drew attention to the possibility that other active prominences, and even quiescent objects, may be produced by the injection mechanism. If the thermalization of the injected particles takes place near the top of the loop of the magnetic field, a loop prominence should be formed as described. But if it occurred near the bottom of one side of a loop-formed flux tube, the result might be a surgelike object or a loop in which matter is seen to stream up one of the legs and down the other.

7.4. *Interaction with Plages, Sunspots, and Flares*

In this Section we shall discuss some of the most interesting and puzzling interactions between prominences of different types and other forms of solar activity. It seems useful to start out with a description of quiescent prominences in this framework and to include a more general morphological study of them.

7.4.1. The Morphology of Quiescent Prominences

We have seen in Section 7.1.1 that the typical long-lived quiescent prominence—the filament when seen in absorption on the disk—is a huge thin sheet of plasma, some 200,000 km long and standing nearly vertically in the solar atmosphere, often reaching high into the corona. Let us first consider the distribution of such prominences on the sun.

It was known to Secchi (1875–77) that the distribution of prominences with latitude is similar to that of sunspots. In addition, L. and M. d'Azambuja (1948) found that there are also polar prominences, so that one has four prominence zones on the sun, two in each hemisphere. Of these, the zones in low latitudes are generally the more important, and, like the sunspot zones, they migrate toward the equator during the sunspot cycle, remaining about 10 degrees behind the sunspot zones. The high-latitude zones develop about three years after sunspot maximum and migrate toward the poles (Lockyer, 1931; L. and M. d'Azambuja, 1948), where the prominences seem to dissolve as the polar cap fields change polarities (Hyder, 1965a). Figure 7.11 shows the frequencies of sunspots and prominences during several solar cycles (Abetti, 1963).

Both Moss (1946) and the d'Azambujas found that all individual prominences (not the prominence zones), equatorial and polar, migrate toward the poles during the 11-year cycle. The drift velocity given is about 1 degree per solar rotation, or 5×10^2 cm/sec. However, Becker (1956) relates this seeming poleward migration of equatorial prominences to the effect of an asymmetric growth in a poleward direction of the filaments along their longest axis. The observations are difficult to interpret, and it is probably premature to try to draw final conclusions. It is, however, of importance to resolve this problem since we know that other facets of activity, like magnetic plages, migrate poleward (see Chapter 4).

The development of filaments has been extensively studied by L. and M. d'Azambuja (1948). Many of them form near sunspot groups and almost always in a pre-existing plage area. This strongly suggests that a magnetic field is a necessary condition for the existence of quiescent prominences, and

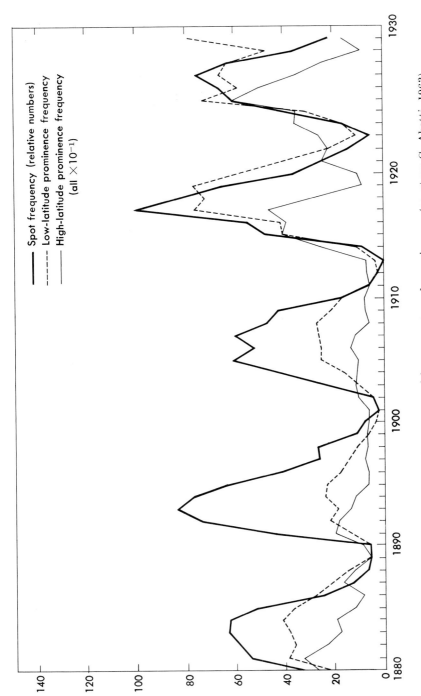

FIGURE 7.11.   The 11-year period as portrayed by sunspots and prominences (courtesy G. Abetti, 1963)

in Section 7.2.5 we have seen that actual measurements are consistent with this conclusion. Many filaments seem to disappear for a day or two after they have formed and then reappear in the same or similar shape (see Section 7.4.4.1 for further details). They mainly grow in length and reach dimensions of 10^5 km after a week from the time they can first be distinguished. Roughly speaking, the length of a filament increases 10^5 km per rotation. The initial orientation of filaments seems to be more or less in meridional planes. Because of this, differential rotation will strongly influence the shape of filaments, and the older the prominence, the more it will follow latitude circles. Old prominences may be observed nearly end-on at the limb.

Filaments may last for many solar rotations and finally—if they have not disappeared before—reach a polar boundary the latitude of which varies with the sunspot cycle. This boundary is referred to as the "polar crown." It is often possible to follow individual equatorial prominences on their way to the polar crown. Whether filaments, on the other hand, initially are formed at these polar latitudes is not known (Kiepenheuer, 1953a).

7.4.2. Association between Plages and Quiescent Prominences

We have seen that many filaments form near spot groups and generally in areas outlined by chromospheric or photospheric plages (faculae). We have seen in Chapter 4 that these formations are determined by the corresponding magnetic plages.

There are also filaments that form outside spot groups, but they occur within the spot zones and they always form in plage areas. Generally, after two or three rotations the optical plage and the sunspots have disappeared and only the filament may remain, probably supported by a partly surviving magnetic field. We thus picture quiescent prominences as anchored in the magnetic fields of plages (see Figure 7.6). These plages migrate poleward and the filaments should do likewise. From the correlation with plages, one would not expect magnetic fields much in excess of 20 gauss in quiescent prominences, unless some compression takes place whereby the magnetic energy density is significantly increased.

7.4.3. Sunspot Prominences

Many active prominences occur above sunspot groups or in the neighborhood of spots, and it seems reasonable to suppose that this is because of the magnetic fields found there. In this connection, we distinguish between prominences in which matter is "drawn" into sunspot regions and prominences that are shot out of sunspot regions up into the corona, like surges and sprays.

7.4.3.1. *Surges*

Most often the path of surges is directed away from the nearest sunspot (Giovanelli and McCabe, 1958b; Shaposhnikova, 1958), and if the material does not reach velocities in excess of the velocity of escape, the surge is observed to fall back along the same trajectory. Surges tend to recur at the same place (see also Rosseland and Tandberg-Hanssen, 1957; Kiepenheuer, 1960). However, the relationship with sunspots may be the result of a deeper relationship with flares—which occur near sunspot groups. We shall return to this in Section 7.4.4 and here only recall the fact that magnetic fields observed in surges (see Section 7.2.5) may be quite high, 100 to 200 gauss, and that this can be understood if the surge "draws with it" the photospheric sunspot field as it is shot up into the corona. For this to be possible, the energy density connected with the magnetic field must be less than the kinetic energy density of the surge plasma. Taking the number density in the surge to be $n_p = 10^{12}$ cm^{-3}, and its velocity $v = 3 \times 10^7$ cm/sec, we find a kinetic energy density $E_{\text{kin}} \approx 750$ ergs/cm^3. The numbers quoted may approximate an actual surge only to a fair degree of accuracy, but it seems that kinetic energy densities much in excess of 10^3 ergs/cm^3 should not be expected. This would mean that one should not expect magnetic fields much in excess of 150 gauss in this type of active prominence high in the corona.

7.4.3.2. *Loops*

Loop prominences are closely connected with sunspots and have been observed on the limb for many years (McMath and Pettit, 1937, 1938; Sawyer and Brodie, 1938; Pettit, 1943; Ellison, 1944; Waldmeier, 1945, 1957; Bumba and Kleczek, 1961; Dodson-Prince, 1961; Bruzek, 1962, 1964), see Figure 7.12 for two examples of loop structures. It is possible that what these authors have discussed is not a uniquely defined active object. We seem to have to deal with two different types of loops, namely (1) loop prominences that are intimately connected with sunspots, not only with the active region associated with sunspots, which we shall refer to as sunspot loops, and (2) flare loops that seem to grow out of flares; these loops will also occur near sunspots because their triggering or generating flares occur near sunspots. Ellison reported that matter streamed up one leg of the loop and down the other, while Bruzek found matter streaming downward in both legs. The latter result is in agreement both with the picture that loop prominences are condensations, and with the model due to Jefferies and Orrall (Section 7.3.3.3b); the former can only be understood if they are injections from below. However, according to Bruzek (1964), these different types of motions characterize the two different types of loops. What Ellison reported

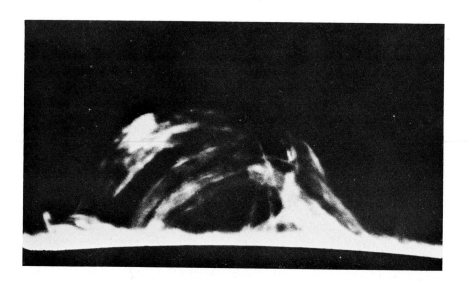

FIGURE 7.12. Two examples of complex loop prominences (courtesy R. Dunn, Sacramento Peak Observatory)

is the kind of motion typical of sunspot loops, which we treat in the rest of this section.

Bumba and Kleczek demonstrated that at least one leg of the loop is anchored in the umbra of sunspots, and they considered the loops themselves as magnetic flux tubes. Since the cross-sections of loops do not seem to change appreciably with height, Bumba and Kleczek argued that the intensity of the magnetic field at the top of loops does not differ much from the value near photospheric levels. This picture implies a very much stronger field than that which can be expected above sunspots at the coronal heights involved (30,000 to 100,000 km) if the field there is due to a dipole, or even monopole, configuration anchored in the sunspots. In the latter case, the field strength has fallen to a few tens of gauss at these heights.

Photographs of sunspot loops do not indicate any significant twisting of the material along the loop, which may mean that there is no strong azimuthal field component in the implied magnetic flux tube. Since the field must be essentially force-free at coronal heights, it seems that the field configuration is given by the interaction between the low-lying parts of the field and the subphotospheric motions. In these layers, the kinetic energy density of the motions dominates over the energy density of the magnetic field and the latter can be twisted easily. The flare loops, which develop after great flares, will be treated in Section 7.4.4.2b.

7.4.3.3. Active region "filaments"

In active regions around sunspots, one often observes comparatively small filament-like objects that are not to be considered as normal filaments, i.e., as quiescent prominences. Their lifetimes are short and even though their shape at any one moment of observation reminds one of quiescent filaments, these prominences are active. Newton's classification (see Table 7.2) includes some of these objects in his class II. At times these prominences may be seen in emission in H_α, indicating excess temperature or, more likely, density. One end of such prominences is often seen to point toward the umbra of a sunspot, and an exchange of matter seems to take place between the prominence and the sunspot.

A closer inspection of active filaments reveals that many of them are surges, sometimes referred to as high-speed dark surges, and some are loops seen in projection on the disk, thereby giving the impression of being dark filaments. Finally, there are genuine "active filaments," small dark and dense filament-shaped prominences that appear as an integral part of many active regions (Smith and Ramsey, 1964). The incidence of flares seems to increase with increasing number of active region filaments in a particular area. It may therefore be that dark filaments are somehow related to the formation of at least some flares.

7.4.4. Prominences and Flares

Probably the most spectacular interaction to be discussed in the present chapter is the prominence-flare coupling. Included here is a complex set of phenomena, and several physical processes are undoubtedly at play. Both quiescent and active prominences may be involved, and the following sections are hardly exhaustive.

7.4.4.1. *Quiescent prominences*

Flares may affect quiescent prominences in different ways. At times only a temporary "activation" takes place, manifested by increased internal motions of the prominence plasma or by oscillations (winkings) of the whole prominence, after which the prominence returns to its previous state without any visible lasting changes. In other instances, the prominence is disturbed to a degree such that it completely disappears, either permanently or, more often, for hours or days.

(a) THE "DISPARITION BRUSQUE" PHENOMENON — Nearly one-half of all low-latitude filaments are seen to disappear temporarily at least once (L. and M. d'Azambuja, 1948). When one makes allowance for the time the filaments spend on the invisible hemisphere, one must conclude that the sudden disappearance phase (the French term is disparition brusque) is a "normal" experience for filaments, and probably all quiescent prominences are subjected to it. We have seen that polar filaments in general are old, and only a few of these undergo sudden disappearances. However, it is premature to conclude that the disparition brusque phase belongs to fairly young objects, since the agency triggering the activation may be latitude-dependent.

L. and M. d'Azambuja further found that some prominences disappear and reappear twice or even three times. The interval between different disappearances may be several weeks. The disappearance may last for a few days or up to a few weeks, and it is permanent in about one third of all cases. When the filament reforms, it appears in very nearly the same shape as the previous one. This fact can be used as an argument that the supporting force in quiescent prominences is a long-lived magnetic field that is not drastically altered by the disparition brusque.

Kiepenheuer (1953a) points out that the disappearance of a prominence may happen in any of the following three ways: (1) The prominence flows down into the chromosphere along well-defined trajectories that often end up in sunspots, (2) The prominence shrinks and disappears that way, (3) The prominence rises into the corona with increasing velocity that may, or may not, exceed the velocity of escape.

The first type of disappearance has been studied in detail by Pan Puh (1939) and Becker (1952). The shape of the trajectories and the often-associated sunspot point to the existence of magnetic fields in determining the streaming motion. But the triggering seems to come in most cases from flares. By correlating the disappearance with the occurrence of specific flares, Bruzek (1951a) found that if the perturbation originates in these flares, it travels with a speed of about 100 km/sec to the filament, where it triggers the activation that may lead to a disparition brusque. Velocities of the same order of magnitude have been deduced for other flare disturbances by Öhman and Öhman (1953) and Öhman, Lindgren, and Lindgren (1962).

Pettit (1925), Waldmeier (1938a, 1939c), and Pan Puh (1939) have studied the third type of disappearance. The first two authors found that the velocity of rise increases in jumps after intervals of 10 to 20 minutes. However, Pan Puh concluded that the data could as well be interpreted in terms of velocities increasing continuously with height, a result that was confirmed by Larmore (1953). Consequently, there is conflicting evidence as to the existence of localized regions in the magnetic field configuration where acceleration takes place. Becker (1952) reported that such regions exist during disappearances of the first type.

The velocity of ascension may reach values much in excess of the velocity of escape, at times exceeding 1000 km/sec (Menzel, Smith, De Mastus, Ramsey, Schnable, and Lawrence, 1956; Bjerke, 1961). However, all parts of the erupting prominence may not show the same velocity (Comper and Kern, 1957); see also Severny and Khokhlova (1953), Olivieri (1956), Cragg (1957), and Shaposhnikova (1958).

The disparition brusque phase seems to be so common that it may be considered part of the "normal" development of quiescent prominences. However, it is due to a perturbation from outside, from a flare or from a sunspot, and extensive studies have been done on the nature of these flare perturbations. We shall return to this in Section 7.5.

It is also probable that sunspots provide the triggering agency. The work in this field is mainly due to Bruzek (1952). He found that there exists a correlation between the time, Δt, from the first appearance of a sunspot to the activation of a nearby filament, and the distance, d, of the filament from the spot. From the Δt, d correlation, Bruzek concluded that there is a perturbation propagating from sunspots with a velocity of about 1 km/sec. Using observations of photospheric magnetic fields, we can link this disturbance to the development and propagation of the magnetic field around forming sunspots. The observations show that there is an expanding elliptic area around the developing sunspot group in which the chromospheric fibrilles become aligned by the magnetic field. The growth of the outer boundary of this area proceeds at about 0.2 km/sec (Bumba and Howard, 1965), and when the disturbance reaches a filament, the latter breaks up in a "disparition-brusque-like" manner. This sunspot-induced disparition brusque should be clearly distinguished from the similar flare-induced phenomenon, which is triggered by a much faster disturbance. The reality of the two perturbation velocities, 100 km/sec from flares and 1 km/sec from sunspots, is difficult to ascertain, based as they are on statistical studies. We shall return to the important implications related to these different types in Section 7.5.

(b) PROMINENCE-INDUCED "FLARINGS" — Bruzek (1951a, 1957) has discussed in considerable detail the situation in which a disparition brusque is followed by a brightening of the chromospheric structure on either side of the site of the disappearing filament. The brightening reaches flare intensity and may last for several hours. These prominence-induced flarings were first described by Waldmeier (1938a) and also mentioned by Martres (1956) and Becker (1957). According to Bruzek, the brightening of the facular structure may be described as strings of bright mottles parallel to the disappearing filament.

In cases like these, we are apparently witnessing the formation of flaring regions at the expense of energy stored in the filament, whether electromagnetic or gravitational (Sturrock and Coppi, 1965; Sturrock and Woodbury, 1965). Hyder (1966b) has tried to develop a model in which the destruction of the magnetic field configuration in filaments can account for the filament-flare relationship. This may be—on a smaller scale of activity—a phenomenon similar to the one mentioned in Section 7.4.3.3 namely the interaction of active-region filaments and flares. In this picture, the flare is secondary to the generating, or at least the triggering, agency of the prominence. In the next Section, 7.4.4.2, we shall discuss another case where the casual dependence is opposite: prominences that are generated by the flares.

(c) "WINKING" FILAMENTS — Under this heading, we discuss a type of filament activation that generally does not lead to a spectacular disparition brusque, but which has revealed the existence of a flare generated disturbance of great importance. The phenomenon of "winking" filaments has been known for many years. It was observed in spectrohelioscopes by Greaves, Newton and Jackson (Dyson, 1930) and studied further by Newton (1935). The phenomenon derives its name from the fact that the filament—which is subjected to more or less vertical oscillations—gives a spectrum whose lines are Doppler-shifted alternatively to the red and violet as the filament is pushed down or lifted up. This will cause the image of the filament to be shifted alternately out of and into the passband of narrow-band H_α filters used for flare patrols, and gives the "winking" impression. The observed winking filament generally shows an initial receding motion followed by from one to four damped oscillations. The frequency of oscillation varies from one filament to another, and does not appear to relate to the importance of the flare. Ramsey and Smith (1966) observed a filament which was disturbed four times in a three-day period, and each time it oscillated with essentially the same frequency. There is further a preferential direction, or rather a cone, in which the disturbance propagates. Filaments lying inside this cone as seen from the flare may be activated, those outside are not.

The work on these activations was continued by Dodson-Prince (1949), Bruzek (1951b, 1958), and Becker (1958) and especially by Moreton (1960, 1965), whose refined photographic technique permits the actual observation of the propagating disturbance as it travels from the flare to the filament with a velocity in the range 500 to 1500 km/sec. This is considerably more than the velocities derived for other disturbances by Bruzek (see Section 7.4.4.1a), but Becker (1958) has reported an exceptional case that indicated a velocity in the range 1500 to 2000 km/sec. Among other significant contributions to the study of these activations, see papers by Moreton and Ramsey (1960) and Dodson-Prince and Hedeman (1964b).

There are basically two ways of explaining the disturbance which propagates from the triggering flare and which causes the winking phenomenon, namely, (1) the disturbance is a plasma cloud or particles whose interaction with the filament material is responsible for the activation, or (2) the disturbance is a wave phenomenon. The observed preferential direction of propagation of the disturbance implies that magnetic fields play an important role and restrict the number of possible types of waves involved.

The first point of view was taken by Athay and Moreton (1961), who envisaged a charge-exchange mechanism between the protons in the disturbance and the neutral hydrogen atoms in the filament, whereby the second quantum level of hydrogen became depopulated. Alternatively, they considered that the observed reduction in the H_α opacity was due to a Doppler shift of the absorption profile. Athay and Moreton concluded that a stream of protons of density 10^9 cm^{-3}, or slightly more, incident on a filament would give rise to a reduction in the opacity in H_α by a factor of about 10, which is sufficient to render the filament transparent. However, this model cannot reasonably predict more than one "winking," neither does it account for the off-band visibility reported by Moreton and by Ramsey and Smith.

Malville (1961) suggested that magnetic fields in the filaments were probably involved, and Hyder (1966a) developed a model where an electromagnetic wave disturbance causes the filament to oscillate under the influence of its own magnetic field (see also Anderson, 1966). We shall follow Hyder's arguments in some detail, taking the frequency of oscillation to be about $\nu_{osc} = 10^{-3}$ sec^{-1} and the decay constant $\gamma \approx 10^{-3}$ sec^{-1} (Ramsey and Smith, 1966). The mass of the filament is supposed to be suspended in the magnetic field supporting the quiescent prominence, in a manner similar to the model of Kippenhahn and Schlüter (Section 7.3.2.2d). The vertical component of the field is B_z, the scale height of the filament is H and a small downward displacement Δz of the filament is supposed to lead to a linear increase in B_z,

$$\Delta B_z = -B_z \, \Delta z / H. \tag{7.48}$$

Under these conditions, one can analyze the filament oscillations in terms of a damped harmonic oscillator, and the frequency ν_{osc} is determined from the equation of motion

$$\frac{d^2z}{dt^2} + \frac{\mu}{M}\frac{dz}{dt} + \frac{K}{M}z = 0 \tag{7.49}$$

and from

$$\nu_{\mathrm{osc}} = \sqrt{\nu_0^2 - \mu^2/16\pi^2 M^2}, \tag{7.50}$$

where ν_0 is the frequency of an undamped harmonic oscillator, $\nu_0 = (1/2\pi)\sqrt{K/M}$; M is the mass of the filament, K the restoring force, and μ the coefficient of friction in the corona in which the filament moves. The ratio K/M can be expressed in terms of the magnetic field in the prominence (through the magnetic tension, $B^2/4\pi H$) and the physical parameters describing it (density ρ, volume V, scale height H):

$$\frac{K}{M} = 2\frac{d}{dz}\left(\frac{B_z^2}{4}\right)\frac{V}{H}\frac{1}{\rho V}. \tag{7.51}$$

Combining Equations (7.48) and (7.51), we find

$$\frac{K}{M} = \left(\frac{B_z}{H}\right)^2 \frac{1}{\pi \rho}. \tag{7.52}$$

This equation may be combined with the following expression for K/M in terms of the frequency of oscillation and the decay constant, that is,

$$K/M = 4\pi^2\nu_{\mathrm{osc}}^2 + \gamma^2$$

to obtain an expression for the vertical field

$$(B_z/H)^2 = \pi\rho(4\pi^2\nu_{\mathrm{osc}}^2 + \gamma^2). \tag{7.53}$$

The frequency ν_{osc} as given by Equation (7.50) depends on the friction experienced by the oscillating filament. The coefficient of friction may be defined in terms of the coefficient of viscosity in the corona $\eta = 2M\,d\gamma/Ac$, where A is the area of the vertical surface of the filament and d the effective distance, perpendicular to A, over which shears exist in the coronal plasma as a result of the winking motions. Hyder inserted the following values for the parameters: $M = 10^{15}$ gm , $H = 3 \times 10^9$ cm , $d = 10^9$ cm , $A = 10^{20}$ cm^2, $\nu_{osc} = 10^{-3}$ sec^{-1}, $\gamma = 10^{-3}$ sec^{-1}, which leads to the following values,

$$B_z \approx 10 \text{ gauss}, \qquad \eta \approx 10^{-9} \text{ poise}.$$

Linhart (1960) has given a relation between the strength of a coronal magnetic field, B_c, and the coefficient of viscosity in the corona

$$\eta = 1.6 \times 10^{-26} n_e^2 / B_c^2 T_c^{1/2}.$$

Using the value for η determined by Hyder and inserting for $n_e = 10^9$ cm^{-3} and for $T_c = 10^6$ °K , we find $B_c \approx 0.13$ gauss . The quoted values of B_z and B_c indicate that an enhancement of the field strength between one and two orders of magnitude is involved in the formation of a quiescent prominence.

In his thought-provoking paper, Hyder implies that the disparition brusque and the winking filament are similar phenomena. The property that distinguishes between them may be the direction of the initial displacement Δz of the filament. If the displacement takes place along the positive z-axis, the filament may completely disappear, but if the displacement is downward (along the negative z-axis), the disturbed filament may undergo oscillations. As the filament is pushed down initially, the density increases rapidly and the motion becomes highly damped.

7.4.4.2. Active prominences

The relationship between active prominences and flares is quite close in many respects. In Section 7.2.2 we mentioned the similarity of their optical spectra. A second indication is the tendency either for flares to spread along trajectories on one or both sides of pre-existing active filaments, or for certain loops to form between different parts of a flare, or for flares to be associated with surge prominences. We note that while the active filament exists before the flare and either may be instrumental in forming the flare or have nothing to do with it, the loops and surges are the result of flare action.

(a) FLARE SURGES — Surges are often seen to be ejected from flares (Newton, 1942; Ellison, 1942; Giovanelli and McCabe, 1958b). When seen on the disk, the surges appear as dark absorption markings most of the time, and when observed at the limb, they look like narrow spikes rising nearly radially to heights of about 50,000 km , usually followed by a more gradual descent along the same path. The rise velocity may exceed 200 km/sec , but the average downward acceleration does not exceed that due to gravitation (Byrne, Ellison and Reid, 1964). According to Gopasyuk and Ogir (1963), all flares are accompanied by surges, and matter may be ejected during the whole lifetime of the flare. If this is so, the surge ejection may be considered a "normal" part of the flare phenomenon, and a study of the acceleration mechanism should possibly lead us to some of the basic physics of flares.

Warwick (1957) called attention to an extreme type of flare ejection, the so-called flare spray. It is characterized by much higher velocities than surges, velocities at or above the velocity of escape (670 km/sec). Also, while the surge is a continuous stream of gas, the spray degenerates into many fragments, only a small number of which fall back into the chromosphere. Observations show that the sprays, like surges, rise with a twisting motion, and a magnetic field seems necessary to prevent such rapidly turning plasma columns from disintegrating. According to Warwick, field strengths of a few hundred gauss are required in the case of sprays.

(b) FLARE LOOPS — Bruzek (1962, 1964) has studied the evolution of loop-prominence systems and their relation to flares in great detail, and the following description is mainly due to him. These loops may be different from the type discussed in Section 7.4.3.2, which is anchored in sunspots. The flare loop always develops from a flare, as small knots of material that grow to form the loop structure. The material streams down both legs of the loop with velocities of the order of 100 km/sec. At the same time, the loop is expanding at a rate of about 10 km/sec, and new loops form above the old one, higher and higher in the corona. When observed on the disk, the loops are seen to bridge two parts of the flare, generally two parallel "flare filaments" which move apart as the loops expand, probably causing the expansion, see also Bruzek (1957), Malville and Moreton (1963). These flare filaments generally originate from a single filament closely aligned along the neutral line in the underlying magnetic plage (class A flare according to Avignon, Martres-Trope and Pick-Gutmann, 1963). After several hours, the loop system has grown to heights of 10^5 km and the whole phenomenon is over in about 12 hours. In disk observations the flare loops may have various shapes, depending on the projection angle, and they may be seen in either emission or absorption.

The flare loops are manifestations of the highest degree of activity observed in the solar atmosphere. They are closely related to sporadic coronal condensations (Waldmeier, 1957) which we shall treat in Chapter 8, and which reveal conditions of high density and very high temperature ($\approx 3 \times 10^6$ to $6 \times 10^6 \, °K$). Furthermore, the loop system is a very stable configuration and is not significantly disturbed by the occurrence of other nearby flares which interfere seriously with prominences of other types. Since we do not know the magnetic configuration associated with flare loops, we can only conjecture that this stability is caused by a stable magnetic field outlining the loop structure.

7.5. *Theoretical Interpretations*

In the previous sections of this chapter, 7.3 and 7.4, we have several times carried the discussion beyond a point which can be defended as being a necessary conclusion drawn from the observations. We have already entered the domain of interpretations. The reason is that it is even more difficult when dealing with prominences than with sunspots or flares to make a sharp distinction between what is model and what is theoretical interpretation— and speculation. Nevertheless, the guiding principle in the previous sections was to use observations in deriving models for the phenomena in question. In so doing, we judged it necessary to treat some of the fundamental problems, while others were left for later discussion. We shall now treat some of these remaining problems in an effort to bring into focus the basic ideas involved.

7.5.1. The Initial Formation of Prominences

The models discussed in Section 7.3 run into difficulties when trying to describe how the prominence "gets started." Similar remarks hold for the flare-generated or flare-triggered prominences of Section 7.4.

7.5.1.1. *Condensations*

In an attempt to solve the problem of the initial formation of condensing prominences, Kuperus (1965) related this phase to the distribution of the mechanical energy flux responsible for the heating of the corona. He used the theory for the generation and propagation of mechanical energy as outlined in Section 3.3.5 [see Equation (3.20)], and assumed that the mechanical energy is transported in the vertical direction by fast-mode hydromagnetic waves (Section 1.5). In this mode, there is a reduction of the absorption coefficient for waves which travel perpendicularly to the magnetic field (Uchida, 1963), the reason being that waves in this direction have a larger propagation velocity than waves in a direction parallel to the field. If we therefore have regions in the atmosphere where there is a horizontal magnetic field, the waves carrying the mechanical energy will not dissipate so easily in these regions as in regions where the magnetic field is mainly vertical. Figure 7.13 shows schematically the magnetic field between two regions with opposite polarities. In region A, according to the foregoing discussion, there will be less dissipation of energy than in regions B. Kuperus argued that if the radiation in regions B is balanced by the mechanical energy dissipation, region A will not be in energy balance because in this region there is a reduction of the absorption coefficient for the fast mode waves involved in the energy transport. Consequently, the plasma in A will lose energy faster

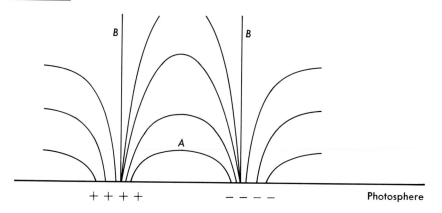

FIGURE 7.13.   Magnetic field configuration in a bipolar region (courtesy M. Kuperus, 1965)

than it can be supplied by the fast mode waves, and the region will cool. Furthermore, region A must also be compressed to keep the cooling gas in pressure equilibrium with the surroundings. This causes a further increase in the radiation (which is proportional to the square of the density) and a decrease in the temperature until the condensing plasma (the prominence) obtains a temperature low enough to keep it in radiative equilibrium.

As matter is compressed in the prominence, there will no longer be hydrostatic equilibrium along the vertical axis. The horizontal magnetic field will sag sufficiently to support the prominence by the magnetic stresses caused by the curvature of the lines of force. Kuperus estimated the field strength necessary—given a particle density, $n = 10^{10}$ cm^{-3}, and a temperature, $T = 10^4$ °K of the prominence plasma, and a radius of curvature, $R = 10^9$ cm for the field lines—from the expression

$$B^2 = 4\pi\rho gR\,,$$

which gives $B \approx 2$ gauss.

Kuperus' idea is interesting in that it ties the formation of prominences to a phenomenon (mechanical energy transport) that is needed also for other purposes. The formation of quiescent prominences can thereby be considered a "normal" occurrence in the solar atmosphere.

7.5.1.2. *Injections*

Models that describe prominences as being formed from below must rely on an injection mechanism for the plasma. We know that copious amounts of particles are generated during flares, and these are the particles used by Jefferies and Orrall (1965b) to account for the matter in loops. It is a widely held view that magnetic fields exist in flare regions in such configurations that particle acceleration is possible, or even likely, see Section 4.3.4.

Another approach has been taken by Jensen (1959), who showed that when a plasma is not in thermal equilibrium an inhomogeneous magnetic field will cause the plasma to move in the field. Under certain conditions, the plasma can be forced to move up into loop structures in the field, thereby accounting for loop prominences and coronal condensations.

Jensen derived an equation of motion for the macroscopic velocity, $v_\parallel$, parallel to the magnetic field **B**. He started from the Vlasov equation [the collisionless Boltzmann equation, Equation (1.28)] for the ions and introduced for the accelerations **F**/m the expressions

$$\frac{\partial w_r}{\partial t} = 0, \qquad \frac{\partial w_\perp}{\partial t} = \frac{w_\parallel w_\perp}{2B} \frac{\partial B}{\partial z}, \qquad \frac{\partial w_\parallel}{\partial t} = -\frac{w_\perp^2}{2B} \frac{\partial B}{\partial z} - g,$$

since the magnetic field was assumed to be constant in time and to have the components in cylindrical coordinates

$$\mathbf{B} = \left[-\frac{1}{2} r \frac{\partial B}{\partial z}, 0, B_z \right].$$

The resulting Vlasov equation for the ion distribution function f is

$$\frac{\partial f}{\partial t} + w_\parallel \frac{\partial f}{\partial z} - \frac{w_\perp^2}{2B} \frac{\partial B}{\partial z} \frac{\partial f}{\partial w_\parallel} - g \frac{\partial f}{\partial w_\parallel} + \frac{w_\parallel w_\perp}{2B} \frac{\partial B}{\partial z} \frac{\partial f}{\partial w_\perp} = 0.$$

By taking the different moments of this equation, one arrives at the equation of continuity, Equation (1.29), and the equation of motion in the z-direction, which is similar to Equation (1.31) and which leads to the following linearized equation of motion in $v_\parallel$ [compare this with Equation (1.33a)],

$$\rho \frac{\partial v_\parallel}{\partial t} + \frac{\partial p_\parallel}{\partial z} + \frac{n}{B} \frac{\partial B}{\partial z} (E_\perp - 2E_\parallel) + \rho g = 0. \tag{7.54}$$

The pressure $p_\parallel$ relates to the component of the random velocity $u_\parallel \equiv w_\parallel - v_\parallel$ by the assumption $\partial \overline{nmu^2}/\partial z = \partial p_\parallel/\partial z$. Equation (7.54) shows that if we have thermal equilibrium, $E_\parallel = 2E_\parallel$ (since there are two degrees of freedom in the perpendicular direction, but only one in the parallel direction) and the magnetic field has no influence on the density distribution (van de Hulst, 1950). But if there are deviations from equipartition, an inhomogeneous ($\partial B/\partial z \neq 0$) magnetic field will change the density distribution of the plasma. This result was derived using the Vlasov equation, which means that the effect will be of importance only in cases where collisions are sufficiently rare.

Under such conditions, the hydrostatic equation becomes, with $\partial B/\partial z = -|\partial B/\partial z|$,

$$\frac{\partial p_{\parallel}}{\partial z} = \frac{n}{B}\left|\frac{\partial B}{\partial z}\right|(E_{\perp} - 2E_{\parallel}) - \rho g. \tag{7.55}$$

Equation (7.55) may be integrated to find the density distribution, provided that we can define a temperature $T_{\parallel}$ that is independent of z. In that case,

$$n = n_0 \exp\left\{\int_0^z\left[\frac{E_{\perp} - 2E_{\parallel}}{2E_{\parallel}B}\left|\frac{\partial B}{\partial z}\right| - \frac{mg}{kT_{\parallel}}\right]dz\right\}. \tag{7.56}$$

Jensen now assumed that the deviations from equipartition ($E_{\perp} \neq 2E_{\parallel}$) were achieved by a changing magnetic field, since only $E_{\perp}$ and not $E_{\parallel}$ is altered by induction. If $\partial B/\partial t > 0$, $E_{\perp}$ is increased and $E_{\perp} - 2E_{\parallel} > 0$, which means that the plasma is diamagnetic and it will be pushed to regions where the magnetic field strength has a minimum. (The condition $\partial B/\partial t < 0$ leads to a paramagnetic plasma which moves to places where the magnetic field is strongest, see also Kiepenheuer, 1938.) To maintain an inverse gradient, the ratio of scale-height, H, to characteristic length, L, of the magnetic field must satisfy the condition

$$H/L > 2E_{\parallel}/(E_{\perp} - 2E_{\parallel}). \tag{7.57}$$

One can find the time scale for the variation in the magnetic field necessary to give deviations from thermal equilibrium large enough to be of interest by writing for the variation of the ion component of $E_{\perp} - 2E_{\parallel}$ with time (see Schlüter, 1957b):

$$\frac{\partial(E_{i,\perp} - 2E_{i,\parallel})}{\partial t} = -\frac{E_{i,\perp} - 2E_{i,\parallel}}{\tau_i} + \frac{E_{i,\perp}}{B}\frac{\partial B}{\partial t},$$

where τ_i is the mean flight time for ions. Any deviation from an isotropic distribution of velocities will be smoothed out in time intervals of the order of τ_i. We require that $\partial(E_{i,\perp} - 2E_{i,\parallel})/\partial t = 0$ in order to maintain the difference $E_{i,\perp} - 2E_{i,\parallel}$. Then, defining the time-scale for the variation of the magnetic field $t_B^{-1} = |(1/B)(\partial B/\partial t)|$, we find

$$t_B = \frac{E_{i,\perp}}{E_{i,\perp} - 2E_{i,\parallel}}\tau_i. \tag{7.58}$$

For the electrons we may assume thermal equilibrium, $E_{e,\perp} = 2E_{e,\parallel}$, since the relaxation time for the electrons is much shorter than for the ions.

Bearing this in mind, we find from Equations (7.57) and (7.58) the condition for the inverse density gradient,

$$t_B < \frac{E_{i,\perp}}{2(E_{i,\parallel} + E_{e,\parallel})} \frac{H}{L} \tau_i. \tag{7.59}$$

As a numerical example, let us consider the conditions in the corona at heights of large loops. Here τ_i is probably of the order of 10 sec, and taking $H/L = 10$, we find from Equation (7.57) $E_\perp > 2.2 E_\parallel$ and from Equation (7.59) $t_B < 60$ sec. This seems to indicate that dense regions can be formed

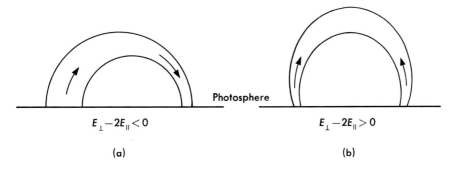

$$E_\perp - 2E_\parallel < 0 \qquad\qquad\qquad E_\perp - 2E_\parallel > 0$$

(a)   (b)

FIGURE. 7.14.   Motions in magnetic loops according to Jensen

as a result of the diamagnetic effect described if the magnetic field undergoes changes with time-scales of the order of a minute. Such changes do not seem unreasonable in active regions. Figure 7.14a shows a magnetic-field configuration which would lead to a loop prominence in which matter would stream up one leg and down the other. Jensen also conceived of other field configurations with different mass motions. Since one has several possible combinations of the parameters involved ($\partial B/\partial t < 0$, $\partial B/\partial t > 0$, $\partial B/\partial z < 0$, $\partial B/\partial z > 0$), a variety of "loop prominence motions" can be constructed, corresponding to injection of matter at the top of the loop as well as at one or both legs of the loop. Figure 7.14b shows motions that would lead to a condensation of matter in the corona at the top of a loop.

7.5.2. Thermal Balance in Quiescent Prominences

In active prominences, like surges and loops, we are witnessing the relaxation of cooling matter, whether it is condensing out of the hot corona or injected into the prominence from below as energetic particles or as a hot plasma cloud. Also, in quiescent prominences it may be that the plasma relaxes in a similar way, but the time constant may be quite different.

7.5.2.1. *Steady-state configurations*

It may be that the prominence plasma exists in quasi-equilibrium configurations in which there is balance between the rate at which energy is supplied to the plasma by heat conduction and the rate at which it is lost by radiation from the prominence. This case was studied by Orrall and Zirker (1961), who found such equilibrium configurations and tested them for stability against temperature perturbations to determine the characteristic time with which the prominences pass from one equilibrium state to another.

The equation describing the equilibrium between thermal conduction and radiative cooling is

$$\nabla \cdot (K \nabla T) = \nabla \cdot \mathbf{F}, \tag{7.60}$$

where T is the kinetic temperature, K the thermal conductivity—see Equation (1.54)—and $\nabla \cdot \mathbf{F}$ the divergence of the radiative flux. The temperature in the center of the prominence is T_p, the coronal temperature T_c. Orrall and Zirker used the expression

$$K = 3 \times 10^{-6} \ T^{5/2} \quad \text{erg deg}^{-1} \ \text{sec}^{-1} \ \text{cm}^{-1} \tag{7.61}$$

for the thermal conductivity (Oster, 1957) in the absence of magnetic fields. If there is a magnetic field $\mathbf{B}$ present, the thermal conductivity transverse to $\mathbf{B}$ will be reduced by a factor $1 + (\omega_B \tau)^2$, see Equation (1.61), and its temperature dependence will be changed, $(\omega_B \tau)^2 \propto T^3$, see Equation (1.62), where $\omega_B = eB/mc$ and τ is the collision interval. For electrons in prominences and in the corona, $\omega_B \tau > 1$ for magnetic fields smaller than 1 gauss. Under such conditions, the effective thermal conductivity is largely due to ions (Rosenbluth, 1958), and Orrall and Zirker used the expression

$$K = 6 \times 10^{-17} \ n_e^2/B^2 T^{1/2}. \tag{7.62}$$

Their discussion of the divergence of the radiative flux led Orrall and Zirker to the following expression, valid for optically thin conditions in the prominence,

$$\nabla \cdot \mathbf{F} = 1.75 \times 10^{-23} n_e^2, \tag{7.63}$$

which is independent of temperature. Both free–free, free–bound, and line emission were included.

By inserting Equations (7.61) and (7.63) in Equation (7.60), we find the equation describing the equilibrium condition in the absence of magnetic fields. Orrall and Zirker solved this equation and found equilibrium configurations such that the high-temperature portions of the prominence were far too large. Next, to account for the effect of a magnetic field, one inserts

Equations (7.62) and (7.63) in (7.60). The solution shows that in this case the magnetic field almost completely determines the width of the prominence, the value of the temperature T_p being of little importance. When the magnetic field is important, the width of the prominence threads is very small, 24 km in one numerical example quoted by the authors. They imply that when the prominence is optically deep in some of the crucial radiations, the models will be in better agreement with observations.

This line of reasoning was adopted by Doherty and Menzel (1965), who treated the transfer of radiation in the resonance lines of hydrogen and of neutral and ionized helium. They arrived at models similar to Orrall's and Zirker's. The central temperature minimum was somewhat lower; at a density of $n_e = 2 \times 10^{11}$ cm^{-3} the temperature should be close to 10^4 °K .

7.5.2.2. The heating of prominences

If no quasi-equilibrium configuration exists, Equation (7.60) must be replaced by the general equation

$$c_v \frac{\partial T}{\partial t} + p \frac{\partial}{\partial t}\left(\frac{1}{\rho}\right) = \nabla \cdot (K\nabla T) - \nabla \cdot \mathbf{F} + \nabla \cdot \mathbf{Q}, \qquad (7.64)$$

where c_v is the specific heat per unit volume and $\nabla \cdot \mathbf{Q}$ the source of coronal heating, the mechanical energy flux. We shall assume that this heating mechanism is not operative inside the prominence and put $\nabla \cdot \mathbf{Q} = 0$. A lower limit to the time it would take to heat the prominence from the initial temperature T_p to coronal values due to heat conduction can then be found by neglecting the radiative losses (the term $\nabla \cdot \mathbf{F}$) in Equation (7.64). This is the avenue followed by Rosseland, Jensen and Tandberg-Hanssen (1958) and Ioshpa (1965). Furthermore, for quiescent prominences we consider the cooling isobaric, $p = R\rho T = $ constant, and in the one-dimensional case Equation (7.64) takes the following form

$$c_p\rho = \frac{\partial}{\partial x}\left(K \frac{\partial T}{\partial x}\right). \qquad (7.65a)$$

Ioshpa used the expression $K = AT^{5/2}$ for the thermal conductivity and, since $c_p\rho = \frac{5}{2}kn_e$, wrote Equation (7.65a) in the form

$$\frac{\partial T}{\partial t} = \frac{2A}{5kn_e} \frac{\partial}{\partial x}\left(T^{5/2} \frac{\partial T}{\partial x}\right), \qquad (7.65b)$$

for which he gave an approximate solution, subject to the boundary conditions

$$T(0, t) = T_c \qquad \text{and} \qquad T(x, 0) = 0.$$

The initial boundary between the prominence and corona is $x = 0$. The solution may be written

$$T = T_c[1 - x/(atT_c^{5/2})^{1/2}]^{2/5}. \tag{7.66}$$

Equation (7.66) portrays a thermal wave with a steep front. At any time t, the width of the zone in which the temperature drops from $0.4T$ to 0 is approximately $\frac{1}{10}$ the thickness of the already heated region. If, for example, the prominence has a thickness of 10^9 cm, it will be heated in $t = 2.5 \times 10^3$ sec, and if the prominence consists of fine structure threads of thickness 10^8 cm, the time to heat it to coronal temperatures is 25 seconds. Similar results are due to Severny and Khokhlova (1953) and Shklovsky (1962).

The existence of a magnetic field in the prominence with a significant component transverse to the heat flow will drastically alter these estimates. While heat conduction along the field is the same as in the absence of the field, we have seen that the conduction perpendicular to the field is reduced by the factor $1 + (\omega_B \tau)^2$ [Equation (1.61)]. Therefore, to increase the time-scale above by a factor of 10^4, for example, it is sufficient to have a transverse magnetic field of less than 1 gauss. However, even though the transverse conductivity is greatly reduced, there will be an additional heat flow in a direction perpendicular to both the magnetic field and the temperature gradient, i.e., in the direction $\mathbf{B} \times \nabla T$ (the Righi-Leduc effect). The corresponding conductivity is $\omega_B \tau$ times the direct conductivity [see Equation (1.63)] and may be of importance for some geometrical configurations in prominences (Tandberg-Hanssen, 1960; Orrall and Zirker, 1961).

7.5.3. The Nature of Prominence Magnetic Fields

Both observations and theoretical studies as presented in this chapter strongly suggest that prominences owe their shape and motion, and probably their existence, to magnetic fields. Different types of prominences require different types of magnetic fields. For some we have a fair understanding of the origin and nature of the fields involved; for others our interpretation of observations and models is little more than an educated guess.

7.5.3.1. *Quiescent prominences*

The dominating magnetic field in this case is the field of magnetic plages whose lines of force connect regions of opposite polarities in these plages. The prominence material collects in those parts of the field where it is more or less horizontal, i.e., along the "neutral line" between the polarities as observed in the longitudinal component. We know little about the origin of the magnetic field that defines these plages and how this field relates to the magnetic fields of sunspots that may occur within the plage field.

As the filament grows older, the effect of the sun's differential rotation will cause the filament to become aligned more and more parallel to the equator. It is to be expected that a magnetic field component along the filament will develop, and the simple picture portrayed in Figure 7.6 is too idealized. Observations of magnetic fields in filaments should therefore reveal longitudinal components regardless of how the filament is viewed (Rust, 1966b). The increased twisting of the field with age may also conceivably lead to instabilities that can be triggered by disturbances of a different kind (see Section 7.5.4).

7.5.3.2. Surges

From estimates of the kinetic energy of surges (Section 7.4.3.1), we have seen that it is possible to consider the magnetic field observed in surges as an active region field being transported up into the corona by the surge plasma. However, the shape of the trajectory of some surges strongly suggests that the surge plasma is itself being guided along magnetic lines of force, which therefore must exist in the corona above active regions before the surge is shot up from these regions. It is at present not possible to decide which of these alternatives is realized in actual surges, but future observations of magnetic fields in surges should settle the issue.

Regardless of which of the above-mentioned alternatives is the more correct, the low-lying parts of the magnetic field (which is probably due to the nearest sunspot) may be called upon to provide the acceleration mechanism for the surge. Since surges are generally shot out of the active regions from flares, the magnetic acceleration mechanism is probably activated by the redistribution of magnetic field energy that may take place with the occurrence of the flare. In one possible picture of surges, the magnetic field therefore plays a dual role: it provides the acceleration mechanism for the surge and it guides the surge up into the corona, from which it also falls back along the same lines.

7.5.3.3. Loops

(a) SUNSPOT LOOPS — As the name implies, the magnetic field in these loops is provided by the sunspot over, or near, which the loop structure is formed. In somes cases, the loops may funnel a substantial part of the magnetic flux from one spot of a bipolar group to the other. In other loops, only one of the legs may be anchored in a spot and the magnetic flux will then return to other parts of the plage surrounding the spot. The magnetic field in the loop must be very nearly force-free, but little can be said about the intensity of the magnetic field. We have seen in Section 7.4.3.2 that Bumba and Kleczek (1961) interpreted the observed loops as magnetic flux tubes of more or less constant cross section, and deduced from this an essentially constant field intensity with height. However, this may be an oversimplification since the effects of additional parameters have been neglected (changing scale height, pressure differences). From measurements of linear polarization in H_z at the top of a loop system, Hyder (1964) inferred a magnetic field strength of about 60 gauss. Further observations are needed to determine how the field changes along the loop before theoretical arguments can be verified.

(b) FLARE LOOPS — Even less is known about the magnetic field in loops which generally bridge two parts of the flare structure (the two parallel strands that often constitute the main part of a large flare). If the flare is of the two-strand type that forms on either side of a pre-existing filament (Section 7.4.4.1b), one might expect the magnetic field configuration to bear resemblance to that of the filament. One might then picture the field as a long "tunnel" of loops bridging opposite magnetic polarities in the two flare strands. As with sunspot loops, observations of the magnetic field intensity along flare loops are highly desirable and will furnish information of great importance for the theory of such objects.

7.5.4. Prominence Activations

In Section 7.4.4.1c, we treated the phenomenon of winking filaments and discussed Hyder's (1966a) model for the oscillations executed by the prominence. The detailed nature of the perturbation was not studied, but a wave motion was assumed. These perturbations originate in flares and propagate with velocities of the order of 1000 km/sec, with a large spread between less than 400 km/sec and more than 1800 km/sec. The propagation takes place in the chromosphere or the corona at speeds much greater than the velocity of sound, V_s. For comparison, $V_s = 23$ km/sec for a temperature $T = 2 \times 10^4\,°\text{K}$. In Section 7.4.4.1a, we mentioned two other velocities, 1 km/sec and 100 km/sec, for disturbances originating in sunspots and flares, respectively. The 1-km/sec disturbance is subsonic, and we shall return to it in Section 7.5.4.2. The 100-km/sec perturbation may possibly be considered as a slow example of the 1000-km/sec disturbances; we know that the spread in velocity is large for this type.

7.5.4.1. *Activations due to flares*

Anderson (1966) considered the perturbations leading to the winking-filament phenomenon and assumed that they are weak hydromagnetic shocks generated during the flash phase of the flares. The disturbance is guided along magnetic lines of force up into the corona, where it is reflected and refracted and finally arrives at the chromosphere. If the disturbance encounters a filament, the latter will be pushed down by the shock and forced to oscillate. The dominant wave frequency, ω_0, of the disturbance is considerably greater than the critical frequency, ω_a [see Equation (1.155)], and we are in the high-frequency domain of acoustic wave modes. Observations show that ω_0 is of the order of 0.3 rad/sec, while at chromospheric temperatures $\omega_a = \gamma g/2 V_s \approx 0.02$ rad/sec . Hence, we do not expect the gravitational field to affect the disturbance significantly. Anderson considered the propagation to take place in a magnetic field approximated by

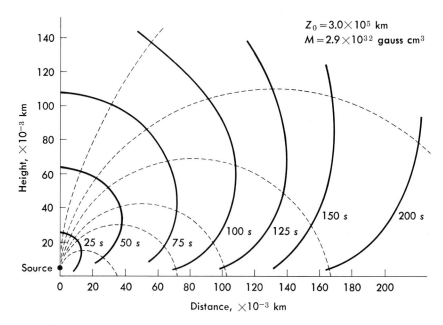

FIGURE 7.15. Propagation of flare disturbance in the corona (courtesy G. Anderson, 1966)

that of a magnetic dipole with moment M situated below the photosphere. By using a ray-tracing technique (Haselgrove, 1954, 1957; Budden, 1961), he then determined the path of the weak shock and the time of arrival at different distances in the chromosphere away from a flare source which was placed above the magnetic dipole. Figure 7.15 shows the assumed magnetic-field configuration in the corona and the propagation of the wave front. For instance, the disturbance will arrive in the chromosphere at a distance of 140,000 km from the source after about 150 sec. From the observed activation of a prominence situated at this distance, we deduce a perturbation velocity of slightly less than 1000 km/sec.

The assumed model for the magnetic field in the corona is idealized and will not describe actual field configurations too well. Also, the choice of the particular wave mode and the shape of the shock may be somewhat arbitrary, but the idea of using slightly nonlinear hydromagnetic waves to describe the disturbance is interesting, and further studies along these lines may explain other aspects of the disturbance (directivity of the disturbance, interaction with spicules, etc.).

7.5.4.2. *Activations due to sunspots*

The direct observation of this phenomenon (Bumba and Howard, 1965) shows that the disturbance is to be linked with the electromagnetic field propagating away from developing sunspots. We shall try to treat this by following Giovanelli (1947), who compared the growing magnetic field of a sunspot with the field resulting from a continuously oscillating magnetic dipole (Section 6.3.2.1e). The electromagnetic field set up around the dipole is given by Equations (6.59) and (6.60), and Giovanelli showed that the magnetic field would grow as if propagated with a velocity

$$V_{\text{dist}} \approx 3(2\omega c^2/\sigma)^{1/2}, \qquad (7.67)$$

where ω is the frequency of the dipole oscillation and σ the electric conductivity. To make a rough estimate of this velocity, we take $\omega = 5 \times 10^{-6}$ sec^{-1} and $\sigma = 10^8$ sec^{-1}. This gives $V_{\text{dist}} \approx 0.3$ km/sec, not unlike the velocities inferred by Bruzek (1952) and by Bumba and Howard (1965).

The phenomenon treated here is apparently quite different from the flare-induced disturbances treated in the previous Section. If the propagating magnetic field encounters a filament, the interaction between the filament magnetic field (a modified plage field) and the disturbance may possibly be quite different from the interaction between a filament and a flare-induced disturbance. Bumba and Howard's observation showed that the filament that was hit by the slow disturbance did not undergo winking motions or an abrupt disappearance, but broke up over a period of two days. This may indicate that the two magnetic fields involved interacted in such a way as to profoundly alter the magnetic field configuration of the filament.

7.5.5. Filaments and Sympathetic Flares

In Section 6.1.2.2, we discussed sympathetic flares and indicated that the existence of a filament may be necessary for the second flare to occur. This inference was based on observations (S. Smith, 1965) of disturbances propagating from flares and interacting with dark filaments which were found in the location of the ensuing sympathetic flares. It is an interesting fact, which may be of great importance, that there is a considerable time lag (from a few minutes to more than thirty minutes) between the onset of the filament activation and the start of the sympathetic flare, which presumably occurs below the filament. One may therefore divide the phenomenon of sympathetic flares into two parts, namely (1) a flare-induced filament activation, followed by (2) a filament-induced flare. If this picture is correct, it gives further evidence that the optical flare forms at the expense of energy stored in the filament (Section 7.4.4.1b). Research along these lines may open new vistas in our understanding of flare-prominence interactions, and may be useful in flare-prediction schemes.

The solar corona during the total solar eclipse of 20 July, 1963, photographed at Talkeetna, Alaska by R. R. Fisher of the High Altitude Observatory's 1963 eclipse expedition.

The Active Corona | 8

8.1. *Introduction and Observations*

Plages, sunspots, flares and prominences are all signs of activity and disappear under quiet conditions in the solar atmosphere. A similar state of affairs may exist for the corona, but this part of the atmosphere is generally considered to consist of two parts: the quiet and the active corona. We have treated the minimum-activity corona and several aspects of the active corona (radio and X-ray plages, etc.) in Section 3.3 and shall in this chapter deal with some of the remaining problems of the active corona. An excellent book on the corona has recently been published by Billings (1966), and the reader is referred to this book for further details. We shall rely on his book for many of the observations and descriptions to be presented in the following.

8.1.1. The Unobservable Quiet Corona

Secchi (1875) was probably the first to realize that the form of the corona changes during the solar cycle, and when sufficient photographs became available, Young (1896) distinguished between the maximum type and the minimum type of coronal structure. At times of sunspot maximum, the corona is more or less spherical and can be observed in white light or at radio frequencies out to distances of many solar radii (Section 3.3.1). When the activity diminishes, as measured by the occurrence of plages, sunspots and prominences, the corona shrinks, especially at the poles. We then observe the typical minimum corona, which is characterized by fairly long low-latitude *streamers* and short polar *plumes* (see Figure 8.1). The streamers are found above magnetic plages, and one might conjecture that under extremely quiet conditions (such as have not been realized at least in recent times) most of the equatorial corona would also disappear. Therefore, there is at least a philosophical question whether a true "quiet corona" really exists.

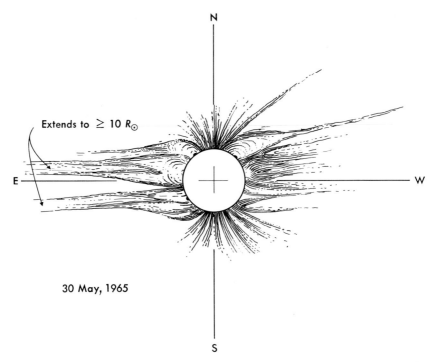

FIGURE 8.1.   Drawing of the corona near sunspot minimum (drawing courtesy J. D. Bohlin, High Altitude Observatory; from photographs by S. Smith, NASA Ames Research Center)

In praxis, it certainly does, and different aspects of it have been discussed in Section 3.3. For detailed drawings of coronal features, see Bugoslovskaya (1949) and Vsekhsvjatsky (1963).

8.1.2. Coronal Features of Different Degrees of Activity

We shall now describe a number of different coronal forms that are manifestations of increasing importance of solar activity.

8.1.2.1. *Polar plumes*

During periods of minimum solar activity, the polar region (latitudes higher than about 70 degrees) is characterized by the presence of polar plumes. These appear as nearly vertical cylindrical columns of cross section of about 7000 km and reach to heights of several hundred thousand km. We do not know the distribution of these plumes over the solar surfaces; they may be imbedded in an ambient structureless coronal plasma, or this seemingly structureless corona may itself be unresolved plumes. Furthermore, we do not know whether the plumes are the basic structure of the entire corona but are seen only under special conditions near the poles, always being masked by other structures due to higher activity at lower latitudes. It seems that the plumes are the basic structure element of the minimum (if not completely quiet) corona just as the spicules are the basic quiescent chromosphere. But only speculations can be made as to whether the plumes play a role in the energy balance of the corona, similarly as spicules provide the coupling between photosphere and chromosphere, regardless of activity.

8.1.2.2. Helmets

Above magnetic plages in which quiescent prominences occur one often sees streamer-like structures referred to as *helmets*. Billings (1966) describes their characteristic appearance as a broad spade shape with the prominence—observed edge-on above the disk—at the axis of symmetry. The broadest part of the helmet is about one-half solar radius, and the upper end draws toward a sharp point at one or two radii above the limb. Right above the prominence, one generally observes a series of arch- or loop-like structures (see Figure 8.1, where a helmet is visible in the NW quadrant).

8.1.2.3. Streamers

This designation is reserved for the coronal structures that extend out to several solar radii above developing magnetic plages in which sunspots, but not quiescent prominences, may occur. The streamers have a fairly uniform cross section, or may spread out somewhat in the outer parts. These are the structures that give the minimum corona its characteristic appearance (see Figure 8.1, where two long streamers are seen on the east limb). The lowest part of streamers forms the more or less homogeneous enhancement; see the following discussion.

8.1.2.4. Enhancements

Enhancements (Billings, 1966) may appear over any sunspot group and are identical to the *permanent condensations* described by Waldmeier (1956). They are not permanent but outlast the life of the associated sunspot group and are, at least at times, even longer-lived than the lower-lying plage (Nagasawa and Nakagomi, 1965). During periods of high solar activity, enhancements can also be found in polar regions. Their emission spectrum is characterized by the red (Fe X, 6374 Å) and green (Fe XIV, 5303 Å) coronal lines. An enhancement is typically about five times as bright as the normal corona and has a diameter of more than 10^5 km. Their outward extension is the above-mentioned streamer.

8.1.2.5. *Condensations*

Over very active sunspot groups in the inner, dense portion of an enhancement, there may occur a short-lived (hours or days) high-temperature *condensation.* This is identical to Waldmeier's (1956) *sporadic condensation,* and is probably the region where the greatest optical activity in the solar atmosphere is found. The diameter is typically a few ten-thousand km. The condensation may take the shape of a bright white knot just above a loop prominence, or it may itself be loop-formed. In white light it looks like a white prominence (Waldmeier, 1962). Spectroscopically, condensations are characterized by a strong continuum and lines of highly ionized calcium, the lines of Ca XIII, 4086 Å and Ca XV, 5445 Å and 5694 Å—the yellow coronal lines.

8.1.3. The Outer Extension of the Corona

The solar wind model of the corona (Parker, 1961) predicts a certain flux of particles escaping out through interplanetary space at times of solar minimum activity. We have seen (Section 3.3.2) that satellite observations

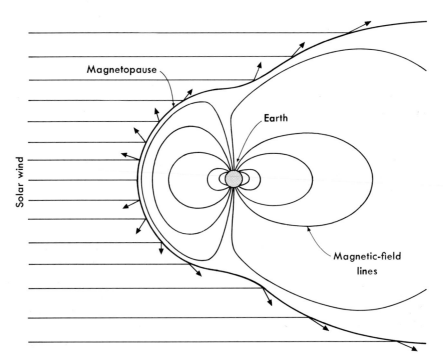

FIGURE 8.2.   Simplified representation of the interaction of the solar wind plasma with the earth's magnetic field (courtesy N. F. Ness, 1966)

indicate a steady stream of particles with a density near the earth of about one particle per cm³ and a velocity of a few hundred km/sec, maybe 300 km/sec. During times of increased activity, both the particle density and the velocity increase, and this dynamic extension of the corona must reach out far beyond the earth's orbit.

The solar wind—at minimum activity as well as during increased activity—interacts with the earth's magnetic field, and the effect of the extended corona on the earth's magnetosphere is pictured in the simplified representation of Figure 8.2 (Ness, 1966). The boundary of the magnetosphere, the magneto-pause, is shown distorted by the solar wind plasma, and direct impacts of the plasma particles with the magnetic field leading to reflections are indicated with arrows.

A wealth of interesting questions are connected with this and other aspects of solar–terrestrial relationships. However, it is outside the scope of this book to pursue the matter further, and the reader is instead referred to Ellison (1955), Le Galley (1963), and others.

8.2. *Models*

8.2.1. Polar Plumes

Cowling (1957) mentioned as a possible explanation for the polar plumes an accumulation of matter in vertical columns along lines of force of a general polar magnetic field. We have seen (Section 4.3.3) that the existence of a general solar field is dubious, but there will be patches of magnetic field due to magnetic plages that have migrated toward the poles from the sunspot zones. Cowling remarked that in a field initially vertical and uniform, an increased density in a particular vertical column would produce a lateral expansion of the lines of force until the decreased magnetic pressure in the column compensates for the increased gas pressure. Since the gas pressure is less than 5×10^{-2} dyne/cm² at the base of the corona and falls off with height, a field of only 1 gauss would be sufficient to maintain the shape of the polar plumes.

From the brightness fluctuations observed when tracing across the polar regions on 1954 eclipse plates, Waldmeier (1961c) determined the density in plumes to be five times that of the interplume plasma. Waldmeier's result pertains to the most extreme minimum observed, but similar results had been obtained by van de Hulst (1950) and Hepburn (1955) using other eclipse observations.

8.2.2. Helmets and Streamers

Models have been deduced for the low-lying features in the corona, for the enhancements and, especially for the condensations. On the other hand, few concrete facts have been combined for streamers of different kinds (helmets and active-region streamers) to build detailed models. The significance that helmets are found above "organized" magnetic plages with quiescent prominences while young active regions occur near the base of streamers may not be obvious. However, the difference is probably to be sought in the configurations of the magnetic fields in the two cases. The helmets may be considered outlined by the upper part of the magnetic field configuration whose lower part supports the prominence (compare Figure 7.13). A helmet is therefore probably a long-lived phenomenon (months), as the stable field configuration would indicate.

Above active regions where no filament has formed, the magnetic lines of force form configurations that will change as the active region changes. The streamers occurring there typically have lifetimes of the order of weeks.

According to Saito (1950), there does not seem to be much difference between the density gradients in helmets and streamers. In both cases, he approximated the density distribution by the formula

$$n_e = 1.9 \times 10^7/r^3, \qquad 1.5 < r < 4.0, \qquad (8.1)$$

where r is the distance in units of the solar radius. On the other hand, Hepburn (1955) concluded that the great streamer observed at the 1952 eclipse revealed a much flatter density gradient than the helmet on the SW limb seen at the same eclipse.

A striking feature of helmets is a dark region just above the quiescent prominence, and above and around this dark region one often sees alternate dark and bright arches concentric with the prominence (Obashev, 1961). The electron density in the dark region has been estimated by von Klüber (1961), who found that very little electron scattering takes place in this area, which may be considered a local vacuum. We can think of the vacuum as being due to the material condensing onto the lower-lying quiescent prominence, carrying the magnetic field with it (Billings, 1966). See also Figure 7.13, in which the prominence forms in region A.

8.2.3. Enhancements

8.2.3.1. *The radio plage*

On cm and dm wavelengths, one observes the slowly varying component of radio emission which comes from low and intermediate coronal heights (Section 4.2.3). There is a high correlation between the intensity of this component and the sunspot number or, better, the area of plages (Covington, 1954; Firor, 1959b; Kundu, 1959; Christiansen *et al.*, 1960; Moutot and Boischot, 1961). The radio emission can be understood in terms of thermal radiation at a temperature and density both slightly higher than in the surrounding undisturbed corona. In other words, the radio emission comes from radio plages whose lowest parts we identify with the optically observed enhancements.

In the lower parts of the radio plage, as observed for instance on a wavelength of 3 cm, one sees at times small, embedded, bright regions overlying very active sunspots. These regions give rise to the circularly polarized radio emission known as *the gradual rise and fall* with a lifetime of the order of minutes or hours. We identify these regions with the optically observed condensations (Newkirk, 1961). Since the gradual-rise-and-fall component of radio emission is partly circularly polarized, it is likely that the sunspot magnetic field is of importance in condensations. The fact that many condensations are loop-shaped supports this view.

8.2.3.2. *Newkirk's model*

In his model, Newkirk (1961) referred to the electron density, n_1, in the corona outside enhancements and assumed

$$n_1 = n_0\, 10^{4.32/r}, \tag{8.2}$$

where $n_0 = 4.2 \times 10^4$ and r is the distance from the center of the sun in units of the sun's radius. For the density in the enhancement, he took

$$n = n_1[1 + a\, e^{-b^2}], \tag{8.3}$$

that is, a Gaussian distribution around the vertical axis of the assumed cylindrical enhancement. The best values for a and b were found by a least-square analysis of K-coronameter observations of enhancements. The main results are that the density in an enhancement is larger by a small factor (2 or 3) than the density in the adjacent corona and that the temperature, 1 to $2 \times 10^6\ °K$, is about the same as outside the enhancement.

8.2.4. Condensations

8.2.4.1. *Waldmeier and Müller's model*

Waldmeier and Müller (1950) considered a typical condensation to have a diameter of about 125,000 km and to be about five times as bright as the normal corona. The model consists of hemispherical shells of equal density, ranging from $6.3 \times 10^9\ cm^{-3}$ in the center to $1.6 \times 10^9\ cm^{-3}$ in the outermost shell. This model was used to explain the slowly varying component at a wavelength of 10 cm, but it was not possible to distinguish between two versions of the model: one with a uniform temperature of 1.4×10^6 °K and one in which the temperature decreased from 6×10^6 °K in the core. Because of the strong yellow coronal line emission from bright condensations, the latter alternative is to be considered the more correct, even though 6×10^6 °K is probably somewhat extreme. Also, we have seen that the slowly varying component more likely comes from enhancements.

8.2.4.2. *Waldmeier's model*

This model (Waldmeier, 1963) refers to the brilliant condensation observed during the 1962 eclipse, a condensation the author referred to as a "white prominence." There are two versions of the model. In one, Waldmeier assumed cylindrical symmetry; the other model has an elliptical horizontal cross section corresponding to the underlying plage. The electron densities computed from these geometrical models do not differ much, ranging—on the axis of symmetry—from 6.3×10^9 cm^{-3} at $r = 1.02$ to 3×10^8 cm^{-3} at $r = 1.3$.

8.2.4.3. *Nishi and Nakagomi's model*

Nishi and Nakagomi (1963) used observations of the intensities of coronal lines (Fe X, 6374 Å; Fe XIV, 5303 Å; Ca XV, 5694 Å) and the intensity of the radio emission at 21 cm to construct their model. The model consists of a core and a surrounding part. The electron temperature in the core—the yellow-line region—is taken to be 4×10^6 °K. The surrounding region, from which the green and the red lines come, consists of two temperature domains, 2.4×10^6 °K (the green line region) and 1.7×10^6 °K (the red line region). Nishi and Nakagomi's model thus encompasses both the central condensation and the more extended enhancement. The 21-cm radio flux to be expected for different values of the electron density was calculated from Equation (4.9c), which here takes the form

$$F_{21} = (2k/\lambda^2) \int d\Omega \int T_e(\tau)\, e^{-\tau}\, d\tau, \qquad (8.4)$$

and the electron density was determined from the best fit. In Equation (8.4), $d\Omega$ is the solid angle of the emitting source, and the optical depth $d\tau$ is calculated from Equation (4.10).

The resulting model for the condensation has an electron density in excess of 5×10^9 cm^{-3} and contributes little to the 21-cm flux. The enhancement has a fine structure consisting of the hot green-line region and the cooler red-line region. In these elements, the density is 10^9 cm^{-3} or more, and most of the 21-cm flux originates there.

8.2.4.4. *Saito and Billings' model*

Saito and Billings' (1964) model refers, like Waldmeier's, to the condensation observed at the 1962 eclipse. According to these authors, the condensation consists mainly of three loops, and they attempted to describe the density distribution in the condensation in terms of cylindrical symmetry around the axis of the principal loop system. The concentration of matter in the condensation therefore was assumed to be higher than in Waldmeier's model, and the value of n_e came out about twice the value given by Waldmeier. Apart from this, the agreement is good and the analysis shows that the density in bright condensations is about 10^{10} cm^{-3} in the dense parts. Furthermore, the fact that these active condensations have a loop structure may be of great significance and should be considered a major part of the model.

The Ca XV lines often show Doppler shifts, indicating that the condensation moves with typical velocities of up to 25 km/sec. On the other hand, turbulence seems to be of little importance in broadening the lines, and the most likely ion kinetic temperature is in excess of 4×10^6 °K (Boardman and Billings, 1966), maybe between 5 and 6×10^6 °K.

8.3. *Relationship to Flares and Active Prominences*

8.3.1. Radio Bursts and the Active Corona

We mentioned in Section 6.1.5 that different kinds of radio bursts—which all occur in the corona—are related to flares. We also treated the different possibilities of accounting for the radio disturbances in terms of shock waves, plasma oscillations, and synchrotron emission (see Figures 6.5, 6.6 and 6.7). In this section we shall discuss the radio bursts in their relation to the corona.

The occurrence of type III bursts, which are caused by a very fast (velocity of the order of $\frac{1}{3}$ to $\frac{1}{2}c$) moving disturbance (pulses of low-density electrons), increases with the importance of the flare (Wild, Roberts, and Murray, 1954; Malville, 1961), and if the flare produces a flare–surge, this increases by a factor of two the probability of an associated type III burst (Swarup, Stone, and Maxwell, 1960). This simply indicates that the more active a flare region is in accelerating plasma clouds and particle streams, the greater is the probability that bursts will be observed in the corona, where they are generated by the interaction of the particles with the coronal matter in the active corona above plages. The solar-wind plasma apparently carries with it photospheric magnetic fields (Ness and Wilcox, 1965), and it is reasonable to suppose that this transport also takes place above active regions. As we go up into the corona high above active regions, the magnetic field seems to become more or less radial, or rather, deviates sufficiently from the radial direction to be approximately describable in terms of Archimedes spirals that map the trajectories of the plasma streams moving radially outward from a rotating sun (Ness, Scearce, Seek, and Wilcox, 1965). The coronal streamers may thus be regarded as the paths along which the complex flare-initiated disturbances travel out into the outer corona, as different types of excess radio noise are generated by the interaction with the local plasma. Whether the streamer is formed by a slow outflow of plasma only slightly enhanced above active regions, or whether the violently ejected flare material provides a major part of the streamer plasma is not clear.

Observation of the scattering of extrasolar radio waves by the corona gives support to the picture of a near-radial magnetic field model in the outer corona. The Crab Nebula comes behind the corona, as seen from the earth once a year, and the radio waves from the Crab Nebula will be scattered, on their way to the earth, by the coronal particles. The orientation of the scattering particles indicates that the magnetic field in the corona is more or less radial at a distance of several solar radii (Hewish, 1958; Vitkevich and Panovkin, 1959) or at least shows some preference for a radial orientation (Erickson, 1964).

Lower in the corona, extensive plasma clouds may become trapped in the magnetic field and the synchrotron radiation from these regions is believed responsible for the continuous radio emission known as type IV bursts. The regions may be considered part of the coronal streamer overlying the particular condensation associated with the flare. Again, we see the overriding importance of the "particle flare" when dealing with the total picture of these disturbances—a point of view discussed in Chapter 6.

8.3.2. Coronal Loops

In the two preceding Chapters we have repeatedly had the opportunity to see how often loop structures are realized in flares and active prominences. We also encounter this basic geometric form in coronal structures. The optical coronal feature most closely associated with flares is the coronal condensation emitting the Ca XV lines (Billings, 1966), and these yellow-line regions often take the shape of loops. Also, the regions emitting the green coronal line (Fe XIV, 5303 Å) may show loop structure (Evans, 1957). Zirin (1959, 1964) has drawn attention to the complex interplay between what we generally consider flare manifestations and what is called coronal activity. He has observed limb events in which strong continuous radiation is emitted from a coronal plasma cloud just prior to the occurrence of a flare. Then, with the release of the flare energy, coronal lines were observed and copious amounts of particles were accelerated.

Often the coronal loops, as observed in the yellow coronal line or in the iron lines (Fe X, 6374 Å and Fe XIV, 5303 Å), nearly coincide with active loop prominences (Newkirk, 1957; Karimov and Shilova, 1959). Newkirk showed that the coronal velocity, v_{cor}, inferred from the Doppler displacement of the red coronal line, has a mean value of $\bar{v}_{cor} = 14$ km/sec , while the corresponding prominence velocity, v_{prom}, deduced from the Hα line, gave $\bar{v}_{prom} = 34$ km/sec . Consequently, even though the coronal and prominence loops are closely related, the plasmas making up the two different temperature domains still move at least to a certain extent independently of each other.

The coronal loop structure and its close relationship to loop prominences strongly suggest the influence of magnetic fields. These could be the coronal counterparts of the magnetic fields of the underlying active region. Even if we did not have the velocity measurements mentioned above, it is clear that the loop configuration cannot be in static equilibrium. Both temperature and density are higher than in the surrounding corona, and we now also imply that the magnetic field in the loops is increased relative to its value outside. A dynamic model should include a description of the preflare injection of matter into the coronal condensation, the trapping of the plasma by the magnetic field in the loop structure, expansion or contraction of the magnetic flux tubes giving rise to the observed velocities, the high excitation conditions brought about by the excess heating process over the plage, and the final dumping of the coronal material due to some kind of disturbance. Different aspects of this complex chain of events have been discussed in Chapters 4, 6, and 7. While a comprehensive physical picture of this—the most dramatic manifestation of solar activity—is slowly emerging, much still remains to be done.

References

ABEL, W. C., J. H. CHISHOLM, P. L. FLECK, and J. C. JAMES, 1961, "Radar Reflections from the Sun at Very High Frequencies," *J.G.R. 66*, 4303.

ABETTI, G., 1929, "Solar Physics," *Handbuch der Astrophysik 4*, 57.

——1963, *The Sun* (2nd ed.) (translated by Sidgwick), London: Faber and Faber.

ABHYANKAR, K. D. and A. S. RAMANATHAN, 1955, "Equivalent Widths of Atomic Lines in Sunspot Spectra," *Ap. J. 121*, 739.

ACTON, L., 1964, "X-radiation of the Sun," Ph.D. Diss., University of Colorado.

AKHIEZER, A. I., I. G. PROKHODA, and A. G. SITENKO, 1957, "On the Scattering of Electromagnetic Waves in a Plasma," *J. E. T. P. (USSR) 33*, 750.

ALEXANDER, E., U. FELDMAN, B. S. FRAENKEL, and S. HOORY, 1965, "$3p^6$–$3p^53d$ Transitions of Fe IX and Ni XI in the Solar Spectrum," *Nature 206*, 176.

ALFVÉN, H., 1940, "Tentative Theory of Solar Prominences," *Ark. Mat. Astron. Fys. 27A*, No. 20.

——1941, "On the Solar Corona," *Ark. Mat. Astron. Fys. 27A*, No. 25.

——1943a, "On Sunspots and the Solar Cycle," *Ark. Mat. Astron. Fys. 29A*, No. 12.

——1943b, "On the Existence of Electromagnetic-hydromagnetic Waves," *Ark. Mat. Astron. Fys. 29B*, No. 2.

——1945a, "Magneto-hydrodynamic Waves and Sunspots I," *M. N. 105*, 3.

——1945b, "Sunspots and Magneto-hydrodynamic Waves II," *M. N. 105*, 382.

——1947, "Granulation, Magneto-hydrodynamic Waves, and the Heating of the Solar Corona," *M.N. 107*, 211.

——1950, *Cosmical Electrodynamics*, London: Clarendon Press.

——1958, "Interplanetary Magnetic Field," *I. A. U. Symposium No. 6*, p. 284.

ALLEN, C. W., 1940, "Stark Effect and Damping Factor in the Fraunhofer Spectrum," *M. N. 100*, 4.

——1946, "The Spectrum of the Corona at the Eclipse of 1940, October 1," *M. N. 106*, 137.

——1960, "Oscillator Strengths of Neutral Atoms of the Iron-Group," *M. N.* *121*, 299.

——1963, *Astrophysical Quantities* (2nd ed.), London: Athalone Press.

ALTSCHULER, M., 1964, "Interaction of Fast Charged Particles with the Coronal Plasma," Ph. D. Diss., Yale University.

ALY, M. K., J. W. EVANS, and F. Q. ORRALL, 1963, "A Photometric Study of the Continuum and Seventeen Emission Lines in the Inner Solar Corona," *Ap. J.* *136*, 956.

ANANTHAKRISHNAN, R. and P. MADHAVAN NAYAR, 1953, "Discussion of the Results of Observations of Solar Prominences made at Kodiakanal from 1904 to 1950," *Kodiakanal Obs. Bull.* No. 137, 194.

ANDERSON, G. F., 1966, "Transient Flare-Associated Phenomena in the Solar Atmosphere," Ph. D. Diss., University of Colorado.

ANDERSON, K. A. and J. R. WINCKLER, 1962, "Solar Flare X-ray Burst on September 28, 1961," *J. G. R.* *67*, 4103.

ATHAY, R. G., 1959, "The Number of Spicules in the Middle Chromosphere," *Ap. J.* *129*, 164.

——1963, "Excitation of Chromospheric He I," *Ap. J.* *137*, 931.

——and C. L. HYDER, 1963, "Coronal Ionization by Two-Step Collision Process," *Ap. J.* *137*, 21.

——and D. H. MENZEL, 1956, "A Model of the Chromosphere from the Helium and Continuum Emissions," *Ap. J.* *123*, 285.

——and G. E. MORETON, 1961, "Impulsive Phenomena of the Solar Atmosphere I. Some Optical Events Associated with Flares Showing Explosive Phase," *Ap. J.* *133*, 935.

AVIGNON, Y., A. BOISCHOT, and P. SIMON, 1959, "Observations interférométriques à 169 Mc/s des centres R, sources des orages de bruit," *Paris Symposium on Radio Astronomy* (R. N. Bracewell, Ed.), p. 240, Stanford University Press.

——and A. M. MALINGE, 1961, "Dimensions du soleil calme sur 169 MHz," *C. R* *253*, 2859.

——M. J. MARTRES-TROPE, and M. PICK-GUTMANN, 1963, "Identification d'une classe d'éruptions chromosphériques responsables des absorptions ionosphériques polaires," *C. R. 256*, 2112.

BABCOCK, H. D., 1940, "Annual Report of the Director of the Mt. Wilson Observatory, 1939–40," *Carnegie Inst. Washington Year Book* No. 39, 9.

——1945, "Chemical Compounds in the Sun," *Ap. J.* *102*, 154.

——and H. W. BABCOCK, 1952, "Mapping the Magnetic Fields of the Sun," *The Sun* (G. Kuiper, Ed.), p. 704, Chicago: University of Chicago Press.

——and H. W. BABCOCK, 1955, "The Sun's Magnetic Field, 1952–1954," *Ap. J.* *121*, 349.

BABCOCK, H. W., 1953, "The Solar Magnetograph," *Ap. J.* *118*, 387.

——1960, "The Magnetism of the Sun," *Sci. Amer. 202* (February), 52.

——1961, "The Topology of the Sun's Magnetic Field and the 22-year Cycle," *Ap. J.* *133*, 572.

——1963, "The Sun's Magnetic Field," *Ann. Rev. Astron. Ap. 1*, 41.

BAHNG, J. and M. SCHWARZSCHILD, 1961, "Lifetime of Solar Granules," *Ap. J.* *134*, 312.

——and M. SCHWARZCHILD, 1963, "Hydrodynamic Oscillations in the Solar Chromosphere," *Ap. J. 137*, 901.

BATCHELOR, G. K., 1950, "On the Spontaneous Magnetic Field in a Conducting Liquid in Turbulent Motion," *Proc. Roy. Soc. (London) A 201*, 405.

BECKER, U., 1952, "Zur Bewegung von Protuberanzen," *Naturwiss. 39*, 139.

——1956, "Über die Entwicklung langlebiger Filamente und ihre Orientierung auf der Sonnenscheibe," *Z. Ap. 40*, 65.

——1957, "Der Filamentaufstieg von August 9, 1956," *Z. Ap. 42*, 85.

——1958, "Über die Fernauslösung von Eruptionen," *Z. Ap. 44*, 243.

BECKERS, J. M., 1964, "On the Relation between Solar Granules and Spicules," *Ap. J. 140*, 1339.

BEGGS, D. W. and H. VON KLÜBER, 1956, "A Solar Magnetograph," *Nature 178*, 1412.

——and H. VON KLÜBER, 1964, "Measurements of the General Magnetic Field of the Sun with a Magnetograph," *M. N. 127*, 133.

BEHR, A. and H. SIEDENTOPF, 1952, "Zur Statistik von Sonneneruptionen," *Z. Ap. 30*, 177.

BELL, B. and H. GLAZER, 1959, "Some Sunspot and Flare Statistics," *Smithsonian Contributions to Astrophysics 3*, 25.

BELL, P. R., 1948, "The Use of Anthracene as a Scintillation Counter," *Phys. Rev. 73*, 1405.

BERGSTRÖM, I., 1955, "Auger Electrons Emitted from Radioactive Atoms," *Beta and Gamma Ray Spectroscopy* (K. Siegbahn, Ed.), p. 624, New York: Interscience Press.

BETHE, H. A., 1933, "Quantenmechanik der Ein- und Zwei- Elektronenprobleme," *Handbuch der Physik* (2nd ed.) *24/1*, 273.

BHATNAGAR, P. L., M. KROOK, and D. H. MENZEL, 1951, "Dynamics of Ionized Media," *Report of Conference on Dynamics of Ionized Media*, University College, London.

BIERMANN, L., 1941, "Der gegenwärtige Stand der Theorie konvektiver Sonnen-modelle," *Vierteljahrschrift Astron. Gesellschaft 76*, 194.

——1946, "Zur Deutung der chromosphärischen Turbulenz und des Exzesses der UV-Strahlung der Sonne," *Naturwiss. 33*, 118.

——1950, "Über den Ursprung der Magnetfelder auf Sternen und im interstellaren Raum," *Z. Naturforsch. 5a*, 65.

——1951, "Kometenschweife und solare Korpuskularstrahlung," *Z. Ap. 29*, 274.

——1952, "Über den Schweif des Kometen Halley im Jahre 1910," *Z. Naturforsch. 7a*, 127.

——1957, "Solar Corpuscular Radiation and the Interplanetary Gas," *Obs. 77*, 109.

BILLINGS, D. E., 1959, "Distribution of Matter with Temperature in the Emission Corona," *Ap. J. 130*, 961.

——1962, "Spectroscopic Limitation on Coronal Heating Mechanisms," *Ap. J. 137*, 592.

——1966, *A Guide to the Solar Corona*, New York: Academic Press.

——and W. O. ROBERTS, 1953, "Isophotal Photometry of a Solar Flare," *Ap. J. 118*, 429.

BIRKS, J. B., 1953, *Scintillation Counters*, New York: McGraw-Hill.

BISHOP, A. S., 1966, "Talk on Roadblocks in the Path of Controlled Fusion," *AEC Research and Development Report*, MATT-412, Princeton University.

BISWAS, S., C. E. FICHTEL, and D. E. GUSS, 1962, "A Study of the Hydrogen, Helium and Heavy Nuclei in the November 12, 1960, Solar Cosmic Ray Event," *NASA Rep. X-611-62-27*, Goddard Space Flight Center.

——P. S. FREIER, and W. STEIN, 1962, "Solar Protons and α Particles from the September 3, 1960, Flares," *J. G. R. 67*, 13.

BJERKE, K., 1961, "Visual Determinations of Ascending Velocities in Some Eruptive Solar Prominences," *Ark. Astron. 2*, No. 13, 145.

BJERKNES, V., 1926, "Solar Hydrodynamics," *Ap. J. 64*, 93.

BLACKWELL, D. E., D. W. DEWHIRST, and A. DOLLFUS, 1959, "The Observation of Solar Granulation from a Manned Balloon I. Observational Data and Measurement of Contrast," *M. N. 119*, 98.

BLAKE, R. L., T. A. CHUBB, H. FRIEDMAN, and A. E. UNZICKER, 1963, "Interpretation of X-ray Photograph of the Sun," *Ap. J. 137*, 3.

BOARDMAN, W. J. and D. E. BILLINGS, 1966, private communication.

BOHM, D. and E. P. GROSS, 1949a, "Theory of Plasma Oscillations A. Origin of Medium-like Behavior," *Phys. Rev. 75*, 1851.

——and E. P. GROSS, 1949b, "Theory of Plasma Oscillations B. Excitation and Damping Oscillations," *Phys. Rev. 75*, 1864.

BÖHM-VITENSE, E., 1951, "Der Aufbau der Sternatmosphären IV. Kontinuierliche Absorption und Strenung als Funktion von Druck und Temperatur," *Z. Ap. 28*, 81.

——1953, "Die Wasserstoffkonvektionszone der Sonne," *Z. Ap. 32*, 135.

——1954, "Über die Temperatur- und Druckschichtung der Sonnenatmosphäre," *Z. Ap. 34*, 209.

BOISCHOT, A., 1958, "Étude du rayonnement radioélectrique solaire sur 169 MHz, à l'aide d'un grand interféromètre à réseau," *Ann. d'Ap. 21*, 273.

BRATIICHUK, M. V., 1961, "Results of Spectrophotometry of Several Prominences," *Publ. Kiev Obs. 9*, 11.

BRAY, R. J. and R. E. LOUGHHEAD, 1958, "Observations of Changes in the Photospheric Granules," *Aust. J. Phys. 11*, 507.

——and R. E. LOUGHHEAD, 1959, "High Resolution Observations of the Granular Structure of Sunspot Umbrae," *Aust. J. Phys. 12*, 320.

——and R. E. LOUGHHEAD, 1964, *Sunspots*, New York: Wiley.

BRILLOUIN, L., 1926, "Remarques sur la méchanique ondulatoire," *J. Phys. Rad. Ser. 6, 7*, 353.

BROXON, J. W., 1942, "Relation of the Cosmic Radiation to Geomagnetic and Heliophysical Activities," *Phys. Rev. 62*, 508.

BROWN, A., 1958, "On the Stability of a Hydromagnetic Prominence Model," *Ap. J. 128*, 646.

BRUCE, C. E. R., 1944, *A New Approach in Astrophysics and Cosmogony*, London.

——1963, "Cosmic Electrical Discharges," *J. Inst. Electr. Engrs. 9*, 356.

BRUZEK, A., 1951a, "Über eine ungewöhnliche chromosphärische Eruption," *Anz. Math.-Naturwiss. Kl. Österr. Akad. Wiss. 12*, Nr. 6, 145 (*Mitt. Sonnenobser. Kanzelhöhe* Nr. 4).

——1951b, "Beobachtungen über das Verhalten von Filamenten während chromosphärischer Eruptionen," *Z. Ap. 28*, 277.

——1952, "Über die Ursache der 'plötzlichen' Filamentauflösungen," *Z. Ap. 31*, 99.

——1957, "Über eruptionsartige Fackeln bei Filamentaufstiegen," *Z. Ap. 42*, 76.

——1958, "Die Filamente und Eruptionen eines Aktivitätszentrums," *Z. Ap. 44*, 183.

——1960, "Beobachtungen über die Beziehungen zwischen Eruptionen und Fleckenfeldern," *Z. Ap. 50*, 110.

——1962, "Über Fleckenprotuberanzen vor der Sonnenscheibe," *Z. Ap. 54*, 225.

——1964, "On the Association between Loop Prominences and Flares," *Ap. J. 140*, 746.

BUDDEN, K. G., 1961, *Radio Waves in the Ionosphere*, London: Cambridge University Press.

BUGOSLAVSKAYA, E. J., 1949, "Structure of the Solar Corona," *Publ. Sternberg Astron. Inst. (Moscow) 19*, 1.

BULLARD, E. C., 1949, "The Magnetic Field within the Earth," *Proc. Roy. Soc. (London) A 197*, 433.

——1955, "The Magnetic Fields of Sunspots," *Vistas in Astronomy 1*, 685.

BUMBA, V., 1958, "Relation between Chromospheric Flares and Magnetic Fields of Sunspot Groups," *Iz. Krim. Ap. Obs. 19*, 105.

——1960a, "Results of the Investigation of the Single Sunspot Magnetic Field," *Iz. Krim. Ap. Obs. 23*, 212.

——1960b, "Results of the Study of the Evershed Effect in Single Sunspots," *Iz. Krim. Ap. Obs. 23*, 253.

——1960c, "The Connection between the Magnetic Field and Motion in Single Sunspots," *Iz. Krim. Ap. Obs. 23*, 277.

——1962, "Contribution to the Study of the Magnetic Field in Sunspot Umbrae," *B. A. C. 13*, 42.

——and R. HOWARD, 1965, "A Study of the Development of Active Regions on the Sun," *Ap. J. 141*, 1492.

——and J. KLECZEK, 1961, "On a Sunspot Group with an Outstanding Loop Activity," *Obs. 81*, 141.

BURGESS, A., 1964, "Dielectronic Recombination and the Temperature of the Solar Corona," *Ap. J. 139*, 776.

BURNIGHT, T.R., 1949, "Soft X-radiation in the Upper Atmosphere," *Phys. Rev. 76*, 165.

BYRNE, F. N., M. A. ELLISON, and J. H. REID, 1964, "A Survey of Solar Flare Phenomena," *Space Sci. Rev. 3*, 319.

CARRINGTON, C., 1859, "Description of a Singular Appearance Seen in the Sun on September 1, 1859." *M. N. 20*, 13.

CELSIUS, A., 1735, "Historia Eclipseos Solis, quae totalis cum mora Scandinaviae, praecipue Gothiae, incolis apparuit Anno 1733 die 2 Maji horis vespertinis," *Acta Lit. et Sci. Sueciae 4*, 48.

CHANDRASEKHAR, S., 1952, "A Statistical Basis for the Theory of Stellar Scintillation," *M. N. 112*, 475.

—— 1954, "On Characteristic Value Problems in High Order Differential Equations which Arise in Studies on Hydrodynamic and Hydromagnetic Stability," *Amer. Math. Monthly Supp. 61*, 32.

—— 1955, "The Gravitational Instability of an Infinite Homogeneous Medium when a Coriolis Acceleration is Acting," *Vistas in Astronomy 1*, 344.

—— 1961, *Hydrodynamics and Hydromagnetic Stability*, Oxford: Clarendon Press.

—— and F. H. BREEN, 1946, "On the Continuous Absorption Coefficient of the Negative Hydrogen Ion, III," *Ap. J. 104*, 430.

—— and E. FERMI, 1953, "Problems of Gravitational Stability in the Presence of a Magnetic Field," *Ap. J. 118*, 116.

CHAPMAN, S., 1916, "On the Law of Distribution of Molecular Velocities and On the Theory of Viscosity and Thermal Conduction in a Non-Uniform Simple Monatomic Gas," *Phil. Trans. Roy. Soc. (London) A 216*, 279.

—— 1943, "Address on Magnetism in the Sun's Atmosphere," *M. N. 103*, 117.

—— 1954, "The Viscosity and Thermal Conductivity of a Completely Ionized Gas," *Ap. J. 120*, 151.

—— 1957, "Notes on the Solar Corona and the Terrestrial Ionosphere," *Smithsonian Contributions to Astrophysics 2*, 1.

—— and T. G. COWLING, 1952, *Mathematical Theory of Non-uniform Gases* (2nd ed.), London: Cambridge University Press.

CHEVALIER, S., 1908, "Contribution to the Study of the Photosphere," *Ap. J. 27*, 12.

—— 1916, "Appendice à l'étude photographique des diamètres polaire et équatorial du soleil," *Ann. Obs. Zô-Sè 9*, B1.

CHISTYAKOV, V. F., 1961, "A Study of the Wilson Effect in Sunspots," *A. Zhurn. 38*, 617 (*Sov. Astron. 5*, 471).

CHRISTIANSEN, W. N., 1953, "A High-resolution Aerial for Radio Astronomy," *Nature 171*, 831.

—— and D. S. MATHEWSON, 1959, "La compasante lentement variable du rayonnement solaire sur **169 Mc/s**," *Paris Symposium on Radio Astronomy* (R. N. Bracewell, Ed.), p. 140, Stanford University Press.

—— et al., 1960, (CHRISTIANSEN, W. N., D. S. MATHEWSON, J. L. PAWSEY, S. F. SMERD, A. BOISCHOT, J. F. DENISSE, P. SIMON, T. KAKINUMA, H. DODSON-PRINCE, and J. FIROR) "A Study of a Solar Active Region Using Combined Optical and Radio Techniques," *Ann. d'Ap. 23*, 75.

CHUBB, T. A., H. FRIEDMAN, and R. W. KREPLIN, 1960, "Measurements Made of High-energy X-rays Accompanying Three Class 2 + Solar Flares," *J. G. R. 65*, 1831.

—— H. FRIEDMAN and R. W. KREPLIN, 1961, "X-ray Emission Accompanying Solar Flares," *Liege Symposium Les Spectres des Astres dans l'Ultraviolet Lointain*, p. 216, University of Liege.

CILLIÉ, G. G., 1932, "The Hydrogen Emission in Gaseous Nebulae," *M. N. 92*, 820.

CIMINO, M., 1945, "Un'oscillazione ventiduennale vel diametro solare," *Comm. Pont. Acad. Sci. 8*, 485.

—— 1953, "Le variazioni del diametro solare osservate all'Osservatorio Astronomico di Roma e le recenti teorie elettrodinamiche stellari," *Accad. Naz. Lincei*, 220.

CLINE, T. L., G. H. LUDWIG, and F. B. McDONALD, 1964, "Detection of Interplanetary 3- to 12-MeV Electrons," *Phys. Rev. Letters 13*, 786.

COMPER, W. and R. KERN, 1957, "Die Eruption (Flare) und der Protuberanzenaufstieg vom 4 Juni 1956," *Z. Ap. 43*, 20.

CONWAY, M. T., 1952, "A Study of the Profile of the Hydrogen Hα Line in the Spectra of Solar Prominences," *Proc. Roy. Irish Acad. 54A*, 311.

COOPER, J. W., U. FANO, and F. PRATS, 1963, "Classification of Two-Electron Excitation Levels of Helium," *Phys. Rev. Letters 10*, 518.

COPPI, B., 1964, "Gravitational Instabilities in a Compressible Collisional Plasma Layer," *Ann. Phys. 30*, 178.

CORRELL, M., M. HAZEN, and J. BAHNG, 1956, "Motions of Prominences," *Ap. J. 124*, 597.

—— and W. O. ROBERTS, 1958, "Atmospheric Magnetic Fields above Active Solar Region of April 13, 1950," *Ap. J. 127*, 726.

COVINGTON, A. E., 1948, "Solar Noise Observations on 10.7 Centimeters," *Proc. Inst. Radio Engrs. 36*, 454.

—— 1954, "Solar Noise at 10 cm," *J.G.R. 59*, 163.

COWLING, T. G., 1934, "The Magnetic Field of Sunspots," *M.N. 94*, 39.

—— 1945, "On the Sun's General Magnetic Field," *M.N. 105*, 166.

—— 1946, "The Growth and Decay of the Sunspot Magnetic Field," *M. N. 106*, 218.

—— 1953, "Solar Electrodynamics," *The Sun* (G. Kuiper, Ed.), p. 532, Chicago: University of Chicago Press.

—— 1955, "Dynamo Theories of Cosmic Magnetic Fields," *Vistas in Astronomy 1*, 313.

—— 1957, *Magnetohydrodynamics*, New York: Interscience Press.

CRAGG, T. A., 1957, "The Eruptive Prominence of May 18, 1956," *P. A. S. P. 69*, 268.

CULHANE, J. L., A. P. WILLMORE, K. A. POUNDS, and P. W. SANFORD, 1964, "Variability of the Solar X-Ray Spectrum Below 15 Å," *Space Res. IV*, 741.

CURTISS, C. F. and J. O. HIRSCHFELDER, 1949, "Transport Properties of Multicomponent Gas Mixtures," *J. Chem. Phys. 17*, 550.

DANIELSON, R. E., 1961a, "The Structure of Sunspot Penumbras I. Observations," *Ap. J. 134*, 275.

—— 1961b, "The Structure of Sunspot Penumbras II. Theoretical," *Ap. J. 134*, 289.

DAVIDSON, C. R. and F. J. M. STRATTON, 1927, "Report on the Total Solar Eclipse of 1926 January 14," *Mem. Roy. Astron. Soc. 64*, Part 4, Section 4, 105.

D'AZAMBUJA, L., 1939, "La coopération internationale pour l'observation continue du soleil et ses premiers résultats," *L'Astronomie 53*, 97.

—— and M. D'AZAMBUJA, 1948, "Étude d'ensemble des protubérances solaire et de leurs evolution," *Ann. Obs. Paris-Meudon 6*, No. 7.

DEBYE, P., 1919, "Das molekulare elektrische Feld in Gasen," *Physik Z. 20*, 160.

DEINZER, W., 1960, "Zur magneto-hydrostatischen Theorie der Sonnenflecken," *Mitt. Astron. Gesellschaft.*, p. 7.

―― 1962, "Zur magneto-hydrostatischen Theorie der Sonnenflecken," Diss., Max-Planck-Institut für Physik und Astrophysik.

―― 1965, "On the Magneto-Hydrostatic Theory of Sunspots," *Ap. J. 141*, 548.

DE JAGER, C., 1959, "Structure and Dynamics of the Solar Atmosphere," *Handbuch der Physik 52*, 80.

―― 1960, "The X-Ray Radiation of the Sun," *Space Res. I*, 628.

―― 1963, "The Sun as a Source of Interplanetary Gas," *Space Sci. Rev. 1*, 487.

DE LA RUE, W., 1868, "On the Solar Eclipse of August 18th, 1868," *M. N. 29*, 73.

DENISSE, J. F., 1960, "Les phénomènes radioélectriques solaires et leur interprétation physique," *U. R. S. I. XIII General Assembly, Commission V Report*, London.

――and J. L. DELCROIX, 1961, *Théorie des ondes dans les plasmas*, Paris: Dunod.

DESLANDRES, H., 1910, "Recherches sur l'atmosphère solaire; photographie des couches gazeuses supérieures; étude simultanée des formes et des mouvements des vapeurs," *Ann. Obs. Paris-Meudon 4*, I, 1.

DODSON-PRINCE, H. W., 1949, "Position and Development of the Solar Flares of May 8 and 10, 1949," *Ap. J. 110*, 382.

―― 1958, "Studies at the McMath–Hulbert Observatory of Radio Frequency Radiation at the Time of Solar Flares," *Proc. Inst. Radio Engrs. 46*, 149.

―― 1961, "Observation of Loop-Type Prominences in Projection Against the Disk at the Time of Certain Solar Flares," *Proc. Natl. Acad. Sci. 47*, 901.

――and E. R. HEDEMAN, 1949, "The Frequency and Positions of Flares within Three Active Sunspot Areas," *Ap. J. 110*, 242.

――and E. R. HEDEMAN, 1961, "Photographic Observations of Certain Flares Associated with Polar Cap Absorption," *Ark. Geofys. 3*, 469.

――and E. R. HEDEMAN, 1964a, "Problems of Differentiation of Flares with Respect to Geophysical Effects," *Planet. Space Sci. 12*, 393.

――and E. R. HEDEMAN, 1964b, "Moving Material Accompanying the Flare of 1959 July 16^d 21^h 14^m U.T.," *AAS–NASA Symposium on the Physics of Solar Flares, 1963*, p. 15.

DOHERTY, L. R. and D. H. MENZEL, 1965, "Filamentary Structure in Solar Prominences," *Ap. J. 141*, 251.

DOLLFUS, A., 1958, "Un polarimètre photoélectrique très sensible pour l'étude du soleil," *C. R. 246*, 2345.

――and J. -L. LEROY, 1962, "Un magnetomètre mesurant les champs magnétiques perpendiculaires au rayon visuel. Applications à l'étude des champs radiaux autour des taches," *Trans. I.A.U. 11B*, 438.

DUNGEY, J. W., 1953a, "Conditions for the Occurrence of Electrical Discharges in Astrophysical Systems," *Phil. Mag. 44*, 725.

―― 1953b, "A Family of Solutions of the Magneto-Hydrostatic Problem in a Conducting Atmosphere in a Gravitational Field," *M. N. 113*, 180.

―― 1958a, "The Neutral Point Discharge Theory of Solar Flares. A Reply to Cowling's Criticism," *I. A. U. Symposium No. 6*, paper 15, p. 135.

―― 1958b, *Cosmic Electrodynamics*, London: Cambridge University Press.

DUNN, R., J. T. JEFFERIES, and F. Q. ORRALL, 1960, "The Line and Continouus Emission Observed in Two Limb Flares," *Obs. 80*, 31.

DYSON, F. (Astronomer Royal), 1930, "A Solar Eruption on 1930 November 25," *M. N. 91*, 239.

EARL, J. A., 1961, "Cloud-Chamber Observations of Primary Cosmic-Ray Electrons," *Phys. Rev. Letters 6*, 125.

EDDINGTON, A. S., 1942, "Conditions in the Hydrogen Convection Zone," *M. N. 102*, 154.

EDLÉN, B., 1942, "Die Deutung der Emissionslinien im Spektrum der Sonnenkorona," *Z. Ap. 22*, 30.

—— 1954, "On the Identification of Ca XV and A XIV in the Solar Corona," *M. N. 114*, 700.

ELIASSEN, A. and E. KLEINSCHMIDT, 1957, "Dynamic Meteorology," *Handbuch der Physik 48*, 1.

ELLERMAN, F., 1917, "Solar Hydrogen 'Bombs'," *Ap. J. 46*, 298.

ELLISON, M. A., 1942, "Some Studies of the Motions of Hydrogen Flocculi by Doppler Displacements of the Hα Line," *M. N. 102*, 11.

—— 1944, "Sunspot Prominences—Some Comparisons between Limb and Disk Appearances," *M. N. 104*, 22.

—— 1946, "Visual and Spectrographic Observations of a Great Solar Flare, 1946 July 24," *M. N. 106*, 500.

—— 1955, *The Sun and Its Influence*, London: Routledge and Paul.

—— 1963, "Energy Release in Solar Flares," *Quart. J. Roy. Astron. Soc. (London) 4*, 62.

—— S. M. P. McKENNA, and J. H. REID, 1960a, "The Solar Flare of 1960 April 1," *Obs. 80*, 149.

—— S. M. P. McKENNA, and J. H. REID, 1960b, "Cape Lyot Heliograph Results," *Dunsink Obs. Publ. 1*, 39.

—— S. M. P. McKENNA, and J. H. REID, 1961a, "Flares Associated with the 1960 November Event and the Flare Nimbus Phenomenon," *M. N. 122*, 491.

—— S. M. P. McKENNA, and J. H. REID, 1961b, "Cape Photoheliographic Results II. The 3 + Flare of 1960 June 1 and Its Influence on the H-alpha Striation Pattern," *Dunsink Obs. Publ. 1*, 53.

—— S. M. P. McKENNA, and J. H. REID, 1962, "Cosmic Ray Flares Associated with the 1961 July Event," *M. N. 124*, 263.

ELSASSER, W. M., 1946a, "Induction Effects in Terrestrial Magnetism Part I. Theory," *Phys. Rev. 69*, 106.

—— 1946b, "Induction Effects in Terrestrial Magnetism Part II. The Secular Variation," *Phys. Rev. 70*, 202.

—— 1947, "Induction Effects in Terrestrial Magnetism Part III. Electric Modes," *Phys. Rev. 72*, 821.

—— 1950, "The Hydromagnetic Equations," *Phys. Rev. 79*, 183.

—— 1956, "Hydromagnetic Dynamo Theory," *Rev. Mod. Phys. 28*, 135.

ELWERT, G., 1952, "Über die Ionisations- und Rekombination- Prozesse in einem Plasma und die Ionisationsformel der Sonnenkorona," *Z. Naturforsch. 7a*, 432.

—— 1954, "Die weiche Röntgenstrahlung der ungestörten Sonnenkorona," *Z. Naturforsch. 9a*, 637.

—— 1961, "Theory of X-Ray Emission of the Sun," *J. G. R. 66*, 391.

ENSKOG, D., 1917, "Kinetische Theorie der Vorgänge in mässig verdünnten Gasen," Inaug. Diss, Uppsala.

ERICKSON, W. C., 1964, "The Radio-Wave Scattering Properties of the Solar Corona," *Ap. J. 139*, 1290.

ESHLEMAN, V. R., R. C. BARTHLE, and P. B. GALLAGHER, 1960, "Radar Echoes from the Sun," *Science 131*, 329.

EVANS, J. W., 1940, "The Quartz Polarizing Monochromator," *P. A. S. P. 52*, 305.

—— 1949, "The Birefringent Filter," *J. Opt. Soc. Amer. 39*, 229.

—— 1957, "Observations of the Solar Emission Corona outside Eclipse," *P. A. S. P. 69*, 421.

—— 1959, "Flare-Associated Magnetic Activity in the Sun," *A. J. 64*, 330.

—— and R. MICHARD, 1961, "Spectral Line Studies of Granulation Paper 4," *Trans. I. A. U. 11B (Proceedings, 1961, Berkeley)*, p. 201.

—— and R. MICHARD, 1962, "Observational Study of Macroscopic Inhomogeneities in the Solar Atmosphere III. Vertical Oscillatory Motions in the Solar Photosphere," *Ap. J. 136*, 493.

EVERSHED, J., 1909, "Radial Movement in Sun-spots," *M. N. 69*, 454.

—— 1939, "Note on the Zeeman Effect in Sunspot Spectra," *M. N. 99*, 217.

—— 1941, "Speech on the Zeeman Effect in Sunspot Spectra," *Obs. 64*, 154.

FERMI, E., 1949, "On the Origin of the Cosmic Radiation," *Phys. Rev. 75*, 1169.

—— 1954, "Galactic Magnetic Fields and the Origin of Cosmic Radiation," *Ap. J. 119*, 1.

FERRARO, V. C. A., 1937, "The Non Uniform Rotation of the Sun and Its Magnetic Field," *M. N. 97*, 458.

FICHTEL, C. E. and D. E. GUSS, 1961, "Heavy Nuclei in Solar Cosmic Rays," *Phys. Rev. Letters 6*, 495.

FIROR, J., 1959a, "The Quiet Sun at 88 Cm Wavelength," *Paris Symposium on Radio Astronomy* (R. N. Bracewell, Ed.), p. 107, Stanford University Press.

—— 1959b, "Solar Radio Bright Spots at 88 Cm Wavelength," *Paris Symposium on Radio Astronomy* (R. N. Bracewell, Ed.), p. 136, Stanford University Press.

—— and H. ZIRIN, 1963, "Relative Populations of Fe in the Corona," *The Solar Corona* (J. W. Evans, Ed.), p. 27, New York: Academic Press.

FOKKER, A. D., 1960, "Studies of Enhanced Solar Radio Emission at Frequencies Near 200 MHz," Diss., Leiden University.

—— 1963, "Type IV Solar Radio Emission," *Space Sci. Rev. 2*, 70.

FORBUSH, S. E., 1946, "Three Unusual Cosmic-Ray Increases Possibly due to Charged Particles from the Sun," *Phys. Rev. 70*, 771.

FORTINI, T., 1949, "Analisi periodale col methodo di Schuster della curva di variazione del diametro solare ottenuta al Campidoglio dal 1877 al 1937 ed a M. Mario dal 1937 al 1947," *Memorie Soc. Astron. Italiana 20*-4.

FRENKEL, J., 1945, "On the Origin of Terrestrial Magnetism," *Akad. Nauk. C.R. USSR 49*, 98.

FRIEDMAN, H., 1960, "The Sun's Ionizing Radiations," *Physics of the Upper Atmosphere* (J. A. Ratcliffe, Ed.), Chapter 4, p. 133, New York: Academic Press.

—— T. A. CHUBB, J. E. KUPPERIAN, R. W. KREPLIN, and J. C. LINDSAY, 1958,

"X-Ray and Ultraviolet Emission of Solar Flares," *Ann. de Geophys. 14*, 232.

—— S. W. LICHTMAN, and E. T. BYRAN, 1951, "Photon Counter Measurements of Solar X Rays and Extreme Ultraviolet Light," *Phys. Rev. 83*, 1025.

FRITZOVÁ, L., 1959, "On the Frequency Distribution of Intervals between Successive Flares," *B. A. C. 10*, 145.

GAUNT, J. A., 1930, "Continuous Absorption," *Phil. Trans. Roy. Soc. (London) A 229*, 163.

GERSHMAN, B. N., V. L. GINZBURG, and N. G. DENISOV, 1957, "The Propagation of Electromagnetic Waves in a Plasma (Ionosphere)," *Uspekhi Fiz. Nauk. 61*, 561.

GIACCONI, R., W. P. REIDY, T. ZEHNPFENNIG, J. C. LINDSAY, and W. S. MUNEY, 1965, "Solar X-Ray Images Obtained Using Grazing Incidence Optics," *Ap. J. 142*, 1274.

GIANNUZZI, M. A., 1953, "Riduzione delle osservazioni dei diametri solari orizzontali, osservati a Greenwich, dal 1851 al 1937 e conferma della oscillazione con periodo di 23 anni trovata al Campidoglio," *Memorie Soc. Astron. Italiana 24-3*.

—— 1955a, "Sulla variabilita del raggio solare," *Accad. Naz. Lincei 19*, 277.

—— 1955b, "Riduzione delle osservazioni dei diametri solari verticali osservati a Greenwich dal 1851 al 1937 e conferma della oscillazione con period di 23 anni trovata al Campidoglio (Roma)," *Memorie Soc. Astron. Italiana 26-4*.

GINZBURG, V. L. and S. N. SYROVATSKII, 1964, *The Origin of Cosmic Rays* (translated by H. S. H. Massey), New York: Macmillan.

—— and V. V. ZHELEZNYAKOV, 1958, "On the Possible Mechanisms of Sporadic Solar Radio Emission (Radiation in an Isotropic Plasma)," *A. Zhurn. 35*, 694 (*Sov. Astron. 2*, 653).

—— and V. V. ZHELEZNYAKOV, 1959, "On the Propagation of Electromagnetic Waves in the Solar Corona Taking into Account the Influence of the Magnetic Field," *A. Zhurn. 36*, 233 (*Sov. Astron. 3*, 235).

GIOVANELLI, R. G., 1939, "The Relations between Eruptions and Sunspots," *Ap. J. 89*, 555.

—— 1946, "A Theory of Chromospheric Flares," *Nature 158*, 81.

—— 1947, "Magnetic and Electric Phenomena in the Sun's Atmosphere Associated with Sunspots," *M. N. 107*, 338.

—— 1948, "Chromospheric Flares," *M. N. 108*, 163.

—— 1949, "A Note on Heat Transfer in the Upper Chromosphere and Corona," *M. N. 109*, 372.

—— and M. K. MCCABE, 1958a, "The Distribution of Flare Heights as Derived from Limb Flares," *Aust. J. Phys. 11*, 130.

—— and M. K. MCCABE, 1958b, "The Flare-Surge Event," *Aust. J. Phys. 11*, 191.

GOLD, T., 1958, "The Magnetic Field in the Corona," *I. A. U. Symposium No. 6*, p. 275.

—— and F. HOYLE, 1960, "On the Origin of Solar Flares," *M. N. 120*, 89.

GOLDBERG-ROGOZINSKAYA, N. M., 1965, "Helium Lines in Chromospheric Flare Spectra, II," *Iz. Glavnoi Astron. Obs. 24*, No. 178, 35.

GOPASYUK, S. I., 1960, "An Investigation of Chromospheric Flares at the Initial Stage of Their Development," *Iz. Krim. Ap. Obs. 23*, 331.

—— 1961, "Variations of the Magnetic Field and Sunspot Configurations during Solar Flares—A Determination of the Total Energy of Flares," *A. Zhurn. 38*, 209 (*Sov. Astron. 5*, 158).

—— 1962, "The Motion of Spots Connected with Solar Flares and the Possible Character of Energy Exit from Flare Regions," *Iz. Krim. Ap. Obs. 27*, 110.

—— and M. B. OGIR, 1963, "The Connection between Flares and Surges on the Sun," *Iz. Krim. Ap. Obs. 30*, 185.

—— M. B. OGIR, A. B. SEVERNY, and E. F. SHAPOSHNIKOVA, 1962, "The Structure of Magnetic Fields and Its Variations in Flare Regions," *Iz. Krim. Ap. Obs. 29*, 15.

GORDON, I. M., 1960, "The Nature of γ Emission in Solar Flares and the Formation of Cosmic Particles in Active Solar Regions," *A. Zhurn. 37*, 934 (*Sov. Astron. 4*, 873).

GRANT, R., 1852, *History of Physical Astronomy*, London: Robert Baldwin.

GROTRAIN, W., 1931a, "Ergebnisse der Potsdamer Expedition zur Beobachtung der Sonnenfinsternis am 9 Mai 1929 in Takengon (Nordsumatra) 1. Spektroskopische Untersuchungen an Korona und Protuberanzen," *Z. Ap. 2*, 106.

—— 1931b, "Ergebnisse der Potsdamer Expedition zur Beobachtung der Sonnenfinsternis am 9 Mai 1929 in Takengon (Nordsumatra) 6. Über die Intensitätsverteilung des kontinuierlichen Spektrums der inneren Korona," *Z. Ap. 3*, 199.

—— 1939, "Zur Frage der Deutung der Linien im Spektrum der Sonnenkorona," *Naturwiss. 27*, 214.

GUREVICH, L. E. and A. LEBEDINSKI, 1945, "The Magnetic Field of the Sunspots," *C.R. Acad. Sci. USSR. 49*, 92.

GUSEINOV, R. E., 1963, "The Possibility of Application of the 'Radiating' Electron Theory to Describe the Generation of γ Radiation in Chromospheric Flares," *A. Zhurn. 40*, 584 (*Sov. Astron. 7*, 444).

GUTMANN, M. and J. L. STEINBERG, 1959, "Resultats preliminaires obtenus avec l'interferomètre à 8 antennes sur 3 cm de longueur d'onde," *Paris Symposium on Radio Astronomy* (R. N. Bracewell, Ed.), p. 123, Stanford University Press.

HAEFF, A. V., 1949, "On the Origin of Solar Radio Noise," *Phys. Rev. 75*, 1546.

HALE, G. E., 1907, "A Vertical Coelostat Telescope," *Ap. J. 25*, 68.

—— 1908a, "Preliminary Note of the Rotation of the Sun as Determined from the Motions of the Hydrogen Flocculi," *Ap. J. 27*, 219.

—— 1908b, "Solar Vortices," *Ap. J. 28*, 100.

—— 1913, "Preliminary Results of an Attempt to Detect the General Magnetic Field of the Sun," *Ap. J. 38*, 27.

—— 1914, "The Zeeman and Stark Effects," *P. A. S. P. 26*, 146.

—— 1929, "The Spectrohelioscope and Its Work. I. History, Instruments, Adjustments, and Methods of Observation," *Ap. J. 70*, 265.

—— 1930, "The Spectrohelioscope and Its Work. II. The Motions of the Hydrogen Flocculi Near Sun-spots," *Ap. J. 71*, 73.

—— 1931a, "The Spectrohelioscope and Its Work. III. Solar Eruptions and Their Apparent Terrestrial Effects," *Ap. J. 73*, 379.

—— 1931b, "The Spectrohelioscope and Its Work. IV. Methods of Recording Observations," *Ap. J. 74*, 214.

——and F. Elleman, 1903, "The Rumford Spectroheliograph of the Yerkes Observatory," *Publ. Yerkes Obs. 3*, Part I, 3.

——and S. B. Nicholson, 1938, "Magnetic Observations of Sunspots 1917–1924, Part 2," *Publ. Carnegie Inst.* No. 498, Part 2.

——F. H. Seares, A. van Maanen, and F. Ellerman, 1918, "The General Magnetic Field of the Sun: Apparent Variation of Field-Strength with Level in the Solar Atmosphere," *Ap. J. 47*, 206.

Hansky, A., 1904, "Sur la grande période de l'activité solaire," *Bull. Acad. Imp. Sci. (St. Petersburg), Phys.-Math. 20*, No. 4, 145.

——1905, "Photographies de la granulation solaire faites à Poulkovo," *Pulkovo Mitt. 1*, 81.

Harris, D. L., 1948, "On the Line-Absorption Coefficient due to Doppler Effect and Damping," *Ap. J. 108*, 112.

Harvey, J. W., 1966, private communication.

Haselgrove, J., 1954, "Ray Theory and a New Method for Ray Tracing," *Rep. Conf. on Phys. of Ionosphere*, p. 355.

——1957, "Oblique Ray Paths in the Ionosphere," *Proc. Phys. Soc. 70B*, 653.

Haupt, H., 1955, "Eine ungewöhnliche Spektralaufnahme einer Protuberanz am Koronographen," *Mitt. Obs. Kanzelhöhe* No. 6.

Hayakawa, S., J. Nishimura, H. Obayashi, and H. Sato, 1964, "Acceleration Mechanisms of Cosmic Rays II," *Prog. Theoret. Phys. Suppl.* No. 30, 86.

Hepburn, N., 1955, "A Photometric Study of the Solar Corona," *Ap. J. 122*, 445.

Hewish, A., 1957, "Radio Observations of the Solar Corona at Sunspot Minimum," *I.A.U. Symposium No. 4*, p. 298.

——1958, "The Scattering of Radio Waves in the Solar Corona," *M. N. 118*, 534.

Hey, J. S., 1946, "Solar Radiations in the 4–6 Metre Radio Wavelength Band," *Nature 157*, 47.

Hines, C. O., 1960, "Internal Atmospheric Gravity Waves at Ionospheric Heights," *Cand. J. Phys. 38*, 1441.

Hirayama, T., 1961, "Physical Structure of Limb Flares," *P. A. S. Japan 13*, 152.

——1963, "A Model of the Solar Quiescent Prominence and the Effect of the Solar UV Radiation on the Prominence," *P. A. S. Japan 15*, 122.

——1964, "Solar Quiescent Prominence and the Energy Balance," *P. A. S. Japan 16*, 104.

Hofstader, R., 1948, "Alkali Halide Scintillation Counters," *Phys. Rev. 74*, 100.

Holmes, J., 1961, "A Study of Sunspot Velocity Fields using a Magnetically Undisturbed Line," *M. N. 122*, 301.

Holtsmark, J., 1919, "Über die Verbreitung von Spektrallinien," *Ann. Physik 58*, 577.

Houtgast, J. and A. van Sluiters, 1948, "Statistical Investigations Concerning the Magnetic Fields of Sunspots I," *B. A. N. 10*, 325.

Howard, R., 1958, "Excitation Temperatures and Turbulent Velocities in Sunspots," *Ap. J. 127*, 108.

——1959, "Observations of Solar Magnetic Fields," *Ap. J. 130*, 193.

——and H. W. Babcock, 1960, "Magnetic Fields Associated with the Solar Flare of July 16, 1959," *Ap. J. 132*, 218.

——and A. B. Severny, 1963, "Solar Magnetic Fields and the Great Flare of July 16, 1959," *Ap. J. 137*, 1242.

Hoyle, F., 1949, *Some Recent Researches in Solar Physics*, London: Cambridge University Press.

——and N. C. Wickramasinghe, 1961, "A Note on the Origin of the Sun's Polar Field," *M. N. 123*, 51.

Huggins, W., 1869, "Note on a Method of Viewing the Solar Prominences without an Eclipse," *Proc. Roy. Soc. (London) 17*, 302.

Hyder, C. L., 1964, "Magnetic Fields in the Loop Prominence of March 16, 1964," *Ap. J. 140*, 817.

——1965a, "The 'Polar Crown' of Filaments and the Sun's Polar Magnetic Fields," *Ap. J. 141*, 272.

——1965b, "The Polarization of Emission Lines in Astronomy II. Prominence Emission-line Polarization and Prominence Magnetic Fields," *Ap. J. 141*, 1374.

——1966a, "Winking Filaments and Prominence and Coronal Magnetic Fields," *Z. Ap. 63*, 78.

——1966b, private communication.

I. A. U., 1955, "Report of the Working Group on Flare Classification," *I. A. U. Trans. IX General Assembly*, Dublin, p. 146.

——1964, "Report of the Working Committee of Commission 10, Commission de l'Activite Solaire," *I.A.U. Rep. XII General Assembly*, Hamburg.

Ikhsanova, V. N., 1959, "Solar Observations with the Large Pulkovo Radio Telescope at 3.2-cm Wavelength," *Paris Symposium on Radio Astronomy* (R. N. Bracewell, Ed.), p. 171, Stanford University Press.

Inglis, D. R. and E. Teller, 1939, "Ionic Depression of Series Limits in One-Electron Spectra," *Ap. J. 90*, 439.

Ioschpa, B. A., 1962, "Measurement of Magnetic Fields in Solar Prominences," *Geomagnetism and Aeronomy 2*, 149.

——1963, "Magnetic Fields in Solar Prominences," *Geomagnetism and Aeronomy 3*, 903.

——1965, "The Heating of a Prominence," *A. Zhurn. 42*, 754 (*Sov. Astron. 9*, 583, 1966).

Ivanov-Kholodny, G. S., 1955, "Spectrophotometric Studies of Hydrogen and Helium in Prominences I," *Iz. Krim. Ap. Obs. 13*, 112.

——1958, "The Deviation of the Profiles of Emission Lines of the Prominences from the Doppler Profile," *Iz. Krim. Ap. Obs. 18*, 109.

——1959, "The Electron Density in Solar Prominences," *A. Zhurn. 36*, 589 (*Sov. Astron. 3*, 578, 1960).

Janssen, P. J., 1868, "Indication de quelques-uns des résultats obtenus à Cocanada, pendant l'eclipse du mois d'août dernier, et à la suite de cette éclipse," *C. R. 67*, 838.

——1896, "Mémoire sur la photographie solaire," *Ann. Obs. Paris-Meudon 1*, 91.

Jefferies, J. T., 1953, "Emission of Radiation from Model Hydrogen Chromospheres," *Aust. J. Phys. 6*, 22.

——and F. Q. Orrall, 1958, "On the Interpretation of Prominence Spectra I. Balmer Series Line Widths," *Ap. J. 127*, 714.

——and F. Q. Orrall, 1961a, "On the Interpretation of Prominence Spectra II.

The Line and Continuous Spectrum of the Spray-type Limb Event of March 7, 1959," *Ap. J. 133*, 946.

——and F. Q. ORRALL, 1961b, "On the Interpretation of Prominence Spectra III. The Line and Continuous Spectrum of a Loop Prominence and Limb Flare," *Ap. J. 133*, 963.

——and F. Q. ORRALL, 1961c, "On the Interpretation of Prominence Spectra IV. The Balmer and Paschen Continua in a Quiet Prominence," *Ap. J. 134*, 747.

——and F. Q. ORRALL, 1962, "On the Interpretation of Prominence Spectra V. The Emission Lines in Quiescent Prominences," *Ap. J. 135*, 109.

——and F. Q. ORRALL, 1963, "On the Interpretation of Prominence Spectra VI. Temperature Determination and a Model for Quiescent Prominences," *Ap. J. 137*, 1232.

——and F. Q. ORRALL, 1965a, "Loop Prominences and Coronal Condensations I. Non-thermal Velocities within Loop Prominences," *Ap. J. 141*, 505.

——and F. Q. ORRALL, 1965b, "Loop Prominences and Coronal Condensations II. The Source of Mass and Energy and a Model of the Loop Prominence Mechanism," *Ap. J. 141*, 519.

——E. v. P. SMITH and H. J. SMITH, 1959, "The Flare of September 18, 1957," *Ap. J. 129*, 146.

——and R. N. THOMAS, 1958, "Source Function in a Non-equilibrium Atmosphere II. Depth Dependence of Source Function for Resonance and Strong Subordinate Lines," *Ap. J. 127*, 667.

——and R. N. THOMAS, 1959, "Source Function in a Non-equilibrium Atmosphere III. The Influence of a Chromosphere," *Ap. J. 129*, 401.

——and R. N. THOMAS, 1960, "Source Function in a Non-equilibrium Atmosphere V. Character of the Self-reversed Emission Cores of Ca^+ H and K," *Ap. J. 131*, 695.

JEFFERY, A. and T. TANIUTI, 1966, "Magnetohydrodynamic Stability and Thermonuclear Containment: An Introduction," *Magnetohydrodynamic Stability and Thermonuclear Containment* (A. Jeffery and T. Taniuti, Eds.), p. 1, New York: Academic Press.

JENSEN, E., 1955, "On Tubes of Magnetic Force Embedded in Stellar Material," *Ann. d'Ap. 18*, 127.

——1959, "On the Dynamics of Prominences and Coronal Condensations," *Ap. Norv. 6*, 93.

——J. NORDÖ, and T. S. RINGNES, 1955, "Variations in the Structure of Sunspots in Relation to the Sunspot Cycle," *Ap. Norv. 5*, 167.

——and F. Q. ORRALL, 1963, "Observational Study of Macroscopic Inhomogeneities in the Solar Atmosphere IV. Velocity and Intensity Fluctuations Observed in the K line," *Ap. J. 138*, 252.

JOHNSON, H. R., 1960, "Helium Equilibrium in the Solar Atmosphere," Ph.D. Diss., University of Colorado.

JONES, W., 1965, "Generation of Small-scale Oscillations in the Solar Atmosphere," *NCAR Preprint PM 65-27*.

JORDAN, C., 1965, "Wavelengths, Intensities and Identifications of Solar Emission Lines between 1994 Å and 13.7 Å," *Communications University London Obs. 68*.

KAHN, F. D., 1961, "Sound Waves Trapped in the Solar Atmosphere I," *Ap. J. 134*, 343.

—— 1962, "Sound Waves Trapped in the Solar Atmosphere II," *Ap. J. 135*, 547.

KAKINUMA, T. and G. SWARUP, 1962, "A Model for the Sources of the Slowly Varying Component of Microwave Solar Radiation," *Ap. J. 136*, 975.

KALLMANN, H., 1949, "Quantitative Measurements with Scintillation Counters," *Phys. Rev. 75*, 623.

KARIMOV, M. G. and N. S. SHILOVA, 1959, "Connection between the Motion of Matter in the Corona and the Prominences," *Bull. Astron. Inst. Acad. Sci. Kazakh. SSR 9*, 10 (*Amer. Rocket Soc. J. Suppl. 31*, 970, 1961).

KATO, S., 1963, "On the Generation of Acoustic Noise from Turbulent Atmosphere II," *P. A. S. Japan 15*, 204.

KAWABATA, K., 1960, "The Relationship between Post-burst Increases of Solar Microwave Radiation and Sudden Ionospheric Disturbances," *Rep. Ionos. Space Res. Japan 14*, 405.

KAWAGUCHI, I. 1964, "Effect of the Ultraviolet Radiation on the Ionization and Excitation of Matter in Prominences I. Effect of the Lyman Continuous Radiation on Hydrogen Atoms," *P. A. S. Japan 16*, 86.

—— 1965, "Effect of the Ultraviolet Radiation on the Ionization and Excitation of Matter in Prominences II. Continuous Spectra," *P. A. S. Japan 17*, 367.

KAZACHEVSKAYA, T. V. and A. B. SEVERNY, 1958, "The Hydrogen Spectrum of Flares," *Iz. Krim. Ap. Obs. 19*, 46.

KEENAN, P. C., 1938, "Dimensions of the Solar Granules," *Ap. J. 88*, 360.

KIEPENHEUER, K. O., 1938, "Zur Dynamik der Sonnenprotuberanzen," *Z. Ap. 15*, 53.

—— 1951, "The Nature of Solar Prominences," *P. A. S. P. 63*, 161.

—— 1953a, "Solar Activity," *The Sun* (G. Kuiper, Ed.), Chapter 4, p. 322, Chicago: University of Chicago Press.

—— 1953b, "Über die Beziehung zwischen Protuberanzen und Korona," *Accad. Naz. Lincei, Convegno Volta 11*, 148.

—— 1959, "Über die Verdichtung der Koronamaterie," *Z. Ap. 48*, 290.

—— 1960, "The Optical Phenomena Forming a Solar Center of Activity," *Soc. Ital. Fisica, Scuola Internaz. Fisica Enrico Fermi*, p. 39.

—— 1965, "About the Flare Problem," *The Solar Spectrum* (C. de Jager, Ed.), p. 240, Holland: D. Reidel.

KINMAN, T. D., 1952, "Motions in the Sun at the Photospheric Level II. The Evershed Effect in Sunspot Mt. Wilson No. 9987," *M. N. 112*, 425.

—— 1953, "Motions in the Sun at the Photospheric Level III. The Evershed Effect in Sunspots of Different Sizes," *M. N. 113*, 613.

KINOSHITA, S., 1910, "The Photographic Action of the α-Particles Emitted from Radioactive Substances," *Proc. Roy. Soc. (London) A 83*, 432.

KIPPENHAHN, R., 1963, "Stars with Helium Rich Cores," *Scuola Internaz. Fisica, Varenna, Italy*, p. 330, New York: Academic Press.

—— and A. SCHLÜTER, 1957, "Eine Theorie der solaren Filamente," *Z. Ap. 43*, 36.

—— S. TEMESVÁRY, and L. BIERMANN, 1958, "Sternmodelle I. Die Entwicklung der Sterne de Population II.," *Z. Ap. 46*. 257.

KIRCHHOFF, G., 1850, "Über das Gleichgewicht und die Bewegung einer elastischen Scheibe," *Crelle's Journal 40*, 51.

KLECZEK, J., 1957, "Condensation of Solar Prominences I. Equation of Isobaric Cooling," *B. A. C. 8*, 120.

—— 1958, "Condensation of Solar Prominences II. AS Type," *B. A. C. 9*, 115.

—— 1964, "Mass Balance in Flare Loops," *AAS-NASA Symposium on the Physics of Solar Flares, 1963*, p. 77.

KOCH, H. W. and J. W. MOTZ, 1959, "Bremsstrahlung Cross-section Formulas and Related Data," *Rev. Mod. Phys. 31*, 920.

KOPECKÝ, M., 1958, "Sonnenfleckengruppen in heliographischen Breiten $\geq 40°$," *B. A. C. 9*, 34.

—— 1962, "The Dependence of the Average Importance of Sunspot Groups on Heliographic Latitude and the Phase of the 11-year Cycle," *B. A. C. 13*, 63.

—— 1963, "Physical Interpretation of the 80-year Period of Solar Activity," *B. A. C. 13*, 240.

KORNILOV, A. I., 1961, "Spectrophotometry of Sunspots," *Publ. Sternberg Astron. Inst.* No. 117, 27.

KOTLYAR, L. M., 1960, "A New Design of a Differential Photometer for a Solar Magnetograph," *A. Zhurn. 37*, 469 (*Sov. Astron. 4*, 445).

KOZHEVNIKOV, N. I. and V. D. KUZ'MINYKH, 1964, "Structure of a Facula," *A. Zhurn. 41*, 323 (*Sov. Astron. 8*, 251).

KRAMERS, H. A., 1923, "On the Theory of X-ray Absorption and of the Continuous X-ray Spectrum," *Phil. Mag. 46*, Series 6, 836.

—— 1926, "Wellenmechanik und halbzahlige Quantisierung," *Z. Phys. 39*, 828.

KREMER, P., 1930, "On the Ratio of the Number of Ca^+ Atoms in the Solar Atmosphere over Faculae and over Corresponding Parts of the Solar Surface near the Limb," *Proc. Roy. Acad.* (*Amsterdam*) *33*, 379.

KREPLIN, R. W., 1961, "Solar X-rays," *Ann. de Geophys. 17*, 151.

—— T. A. CHUBB, and H. FRIEDMAN, 1962, "X-ray and Lyman-alpha Emission from the Sun as Measured from the NRL SR-1 Satellite," *J. G. R. 67*, 2231.

KRUSE, U. W., L. MARSHALL, and J. R. PLATT, 1956, "Synchrotron Radiation in the Sun's Radio Spectrum," *Ap. J. 124*, 601.

KUHN, H. and F. LONDON, 1934, "Limitation of the Potential Theory of the Broadening of Spectral Lines," *Phil. Mag. 18*, 983.

KULSRUD, R. M., 1955, "Effect of Magnetic Fields on Generation of Noise by Isotropic Turbulence," *Ap. J. 121*, 461.

KUNDU, M. R., 1959, "Structures et propriétés des sources d'activité solaire sur ondes centimétriques," *Ann. d'Ap. 22*, 1.

—— 1961, "Bursts of Centimeter-wave Emission and the Region of Origin of X-rays from Solar Flares," *J. G. R. 66*, 4308.

—— 1965, *Solar Radio Astronomy*, New York: Interscience Press.

KUPERUS, M., 1965, "The Transfer of Mechanical Energy in the Sun and the Heating of the Corona," *Res. Astron. Obs. Utrecht 17*(1), 1.

KUZ'MINYKH, V. D., 1962, "Study of the Contrast between Faculae and the Photosphere in the Region $\lambda\lambda$ 3755–6800 Å," *A. Zhurn. 39*, 965 (*Sov. Astron. 6*, 751).

——1963, "Dependence of the Contrast of Faculae on Wavelength. Determination of the Spectrophotometric Temperatures of Faculae," *A. Zhurn. 40*, 419 (*Sov. Astron. 7*, 323).

——1964, "Model of an Average Facula," *A. Zhurn. 41*, 692 (*Sov. Astron. 8*, 551).

LABORDE, G., 1961, "Étude de la photoshère et des taches solaires à l'aide des bandes moléculaires," *Ann. d'Ap. 24*, 89.

LAMB, H., 1908, "On the Theory of Waves Propagated Vertically in the Atmosphere," *Proc. London Math. Soc. (2) 7*, 122.

——1945, *Hydrodynamics* (6th ed.), Dover.

LARMOR, J., 1919 and 1927, "How could a Rotating Body such as the Sun become a Magnet? (with Appendix, 1927: On the Solar Magnetic Fields)," *Rep. Brit. Assoc. Adv. Sci., Bournemouth*, 159.

LARMORE, L., 1953, "Study of the Motions of Solar Prominences," *Ap. J. 118*, 436.

LEE, Y. W., 1960, *Statistical Theory of Communication*, New York: Wiley.

LE GALLEY, D. P. (Editor), 1963, *Space Science 1963*, New York: Wiley.

LEIGHTON, R. B., 1957, "Some Observations of Solar Granulation," *P. A. S. P. 69*, 497.

——1959, "Observations of Solar Magnetic Fields in Plage Regions," *Ap. J. 130*, 366.

——1960, "Speech on Velocity Fields on the Sun," *I. A. U. Symposium No. 12*, p. 321.

——1964, "Transport of Magnetic Fields on the Sun," *Ap. J. 140*, 1547.

——R. W. NOYES, and G. W. SIMON, 1962, "Velocity Fields in the Solar Atmosphere I. Preliminary Report," *Ap. J. 135*, 474.

LENZ, W., 1933, "Allgemeine Theorie der Verbreiterung von Spektrallinien," *Z. Phys. 80*, 423.

LEROY, J. -L., 1960, "Interprétation de la polarisation de la lumière des taches solaires," *C. R. 251*, 1720.

——1962, "Contributions à l'étude de la polarisation de la lumière solaire," *Ann. d'Ap. 25*, 127.

LE SQUEREN, A. -M., 1963, "Étude des orages radioéléctriques solaires sur 169 MHz à l'aide de l'interferomètre en croix de la station de Nançay," *Ann. d'Ap. 26*, 97.

LIGHTHILL, M. J., 1952, "On Sound Generated Aerodynamically. I. General Theory," *Proc. Roy. Soc. (London) A 211*, 565.

——1954, "On Sound Generated Aerodynamically. II. Turbulence as a Source of Sound," *Proc. Roy. Soc. (London) A 222*, 1.

LINDHOLM, E., 1942, "Über die Verbreiterung und Verschiebung von Spektrallinien," Diss., Uppsala.

LINHART, J. G., 1960, *Plasma Physics*, Amsterdam: North-Holland Publ. Co.

LIVSHITS, M. A., 1963, "A Facula Model," *A. Zhurn. 40*, 38 (*Sov. Astron. 7*, 28).

LOCKYER, J. N., 1868a, "Lettre à M. W. de la Rue sur une méthode employée par M. Lockyer pour observer en temps ordinaire le spectre des protubérances signalées dans les éclipses totales du soleil," *C. R. 67*, 836.

——1868b, "Sur les protubérances solaires (extrait d'une lettre à M. Warren de la Rue)," *C. R. 67*, 949.

LOCKYER, W. J. S., 1931, "On the Relationship between Solar Prominences and the Forms of the Corona," *M. N. 91*, 797.

LORENTZ, H. A., 1905a, "Over de absorptie—en emissiebanden van gasvormige lichamen I," *Proc. Roy. Acad. (Amsterdam) 14*, 518.

—— 1905b, "Over de absorptie—en emissiebanden van gasvormige lichamen II," *Proc. Roy. Acad. (Amsterdam) 14*, 577.

LOUGHHEAD, R. E. and R. J. BRAY, 1959, "Observations of Faculae Bordering Small Sunspots Near the Limb," *Aust. J. Phys. 12*, 97.

—— and R. J. BRAY, 1960a, "The Lifetime and Cell Size of the Granulation in Sunspot Umbrae," *Aust. J. Phys. 13*, 139.

—— and R. J. BRAY, 1960b, "Granulation Near the Extreme Solar Limb." *Aust. J. Phys. 13*, 738.

LUDWIG, C., 1856, "Diffusion zwischen ungleich erwärmten Orten gleich zusammengesetzter Lösungen," *Akad. Wiss. Wien. S. -B. 20*, 539.

LUNDQUIST, S., 1952, "Studies in Magneto-hydrodynamics," *Ark. Fys. 5*, 297.

LÜST, R. and H. ZIRIN, 1960, "Condensation of Prominences from the Corona," *Z. Ap. 49*, 8.

LYOT, B., 1930, "La couronne solaire étudiée en dehors des éclipses," *C. R. 191*, 834.

—— 1931, "Photographie de la couronne solaire en dehors des éclipses," *C. R. 193*, 1169.

—— 1936, "Observations des protubérances solaires faites au Pic du Midi en 1935," *C. R. 202*, 392.

—— 1938a, "La couronne solaire et les protubérances avant et après l'éclipse du 19 juin 1936," *L'Astronomie 52*, 193.

—— 1938b, "Observations de la couronne solaire et des protubérances faites au Pic du Midi en 1937," *C. R. 206*, 648.

—— 1939, "A Study of the Solar Corona and Prominences without Eclipses," *M. N. 99*, 580.

—— 1944, "Le filtre monochromatique polarisant et ses applications en physique solaire," *Ann. d'Ap. 7*, 31.

MACRIS, C., 1953, "Recherches sur la granulation photosphérique," *Ann. d'Ap. 16*, 19.

MADDEN, R. P. and K. CODLING, 1963, "New Autoionizing Atomic Energy Levels in He, Ne and Ar," *Phys. Rev. Letters 10*, 516.

—— and K. CODLING, 1964, "Recently Discovered Auto-ionizing States of Krupton and Xenon in the λ380–600 Å Region," *J. Opt. Soc. Amer. 54*, 268.

MAKITA, M., 1963, "Physical States in Sunspots," *P. A. S. Japan 15*, 145.

—— and M. MORIMOTO, 1960, "Photoelectric Study of Sunspots," *P. A. S. Japan 12*, 63.

MALITSON, H. H. and W. R. WEBBER, 1963, *Solar Proton Manual, NASA TR-R-169*, Chapter 1.

MALTBY, P., 1960, "Note on the Evershed Effect in Sunspots," *Ann. d'Ap. 23*, 983.

—— 1964, "On the Velocity Field in Sunspots," *Ap. Norv. 8*, 205.

MALVILLE, J. M., 1961, "Studies of Fast-drift Bursts and Related Phenomena," Ph. D. Diss., University of Colorado.

—— 1964, "The Association of Energetic Particles with Solar Flares," *AAS-NASA Symposium on the Physics of Solar Flares, 1963*, p. 257.

——and G. E. MORETON, 1963, "The Expansion of Flare Filaments," *P. A. S. P.* **75, 176**.

MARGENAU, H., 1932, "Pressure Shift and Broadening of Spectral Lines," *Phys. Rev. 40*, 387.

MARSHALL, L., 1957, "Coronal Streaming in Solar Sunspot Prominences," *Ap. J. 126*, 177.

MARTRES, M. -J., 1956, "Disparition brusque d'une protubérance observée à l'héliographe monochromatique le 9 août 1956," *L'Astronomie 70*, 401.

——R. MICHARD and I. SORU–ISOVICI, 1966a, "Étude morphologique de la structure magnétique des régions actives en relation avec les phénomènes chromosphériques et les éruptions solaires. I. Classification magnétique et éruptivité," *Ann. d'Ap. 29*, 245.

——R. MICHARD and I. SORU–ISCOVICI, 1966b, "Étude morphologique de la structure magnétique des régions actives en relation avec les phénomènes chromosphériques et les éruptions solaires. II. Localisation des plages brillantes, filaments et éruptions," *Ann. d'Ap. 29*, 249.

——and M. PICK, 1962, "Caractères propres aux éruptions chromosphériques associées à des emissions radioéléctriques," *Ann. d'Ap. 25*, 293.

MASSEY, H. S. W. and B. L. MOISEIWITSCH, 1954, "The Application of Variational Methods to Atomic Scattering Problems IV. The Excitation of the 2^1S and 2^3S States of Helium by Electron Impact," *Proc. Roy. Soc. (London) A 227*, 38.

MATTIG, W., 1953, "Die radiale Verteilung der Magnetischen Feldstärke in normalen Sonnenflecken," *Z. Ap. 31*, 273.

—— 1958, "Zur Linienabsorption im inhomogenen Magnetfeld der Sonnenflecken," *Z. Ap. 44*, 280.

MAXWELL, J. C., 1867, "On the Dynamical Theory of Gases," *Phil. Trans. Roy. Soc. (London) 157*, 49.

McCREA, W. H., 1929, "The Mechanics of the Chromosphere," *M. N. 89*, 718.

McLEAN, D. J., 1959, "Solar Radio Emission of Spectral Type IV and Its Association with Geomagnetic Storms," *Aust. J. Phys. 12*, 404.

McMATH, R. R., O. C. MOHLER, and H. DODSON, 1960, "Solar Features Associated with Ellerman's 'Solar Hydrogen Bombs'," *Proc. Natl. Acad. Sci. 46*, 165.

——and E. PETTIT, 1937, "Prominences of the Active and Sunspot Types Compared," *Ap. J. 85*, 279.

——and E. PETITT, 1938, "Prominence Studies," *Ap. J. 88*, 244.

MENZEL, D. H., 1950, "Origin of Sunspots," *Nature 166*, 31.

——and L. R. DOHERTY, 1963, "The Evolution of Solar Prominences," *The Solar Corona* (J. W. Evans, Ed.), p. 159, New York: Academic Press.

——and J. W. EVANS, 1953, "The Behavior and Classification of Solar Prominences," *Accad. Naz. Lincei, Convegno Volta 11*, 119.

——and C. L. PEKERIS, 1936, "Absorption Coefficients and Hydrogen Line Intensities," *M. N. 96*, 77.

—— E. v. P. SMITH, H. DE MASTUS, H. RAMSEY, G. SCHNABLE, and R. LAWRENCE, 1956, "The Record Prominence of 10 February 1956," *A. J. 61*, 186.

MEYER, P., E. N. PARKER, and J. A. SIMPSON, 1956, "Solar Cosmic Rays of February, 1956, and Their Propagation through Interplanetary Space," *Phys. Rev. 104*, 768.

—— and R. VOGT, 1962, "Some Properties of the Primary Cosmic Ray Electrons," *J. Phys. Soc. Japan 17, A-III*, 5.

MEYERMANN, B., 1950, "Zur Pulsation der Sonne," *A. N. 279*. 45.

MICHARD, R., 1951, "Remarques sur l'effet Evershed," *Ann. d'Ap. 14*, 101.

—— 1953, "Contribution à l'étude physique de la photosphère et des taches solaires," *Ann. d'Ap. 16*, 217.

—— 1959, "Spectroscopie des eruptions solaires dans le programme français de l'A. G. I.," *Ann. d'Ap. 22*, 887.

—— 1961, "Formation des raies de Fraunhofer en présence d'un champ magnétique," *C. R. 253*, 2857.

—— Z. MOURADAIN, and M. SEMEL, 1961, "Champs magnétiques dans un centre d'activité solaire avant et pendant une eruption," *Ann. d'Ap. 24*, 54.

MILLS, B. Y. and A. G. LITTLE, 1953, "A High Resolution Aerial System of a New Type," *Aust. J. Phys. 6*, 272.

MILNE, E. A., 1924, "An Astrophysical Determination of the Average Life of an Excited Calcium Atom," *M. N. 84*, 354.

MINNAERT, M., 1936, "Die theoretische Intensitätsverteilung in den äusseren Flügeln der Fraunhoferschen Linien," *Z. Ap. 12*, 313.

—— 1953, "The Photosphere," *The Sun* (G. Kuiper, Ed.), p. 88, Chicago: University of Chicago Press.

—— and A. J. M. WANDERS, 1932, "Zur Theorie der Sonnenflecke," *Z. Ap. 5*, 297.

MITCHELL, S. A., 1935, *Eclipses of the Sun*, New York: Columbia University Press.

MITROPOLSKAYA, O. N., 1954, "A Study of Physical Conditions in Solar Faculae," *Iz. Krim. Ap. Obs. 11*, 152.

—— 1955, "Line Profiles of Hydrogen Hα and Hβ in Faculae and the Photosphere," *Iz. Krim. Ap. Obs. 15*, 130.

MOHLER, O. C., 1960, "Fraunhofer Lines and Heights in the Sun's Atmosphere," *Sky and Telescope 20*, No. 3, 124.

—— and L. GOLDBERG, 1956, "The Width of the Infrared Helium Line in the Solar Spectrum," *Ap. J. 124*, 13.

MOORE, D. W. and E. A. SPIEGEL, 1964, "The Generation and Propagation of Waves in a Compressible Atmosphere," *Ap. J. 139*, 48.

MORETON, G. E., 1960, "Hα Observations of Flare-Initiated Disturbances with Velocities ~1000 km/sec," *A. J. 65*, 494.

—— 1965, "Flare-Associated Filament Changes," *I. A. U. Symposium No. 22*, p. 371.

—— and H. RAMSEY, 1960, "Recent Observations of Dynamical Phenomena Associated with Solar Flares," *P. A. S. P. 72*, 357.

MORIYAMA, F., 1961, "On the Thermal Radio Emission from the Sun and Galactic H II Regions," *Ann. Tokyo Astron. Obs. 7*, 127.

MOROZHENKO, N. N., 1963, "Study of the Physical Properties of Protuberances with Metal Lines," *Bull. Main Astron. Obs. Kiev 5*, No. 1, 93.

Moss, W., 1946, "The Distribution and Movements of Solar Prominence Areas," *Ann. Solar Obs. Cambridge* 3(3), 119.

Mott, N. F. and H. S. W. Massey, 1949, *The Theory of Atomic Collisions*, Oxford: Clarendon University Press.

Moutot, M. and A. Boischot, 1961, "Étude du rayonnement thermique des centres d'activité solaire sur 169 MHz," *Ann. d'Ap. 24*, 171.

Nagasawa, S. and Y. Nakagomi, 1965, "Green Corona before the Birth and after the Death of a Calcium Plage," *Rep. Ionos. Space Res. Japan 19*, 339.

Namba, O., 1960, "A Preliminary Report on the Observation of Infrared Lines in Solar Faculae with Special Reference to the He I Line at 10830 Å," *Ann. d'Ap. 23*, 902.

—— 1963, "The Profile of the Infrared He I Line in Solar Faculae," *B. A. N. 17*, 93.

Ness, N. F., 1966, "Earth's Magnetic Field: A New Look," *Science 151*, 1041.

—— C. S. Scearce, J. B. Seek, and J. M. Wilcox, 1965, "A Summary of Results from the IMP-1 Magnetic Field Experiment," *NASA Report X-612-65-180*, Goddard Space Flight Center.

—— and J. M. Wilcox, 1965, "Extension of the Photospheric Magnetic Field into Interplanetary Space," *NASA Report X-612-65-79*, Goddard Space Flight Center.

Newkirk, G., 1957, "Doppler Motions in the Corona," *Ann. d'Ap. 20*, 127.

—— 1959, "A Model of the Electron Corona with Reference to Radio Observations," *I. A. U. Symposium No. 9*, p. 149.

—— 1961, "The Solar Corona in Active Regions and the Thermal Origin of the Slowly Varying Component of Solar Radio Radiation," *Ap. J. 133*, 983.

Newton, H. W., 1934, "The Distribution of Radial Velocities of Dark Hα Markings near Sunspots," *M. N. 94*, 472.

—— 1935, "Note on Two Allied Types of Chromospheric Eruptions," *M. N. 95*, 650.

—— 1942, "Characteristic Radial Motions of Hα Absorption Markings Seen with Bright Eruptions on the Sun's Disk," *M. N. 102*, 2.

—— and M. L. Nunn, 1951, "The Sun's Rotation Derived from Sunspots 1934–1944 and Additional Results," *M. N. 111*, 413.

Ney, E. P. and W. Stein, 1962, "Solar Protons in November, 1960," *J. Phys. Soc. Japan 17*, A-II, 345.

Nicholson, S. B., 1933, "The Area of a Sun-spot and the Intensity of Its Magnetic Field," *P. A. S. P. 45*, 51.

Nikulin, N. S., A. B. Severny, and V. E. Stepanov, 1958, "The Solar Magnetograph of the Krimean Astrophysical Observatory," *Iz. Krim. Ap. Obs. 19*, 3.

Nishi, K., 1962, "The Observation of the Structure of the Magnetic Field in Sunspots," *P. A. S. Japan 14*, 325.

—— and Y. Nakagomi, 1963, "A Model of the Coronal Condensation," *P. A. S. Japan 15*, 56.

Noyes, R. W. and R. B. Leighton, 1963, "Velocity Fields in the Solar Atmosphere III. The Oscillatory Field," *Ap. J. 138*, 631.

Obashev, S. O., 1961, "On the Structure of the Corona over Prominences," *Bull. Astron. Inst. Acad. Sci. Kazahk. SSR 12*, 78.

O'BRIEN, P. A., 1953, "The Radio 'Brightness' Across the Solar Disk at a Wavelength of 1.4 Metres and Its Relation to the Coronal Line Emission," *Obs. 73*, 106.

ÖHMAN, Y., 1938, "A New Monochromator," *Nature 141*, 157.

—— 1947, "Results from Observations of the Total Solar Eclipse of 1945 July 9, I. The Polarization of the Corona," *Stockholm Obs. Ann. 15*, No. 2.

—— 1950, "The Use of Savart Fringes in the Observation of Zeeman Effects in Sunspots," *Ap. J. 111*, 362.

—— A. LINDGREN and U. LINDGREN, 1962, "A Photometric Study of Activations of Prominences probably due to Moving Disturbances on the Sun," *Arkiv Astron. 3*, 121.

—— and N. ÖHMAN, 1953, "On a Disturbance in a Prominence Probably Initiated by a Distant Flare," *Obs. 73*, 203.

OLIVIERI, G., 1956, "Disparition brusque d'une protubérance au bord solaire," *L'Astronomie 70*, 120.

ORRALL, F. Q., 1962, "Temperature Determination in Solar Prominences," *Temperature Measurement and Control Sci. Industry 3*, I, 723.

—— and R. G. ATHAY, 1957, "Physical Conditions in Solar Prominences," *A. J. 62*, 28.

—— and J. B. ZIRKER, 1961, "Heat Conduction and the Fine Structure of Solar Prominences. I. Optically Thin Model Prominences," *Ap. J. 134*, 72.

OSTER, L., 1957, "Viskosität, elektrische und thermische Leitfähigkeit Stellarer Materie," *Z. Ap. 42*, 228.

—— and M. ALTSCHULER, 1964, "Electromagnetic Radiation from Plasma Oscillations," *AAS-NASA Symposium on the Physics of Solar Flares, 1963*, p. 377.

OSTERBROCK, D. E., 1961, "The Heating of the Solar Chromosphere, Plages, and Corona by Magnetohydrodynamic Waves," *Ap. J. 134*, 347.

PAGEL, B. E. J., 1956, "A Model Atmosphere for the Solar Limb Based on Continuum Observations," *M. N. 116*, 608.

—— 1957, "The Emission of Continuous Radiation in Stellar Atmospheres," *Ap. J. 125*, 298.

—— 1959, "Note on Collisional Dissociation of the H⁻ Ion in the Solar Atmosphere," *M. N. 119*, 609.

PANNEKOEK, A. and N. W. DOORN, 1930, "Photometry of the Chromosphere and the Corona," *Verh. Akad. Wetensch. (Amsterdam) 14*, No. 2.

PAN PUH, 1939, "Recherches sur le mouvement des protubérances solaires," *Ann. Obs. Paris-Meudon 8*, Nr. 4, 52.

PARKER, E. N., 1955, "The Formation of Sunspots from the Solar Toroidal Field," *Ap. J. 121*, 491.

—— 1957a, "Acceleration of Cosmic Rays in Solar Flares," *Phys. Rev. 107*, 830.

—— 1957b, "Sweet's Mechanism for Merging Magnetic Fields in Conducting Fluids," *J. G. R. 62*, 509.

—— 1958a, "Dynamics of the Interplanetary Gas and Magnetic Fields," *Ap. J. 128*, 664.

—— 1958b, "Origin and Dynamics of Cosmic Rays," *Phys. Rev. 109*, 1328.

—— 1960, "The Hydrodynamic Theory of Solar Corpuscular Radiation and Stellar Winds," *Ap. J. 132*, 821.

—— 1961, "Sudden Expansion of the Corona Following a Large Solar Flare and the Attendant Magnetic Field and Cosmic-Ray Effects," *Ap. J. 133*, 1014.

—— 1962, "Dynamics of the Geomagnetic Storm," *Space Sci. Rev. 1*, 62.

—— 1963, "The Solar-Flare Phenomenon and the Theory of Reconnection and Annihilation of Magnetic Fields," *Ap. J. Suppl. 8*, No. 77, 177.

PAWSEY, J. L. and R. N. BRACEWELL, 1955, *Radio Astronomy*, London: Oxford University Press.

PECKER-WIMEL, C., 1960, "Étude des spectres pris par Bernard Lyot à l'éclipse de Khartourm du 23 février 1952," *Ann. d'Ap. 23*, 764.

PECKER, J.-C. and E. SCHATZMAN, 1959, *Astrophysique Générale*, Paris: Masson et Cie.

PETERSON, L. E. and J. R. WINCKLER, 1959, "Gamma-Ray Burst from a Solar Flare," *J. G. R. 64*, 697.

PETSCHEK, H. E., 1964, "Magnetic Field Annihilation," *AAS-NASA Symposium on the Physics of Solar Flares, 1963*, p. 425.

PETTIT, E., 1919, "The Great Eruptive Prominence of May 29 and July 15, 1919," *Ap. J. 50*, 206.

—— 1925, "The Forms and Motions of the Solar Prominences," *Publ. Yerkes Obs. 3*, IV, 205.

—— 1932, "Characteristic Features of Solar Prominences," *Ap. J. 76*, 9.

—— 1936, "The Motions of Prominences of the Eruptive and Sun-spot Types," *Ap. J. 84*, 319.

—— 1943, "The Properties of Solar Prominences as Related to Type," *Ap. J. 98*, 6.

—— 1950, "The Evidence for Tornado Prominences," *P. A. S. P. 62*, 144.

—— and S. B. NICHOLSON, 1928, "Stellar Radiation Measurements," *Ap. J. 68*, 279.

PEYTURAUX, R., 1955, "Étude du fond continu du spectre solaire IV. L'assombrissement centre-bord du soleil entre 3190 Å et 23130 Å," *Ann. d'Ap. 18*, 34.

PIDDINGTON, J. H., 1956, "Solar Atmospheric Heating by Hydromagnetic Waves," *M. N. 116*, 314.

—— 1958, "Some Effects of Hydromagnetic Waves in the Solar Atmosphere," *I. A. U. Symposium No. 6*, paper 16, p. 141.

PLASKETT, H. H., 1954, "Motions in the Sun at the Photospheric Level V. Velocities of Granules and of Other Localized Regions," *M. N. 114*, 251.

POLUPAN, P. N. and N. A. YAKOVLIN, 1965, "Investigation of a Chromospheric Limb Flare," *A. Zhurn. 42*, 764 (*Sov. Astron. 9*, 590, 1966).

POTTASCH, S. R. and R. N. THOMAS, 1960, "Thermodynamic Structure of the Outer Solar Atmosphere VI. Effect of Departures from the Saha Equation on Inferred Properties of the Low Chromosphere," *Ap. J. 132*, 195.

POUNDS, K. A. and P. W. SANFORD, 1963, "Rocket Measurements of the Sun's X-ray 'Tail' with a Simple Photographic Detector," *Proc. Internat. Conf. Ionos., London, 1962*, p. 50, London: Inst. Phys. and Phys. Soc.

PROUDMAN, I., 1952, "The Generation of Noise by Isotropic Turbulence," *Proc. Roy. Soc. (London)* A *214*, 119.

PURCELL, J. D. and R. TOUSEY, 1960, "The Profile of Solar Hydrogen-Lyman-α," *J. G. R. 65*, 370.

RAMSEY, H. and S. F. SMITH, 1966, "Flare-Initiated Filament Oscillations," *A. J. 71*, 197.

REDMAN, R. O. and H. ZANSTRA, 1952, "The Continuous Spectrum of a Prominence Observed at the Total Solar Eclipse of 1952 February 25," *Proc. Nederl. Akad. Wetensch. 55 B*, 598.

REICHEL, M., 1953, "Zur Theorie der Spektroheliogramme," *Z. Ap. 33*, 79.

REYNOLDS, G. T., F. B. HARRISON, and G. SALVINI, 1950, "Liquid Scintillation Counters," *Phys. Rev. 78*, 488.

RICHARDSON, R. S., 1931, "An Investigation of Molecular Spectra in Sunspots," *Ap. J. 73*, 216.

—— 1933, "A Photometric Study of Sunspots and Faculae," *Ap. J. 78*, 359.

—— 1936, "Annual Report of the Director," *Mt. Wilson Obs. Yearbook*, No. 35, 171.

—— 1939, "The Intensities of Sunspots from Center to Limb in Light of Different Colors," *Ap. J. 90*, 230.

—— 1941, "The Nature of Solar Hydrogen Vortices," *Ap. J. 93*, 24.

—— 1948, "Sunspot Groups of Irregular Magnetic Polarity," *Ap. J. 107*, 78.

—— 1950, "The Spectra of Two Active Regions Observed at the Sun's Limb," *Ap. J. 111*, 572.

—— 1951, "Characteristics of Solar Flares," *Ap. J. 114*, 356.

—— and R. MINKOWSKI, 1939, "The Spectra of Bright Chromospheric Eruptions from λ3300 to λ11500," *Ap. J. 89*, 347.

RIDDIFORD, L. and S. T. BUTLER, 1952, "The Origin of Cosmic Rays in Solar or Stellar Disturbances," *Phil. Mag. 43*, 447.

RIGUTTI, M. and D. RUSSO, 1961, "Lo spettro di una protuberanza quiescente osservata nell'eclisse solare del 15 febbraio 1961," *Accad. Naz. Lincei*, Series 8, *30*, 487.

RINGNES, T. S., 1964, "Secular Variations of Sunspots with Lifetimes from Two to Eight Days," *Ap. Norv. 8*, No. 7, 161.

—— and E. JENSEN, 1960, "On the Relation between Magnetic Fields and Areas of Sunspots in the Interval 1917–1956," *Ap. Norv. 7*, 99.

ROBERTS, W. O., 1945, "A Preliminary Report on Chromospheric Spicules of Extremely Short Lifetime," *Ap. J. 101*, 136.

—— and D. E. BILLINGS, 1955a, "A Hypothesis for the Origin of Solar Flares," *A. J. 60*, 176.

—— and D. E. BILLINGS, 1955b, "A Hypothesis for the Origin of Solar Flares," *H. A. O. Solar Res. Memo.* No. 33.

ROGERSON, J. B., 1961, "On Photospheric Faculae," *Ap. J. 134*, 331.

ROKA, E. G.v., 1950, "Über die Berechnung der Magnetfelder von Sonnenflecken," *Z. Ap. 27*, 15.

ROSA, P., 1871, "Studi intorno ai diametri solari," *Boll. dell'Osservatorio del Collegio Romano 10*, 97.

RÖSCH, J., 1955, "Fluctuations de température dans le tube d'une lunette astronomique," *J. Phys. Rad. 16*, 54S.

—— 1956, "Étude de l'agitation des images télescopiques par la méthode de Hartmann," *Astronomical Optics* (Z. Kopal, Ed), p. 310, Amsterdam: North-Holland Publ. Co.

—— 1957, "Photographies de la photosphère et des taches solaires," *L'Astronomie* 71, 129.

ROSENBLUTH, M. N., 1956, "Stability of the Pinch," *Los Alamos Sci. Lab. LA-2030.*

—— 1958, "Transport Properties of Ionized Gases in a Magnetic Field," *Transport Properties in Gases* (A. B. Cambel and J. B. Fenn, Eds.), p. 174, Northwestern University Press.

ROSSELAND, S., 1926, "On the Transmission of Radiation Through an Absorbing Medium in Motion, with Applications to the Theory of Sunspots and Solar Rotation," *Ap. J. 63,* 342.

—— 1929, "Viscosity in the Stars," *M. N. 89,* 49.

—— 1936, "On the Theory of Rotating Stars I," *Ap. Norv. 2,* 173.

—— E. JENSEN, and E. A. TANDBERG–HANSSEN, 1958, "Some Considerations on Thermal Conduction and Magnetic Fields in Prominences," *I.A.U. Symposium No. 6,* p. 150.

—— and E. A. TANDBERG–HANSSEN, 1957, "On Some Solar Disturbances on 18 August and 24 September 1956," *Ap. Norv. 5,* 279.

RUSSELL, H. N., 1921, "Note on Cooling by Expansion in Sun-spots," *Ap. J. 54,* 293.

RUSSELL, P. C., 1965, "Further Soft X-ray Images of the Sun," *Nature 206,* 281.

—— and K. A. POUNDS, 1966, "Improved Resolution X-ray Photographs of the Sun," *Nature 209,* 490.

RUST, D., 1966a, "Measurement of Magnetic Fields in Solar Prominences," *A. J. 71,* 178.

—— 1966b, "Measurement of the Magnetic Fields in Quiescent Solar Prominences," Ph. D. Diss., University of Colorado.

SAHA, M. N., 1920, "Ionization in the solar chromosphere," *Phil. Mag. 40,* 472.

—— 1921, "On the Problems of Temperature Radiation of Gases," *Phil. Mag. 41,* 267.

SAITO, K., 1950, "Brightness and Polarization of the Solar Corona," *Ann. Tokyo Astron. Obs. 3,* 3.

—— and D. E. BILLINGS, 1964, "Polarimetric Observations of a Coronal Condensation," *Ap. J. 140,* 760.

SAWER, H. E. and J. BRODIE, 1938, "Effect of Projection Factor on Time-Distance Plots of Motions in Loops of Class III Prominences," *Publ. Obs. Univ. Michigan 7,* 79.

SCHATZMAN, E., 1949, "The Heating of the Solar Corona and Chromosphere," *Ann. d'Ap. 12,* 203.

—— 1961, "Modèles de taches solaires et protubérances de bord de taches," *Ann. d'Ap. 24,* 251.

—— 1963, "On the Acceleration of Particles in Shock Fronts," *Ann. d'Ap. 26,* 234.

—— 1965, "Particle and Radio Emission from the Sun," *The Solar Spectrum* (C. de Jager, Ed.), p. 313, Holland: D. Reidel.

SCHIRMER, H., 1950, "Über die Ausbreitung von Stosswellen in der Sonnenatmosphäre," *Z. Ap. 27*, 132.

SCHLÜTER, A., 1950, "Dynamik des Plasmas I. Grundgleichungen, Plasma in gekreuzten Feldern," *Z. Naturforsch. 5a*, 72.

—— 1957a, "Solar Radio Emission and the Acceleration of Magnetic-Storm Particles," *I. A. U. Symposium No. 4*, p. 356.

—— 1957b, "Der Gyro-Relaxations-Effeckt," *Z. Naturforsch. 12a*, 822.

—— and S. TEMESVÁRY, 1958, "The Internal Constitution of Sunspots," *I. A. U. Symposium No. 6*, p. 263.

SCHMIDT, H. and F. MEYER, 1966, "Generation and Propagation of Oscillatory Motions in the Solar Atmosphere," *Trans. I. A. U. 12B*, 559.

—— and J. B. ZIRKER, 1963, "On the Oscillations of the Solar Atmosphere," *Ap. J. 138*, 1310.

SCHWABE, H., 1844, "Periodicität der Sonnenflecken," *A. N. 21*, 234.

SCHWARZSCHILD, K., 1906, "Über die totale Sonnenfinsternis vom 30 August 1905," *Astron. Mitt. Göttingen 13*.

SCHWARZSCHILD, M., 1948, "On Noise Arising from the Solar Granulation," *Ap. J. 107*, 1.

—— 1959, "Photographs of the Solar Granulation Taken from the Stratosphere," *Ap. J. 130*, 345.

SCHWINGER, J., 1949, "On the Classical Radiation of Accelerated Electrons," *Phys. Rev. 75*, 1912.

SEARES, F. H., 1913, "The Displacement-Curve of the Sun's General Magnetic Field," *Ap. J. 38*, 99.

SEATON, M., 1962, "The Temperature of the Solar Corona," *Obs. 82*, 111.

SECCHI, A., 1868, "Troisième note sur les spectres stellaires," *C. R. 66*, 398.

—— 1872, "Sulle variazioni dei diametri solari osservati a Palermo e a Roma da A. Secchi, P. Rosa e G. Cacciatore," *Memorie Soc. Spettroscopisti Italiani 1*, 97.

—— 1873, "Nouvelles recherches sur le diamètre solaire," *C. R. 77*, 253.

—— 1875–1877, *Le Soleil*, Vols. 1 and 2, Paris: Gauthier-Villars.

SERVAJEAN, R., 1961, "Contribution a l'étude de la cinématique de la matière dans les taches et la granulation solaires," *Ann. d'Ap. 24*, 1.

SEVERNY, A. B., 1950, "Investigations of Intensity Variations in Solar Prominences," *Dokl. Akad. Nauk. 73*, 475.

—— 1954a, "Investigation of the Physical Conditions in Solar Prominences by Emission Lines with Self-absorption," *Iz. Krim. Ap. Obs. 12*, 33.

—— 1954b, "Concerning Self-absorption of Radiation and Physical Conditions in Solar Prominences," *A. Zhurn. 31*, 131.

—— 1956, "Fine Structure in Solar Spectra," *Obs. 76*, 241.

—— 1957, "Some Results of Investigations of Nonstationary Processes on the Sun," *A. Zhurn. 34*, 684 (*Sov. Astron. 1*, 668).

—— 1958a, "The Appearance of Flares in Neutral Points of the Solar Magnetic Field and the Pinch-Effect," *Iz. Krim. Ap. Obs. 20*, 22.

—— 1958b, "On the Production of High-Energy Particles and Hard Radiation in Solar Flares," *Sov. Phys. (Doklady) 3*, 698.

—— 1958c, "Nonstationary Processes in Solar Flares as a Manifestation of the Pinch Effect," *A. Zhurn. 35*, 335 (*Sov. Astron 2*, 310).

—— 1959a, "Fine Structure of the Magnetic Field and Depolarization of Radiation in Sunspots," *A. Zhurn. 36*, 208 (*Sov. Astron. 3*, 214).

—— 1959b, *Solar Physics* (translated by G. Yankovsky), Moscow: Foreign Languages Publ. House.

—— 1960, "On the Nonstationary Continuous Emission of Flares," *Iz. Krim. Ap. Obs. 22*, 67.

—— 1962a, "Magnetically Active Regions on the Sun," *Trans. I. A. U. 11B*, 426.

—— 1962b, "Nonstationary Processes in Solar Magnetic Fields. The Generation of Flares and Heating of Faculae," *Iz. Krim. Ap. Obs. 27*, 71.

—— 1963, "The Location of Great Flares in Magnetic Fields of Spot Groups," *Iz. Krim. Ap. Obs. 30*, 161.

—— 1964, "Solar Flares," *Ann. Rev. Astron. Ap. 2*, 363.

—— and V. L. KHOKHLOVA, 1953, "Studies of Motions and Currents in Solar Prominences," *Iz. Krim. Ap. Obs. 10*, 9.

—— and E. R. MUSTEL, 1955, "A Study of the Chromospheric Flare of June 13, 1950," *Iz. Krim. Ap. Obs. 13*, 82.

—— and V. P. SHABANSKY, 1960, "The Generation of Cosmic Rays in Flares," *A. Zhurn. 37*, 609 (*Sov. Astron. 4*, 583).

—— and V. P. SHABANSKY, 1961, "The Mechanism of Solar Flares and of the Generation of Cosmic Rays in Flares," *Iz. Krim. Ap. Obs. 25*, 88.

—— and V. E. STEPANOV, 1956, "First Observations of Magnetic Fields of Sunspots at the Krimean Astrophysical Observatory," *Iz. Krim. Ap. Obs. 16*, 3.

SHABANSKY, V. P., 1961, "On the Origin and Evolution of Solar Flares and the Generation of Cosmic Rays in Them," *A. Zhurn. 38*, 844 (*Sov. Astron. 5*, 647).

SHAPIRO, R. and F. WARD, 1962, "A Neglected Cycle in Sunspot Numbers," *J. Atmos. Sci. 19*, 506.

SHAPOSHNIKOVA, E. F., 1958, "Filaments Directly Connected with Sunspots," *Iz. Krim. Ap. Obs. 18*, 151.

SHAW, P. E., 1926, "The Electrical Charges from Like Solids," *Nature 118*, 659.

SHIN-HUEI, E., 1961, "A Spectrophotometric Study of Solar Prominences," *Iz. Krim. Ap. Obs. 25*, 180.

SHKLOVSKY, I. S., 1962, *Fizika Solnechnoi Korony*, Chapter IV, p. 189, Moscow: Gosudarstvennoe Izdatel'stvo Fiziko-Matematicheskoi Literaturi (*Physics of the Solar Corona* (translated by L. A. Fenn), London: Pergamon Press, 1965).

—— 1964, "The Inverse Compton Effect as a Possible Cause of the X-ray Radiation of Solar Flares," *Nature 202*, 275.

SIMON, G. W., 1963, "Correlations between Large-Scale Solar Photospheric and Chromospheric Motions, Ca II (K) Emission, and Magnetic Fields," Diss., California Institute of Technology.

—— and R. B. LEIGHTON, 1964, "Velocity Fields in the Solar Atmosphere III. Large-Scale Motions, the Chromospheric Network, and Magnetic Fields," *Ap. J. 140*, 1120.

SIMPSON, J. A., S. R. MIELCZAREK, and J. COOPER, 1964, "Observation of Optically Forbidden Transitions in the Continuum of the Rare Gases by Electron Energy Loss Measurements," *J. Opt. Soc. Amer. 54*, 269.

SITNIK, G. F., 1940, "Dependence of the Intensity of Sunspots from Their Position on the Disk and Their Geometric Area," *A. Zhurn. 17*, 23.

—— 1960, "A Blackbody Model Operable at High Temperature," *A. Zhurn. 37*, 1076 (*Sov. Astron. 4*, 1013).

SMERD, S. F., 1950, "The Polarization of Thermal 'Solar Noise' and a Determination of the Sun's General Magnetic Field," *Aust. J. Sci. Res. 3*, 265.

SMITH, E. v. P., 1962, "Relationships Between H-alpha Intensity, Width and Area of Flares," *GRD Res. Note 74, AFCRL-62-226*.

SMITH, H. J., 1962a, "Some Synoptic Flare Data, 1937–1960," *GRD Res. Note AFCRL-62-827*.

—— 1962b, "A Study of Sacramento Peak Flares III: Sympathetic Flares," *GRD Solar Res. Note No. 58, AFCRL-472 (III)*.

—— 1962c, "The Flares of the November–December Passage of Region 59-AC," *Sac. Peak Res. Note*.

—— and E. v. P. SMITH, 1963, *Solar Flares*, New York: Macmillan.

SMITH, S. F., 1965, "Final Report on Studies of Flare-associated Filament Phenomena," *Lockheed Report No. LR 19038* [Contract NONR 4537 (00)].

—— and H. E. RAMSEY, 1964, "The Flare-Associated Filament Disappearance," *Z. Ap. 60*, 1.

SOBOLEV, V. M., 1958, "On the Excitation of Hydrogen and Helium in Solar Prominences," *Bull. Astron. Obs. Pulkova 20*, 12.

SORET, C., 1879, "Sur l'état d'équilibre que prend au point de vue de sa concentration une dissolution saline primitivement homogène dont deux parties sont portées à des températures différentes," *Arch. Sci. Phys. Nat., Geneve 2*, 48.

—— 1880a, "Sur l'état d'équilibre que prend au point de vue de sa concentration une dissolution saline primitivement homogène dont deux parties sont portées à des températures différentes (deuxième note)," *Arch. Sci. Phys. Nat., Geneve 4*, 209.

—— 1880b, "Influence de la température sur la distribution des sels dans leurs solutions," *C. R. 91*, 289.

SPIEGEL, E. A., 1957, "The Smoothing of Temperature Fluctuations by Radiative Transfer," *Ap. J. 126*, 202.

SPITZER, L., 1956, *Physics of Fully Ionized Gases*, New York: Interscience Press.

SPÖRER, G., 1874, "Beobachtungen der Sonnenflecken zu Anclam," *Publ. Astron. Gesellsch. 13*, 1.

STARK, J., 1916, "Bericht über die Verbreiterung von Spektallinien," *Jahr. Radio Elektr. 12*, 349.

STEIN, W. A. and E. P. NEY, 1963, "Continuum Electromagnetic Radiation from Solar Flares," *J. G. R. 68*, 65.

STEPANOV, V. E., 1958a, "On the Theory of the Formation of Absorption Lines in a Magnetic Field and the Profile of Fe λ 6173 Å in the Solar Sunspot Spectrum," *Iz. Krim. Ap. Obs. 19*, 20.

—— 1958b, "Local Magnetic Fields, Fine Chromospheric Structure and Filaments in Hα," *Iz. Krim. Ap. Obs. 20*, 52.

STEPANYAN, A. A., 1963, "Metallic Line Emission in Flares," *Iz. Krim. Ap. Obs. 29*, 68.

—— and B. M. VLADIMIRSKII, 1961, "On the Emission of High-Energy Particles by the Sun," *A. Zhurn. 38*, 439 (*Sov. Astron. 5*, 326).

STESHENKO, N. and V. KHOKHLOVA, 1960, "Helium Emission of the Chromospheric Flare of September 14, 1958," *Iz. Krim. Ap. Obs. 23*, 322.

STIX, T. H., 1962, *The Theory of Plasma Waves*, New York: McGraw–Hill.

ST. JOHN, C. E., 1913, "Radial Motion in Sunspots I. The Distribution of Velocities in the Solar Vortex," *Ap. J. 37*, 322.

—— 1921, "Solar Faculae and Ionization," *Contributions of the Jefferson Phys. Lab. 15*.

STRATTON, J. A., 1941, *Electromagnetic Theory*, New York: McGraw–Hill.

STUART, F. E. and J. H. RUSH, 1954, "Correlation Analyses of Turbulent Velocities and Brightness of the Photospheric Granulation," *Ap. J. 120*, 245.

STURROCK, P. A., 1966a, "Model of the High-Energy Phase of Solar Flares," *Nature 211*, 695.

—— 1966b, "Explosive and Non-explosive Onsets of Instability," *Phys. Rev. Letters 16*, 270.

—— and B. COPPI, 1964, "A New Model of Solar Flares," *Nature 204*, 61.

—— and B. COPPI, 1965, "A New Model of Solar Flares," *Report SUPR No. 6*, Institute for Plasma Research, Stanford (*Ap. J. 143*, 3, 1966).

—— and E. WOODBURY, 1965, "A New Model for Solar Filaments," *A. J. 70*, 694.

SUEMOTO, Z., 1951, "Electron Temperature of the Chromospheric Eruption," *P. A. S. Japan 3*, 110.

—— and E. HIEI, 1959, "Balmer Series Lines of the Flare and Its Structure," *P. A. S. Japan 11*, 185.

—— E. HIEI, and T. HIRAYAMA, 1962, "Structure of the Flare," *J. Phys. Soc. Japan 17, A-II*, 231.

ŠVESTKA, Z., 1951a, "The H-α Emission from Chromospheric Flares: I. Observations," *B. A. C. 2*, 81.

—— 1951b, "The H-α Emission from Chromospheric Flares: II. General Features of Asymmetry," *B. A. C. 2*, 100.

—— 1951c, "The H-α Emission from Chromospheric Flares: III. Course of Asymmetry," *B. A. C. 2*, 120.

—— 1951d, "The H-α Emission from Chromospheric Flares: IV. Expanding Source of Radiation," *B. A. C. 2*, 150.

—— 1951e, "The H-α Emission from Chromospheric Flares: V. The Flare of August 5, 1949," *B. A. C. 2*, 153.

—— 1951f, "The H-α Emission from Chromospheric Flares: VI. Central Intensity and Line Width," *B. A. C. 2*, 165.

—— 1952, "The H-α Emission from Chromospheric Flares: VII. Broadening of the Line in the Flash State," *B. A. C. 3*, 1.

—— 1957, "Physical Conditions in Chromospheric Flares," *Publ. Astron. Inst. Prague No. 32*.

—— 1960, "Hydrogen Spectrum of the Flare of July 30, 1958," *B. A. C. 11*, 167.

—— 1961, "Spectrum of the Flare of July 20, 1958," *B. A. C. 12*, 73.

—— 1962a, "On a Peculiar Flare Spectrum," *B. A. C. 13*, 30.

—— 1962b, "Evidence of Stark Broadening of Balmer Lines in Flares," *B. A. C. 13*, 236.

—— 1963, "On the Spectral Analysis of Flares," *B. A. C. 14*, 75.

——M. Kopecký, and M. Blaha, 1961, "Qualitative Discussion of 244 Flare Spectra," *B. A. C. 12*, 229.

Swann, W. F. G., 1933, "A Mechanism of Acquirement of Cosmic-Ray Energies by Electrons," *Phys. Rev. 43*, 217.

Swarup, G. and R. Parthasarthy, 1958, "Solar Brightness Distribution at a Wavelength of 60 Centimeters," *Aust. J. Phys. 11*, 338.

——P. H. Stone, and A. Maxwell, 1960, "The Association of Solar Radio Bursts with Flares and Prominences," *Ap. J. 131*, 725.

Sweet, P. A., 1958, "The Neutral Point Theory of Solar Flares," *I. A. U. Symposium No. 6*, Paper 14, p. 123.

Takakura, T., 1960, "Synchrotron Radiation from Intermediate Energy Electrons and Solar Radio Outbursts at Microwave Frequencies," *P. A. S. Japan 12*, 325.

——1961, "Acceleration of Electrons in the Solar Atmosphere and Type IV Radio Outbursts," *P. A. S. Japan 13*, 166.

Tanaka, H. and T. Kakinuma, 1958, "Eclipse Observations of Microwave Radio Sources on the Solar Disk on 19 April 1958," *Rep. Ionos. Res. Japan 12*, 273.

——and T. Kakinuma, 1959, "Polarization of Bursts of Solar Radio Emission at Microwave Frequencies," *Paris Symposium on Radio Astronomy* (R. N. Bracewell, Ed.), p. 215, Stanford University Press.

Tandberg–Hanssen, E. A., 1957, "On the Correlation between Solar Flares and Radio Bursts," *Ap. Norv. 6*, 17.

——1959, "Physical Conditions in Limb Flares and Active Prominences III. The Difference Between the Surge and Loop Prominences of December 19, 1956," *Ap. J. 130*, 202.

——1960, "An Investigation of the Temperature Conditions in Prominences with a Special Study of the Excitation of Helium," *Ap. Norv. 6*, 161.

——1962, "Étude des raies d'émission de He I dans l'atmosphère solaire I. Les profils de la raie triplet infrarouge, λ 10830 Å," *Ann. d'Ap. 25*, 357.

——1963, "Physical Conditions in Limb Flares and Active Prominences VI. Selective Excitation Conditions," *Ap. J. 137*, 26.

——1964, "A Spectroscopic Study of Quiescent Prominences," *Ap. Norv. 9*, 13.

——W. Curtis, and K. Watson, 1959, "The Emission of He I, λ 10830, during the Great Flare of August 26, 1958," *Ap. J. 129*, 238.

——and H. Zirin, 1959, "Physical Conditions in Limb Flares and Active Prominences I. The Loop Prominences of November 12 and 22, 1956," *Ap. J. 129*, 408.

ten Bruggencate, P., 1939, "Die Verbreiterung von Fraunhofer-Linien durch Turbulenz," *Z. Ap. 18*, 316.

——and G. Elste, 1958, "Temperature and Turbulence in Quiescent Prominences Determined from Line-Widths," *Nature 182*, 1154.

——and H. von Klüber, 1939, "Das Spektrum von Sonnenflecken I. Die Temperatur der Flecken," *Z. Ap. 18*, 284.

——and H. von Klüber, 1944, "Temperatur und Elektronendruck in Sonnenflecken," *Nachr. Akad. Wiss. Gött., Math.-Phys. K1.*, 165.

THIESSEN, G., 1946, "Recherches de physique solaire IV. La mesure du champ magnétique général du soleil," *Ann. d'Ap. 9*, 101.

—— 1949, "The Sun's Magnetic Field," *Obs. 69*, 228.

—— 1950, "The Structure of Sunspot-Umbra," *Obs. 70*, 234.

—— 1953, "Die magnetische Feldstärke in Sonnenflecken," *Naturwiss, 40*, 218.

THOMAS, R. N., 1948a, "Superthermal Phenomena in Stellar Atmospheres I. Spicules and the Solar Chromosphere," *Ap. J. 108*, 130.

—— 1948b, "Superthermal Phenomena in Stellar Atmospheres II. Departure from Thermodynamic Equilibrium in an Idealized Chromosphere," *Ap. J. 108*, 142.

—— 1957, "The Source Function in a Non-equilibrium Atmosphere I. The Resonance Lines," *Ap. J. 125*, 260.

—— and R. G. ATHAY, 1961, *Physics of the Solar Chromosphere*, New York: Interscience Press.

THOMPSON, W. B., 1951, "Thermal Convection in a Magnetic Field," *Phil. Mag. 42*, 1417.

TIDMAN, D. A., 1965, "Radio Emission from Shock Waves and Type II Solar Outbursts," *Planet. Space Sci. 13*, 781.

TREANOR, P. J., 1960, "The Spatial Analysis of Magnetic Fields in Sunspots," *M. N. 120*, 412.

UCHIDA, Y., 1960, "On the Exciters of Type II and Type III Solar Radio Bursts," *P. A. S. Japan 12*, 376.

—— 1961, "On the Formation of Solar Chromospheric Spicules and Flare-Surges," *P. A. S. Japan 13*, 321.

—— 1963, "An Effect of the Magnetic Field in the Shock Wave Heating Theory of the Solar Corona," *P. A. S. Japan 15*, 376.

—— 1966, "Resonant Responses of the Solar Atmosphere to the Gravitational-Hydrodynamic Waves," *Ap. J. (147*, 181, 1967).

ULLOA, A., 1779, "Observations on the Total (with Duration) and Annular Eclipse of the Sun, Taken on the 24th of June, 1778, on Board the Espagne, Being the Admiral's Ship of the Fleet of New Spain, in the Passage from the Azores toward Cape St. Vincent's," *Phil. Trans. Roy. Soc. (London) 69*, 105.

UNSÖLD, A., 1938, *Physik der Sternatmosphären* (1st ed.), Berlin: Springer–Verlag.

—— 1947, "Quantitative Analyse des Spektrums einer eruptiven Protuberanz," *Z. Ap. 24*, 22.

—— 1955, *Physik der Sternatmosphären* (2nd ed.), Berlin: Springer-Verlag.

VAN DE HULST, H. C., 1947, "Zodiacal Light in the Solar Corona," *Ap. J. 105*, 471.

—— 1949, "Brightness Variation of the Solar Corona," *Nature 163*, 24.

—— 1950, "On the Polar Rays of the Corona," *B. A. N. 11*, 150.

—— 1953, "The Chromosphere and the Corona," *The Sun* (G. Kuiper, Ed.), p. 207, Chicago: University of Chicago Press.

VAN'T VEER, F., 1961, "Die Bestimmung des Gasdrucks in Sonnenflecken aus Flügelstärken von Fraunhoferlinien I," *Z. Ap. 52*, 165.

—— 1962, "Die Bestimmung des Gasdrucks in Sonnenflecken aus Flügelstärken von Fraunhoferlinien II," *Z. Ap. 55*, 208.

VASSENIUS, B., 1733, "Observatio eclipsis solis totalis cum mora facta Gothoburgi Sveciae sub. elev. poli 57° 40′ 54″ d. 2 Maij, stylo Jul. An. 1733," *Phil. Trans. Roy. Soc. (London)* *38*, 134.

VAUQUOIS, B. 1959, "Étude statistique de la composante lentement variable d'après les observations entre 10,000 et 600 Mc/s," *Paris Symposium on Radio Astronomy* (R. N. Bracewell, Ed.), p. 143, Stanford University Press.

VEDENOV, A. A. and R. Z. SAGDEEV, 1958, "Some Properties of a Plasma with an Anisotropic Ion Velocity Distribution in a Magnetic Field," *The Physics of Plasmas. Akad. Nauk. SSSR* *3*, 278.

VERYARD, R. G. and R. A. EBDON, 1961, "Fluctuations in Tropical Stratospheric Winds," *Meteor. Mag.* *90*, 125.

VETTE, J. I. and F. G. CASAL, 1961, "High-Energy X-rays During Solar Flares," *Phys. Rev. Letters* *6*, 334.

VINOGRADOV, Y. and N. ERYUSHEV, 1963, "X-ray Emission of Flares Originating Behind the Solar Disk," *Iz. Krim. Ap. Obs.* *29*, 141.

VITKEVICH, V. V. and B. N. PANOVKIN, 1959, "On the Structure of the Non-uniformities of the Solar Supercorona," *A. Zhurn.* *36*, 544 (*Sov. Astron.* 3, 529, 1960).

VON KLÜBER, H., 1947, "Über den Nachweis und die Messung lokaler Magnetfelder auf der Sonnenoberfläche," *Z. Ap.* *24*, 121.

—— 1948, "Zur Bestimmung von Zeeman-Effekten im Sonnenspektrum," *Z. Ap.* *25*, 187.

—— 1961, "Photometric Investigation of the Inner Solar Corona Using an Eclipse Plate of 1927 June 29," *M. N.* *123*, 61.

VSEKHSVJATSKY, S. K., 1963, "The Structure of the Solar Corona and the Corpuscular Streams," *The Solar Corona* (J. W. Evans, Ed.), p. 271, New York: Academic Press.

VYAZANITSYN, V. P., 1947, "Spectrophotometric Studies of Solar Prominences," *Iz. Glavnoi Astron. Obs.* *17*, No. 136, 1.

VYSSOTSKY, A. N., 1949, "Astronomical Records in the Russian Chronicles from 1000 to 1600 A. D.," *Meddelanden Lund Obs.* *2*, No. 126, 9.

WADDINGTON, C. J., 1963, "Recent Studies of Solar Cosmic Rays," *IEEE Internat. Convention Record*, Part 5, 271.

WALDMEIER, M., 1938a, "Aufsteigende Protuberanzen," *Z. Ap.* *15*, 299.

—— 1938b, "Chromosphärische Eruptionen," *Z. Ap.* *16*, 276.

—— 1939a, "Die Feinstruktur der Sonnenoberfläche," *Hel. Phys. Act.* *13*, 13.

—— 1939b, "Über die Struktur der Sonnenflecken," *Astron. Mitt. Zurich* No. 138, 439.

—— 1939c, "Bewegung aufsteigender Protuberanzen," *Z. Ap.* *18*, 241.

—— 1941, *Ergebnisse und Probleme der Sonnenforschung*, Leipzig: Geest und Portig.

—— 1942, "Der Aufbau der Sonnenatmosphären," *Hel. Phys. Act.* *15*, 405.

—— 1945, "Das Verhalten der Koronalinien 5694.42 Å," *Astron. Mitt. Zurich* No. 146.

—— 1949a, "Die Sichtbarkeitsfunktion der Sonnenfackeln," *Z. Ap.* *26*, 147.

—— 1949b, "Das Spektrum der Protuberanzen und chromosphärischen Eruptionen im Gebiet 4900–6700 Å," *Z. Ap.* *26*, 305.

—— 1951, "Spektralphotometrische Klassifikation der Protuberanzen," *Z. Ap.* *28*, 208.

—— 1955, *Ergebnisse und Probleme der Sonnenforschung* (2nd ed.), Leipzig: Geest und Portig.

—— 1956, "Analyse einer koronalen Kondensation," *Z. Ap. 40*, 221.

—— 1957, *Die Sonnenkorona II. Struktur und Variationen der Monochromatischen Korona*, Stuttgart: Birkhäuser Verlag Basel.

—— 1958, "Die Komponenten des kontinuierlichen Koronaspektrums," *Z. Ap. 46*, 17.

—— 1961a, *The Sunspot Activity in the Years 1610–1960*, Zurich: Schulthess and Co.

—— 1961b, "Neue Beobachtungen an den b-Linien der Protuberanzen," *Z. Ap. 53*, 142.

—— 1961c, "Ergebnisse der Zürcher Sonnenfinsternisexpedition 1954 VII. Photometrie der Polarstrahlen," *Z. Ap. 51*, 286.

—— 1962, "The Zurich Eclipse Expedition of 1962," *Astron. Mitt. Eidg. Stern. Zurich* No. 248.

—— 1963, "Die koronale Kondensation bei der Sonnenfinsternis vom 5 Februar 1962," *Z. Ap. 56*, 291.

—— and H. MÜLLER, 1950, "Die Sonnenstrahlung im Gebiet von $\lambda = 10$ cm," *Z. Ap. 27*, 58.

WALÉN, C., 1944, "On the Theory of Sun-spots," *Ark. Mat. Astron. Fys. 30A*, No. 15.

—— 1947, "On the Distribution of the Solar General Magnetic Field and Remarks Concerning Geomagnetism and Solar Rotation," *Ark. Mat. Astron. Fys. 33A*, No. 18.

—— 1949, *On the Vibratory Rotation of the Sun*, Stockholm: H. Lindstahl.

WANDERS, A. J. M., 1935, "Die Änderung der Sonnenfleckenintensität über der Scheibe," *Z. Ap. 10*, 15.

WARWICK, C. S. and M. WOOD, 1959, "A Study of Limb Flares and Associated Events," *Ap. J. 129*, 801.

WARWICK, J. W., 1957, "Flare-Connected Prominences," *Ap. J. 125*, 811.

—— 1962, "The Source of Solar Flares," *P. A. S. P. 74*, 302.

—— and C. L. HYDER, 1965, "The Polarization of Emission Lines in Astronomy I. Resonance Polarization Effects in the Field-Free Case," *Ap. J. 141*, 1362.

WASIUTYNSKI, J., 1946, "Studies in Hydrodynamics and Structure of Stars and Planets," *Ap. Norv. 4*.

WEBBER, W. R., 1964, "A Review of Solar Cosmic Ray Events," *AAS-NASA Symposium on the Physics of Solar Flares, 1963*, p. 215.

WEISS, A. A. and R. T. STEWART, 1965, "Solar Radio Bursts of Spectral Type V," *Aust. J. Phys. 18*, 143.

WEISS, N. O., 1964a, "Magnetic Flux Tubes and Convection in the Sun," *M. N. 128*, 225.

—— 1964b, "Convection in the Presence of Restraints," *Phil. Trans. Roy. Soc. (London) A 256*, 99.

WEISSKOPF, V. F. I., 1933, "Die Breite der Spektrallinien in Gasen," *Physik Z. 34*, 1.

——and E. WIGNER, 1930, "Berechnung der natürlichen Linienbreite auf Grund der Diracschen Lichttheorie," *Z. Phys. 63*, 54.

WENTZEL, D. G., 1963a, "Dissipation of Magnetic Energy in a Solar Flare," *A. J. 68*, 299.

——1963b, "Fermi Acceleration of Charged Particles," *Ap. J. 137*, 135.

——1964, "The Origin of Solar Flares and the Acceleration of Charged Particles," *AAS-NASA Symposium on the Physics of Solar Flares, 1963*, p. 397.

WENTZEL, G., 1926, "Eine Verallgemeinerung der Quantenbedingungen für die Zwecke der Wellenmechanik," *Z. Phys. 38*, 518.

WESTCOTT, P., 1964, "The 25- or 26-Month Periodic Tendency in Sunspots," *J. Atmos. Sci. 21*, 572.

WESTFOLD, K. C., 1957, "Magnetohydrodynamic Shock Waves in the Solar Corona, with Applications to Bursts of Radio-frequency Radiation," *Phil. Mag. 2*, 1287.

WHITAKER, W. A., 1963, "Heating of the Solar Corona by Gravity Waves," *Ap. J. 137*, 914.

WHITE, W. A., 1964, "Solar X-rays: Slow Variations and Transient Events," *Space Res. IV*, 771.

WILD, J. P., 1962, "The Radio Emission from Solar Flares," *J. Phys. Soc. Japan 17, A-II*, 249.

——1963, "Fast Phenomena in the Solar Corona," *The Solar Corona* (J. W. Evans, Ed.), p. 115, New York: Academic Press.

——and L. L. MCCREADY, 1950, "Observations of the Spectrum of High-intensity Solar Radiation at Metre Wavelengths I. The Apparatus and Spectral Types of Solar Burst Observed," *Aust. J. Sci. Res. 3*, 387.

——J. D. MURRAY, and W. C. ROWE, 1954, "Harmonics in the Spectra of Solar Radio Disturbances," *Aust. J. Phys. 7*, 439.

——J. A. ROBERTS, and J. D. MURRAY, 1954, "Radio Evidence of the Ejection of Very Fast Particles from the Sun," *Nature 173*, 532.

——S. F. SMERD, and A. A. WEISS, 1963, "Solar Bursts," *Ann. Rev. Astron. Ap. 1*, 291.

WILKINSON, D. H., 1950, *Ionization Chambers and Counters*, London: Cambridge University Press.

WILSON, A., 1774, "Observations on the Solar Spots," *Phil. Trans. Roy. Soc. (London) 64*, 1.

WILSON, C. T. R., 1911, "On a Method of Making Visible the Paths of Ionizing Particles through a Gas," *Proc. Roy. Soc. (London) A 85*, 285.

WINCKLER, J. R., 1961, "Primary Cosmic Rays," *Rad. Res. 14*, 521.

WITTE, B., 1951, "A Contribution to the Study of the Relations between Solar Flares and Sunspot Groups," *H. A. O. Solar Res. Memorandum No. 4*.

WOLF, R., 1855, "Mitteilungen über die Sonnenflecken," *Astron. Mitt. Eidgen. Sternwarte*, No. 1.

——1892, "Die Veränderlichkeit des Sonnendurchmessers," *Handbuch der Astronomie*, Vol. 2, p. 433, §530, Zürich: F. Schulthess.

WOLFENDALE, A. W., 1963, *Cosmic Rays*, New York: Philosophical Library, Inc.

WOOLLEY, R. v. d. R. and C. W. ALLEN, 1948, "The Coronal Emission Spectrum," *M. N. 108*, 292.

——and C. W. ALLEN, 1950, "Ultra-violet Emission from the Chromosphere," *M. N. 110*, 358.

WORMELL, T. W., 1936, "Observations on the Intensity of the Total Radiation from Sunspots and Faculae," *M. N. 96*, 736.

YAKOVKIN, N. A. and M. Y. ZEL'DINA, 1963, "A Spectrophotometric Study of Four Bright Prominences," *A. Zhurn. 40*, 847 (*Sov. Astron. 7*, 643, 1964).

——and M. Y. ZEL'DINA, 1964, "Excitation and Ionization of Hydrogen in Prominences," *A. Zhurn. 41*, 336 (*Sov. Astron. 8*, 262).

YALLOP, B. D., 1961, "Coronal Line Widths and the 'Solar Wind'," *Obs. 81*, 235.

YEFREMOV, A. I., A. L. PODMOSHENSKY, O. N. YEFIMOV, and A. A. LEBEDEV, 1961, "Studies of Solar Short Wave Radiation," *Artificial Earth Satellites (USSR) 10*, 3.

——A. L. PODMOSHENSKY, O. N. YEFIMOV, and A. A. LEBEDEV, 1963, "Investigations of Solar X-rays and Lyman Alpha Radiation on August 19–20, 1960," *Space Res. III*, 843.

YOUNG, C. A., 1896, *The Sun*, New York: D. Appleton.

ZANSTRA, H., 1950, "The Value of Observations of Continuous Spectra in the Chromosphere and Prominences," *Proc. Koninkl. Ned. Akad. Wetenschap. 53*, 1289.

ZHELEZNYAKOV, V. V., 1965, "On the Mechanism of γ-ray Emission by Solar Flares," *A. Zhurn. 42*, 96 (*Sov. Astron. 9*, 73).

ZHURAVLEV, S. S., 1957, "Spectrophotometry of Sunspots," *Publ. Leningrad Univ. Astron. Obs. 17*, 198.

ZIRIN, H., 1957, "Spectre d'une éruption au bord du disque solaire," *C. R. 244*, 2893.

——1959, "Physical Conditions in Limb Flares and Active Prominences II. A Remarkable Limb Flare, December 18, 1956," *Ap. J. 129*, 414.

——1961a, "Physical Conditions in Limb Flares and Active Prominences V. Excitation and Ionization of Helium and Metals," *Ap. J. 135*, 521.

——1961b, "Magnetic Fields in Solar Prominences," *A. Zhurn. 38*, 861 (*Sov. Astron. 5*, 660, 1962).

——1964, "The Limb Flare of November 20, 1960. A Coronal Phenomenon," *Ap. J. 140*, 1216.

——1966, *The Solar Atmosphere*, Waltham, Mass., Blaisdell.

——and A. B. SEVERNY, 1961, "Measurement of Magnetic Fields in Solar Prominences," *Obs. 81*, 155.

——and E. A. TANDBERG–HANSSEN, 1960, "Physical Conditions in Limb Flares and Active Prominences IV. Comparison of Active and Quiescent Prominences," *Ap. J. 131*, 717.

ZIRKER, J. B., 1959, "The High Temperature Excitation of Ionized Helium," *Ap. J. 129*, 424.

ZUIKOV, V. N., 1955, "Spectrophotometry of Solar Prominences," *Iz. Glavnoi Astron. Obs. 20*, No. 155, 22.

ZWAAN, C., 1959, "Curves of Growth for a Large Sunspot," *B. A. N. 14*, 288.

——1965, "Sunspot Models: A Study of Sunspot Spectra," *Res. Astron. Obs. Utrecht 17* (4).

AUTHOR INDEX

Author Index

SUBJECT INDEX

Subject Index

A B C D E F G H I J   5 4 3 2 1 7 0 6 9 8 7